The New

YOU and HEREDITY

ALSO BY AMRAM SCHEINFELD

WOMEN AND MEN

ALL THAT YOU INHERITED

Came in chromosomes like this, shown exactly as they look (after staining) under the microscope

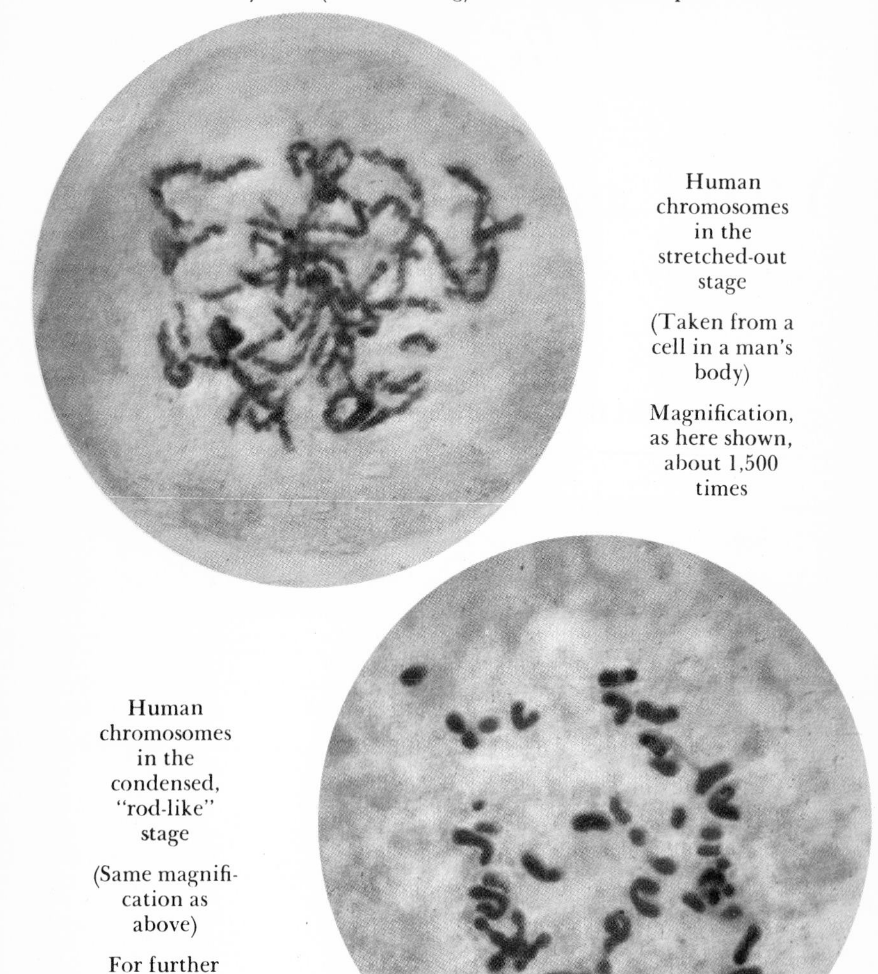

Human chromosomes in the stretched-out stage

(Taken from a cell in a man's body)

Magnification, as here shown, about 1,500 times

Human chromosomes in the condensed, "rod-like" stage

(Same magnification as above)

For further descriptions see text

Both above plates from slides prepared by Dr. Jack Schultz, and photographed under his direction, expressly for this book, by Dr. George T. Rudkin and F. Carroll Beyer. (Color-prints processed by the author.)

The New YOU and HEREDITY

AMRAM SCHEINFELD

With special editing in the medical genetics sections by Dr. Morton D. Schweitzer, and additional aid by others herein mentioned

ILLUSTRATED BY THE AUTHOR

J. B. LIPPINCOTT COMPANY · PHILADELPHIA · NEW YORK

SIXTH IMPRESSION

LIBRARY OF CONGRESS CATALOG CARD NUMBER 51-9156

PRINTED IN THE UNITED STATES OF AMERICA

TO THE MEMORY OF
MY PARENTS
AND MY BROTHER EMMANUEL

CONTENTS

LIST OF ILLUSTRATIONS

PREFACE

No book could have had a more fateful day for its publication than the one on which the first edition of *You and Heredity* made its official bow: *September 2, 1939.**

World War II was in its opening hours, and all humanity was shuddering with the fear of what lay ahead.

Yet, ironically, that September day, with all of its tragic implications, could not have been more appropriate for the publication of a book such as this, dealing with the very essence of human make-up and with many of the points at issue; which sought to tell why human beings, individually and collectively, come to be what they are, and what they can be; which stressed the common origin and interdependence of all peoples; which refuted the theory that war is "natural"; and which, most pointedly, made clear that the known differences among groups of mankind offered no proof whatsoever that any one racial group or nation is inherently "superior" to others, and destined or entitled to become "dominant."

The lack of knowledge or deliberate perversion of these truths contributed greatly to the launching of the war, and may be held chiefly responsible for some of the most terrible acts which preceded or attended it. Even today, with peace and understanding among major human groups far from having been achieved, the same ignorance or perversion of the truths regarding human differences continues to cause untold tragedy.

So it is with a heightened conviction of the importance of making known the established facts about human inheritance—facts which, in the years since 1939, have become much clearer and far more extensive—that I have prepared this completely revised and greatly amplified new edition of my book.

* The book was brought out simultaneously in the United States and England. The first American publication was by the Frederick A. Stokes Company, which was taken over in 1941 by J. B. Lippincott Company, the publishers from then on. A special printing was distributed at the time of publication by the Book-of-the-Month Club; and in 1945, a reprint of the first edition was issued by the Garden City Publishing Company. In England the book was published by Chatto & Windus. Also published have been Spanish, Portuguese, Swedish and Danish translations, but other scheduled translations, into French and Italian, were frustrated by the war developments.

Looking back to the original edition, I may say that despite the unhappy world atmosphere in which it was launched, good fortune smiled on the book in many ways, greatly beyond what might have been anticipated. Selection by the Book-of-the-Month Club contributed enormously to very large sales in the United States, which continued through the years; and the publication of a British edition, and various translations, brought the book to a great many readers in other countries. But what meant most to me, I believe, was the generous endorsement given to the book by scientists in many fields, and its wide adoption for reading and study in educational institutions.

This heartening reception led almost at once to the plan for an ultimate revision, and with it the desire and hope of making the new edition a much better book in all possible ways. But I confess now that I did not envision quite so extensive a remodeling job as has resulted (with almost four-fifths of the book entirely new or completely rewritten, and its size half again as large as that of the original edition).* For this there were a number of reasons.

First, much more is now known about human inheritance. This is hardly surprising when one considers that the whole modern science of heredity is only fifty years old (its "golden jubilee" being celebrated this year), and that a great deal had to be learned about the basic principles before they could be applied on any large scale to the study of complex human traits. With the momentum of researches having steadily increased, and with growing numbers of scientists from other fields having joined in the study, almost as much has been added to the knowledge of human inheritance in the past decade as had come out in the several decades preceding.

So, to the question repeatedly asked the author, "Have you really much *new* to tell about?" a comparison of the index of this book with that of the old one should provide an emphatic answer. The "Rh" factor, the hereditary effects of atomic bombing and atomic radiation, the "Lysenko" theories, the Kinsey studies of sex, and many other new topics have now entered our field of discussion; and innumerable new points will be found regarding the genetic mechanisms, prenatal development, the inheritance of specific dis-

* There would have been justification, by publishing precedents, for giving this book an entirely new title, which was indeed considered. But the feeling prevailed that the old title was so well established that it should be retained with the clarifying prefix of "*The New.*"

eases and defects, features, mental capacities and behavior traits, and evolution, race differences and eugenics.

To be stressed particularly is that, as the science of human heredity has matured, there has come a much clearer perception of the subtler gradations of hereditary influence, and evidence is being evaluated more carefully and soberly. In the earlier years of the science (as in the youth of an individual), there was a tendency to jump at conclusions and think in terms of extremes: to establish a trait as "either" completely hereditary (and if so, due to some simple genetic mechanism), "or" as completely environmental. Today, as we seek to show throughout this book, there is a growing recognition that heredity and environment are constantly interoperating forces in the development of all human traits, although working in different relative degrees with respect to any one given trait. This has led to a great broadening of the field and the scope of discussion, inasmuch as there is hardly an important trait formerly regarded as "directly" hereditary in which some degree of environmental influence is not now perceived; and, conversely, there is hardly an important trait formerly regarded as "purely" environmental in which some hereditary influence cannot be seen at work, through varying degrees of "susceptibility" or "resistance."

Another evidence of the "growing-up" of the science of human heredity is that it finds itself working ever more closely with other sciences, and they with it, resulting in the much more thorough exploration of many areas. Thus, one will find repeatedly in this book reports of new findings which have come through the direct collaborations of geneticists with medical men, anthropologists, psychologists, chemists, physicists, etc. At the same time, the development of human genetics as a specialized science is shown by the fact that it now has its own society and its own journal. (The Human Genetics Society of America, organized in 1948, and its official publication, the *American Journal of Human Genetics,* launched the following year.)

These advances may explain why many of the subjects given relatively scanty treatment in the first edition of our book are now dealt with at much greater length. (Compare, for instance, the previous one-chapter, seven-page discussion of mental diseases and defects with the new two-chapter, twenty-nine-page discussion of these topics. The only section not expanded, but, on the contrary, greatly condensed, is that dealing with my original study of music-talent inheritance. Having placed the detailed evidence on record, it has not been considered necessary to do more now than summarize the principal findings.)

I might add that not the least of the reasons for the greater depth and thoroughness of this new edition is the fact that the author himself, with many more years of study, can reasonably be expected to have learned a lot more. Also, of paramount importance to the book, there has been my much widened personal acqaintanceship with the scientists. In the Preface to the first edition I spoke of writing the book from the viewpoint of an "outsider," ". . . peering into the [heredity] laboratories and reporting back to others what he has seen, heard and learned." The term "outsider" was then quite literally justified, for there were very few scientists whom I knew personally or who knew of me. As the years have gone by the situation has changed, fortunately, to the point where by now I have been privileged to enjoy personal contact with a large proportion of the scientists whose work is dealt with in this book, and can number many of them among my friends.

As a practical consequence of the foregoing, throughout the preparation of this new edition I have had the advantage—to a far greater extent than when writing the first book—of being able to secure data and enlightenment on innumerable points directly from the men engaged in the original researches; and, as chapters and sections were written, of being permitted to call on persons of high authority for their reading and criticism. In many respects, then, this book should be considered as having evolved from the contributions of a large number of individuals, without whose collective aid it certainly could never have achieved such merits as it may now possess.

Leading off my "thank you" notes is that to my close friend and colleague of many years, Dr. Morton D. Schweitzer, one of the best-informed men in the field of medical genetics. In the Preface to the first edition I made acknowledgment of the great service he had rendered with respect to the sections on inherited diseases and defects, and in guiding me in many technical aspects of the book as a whole. While he has again aided me enormously, his participation in the work on this new edition as fully as we both might have wished, was impeded by various circumstances. Among these was his service with the armed forces throughout World War II and for some time thereafter (during most of which period he was in Europe), and, on his return, his removal of residence to Cincinnati. However, by means of extensive correspondence and a number of special visits with me, he was once more able to give much valuable assistance in the editing of the medical genetics sections and the "Black Gene" Tables. In this work he drew generously upon his own voluminous compendium of inherited human diseases and defects (still to be published).

Overseas, my thanks go to Professor J. B. S. Haldane, one of the world's foremost geneticists, who, in editing (and sponsoring) the first edition of my book for British publication, offered numerous suggestions for improvement, many of which have been acted on in this new book. I am greatly indebted also to my esteemed friend Professor Julian Huxley for additional editing and criticisms, which, among other things, helped to spur me toward a complete reworking of the chapter on "Evolution."

Special "thank you" notes go to my very dear and distinguished friends, Dr. Abraham Stone, Dr. Alexander Wiener, Professor Irving Lorge and Dr. David Wechsler, each a leader in his field (Dr. Stone, human reproduction and marriage problems; Dr. Wiener, "blood" genetics; Professor Lorge, education and general psychology; and Dr. Wechsler, clinical psychology), on whom I called repeatedly for information and advice. Moreover, I can hardly overestimate the stimulation and knowledge I derived from my frequent "get-togethers" with them and the many notable guests I met at their homes.

In addition to those mentioned, my indebtedness extends to so large a number of persons for important contributions to this book—for readings and criticisms, for providing photographs, for aid in preparing illustrations, or for other assistance—that, instead of trying to list them all here, I am presenting their names in a special section of "Acknowledgments" following the Preface. Even then, I am sure that I have overlooked some of those who have helped me, and where so, I hope they will forgivingly consider themselves included in the general thanks which I extend to the innumerable workers in all the human sciences who, through their combined efforts, have provided the great wealth of material which has made this book possible.

Finally, with a thought to my greatest indebtedness, I should like to say something of what the study of human heredity has meant to me personally. In the Preface to the first edition I wrote that I was originally led into this study by the practical objective of utilizing some of the facts in a projected work of fiction, and "... before long I discovered that the finding in this field so completely shattered my own preconceived notions and the ideas held by all but an initiated few, as to obliterate my original plans. I became convinced that the most interesting and important task before me was to acquire as thorough a knowledge of the subject as I could and then communicate what I had learned to others."

I may add now that if I have pursued these objectives with growing ardor, it is because I have seen increasingly that the study of human heredity does much more than make one acquainted with how specific traits of body and mind are produced or passed on. Thinking back to my earlier years, I can recall some of my confusion and uncertainty, and a considerable degree of cynicism, regarding human make-up and "human nature," and the possibility of mankind's becoming better. So it is heartening to say, today, that the more science has made clear to me the amazing life processes, the greater has grown my awe and humility, and my respect for the human organism; and the more I have learned about people—what is inherent in them and what is not, how they develop and how they *can* develop—the stronger has grown my faith in them. At a time of continuing conflict and tragedy, of doubt and pessimism, the knowledge of what human beings have the power to become, rather than what they still are, can offer reassurance and hope. I, for one, have never been more convinced than I am now of the fundamental soundness, decency and goodness of the great majority of my fellow men; more certain that their genetic assets far outweigh their liabilities; or more confident that as people the world over really get to know and understand themselves, to make the most of their great endowments, and to give expression to their true impulses to work together for their common good, their lives will be increasingly fuller, worthier and happier.

So, as I welcome you, the reader, into the pages of this book, it is my hope that beyond any interesting or practical information concerning human heredity which you may find here, you will come to share some of this author's faith in our species and his optimism for its future.

AMRAM SCHEINFELD

New York City
October 1, 1950

THANKS AND ACKNOWLEDGMENTS

The author herewith expresses his most profound thanks to the following distinguished individuals for their reading of chapters or sections of this book, as noted, and for their numerous important criticisms and suggestions by which he profited greatly. It should be clear, however, that in extending these thanks no responsibility whatsoever is delegated to those mentioned for any errors of commission or omission which may still be found in this book.

PRE-NATAL LIFE (Ch. 7): Dr. L. W. Sontag, Director, Fels Research Institute, Antioch College

FEATURES (Chs. 11 to 15, incl.): Prof. Wilton M. Krogman, University of Pennsylvania; Dr. Stanley M. Garn, Harvard University

Coloring (skin, hair): Prof. Edward A. Edwards, Harvard Medical School

TWINS, MULTIPLE BIRTHS (Chs. 18, 19): Prof. D. C. Rife, Ohio State University; Prof. Horatio H. Newman (Emeritus), University of Chicago

Dionne Quintuplets: Prof. Norma Ford Walker, University of Toronto

DISEASES AND DEFECTS:

Heart: Dr. Charles A. R. Connor, Medical Director, American Heart Association; Drs. Ernst P. Boas and Harold Aaron, Mt. Sinai Hospital, New York

Cancer: Dr. Clarence C. Little, Director, Jackson Memorial Laboratory, Bar Harbor, Me.

Diabetes: Drs. Elliott P. Joslin and Priscilla White, Joslin Clinic, Boston

Tuberculosis: Dr. F. M. Feldman and associates, National Tuberculosis Association

Baldness: Dr. James B. Hamilton, Long Island College of Medicine, N. Y.

Skin Defects: Dr. Charles R. Rein, New York University, and Dr. George H. Kostant

Teeth Defects: Dr. J. H. Sillman, New York

Eye Defects: Prof. Dan M. Gordon, Cornell University Medical College; Dr. Bernard Kronenberg, New York Eye and Ear Infirmary
Deafness: Dr. Edmund P. Fowler, Sr., Director, Research and Clinics, New York League for Hard of Hearing
Speech Defects: Dr. Beatrice Jacoby, Queens College, New York
Allergies: Dr. Harry Swartz, Harlem Hospital, New York
Blood Diseases: Dr. William Thalhimer, Grasslands State Hospital, Valhalla, N. Y.
Muscle and Nerve Defects: Dr. Israel S. Wechsler, Chief Neurologist, Mt. Sinai Hospital, New York
MENTAL DISEASES AND DEFECTS (Chs. 25 and 26): Dr. Benjamin Malzberg, Director, Bureau of Statistics, New York State Dept. of Mental Hygiene; Dr. Franz J. Kallmann, Columbia University, College of Physicians and Surgeons; Dr. David Wechsler, Chief Psychologist, Bellevue Psychiatric Hospital, New York; Dr. George A. Jervis, Letchworth Village, New York; Dr. Gerhard Sander, University of Wisconsin
Epilepsy: Dr. William Caveness, Associate in Neurology, Columbia University, College of Physicians and Surgeons
SEXUAL ABNORMALITIES (Ch. 27): Prof. Earl T. Engle, Columbia University, College of Physicians and Surgeons
BLOOD TYPES (Ch. 28): Dr. Alexander Wiener, Serologist, Office Chief Medical Examiner, New York City; Dr. Philip Levine, Ortho Research Foundation, Raritan, N. J.
Paternity Tests (Ch. 29): Dr. Wiener
LONGEVITY (Ch. 30): Mr. Mortimer Spiegelman, Assistant Statistician, and Mr. Herbert Marks, Metropolitan Life Insurance Company, New York; Dr. Halbert Dunn, Chief, and associates, National Office of Vital Statistics, Washington, D. C.; Dr. Franz J. Kallmann and Dr. Gerhard Sander (see under "Mental Diseases")
INTELLIGENCE, TALENTS, GENIUS (Chs. 33, 35, 36): Prof. Irving Lorge, Teachers' College, Columbia University
MUSICAL TALENT (Ch. 34): Dr. Harold Seashore, Psychological Corporation, New York; Prof. Louis Thorpe, University of Southern California
BEHAVIOR AND PERSONALITY (Chs. 37, 38): Dr. J. P. Scott, Director of Behavior Studies, Jackson Memorial Laboratory, Bar Harbor, Me.
CRIME (Ch. 39): Prof. Sheldon Glueck, Harvard University

SEX LIFE (Ch. 40): Prof. Alfred C. Kinsey, Indiana University
EVOLUTION (Ch. 41): Dr. George G. Simpson, American Museum of Natural History, New York
Lysenko theories and "acquired characteristics": Prof. Tracy M. Sonneborn, Indiana University
RACE (Chs. 42, 43): Prof. Theodosius Dobzhansky, Columbia University; Prof. Ashley M. F. Montagu, Rutgers University
POPULATION (Ch. 45): Prof. Philip M. Hauser, University of Chicago
EUGENICS (Chs. 45, 46, 47): Dr. Abraham Stone, Director, Margaret Sanger Research Bureau, New York; former Editor *Human Fertility*
Artificial Insemination: Prof. John MacLeod, Cornell University

SPECIAL TOPICS: *Sex determination,* Prof. Carl R. Moore, University of Chicago; *cancer* (hormone therapy), Dr. Frank Adair, Memorial Hospital, New York; *"instincts,"* Prof. A. H. Maslow, Brooklyn College, New York; *transplanting of ova,* Mr. Raymond E. Umbaugh, Essar Ranch, San Antonio, Texas; *behavior* (chemical influences), Dr. Benson Ginsburg, University of Chicago; *gland chart,* Dr. Morton D. Biskind, New York; *chess,* Mr. L. Horowitz, Editor, *Chess Review*

PHOTOGRAPHS

For the unusual color photographs of human chromosomes (Frontispiece) I am indebted to Dr. Jack Schultz, Director of the Department of Genetics, Institute for Cancer Research and Lankenau Hospital Research Institute, Philadelphia; his associate, Dr. George T. Rudkin, and F. Carroll Beyer, the photographer. My thanks also go to Dr. John Rock, of the Harvard Medical School, for the remarkable photograph of the human tubal egg; to Dr. Abraham Stone, for arranging and providing for the photograph of living human sperms; to Dr. Berwind P. Kaufmann, of the Carnegie Institution, for the photograph of fruit-fly chromosomes; and to Mr. Rex D. Billings, of the Belmont Park, Montreal, for the new photograph of the Negro albinos. Also, in the case of the four photographs which I "posed" (the "Identical-Twin Family," the "Undersized and Oversized," the "Musical Patriarch," and the "Cultural Turnabouts"), I am grateful for the fine results obtained by my photographer friend, Mr. Morton Lasser.

CHARTS AND LINE-DRAWINGS

In the preparation of a number of charts, I am indebted for expert guidance to Dr. Stanley M. Garn ("hair form"); Dr. George H. Kostant ("skin pigmentation"); Dr. James B. Hamilton ("baldness"); Dr. Bernard Kronenberg ("eye defects"); Drs. William G. Lennox and William Caveness ("brain waves"); Dr. Alexander Wiener ("Rh-babies"); Messrs. Mortimer Spiegelman and Herbert Marks ("Rocky Road of Life"); Dr. George G. Simpson ("evolution of man").

Also, I am deeply grateful to Harcourt, Brace and Company, publishers of my *Women and Men* (1944), for the loan of five of the original engravings from that book and the permission to reprint the illustrations in this one. (These illustrations appear on pp. 43, 45, 50, 256 and 455.)

And I am again indebted to Prof. Lewis M. Terman and the McGraw-Hill Company for permission to use material from the book, *Sex and Personality,* in the "Sex Life" chapter.

ACKNOWLEDGMENTS FROM THE FIRST EDITION

While only a lesser part of the original *You and Heredity* has been carried over, I am not forgetful of many of the individuals who contributed so much to the success of the first edition and who therefore aided in laying the foundation for this new edition. Among those whom I thanked in the first Preface were: for *initial guidance,* Dr. Henry J. Fry*; for *readings,* Prof S. J. Holmes, Prof. Donald C. Lancefield, Dr. George W. Henry, Dr. Walter Bromberg, Dr. Alfred J. Lotka,* Prof. Raymond Pearl,* Dr. Dwight F. Chapman, Prof. Carl E. Seashore,* Dr. Gene Weltfish, and Frederick Osborn; and for other aid (in sections on disease inheritance), Drs. James Ewing,* May Wilson, Eugene Opie, William Schmidt, Harold Aaron, Emanuel Klein, Nathan Kaliss and Emil Smith.

* Deceased.

CHAPTER 1

THE SCIENCE OF GENETICS

STOP and think about yourself:

In all the history of the world there was never anyone else exactly like you, and in all the infinity of time to come, there will never be another.

Whether or not you attach any importance to that fact, undoubtedly you have often wondered what made you what you are; what it was that you got from your parents and your ancestors and how much of you resulted from your own efforts or the effects of environment; and finally, what of yourself you could pass on to your children.

Until comparatively recent times all this was a matter of theory and speculation. Not until the dawn of this century was anything definitely established about the mechanism of heredity, and for some years thereafter the most important points were bandied about, like footballs, among the biologists. Then, dramatically climaxing a series of some of the most remarkable experiments in all scientific history, the whole field of genetics (the study of heredity and variation among living things) became brilliantly illumined, and what had been theory became fact.

With American geneticists in the vanguard, led by the late Nobel Prize winner, Thomas Hunt Morgan, and a corps of highly gifted associates, the new science was brilliantly explored, and continued research has been proceeding on many broad fronts throughout the world. New data are pouring in with increasing volume. Experiments are repeated countless times, statements checked and rechecked. If the reader is inclined to be skeptical regarding some of the conclusions, let him be advised that no greater skeptics can be found than the geneticists themselves. Their rigid determination to take nothing for granted, and to subject the reports of even their most brilliant colleagues to the severest tests, has made genetics one of the most exact of all biological sciences.

Thus it can be said with assurance that the mechanism of heredity—among humans as among other living and growing things—now stands clearly revealed. While all of its intricacies are by no means fully known, the basic principles are as unmistakably clear as the workings of a watch. Problems of heredity that confounded the greatest thinkers and scientists of the past, from Aristotle to Darwin, have been solved. Long-standing mysteries about birth and development have been unravelled. Endless popular beliefs, theories and superstitions have been completely discredited. Existing social philosophies have been called into question and the way pointed to a reconstruction of humanity itself.

And yet, vitally important as all this is, not much of it has seeped through to the general public, and even among many professional people the knowledge of modern genetics remains hazy. There is some excuse for this. Apart from the fact that it takes a long time for detailed scientific findings to become generally known and accepted, there is the added reason that human genetics is one of the most complicated of sciences, and most of the published reports in the field can have meaning only for the specialist. Even where isolated phases of the subject are popularly treated in newspapers and magazines, the layman is generally left confused through lack of sufficient understanding of the basic principles.

So we come to the purpose of this book, which is:

1. To sift out from the genetics laboratories and various research fields the outstanding facts about heredity directly applicable to human beings.

2. To present these facts in clear-cut, untechnical language, diagrams and illustrations.

3. To point out what their significance may be to the individual and society, and, wherever there is room for argument, to leave the reader to draw his own conclusions.

The steps and processes by which these findings were arrived at will be largely omitted. It is assumed that if you're an average person you do not care two raps about the love life of sea urchins or about the interaction of hereditary factors for coat colors in mice, or what happens when a yellow-bodied *Drosophila melanogaster* (fruit fly) with double-bar eyes and vestigial wings is crossed with a gray-bodied, long-winged, normal red-eyed one. True, without laborious study of these lowlier creatures the geneticists could never have arrived at the facts about human beings, for not the least of their amazing discoveries has been that the mechanism of heredity is almost the same in all living things.

Nevertheless, the facts about the laboratory creatures can wait. What you probably wish to know, as directly as possible, are the answers to the innumerable questions about your own heredity and that of your fellow humans. These questions we hope have been anticipated and answered in the following pages.

The fact has not been overlooked that many readers may already know more or less about the subject of heredity. But for the sake of the many others to whom this may be all quite new, it is our plan to presuppose no previous knowledge whatsoever. So, in the vernacular, we are going to start from "scratch."

CHAPTER 2

LIFE BEGINS AT ZERO

A SPERM and an egg: You, like every other human being and most other animals, began life as just that.

A single sperm enters a single egg and a new individual is started on its way.

Leaving aside for the present the part played by the mother, we know that a father's rôle in his child's heredity is fixed the moment that it is conceived. Whatever it is that the father passes on to his child must be contained within that single sperm.

But to find out exactly what that sperm contains has not been so simple a matter.

Consider, first, its size:

One hundred million sperms may be present in a single drop of seminal fluid. Two billion sperms—two thousand million, as many as were needed to father all the people in the world today—could be comfortably housed in the cap of an ordinary tube of toothpaste!

The microscope had to be well perfected before a sperm could be even seen. Then, in the first flush of discovery, carried away by their desire to believe, just as children and lovers imagine that they

THE HOMUNCULUS (or Manikin) which early scientists believed was contained in the sperm.

After drawings by
(a) Hartsoeker—1694
(b) Dalempatius—1699

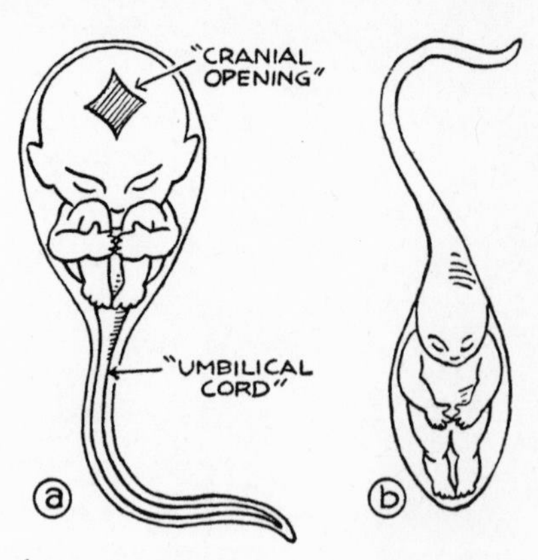

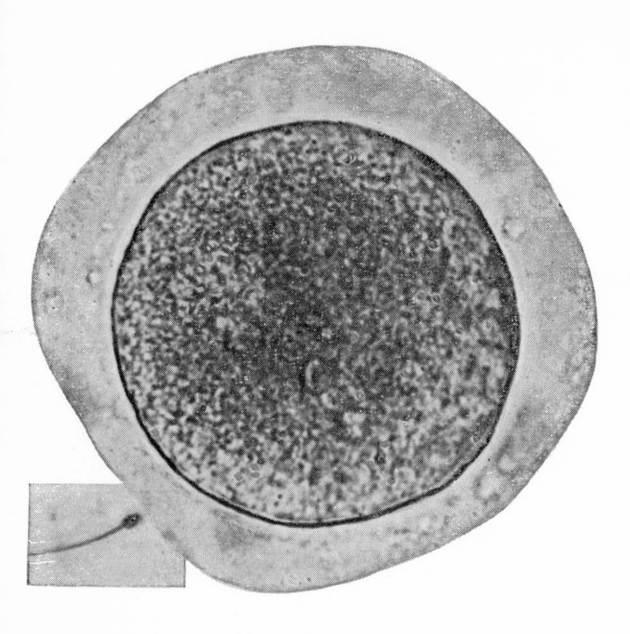

UNFERTILIZED HUMAN TUBAL EGG, WITH SPERM OUTSIDE.

A very rare specimen, recovered from a fallopian tube and photographed by Dr. John Rock. Magnification, as shown, about 500 times. (Outer area of egg: *zona pellucida*. Dark inner circular line: *cell membrane*. Light spot in interior (at left), *nucleus.*)

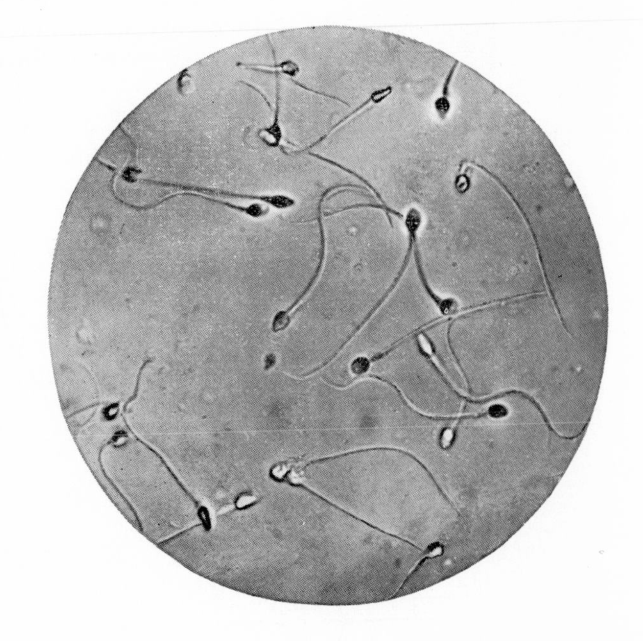

LIVING HUMAN SPERMS, IN MOTION.

From slide prepared by Dr. Abraham Stone, and micro-photographed (1/10,000 second exposure) by Joseph Weber. (Magnification here approximately same as egg above, showing relative proportions.)

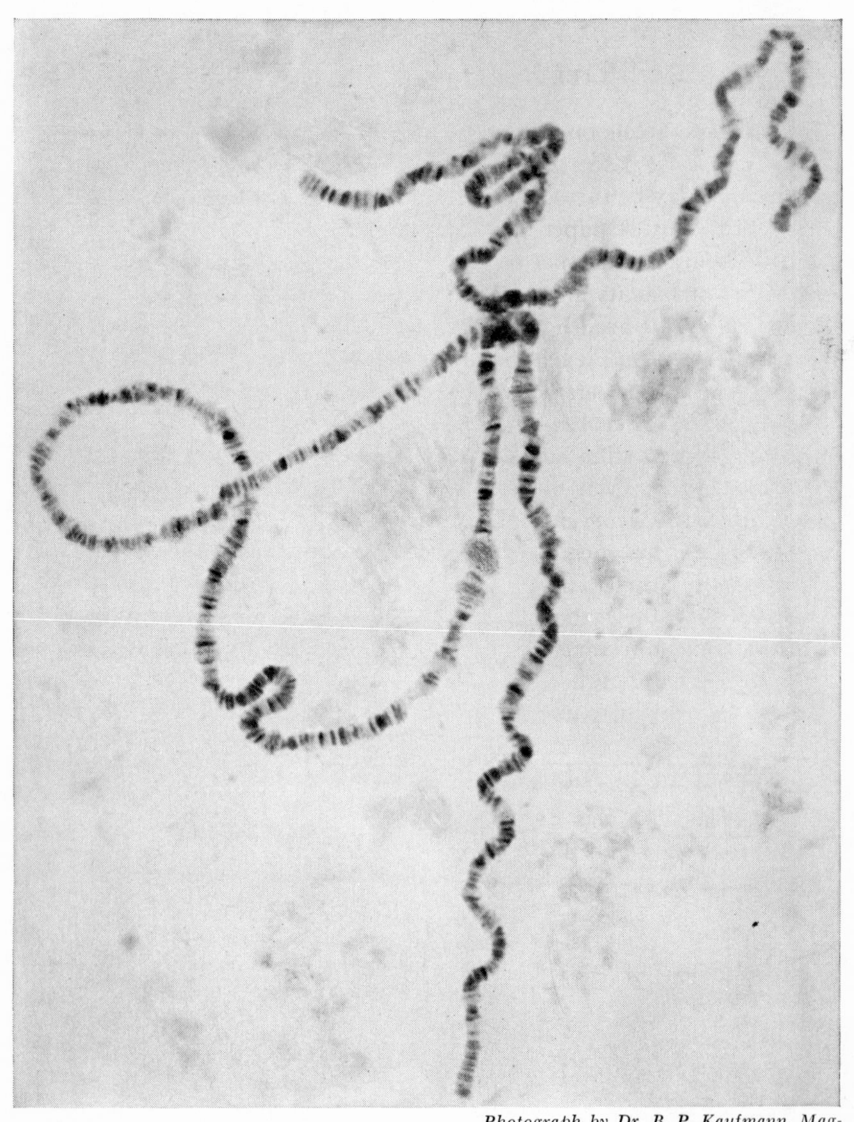

Photograph by Dr. B. P. Kaufmann. Magnification as here shown about 650 times

THE CHROMOSOMES OF THE FRUIT FLY

The fact that the fruit fly (drosophila) has only four different chromosomes (whereas humans have twenty-four), and that these chromosomes develop to unusually large size in its salivary glands, makes it possible to see them microscopically in very great detail. In this photograph the resemblance of the chromosomes to strings of beads is clearly evident, the "beads" being the "genes," or the containers of the genes. Geneticists have "mapped" these chromosomes in great detail, showing the exact location of scores of genes for specific fruit-fly traits. (The "X" chromosome [see Chapter Eight] is the looped one at the left.)

see a man in the moon, some scientists (*circa* 1700 A.D.) reported excitedly that every sperm contained a tiny embryonic being. With professional gravity they gave it the name of "homunculus" (little man), and scientific papers appeared showing careful drawings of the little being in the sperm—although there was some dispute as to whether it had its arms folded or pressed against its side, and whether or not its head had any features.

Presently, however, it became apparent that imagination had run away with scientific perspicacity. The head of the sperm—in which interest rightfully centered, as the tail was merely a means for propelling it—proved to be a solid little mass that defied all attempts at detailed study. Even the great Darwin, who was so right about many things, could never more than guess at what the sperm head comprised—and his guess was a wrong one. Many scientists thought it was hopeless to try to find out. Others concluded that if the sperm head itself could never be dissected and its contents examined, they might still find out what it carried if they could learn what happened *after* it entered the egg. And in this they were right.

Crowning years of painstaking study, we know at last that what

A MARVELOUS MECHANISM: THE HUMAN SPERM

A billion like this can be produced by the average fertile man every week!

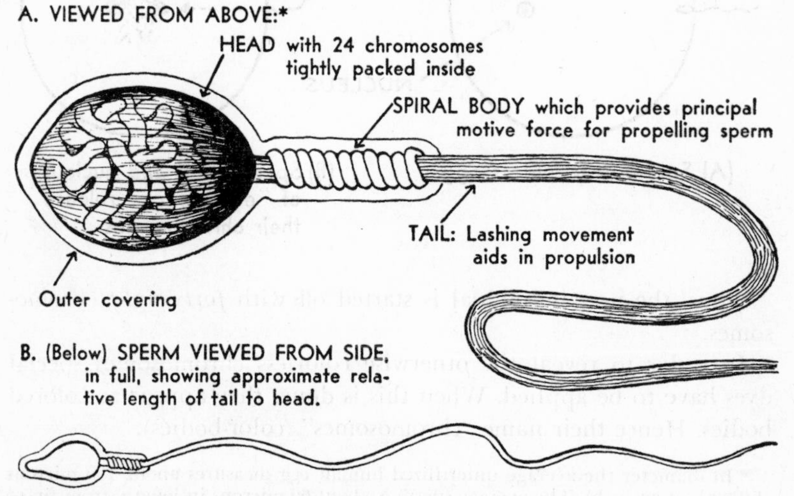

* Upper drawing based in part on diagrammatic reconstruction of human sperm, as seen under electron microscope, in study by Drs. O. S. Culp and John W. Best. (*Journal of Urology*, Feb. 1949.)

a human sperm carries—the precious load that it fights so desperately to deliver—*are twenty-four minute things called chromosomes.*

When the sperm enters the egg and penetrates its substance, the head begins to unfold and reveal itself as having been made up of the twenty-four chromosomes closely packed together. And we know beyond any doubt that *these chromosomes must comprise all the hereditary material contributed by the father.*

What of the egg? Although many thousands of times larger than the sperm, the egg is yet smaller than a period on this page, barely visible to the naked eye. (The weight of a human egg is estimated to be about one-millionth of a gram.)* Under the microscope we see that it consists largely of foodstuffs with the exception of a tiny globule, or nucleus. What that contains we see when the sperm head enters the egg and releases its chromosomes. *Almost at the same time, the egg nucleus breaks up and releases its twenty-four similar chromosomes*—the contribution of the mother to the child's heredity.

FERTILIZATION

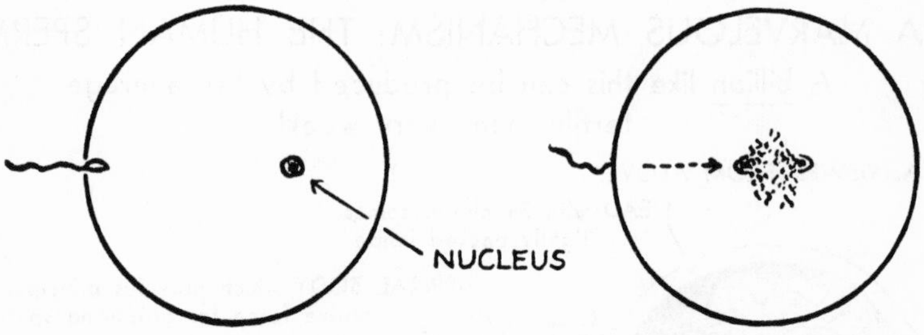

NUCLEUS

(A) Sperm-head enters egg

(B) Sperm-head and nucleus of egg each release their chromosomes.

Thus, the new individual is started off with *forty-eight* chromosomes.

In order to reveal the otherwise colorless chromosomes special dyes have to be applied. When this is done, they appear as colored bodies. Hence their name "chromosomes" (color-bodies).

* In diameter the average unfertilized human egg measures about 130 microns (1/200th of an inch). The average sperm is about 60 microns in length, from tip of head to end of tail, the head alone being about 5 microns long.

But almost immediately another remarkable fact becomes apparent. We find that the chromosomes are of twenty-four different kinds as to shape, size, etc., with one of each kind contributed by each parent. If we could arrange all the pairs in a line they would look like this:

A B C D E F G H I J K L M N O P Q R S T U V W X

How human chromosomes would look if arranged in pairs.

These forty-eight chromosomes comprised all the physical heritage with which you began your life.

By a process of division and redivision, as we shall see in detail later, these initial forty-eight chromosomes are so multiplied that eventually every cell in the body contains an exact replica of each and every one of them. This is not mere theory. If you were willing to lend yourself to a bit of dissection, an expert could take some of your own cells and show you the chromosomes in them looking exactly like those pictured in our Frontispiece.

As we have viewed them up to this point, the chromosomes are in their compressed form. But at certain times they may stretch out into filaments ever so much longer, and then we find that what they consist of apparently are many gelatinous beads closely strung together.

These beads either are, in themselves, or contain the *"genes,"* and *it is the genes which, so far as science can now establish, are the ultimate factors of heredity.*

Has anyone ever seen a gene? Until recently we would have had to answer "No." The best that the most powerful lens-microscopes could reveal were differences in consecutive sections of the chromosomes, in size, width, depth of shading, patterns of striping, etc., which were believed to go with different genes. Then, in the last few years, with the use of the newly perfected "electron" microscope —vastly more powerful than any previously used—two California scientists, Drs. Daniel C. Pease and Richard F. Baker, photographed particles within the chromosomes of fruit flies which they believe *actually are the genes.* The particles—or "genes"—as discernible to the expert eye in published photographs (*Science,* 1949) appear to be usually spindle-shaped or cigar-shaped, with certain variations. Also, in 1949, the *Journal of Heredity* published remarkable photographs of human chromosomes, made by Drs. Jack Schultz and Patricia St. Lawrence, which showed what are quite evidently the gene locations, though without clearly revealing specific genes.*

But whether or not we can ever see human genes in detail, and identify differences in outward appearance among them, we *know*

A CHROMOSOME AT DIFFERENT STAGES

(Beads inside are the genes)

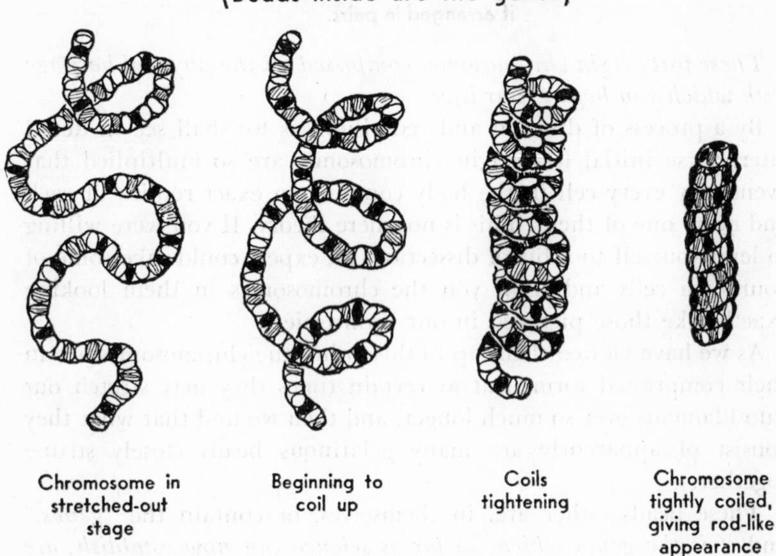

beyond any question from an abundance of evidence that each gene has a definite function in the creation and development of every living person.

Altogether, of all the miraculous particles in the universe, one can hardly conceive of anything more amazing than these infinitesimally tiny units. We say again "infinitesimally tiny" for want of another and better expression. Think of the microscopic size of a

* The later color photographs in our Frontispiece, made in mid-1950 from slides prepared by Dr. Schultz, cannot show the chromosomes in fullest detail because color photography does not permit of as high magnification as does the "electron" microscope photography.

sperm. Then recall that the head of a sperm alone contains twenty-four chromosomes. And now consider that strung in a single chromosome might be anywhere from scores to hundreds of genes—with a single gene, in some cases, able to change the whole life of an individual!

To grasp all this you must prepare yourself for a world in which minuteness is carried to infinity. Contemplating the heavens, you already may have adjusted yourself to the idea of an infinity of bigness. You can readily believe that the sun is millions of miles away; that stars, mere specks of light, may be many times larger than the earth; that the light from a star which burned up six thousand years ago, is reaching us only now; that there are billions of stars in the space beyond space which our most powerful telescopes cannot yet reveal. This is the *infinity of bigness outside of you.*

Now turn to the world *inside* of you. Here there is an *infinity of smallness.* As we trace further and further inward we come to the last units of life that we can distinguish—the genes. And here with our limited microscopes we must stop, just as we are stopped in our exploration of the stars by the limitations of our telescopes. But we can make some pretty good guesses about what the genes are from what we already know about what they can do.

You believe the astronomer when he tells you that, on October 26, in the year 2144, at thirty-four minutes and twelve seconds past twelve o'clock noon there will be a total eclipse of the sun. You believe this because time and again the predictions have come true.

You must now likewise prepare yourself to believe the geneticist when he tells you that a specific gene, whose presence can as yet be only deduced, will nevertheless at such and such a time do such and such things and create such and such effects—*under certain specified conditions.* The geneticist must make many more reservations than the astronomer, for genetics as a science is but a day-old infant compared to astronomy, and the genes are *living substances* whose action is complicated by innumerable factors. But despite all this, so much has already been established about our gene workings that we must stand in greater awe than ever at this latest revelation of how fearfully and wonderfully we are made.

THE HEREDITY PROCESS

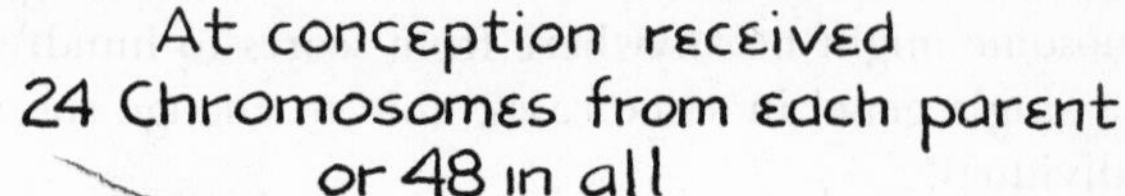

EVERY MAN and EVERY WOMAN
At conception received
24 Chromosomes from each parent
or 48 in all

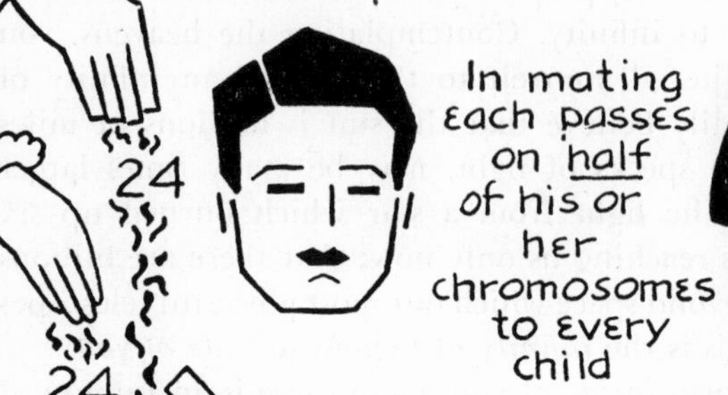

The FATHER'S rôle
is merely that of
passing on half

although she als
acts as incubator
and nourisher for
the egg, con-
tributes no mor

does the Fathe
These 48 chromo-

each passes

CHAPTER 3

THE ETERNAL GERM PLASM

No less important than knowing what heredity is, is knowing what it *is not*. Before we examine the chromosomes and their genes in detail, let us first find out how the sperms, or eggs which carry them, are produced in the parent. That in itself will clear away much of the deadwood of the past with innumerable false theories, beliefs and superstitions about the life processes.

Not so long ago the most learned of scientists believed that whatever it was that the sperms or eggs contained, these were *products* of the individuals, in which were incorporated in some way *extracts* of themselves. That is to say, that each organ or part of a person's body contributed something to the sperm or egg. Darwin, who had gone along with that theory, called these somethings "gemmules."

By the "gemmule" theory, all the characteristics of both parents could be transmitted to the child, to be blended in some mysterious way within the egg and reproduced during development. A child would therefore be the result of what its parents were at the time it was conceived. As the parents changed through life, so would their eggs or sperms, and the chromosomes in them, also change. All that is what scientists used to believe, and what a great many people today still believe—erroneously.

Now we know beyond question that the hereditary properties do not change according to the way the individual changes. For we have learned finally that the chromosomes which the sperms and eggs contain *are not new products of the individual,* and are most certainly not made up of "gemmules" or contributions from the various parts of the body.

As we have seen, a human being starts life as just a single cell containing forty-eight chromosomes. That initial cell must be multiplied countless times to produce a fully developed person, and this is accomplished by a process of division and redivision, as shown in the accompanying illustration.

Continuing in the same way, the two cells become four, the four eight, and this goes on into the billions—the material with which to make the cells, after that in the egg is exhausted, coming from nourishment provided by the mother.

But the cells do not all remain the same, by any means. After the earliest stages, when they are still very limited in number, they

HOW A FERTILIZED EGG-CELL MULTIPLIES

(1) Original cell. (Only four chromosomes shown, for simplification)

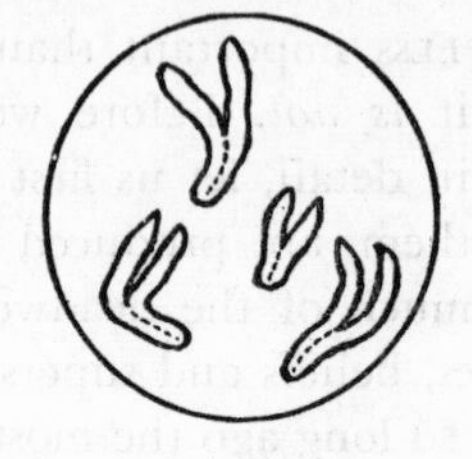

(2) Each chromosome splits in half, lengthwise

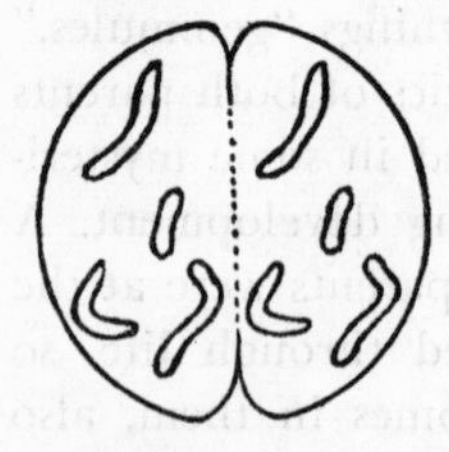

(3) The halved chromosomes go to opposite sides and wall forms between them as cell begins to divide

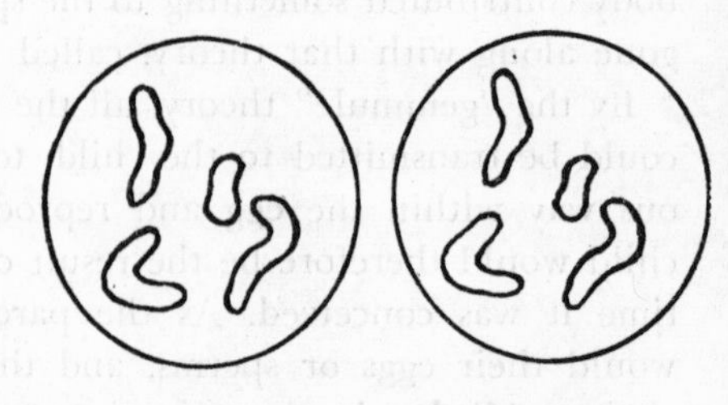

(4) The halved chromosomes grow to full size, resulting in two cells, each a replica of the original

begin "specializing." Some give rise to muscle cells, some to skin, blood, brain, bone and other cells, to form different parts of the body. But a certain number of cells are reserved for another function.

These cells are the germ cells, dedicated to posterity. *It is from these cells that the sperms or eggs are derived.*

When a boy is born, he already has in his testes all the germ cells out of which sperms will eventually be produced. When he reaches puberty, a process is inaugurated that will continue throughout his life—or most of his life, at any rate. In the same way that billions of cells grew from one, millions of more germ cells are manufactured from time to time by division and redivision. Up to a certain point the process is the same as that previously explained—but just before the sperms themselves are to be formed, something different occurs. The chromosomes in the germ cell remain intact and the cell merely splits in half, *each half getting only twenty-four chromosomes, or one of every pair.*

The process of forming the sperms is illustrated on the following page (several stages omitted for simplification). This should make clear how, from a parent germ cell with the regular quota of forty-eight chromosomes, two sperms are formed, each carrying only twenty-four chromosomes. The reason and necessity for this "reduction" division will be explained presently.

Before we go on, let us stop to answer a question which has undoubtedly caused concern to many a man:

"Is it true that the number of sperms in a man is limited, and that if he is wasteful with them in early life, the supply will run out later?"

No, for as we have seen, the sperms are made out of germ cells thrown off without decreasing the "reserve" stock. Endless billions of sperms can continue to be discharged from a man's body (200,000,000 to 500,000,000 or more in a single ejaculation) and the original quota of germ cells will be there to provide more—so long as the necessary machinery functions and the body can supply the material out of which to make them. (However, dissipation to an extreme point which might injure or weaken the body—and similarly, disease, accident or old age—may curtail the production of sperms, or greatly reduce the number of those which will be normal and fertile.)

In the female, although the eggs are also manufactured out of germ cells, the process does not provide for an endless number, running into billions, as in the case of the sperms. The female, when she reaches puberty, will be required normally to mature only one egg a month, for a period of about thirty-five years. So, when a girl baby is born, the fundamental steps in the process have already been taken, and the germ cells have already been turned into eggs. In other words, her ovaries at birth contain tiny clusters of all the eggs (in rudimentary form) which will mature years later. The chromosomes which she will pass on to her future children are also already present within each egg. The maturing process will merely increase the size of the egg by loading it with a store of

HOW SPERMS ARE PRODUCED

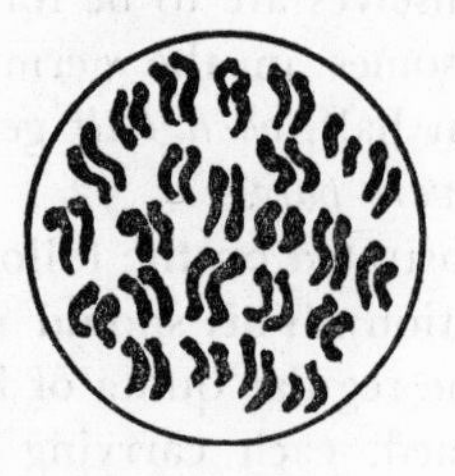

(1) Germ cell, containing forty-eight chromosomes

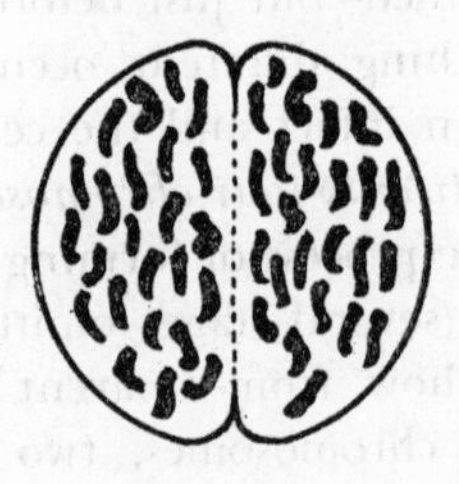

(2) The paired chromosomes separate, going to opposite sides of the cell, and the cell divides

(3) There are now two half-cells, with only twenty-four single chromosomes in each

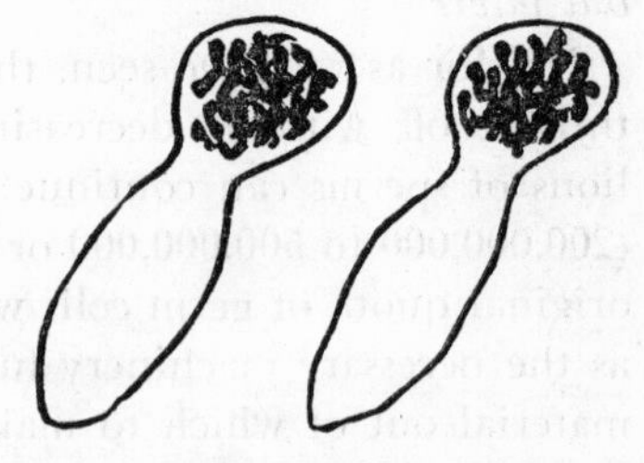

(4) The chromosomes mass together, and part of the cell contents forms a sheath around them

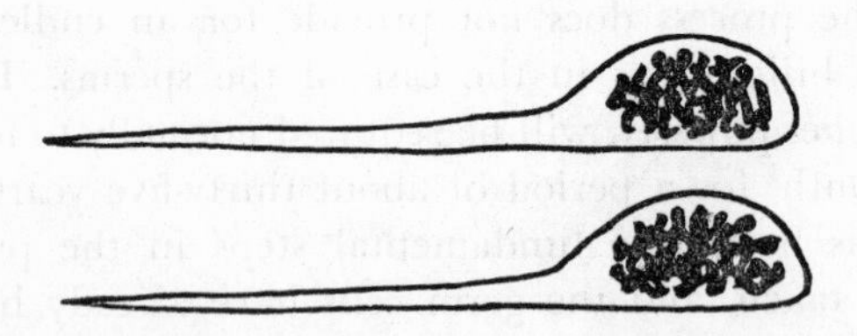

(5) The sheath shapes the chromosomes into a tightly packed mass forming the head. The rest of the cell contents is squeezed out behind to form the tail

food material with which to start a new individual on its way.

Although we need not go into the complicated details of the egg-formation process, it may be pointed out that before the eggs are formed from the germ cells there is a "reduction" division, just as there is in the case of the sperms. This gives each egg, like each sperm, only *half* of the parent's quota of the chromosomes. But when the sperm, with its twenty-four *single* chromosomes, unites with the egg, with its twenty-four corresponding *single* chromosomes, the result is an individual with two each of every chromosome—twenty-four *pairs,* or forty-eight, the required quota for a human being.

If that reduction process hadn't taken place, each sperm or egg would carry forty-eight chromosomes; on uniting they would start off an individual with ninety-six chromosomes; the next generation would begin with 192, and so on to an absurd and impossible infinity. However, this reduction division, it will soon be seen, has much more than a mathematical significance.

One fact should be constantly kept in mind: The sperms or eggs receive chromosomes and genes which are almost invariably replicas of those which the parents themselves received when they were conceived. The rare exceptions are the cases where genes undergo "mutations." These mutations, as we shall see in a later chapter, are changes in the workings of genes which occur at infrequent intervals, either spontaneously, or through some *outside influence* (X-rays, atomic radiation, cosmic rays, strong chemical effects, etc.). Also, rare changes in chromosome structure, such as the hooking on to one chromosome of part of another, may affect the gene workings.

But except for these mutations, the genes remain exactly the same from generation to generation. *No non-hereditary trait in a person's body developed during his or her lifetime can cause the genes to change so that they will produce a similar trait in the child. And nothing that we ourselves or any scientist is now able to do can change the makeup of our germ cells in any specified direction.*

It is as if, when Nature creates an individual, she hands over to him billions of body cells to do with as he wishes, and in addition, wrapped up separately, a small number of special germ cells whose contents are to be passed on to the next generation. And, because Nature apparently does not trust the individual, she sees to it that the hereditary factors in those germ cells are so sealed that he cannot tamper with them or alter them in the slightest degree to suit his purposes.

CHAPTER 4

WHAT WE *DON'T* INHERIT

MEN since the world began have taken comfort in the thought that they could pass on to their children not merely the material possession they had acquired, but also the physical and mental attributes they had developed.

To both types of inheritance, as previously conceived, serious blows have been dealt within recent years. The passing on of worldly goods has been greatly limited by huge inheritance taxes in most countries. But this is as nothing compared to the "inheritance" tax levied by Nature on a man's mental or physical assets—the qualities of mind and body which he might wish to pass on to his children. For with respect to such biological heredity, all pre-existing notions have been shaken by the finding we have just dealt with:

The chromosomes in our germ cells are not affected by any change that takes place within our body cells.

What this means is that no change that we make in ourselves or that is made in us in our lifetimes, for better or for worse, can be passed on to our children through the process of biological heredity. Such changes—made in a person by what he does, or what happens to him—are called *acquired characteristics.* Whether such characteristics could be passed on has provided one of the most bitter controversies in the study of heredity. It has been waged by means of thousands of experiments, and is still being carried on by a stubborn few, including, chiefly, certain Soviet scientists who are motivated by reasons of their own. (We shall deal with them and their theories in a later chapter.) But now that the smoke of battle has cleared away, all qualified geneticists agree that no verified evidence remains to prove that any acquired characteristic can be inherited in human beings.

Reluctantly we must abandon the belief that what we in one generation do to improve ourselves, physically and mentally, can be passed on through our germ plasm to the next generation. It may not be comforting to think that all such improvements will go to the grave with us. And yet the same conclusion holds for the defects developed in us, of the things we may do in our lifetimes to weaken or harm ourselves. If we cannot pass on the good, we likewise cannot pass on the bad.

Why we can't should now be obvious. Knowing that all that we transmit to our children, genetically, are the chromosomes, it means that in order to pass on any change in ourselves, every such change as it occurred would have to be communicated to the germ cells and accompanied by some corresponding change in every specific gene in every specific chromosome concerned with the characteristic involved.

Just imagine that you had a life-sized, plastic statue of yourself and that inside of it was a small, hermetically sealed container filled with millions of microscopic replicas of this statue. Suppose now that you pulled out of shape and enlarged the *nose* of the big statue. Could that, by any means you could conceive, automatically enlarge all the noses on all the millions of little statues inside? Yet that is about what would have to happen if a change in any feature or characteristic of a parent were to be communicated to the germ cells, and thence to the child. It applies to the binding of feet by the Chinese, to circumcision among the Jews, to facial mutilation and distortion among savages, to all the artificial changes made by people on their bodies throughout generations, which have not produced any effect on their offspring. And it applies to the *mind* as well.

Nature performs many seeming miracles in the process of heredity. But it would be too much to ask that every time you took a correspondence course or deepened a furrow in your brain, every gene in your germ cells concerned with the mental mechanism would brighten up accordingly. Or that, with every hour you spent in a gymnasium, the genes concerned with the muscle-building processes would increase their vigor.

Thinking back to your father, you will see that what he was, or what he made of himself in his lifetime, might have little relation to the hereditary factors he passed on to you.

Remember, first, that your father gave you only *half* of his chromosomes—and which ones he gave you depended entirely on chance. It may be possible that you didn't receive a single one of the chromosomes which gave your father his outstanding characteristics.

Aside from this fact, what your father was, or is, may not at all indicate what hereditary factors were in him. The genes, as we shall see presently, do not necessarily *determine* characteristics. What they determine are the *possibilities* for a person's development under given circumstances.

Thus, your father may have been a distinguished citizen or a derelict, a success or a failure, and yet this may provide no clear indication of what chromosomes were in him. But whether or not the nature of his chromosomes did reveal themselves through his characteristics, you can make only a guess as to which of them came to you, by studying unusual traits that your father and you have in common.

What of your mother? The situation with respect to her is different only in that she provided the initial "soil" in which the human seed which was you took root and flourished. Her contribution in the way of chromosomes—half of her own—was essentially the same as your father's. Later we will hear more about the possible effects of the prenatal environment provided by the mother. But that her rôle in heredity is no greater than the father's is clearly proved by the fact that children by and large resemble their mothers no more than their fathers.

You may already be thinking, "What about my children? How much of *myself* did I, or can I, pass on to them?"

Let us first see what you *can't* pass on.

You may have started life with genes that tended to make you a brilliant person, but sickness, poverty, hard luck or laziness kept you from getting an education. *Your children would be born with exactly the same mental equipment as if you had acquired a string of degrees from Yale to Oxford.*

Suppose you are a woman who had been beautiful in girlhood, but, through accident, suffering or hardship, had lost your looks. *The children born to you at your homeliest period would be not one whit different than had you developed into a movie queen.*

Suppose you are a war veteran who was shell-shocked, blinded, crippled and permanently invalided. *If you had a child today his heredity would be basically the same as that of any child you might have fathered in your fullest vigor when you marched off to service.*

Suppose you are old.

The sperms of a man of ninety-five, if he is still capable of producing virile sperms—and there are records of men who were—would be the same in their hereditary factors as when he was sixteen. (Livestock breeders, having established the accuracy of this principle, are now using prize bulls and horses for breeding until the very ends of their lives.) And although the span of reproductive life in a woman is far shorter than in a man, the eggs of a woman of forty-five would be no different in their *genes* from those of her girlhood.

Nevertheless, there may be considerable difference in the offspring born to parents under different conditions. But not because of *heredity*.

The older the mother—at least near forty or beyond—the more likely she is to have had or to have diseases or various bodily disorders, and so the *internal environment* she provides for a child she carries may tend to be less favorable than in her younger years.

But with the mother as well as the father, it is the *external* environment provided which may be most important with respect to children born at different stages of their lives, or under different circumstances. And this obviously refers not merely or even as much to the physical environment as to the psychological environment.

Take this situation: A young man is a teetotaler when he marries and fathers a son. Twenty years later he becomes a drunkard and then fathers another son. Will the second son be more likely to take to drink than the first? Quite definitely. Not because the genes passed on by the man to his second son could be any more "alcoholic," but because the first son had grown up under the influence of a sober father, while the much younger brother will grow up under the influence of a drunken one. There is no evidence whatsoever that drunkenness or other bad *habits* can be inherited directly as such. (Geneticists have kept generations of mice, rabbits, guinea pigs and poultry virtually stupefied with alcohol, without the slightest sign of any transmission of the habit to their offspring.) If children of drunkards are so often drunkards themselves, the most likely and obvious explanation would be, "through precept and example."

As often as not, similarities between child and parent (mother as well as father) which are ascribed to heredity are really the effects of similar influences and conditions to which they have been exposed. In fact, *so interrelated and so dependent on each other are the forces of environment and heredity in making us what we are that they cannot be considered apart, and at every stage in this book will be discussed together.*

Thus where heredity may fall down, environment may be there to carry on. And if you ask, "Can I pass on to my child any of the accomplishments or improvements I have made in myself?" the answer may be, "Yes! You can pass on a great deal—not by heredity, but by training and environment!"

The successful, educated, decent-living father can give his son a better start in life. The athletic father can, by example and training, insure his child a better physique. The healthy, intelligent, alert mother can insure her child a more favorable entry into the world and, after it is born, can influence it for the better in innumerable ways. And just as easily, bad upbringing can thwart or cancel the effects of good heredity.

There are, however, limits to what environment can accomplish. Exaggerated claims made for it in previous years have been refuted by the findings in genetics. The theory of the extreme "behaviorists" that any kind of person could be produced out of any stock by the proper training, has been deflated. On the other hand, the extreme "hereditarians" who in the first flush of discovering the mechanism of heredity attributed everything to its workings, have also been given a setback.

What we will see more and more as we go on in this book is that every individual, in his total makeup and behavior at any time, is the end result of many forces. Only when we deal with specific traits can we be fairly clear as to the relative influences of heredity and environment.

CHAPTER 5

MYTHS OF MATING

OF THE various myths about mating and parenthood, one that has been most ardently cherished is that which many loving couples cling to about "putting themselves in the right state for the conception of a child." To disillusion them may be almost as bad as telling children there is no Santa Claus. But what we have just learned should convince us of the sad, unromantic fact that whether a child is conceived during a glamorous sojourn on sunny strands, or in the depressing air of a dingy tenement, whether in the height of passion or when its parents are barely on speaking terms with one another, the hereditary factors transmitted to it will be not one whit different.

What, then, of a *"love child"?* Popular belief is that a child born out of wedlock is in some ways different from a legitimate child—that it is likely to be more delicate, more sensitive, developing to extremes—sometimes a genius, often a criminal. Weren't Leonardo da Vinci and Alexander Hamilton "illegitimate"? Wasn't *Hitler?* Yes, but it need hardly be stated that Nature never took and still does not take any note of marriage certificates.

An illegitimate child may well be different from a legitimate child—if its *environment* is different. Where society is relentless toward illegitimacy, the child born to an unmarried mother may come into the world and be reared under handicaps which may have continuing effects throughout its life, sometimes in peculiar directions. But wherever consideration is shown to unmarried mothers, where good care is given them during pregnancy, and where the child has anything like a normal start, the factor of illegitimacy has little importance. This is now being proved in thousands of cases where children born out of wedlock are being lovingly and intelligently reared by foster parents.

The *age of parents* is also believed to affect the nature of the child, but where it does, it is only through environmental influences.

A "child of old age," born, let us say, when a mother is in mid-forty and the father in his sixties, frequently appears to be frailer and sicklier than others. The explanation will be found not in any weakness in the parents' germ cells, but, first, in the less favorable intra-uterine environment provided by the older mother (as we noted in the preceding chapter); and, second, in the fact that such late births are so often unwanted and occur mostly where conditions for childbearing are bad. Following birth other factors enter. The "child of old age," surrounded, as is usually the case, by much older brothers, sisters and their friends in addition to the older parents, is frequently pampered and spoiled, and may quite understandably become high-strung and precocious.

In children born to very young mothers (under seventeen), both the intra-uterine and postnatal conditions are also likely to be unfavorable. Immaturity in the mother may not only have physical ill effects on both her and her child, but may be bad psychologically for both, through her lack of social experience.

It should be hardly necessary now to dwell long on certain other erroneous beliefs associated with mating and parenthood which, while prevalent largely among breeders of domestic animals, are also applied to human beings:

—*"Telegony"* is the theory that if a female is mated with two or more successive males, the influence of an earlier sire may carry over to offspring of a later father.

—Similarly, by *"infection"* is meant that a male mated first with an undesirable female (a blooded bull with a "scrub" cow) may communicate some of her characteristics to offspring of the next female with whom he is mated.

—Or that continued mating together may cause a male and female to resemble each other; and that by *saturation* the oftener a female is mated with the same male, the more the successive offspring will resemble him.

In the last two cases, the explanation which should readily occur is that individuals who live together for a long time, whether lower animals or humans, may show common effects of the same environment, diet, habits and other living conditions. Husbands and wives sometimes may get to look alike in the same way that any persons living in the same environment may develop similarities of physique and appearance. One often hears it said of a couple, "You'd think they were brother and sister!" The same environmental influence also tends to increase the resemblance between children and parents.

The myths and superstitions associated with mating and parenthood could fill a book by themselves. Back of all of them lie sometimes coincidences, sometimes mistaken assumptions of paternity, and most often the cropping out of hidden factors (recessive genes)—which will be dealt with more fully further along.

One common question regarding mating may deserve special attention:

"Can there be such a thing as 'conflict' between the chromosomes of one person and another—a genetic incompatibility that would seriously affect or prevent birth of children?"

Yes, but only as applied to certain individuals, not to races, groups or "types" of human beings. This is an important distinction. Later we shall see how in any two given persons there may be specific "dangerous" genes or other genetic factors in each which when combined by their mating may offer serious threats to their prospective offspring. But one should not jump to the conclusion that this would single out persons of radically different surface types. For the fact is that *all* human beings, regardless of "race," "type," "color" or any other classification in which they are placed, are, as members of the same species, sexually and genetically compatible with one another.

No such chromosome incompatibility exists between any two kinds of humans as there does between animals of different species—a cat and a dog, a chicken and a goose, or even a horse and donkey (as our illustration shows).* The tallest, blondest "Nordic" could mate with the smallest, blackest Pygmy and produce children perfectly normal in the eyes of Nature. This, however, has certain qualifications, for if a tall, big-boned European mated with a Pygmy woman, the child might be too large for her to bear without danger to it or to herself. The same, however, would apply to the mating of any extremely large man with a small woman, even of the same race, where sometimes a Caesarean operation is required to deliver the child.

The theory has been advanced that in the mating of parents of

* If you are interested in mules: There are very rare instances where the females have been fertile, for complicated reasons, but the males have been found to be invariably sterile, so that mules cannot perpetuate themselves in a straight line. Lions and tigers are two other related animals which, while genetically distinct, can sometimes be crossbred, producing a "tiglon." Several of these have been in zoos, including one in New York.

MATING

A Cat and a Dog

Cannot mate and have offspring together because they are of different species,

—and their chromosomes differing in kind and number are not compatible.

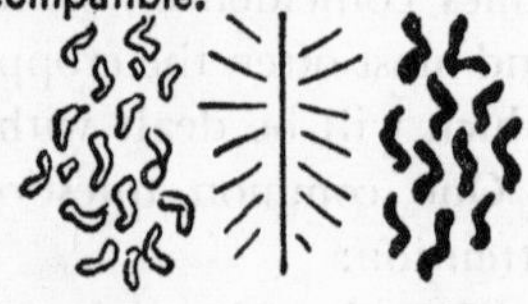

A Horse and a Donkey

Although of different species can mate and produce MULE offspring. But these are sterile (with only rare exceptions) because

A HORSE

produces eggs or sperms containing one kind of chromosomes.

A DONKEY

produces eggs or sperms with another kind of chromosomes.

—While these can work together somehow to produce MULE offspring

— The conflicting chromosomes cannot form in the Mule fertile germ cells.

BUT All Varieties of Human Beings Are Fertile With One Another

Because
—All humans are of the same species with the same kind of chromosomes. Thus, the smallest Pygmy

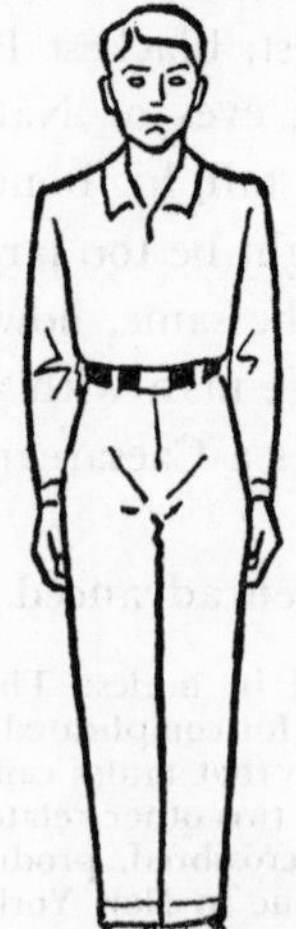

—and the tallest Nordic could mate and produce a child perfectly normal in the eyes of Nature.

radically different types, serious disharmonies may result in the bodily structure and features of their offspring. The evidence on that score is far from conclusive, and until proved otherwise, must be placed among "beliefs" rather than the facts with which we are dealing.

As matters stand the fear of having a freak child because of parental differences in features or bodies need hardly worry any of you who read this. Unless, perhaps, you happen to be a big-jawed circus giant mated to a chinless dwarf.

CHAPTER 6

THE MIRACLE OF *YOU*

WHAT was the most thrilling, hazardous, extraordinary adventure in your life?

Whatever you might answer, you are almost certain to be wrong. For the most remarkable and dramatic series of events that could possibly have befallen you took place before you were born.

In fact, it was virtually a miracle that YOU were born at all!

Consider what had to happen:

First, YOU—that very special person who is YOU and no one else in this universe—could have been the child of only *two specific parents* out of all the untold billions past and present. Assuming that YOU had been ordered up in advance by some capricious Power, it was an amazing enough coincidence that your parents came together. But taking that for granted, what were the chances of their having had YOU as a child? In other words, how many different kinds of children could they have had, or could any couple have, theoretically, if the number was unlimited?

This is not an impossible question. It can be answered by calculating how many different combinations of chromosomes any two parents can produce in their eggs or sperms. For what every parent

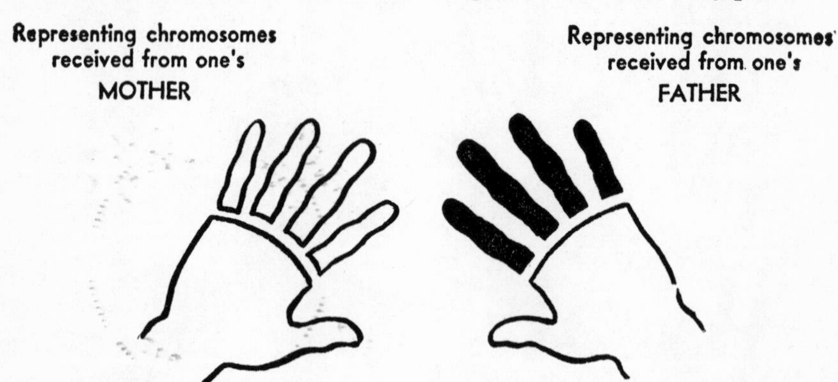

gives to a child is just half of his or her chromosomes—one representative of every pair taken at random. In that fact you will find the explanation of why YOU are different from your brothers and sisters, why no two children (except "identical" twins) can ever be the same in their heredity.

Putting yourself in the rôle of parent, think for a moment of your fingers (thumbs excluded) as if they were four pairs of chromosomes, of which one set had come to you from your father, one set from your mother. (To distinguish between the two, we've made the paternal set black in the Diagram, the maternal set white.)

Now suppose that these "chromosomes" were detachable and that you had countless duplicates of them. If you could give a set of four to every child, and it didn't make any difference whether any "chromosome" was a right- or left-hand one—in other words, whether it had come from your father or your mother—how many different combinations would be possible?

Sixteen (see the Diagram on this page), in which every combination differs from any other in from one to four "chromosomes."

But this is with just *four pairs* involved. If now you put the thumb of each hand into play, representing a *fifth* pair of "chromo-

Illustrating combinations of chromosomes produced with four pair

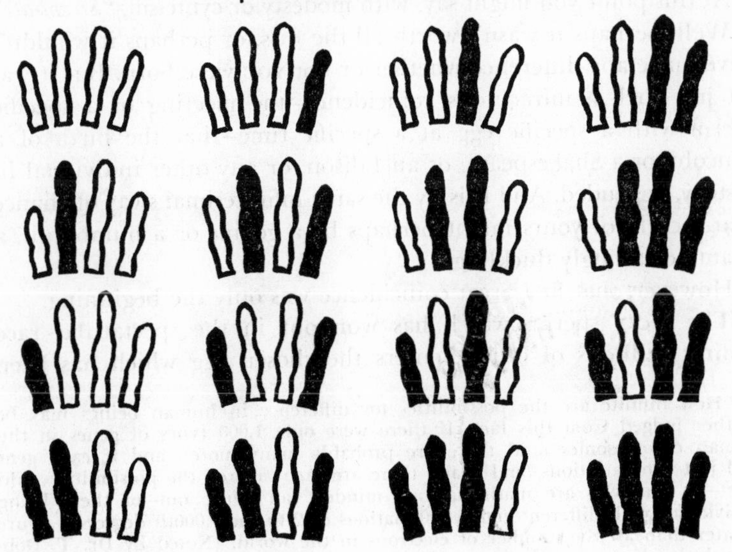

somes," you could produce twice the number of combinations, or thirty-two. In short, as our mathematician friends can quickly see, with every added pair of factors the number of possible combinations is doubled. So in the case of the actual chromosomes, with *twenty-four* pairs involved—where one from each pair is taken at random—every parent can theoretically produce 16,777,216 combinations of hereditary packets, each different from any other in anywhere from one to *all twenty-four chromosomes.*

Whether we are dealing with the millions of sperms released by a male at one time, or the single egg matured by a woman, the chance of any specific combination occurring would be that once in 16,777,216 times.

But to produce a given individual, *both* a specific sperm and a specific egg must come together. So think now what had to happen for YOU to have been born:

At exactly the right instant, the one out of 16,777,216 sperms which represented the *potential half* of you had to meet the one specific egg which held the *other potential half* of you. That could happen only once in some 300,000,000,000,000 times! Adding to this all the other factors involved (as we shall presently see), the chance of there having been or ever being another person exactly like you is virtually nil.*

At this point you might say, with modesty or cynicism, *"So what?"*

Well, perhaps it wasn't worth all the fuss, or perhaps it wouldn't have made any difference whether or not YOU were born. But it was on just such a miraculous coincidence—the meeting of a specific sperm with a specific egg at a specific time—that the birth of a Lincoln, or a Shakespeare, or an Edison, or any other individual in history, depended. And it is by the same infinitesimal sway of chance that a child of yours might perhaps be a genius or a numbskull, a beauty or an ugly duckling!

However, that first great coincidence was only the beginning.

The lucky sperm, which has won out in the spectacular race against millions of others, enters the chosen egg which has been

* How infinite are the possibilities for difference in human beings may be further judged from this fact: If there were only 1,000 types of genes in the human chromosomes (and there are probably many more), and if each gene had just two variations (and again, there are many more), the possibility would exist—as you who are mathematically-minded can figure out—of there being individuals with different gene combinations of 2 to the 1,000th degree—a figure greater than all the number of electrons in the world! (Noted by Dr. T. Dobzhansky.)

waiting in a fallopian tube of the mother. Immediately, as we previously learned, the sperm and the nucleus in the egg each releases its quota of chromosomes, and thus the fertilized egg starts off on its career.

Already, from this first instant, the fertilized egg is an individual with all its inherent capacities mapped out—so far as the hereditary factors can decide. Will the baby have blue eyes or brown eyes? Dark hair or blond hair? Will it have six fingers or a tendency to diabetes? Can it live to 19 or to 90? These and thousands of other characteristics are already largely predetermined by genes in its particular chromosomes.

But as yet the individual consists of only one cell, like the most elemental of living things, i.e., the ameba. To develop it into a full-fledged human being, trillions of cells will be required. How this multiplication is effected we have seen in a previous chapter: The chromosomes split in half and separate, then the cell divides, making *two* cells, each with exact replicas of the forty-eight chromosomes that there were in the original whole. Again the process is repeated, and the two cells become four. Again, and the four cells become eight. So it continues, and as you could figure out if you wished, the doubling process would have to be repeated only forty-five times to provide the twenty-six trillion cells which, it is estimated, constitute a fully developed baby.

However, as the cells go on to "specialize," some divide and multiply much more slowly than others. But regardless of how they multiply or what they turn into, to the very last cell each one will still carry in its nucleus descendants of each of the original forty-eight chromosomes.

CONCEPTION

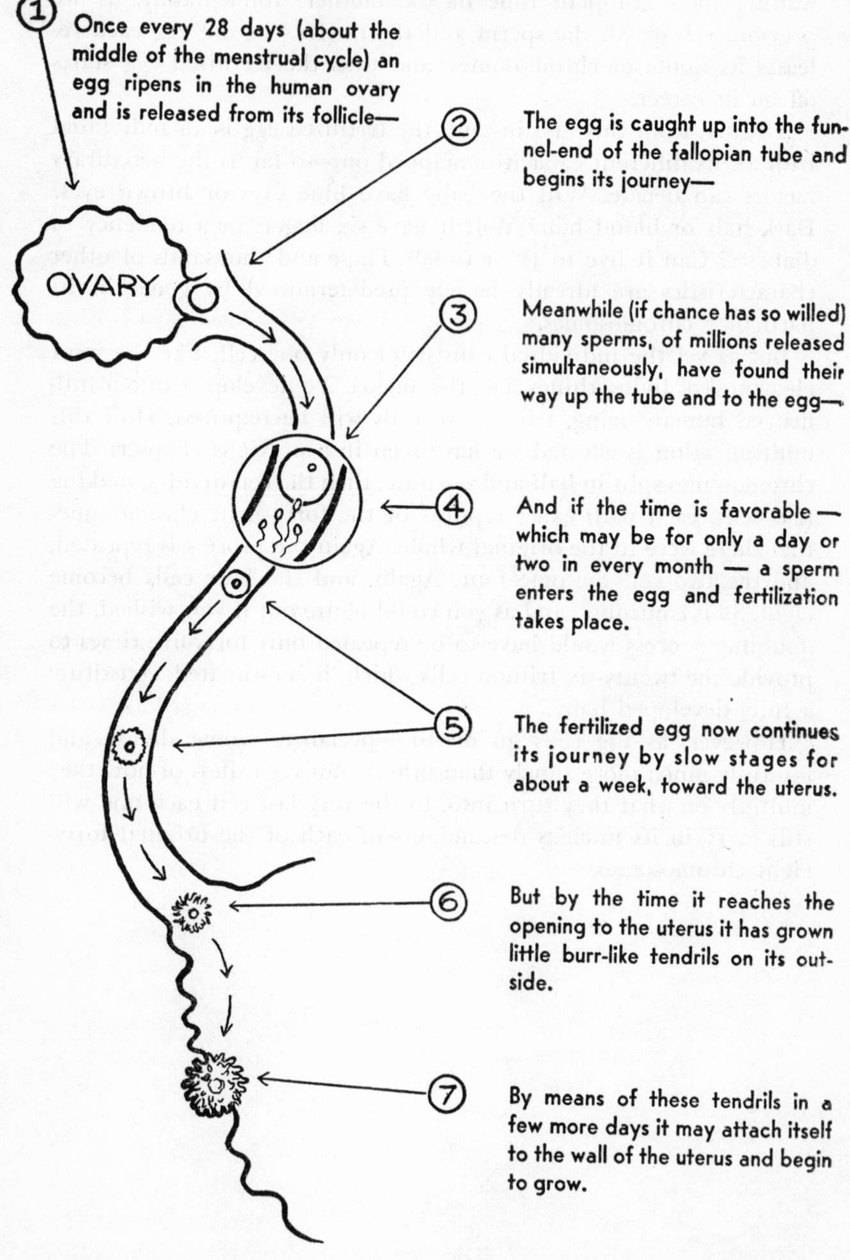

1
Once every 28 days (about the middle of the menstrual cycle) an egg ripens in the human ovary and is released from its follicle—
OVARY
2
The egg is caught up into the funnel-end of the fallopian tube and begins its journey—
3
Meanwhile (if chance has so willed) many sperms, of millions released simultaneously, have found their way up the tube and to the egg—
4
And if the time is favorable — which may be for only a day or two in every month — a sperm enters the egg and fertilization takes place.
5
The fertilized egg now continues its journey by slow stages for about a week, toward the uterus.
6
But by the time it reaches the opening to the uterus it has grown little burr-like tendrils on its outside.
7
By means of these tendrils in a few more days it may attach itself to the wall of the uterus and begin to grow.

NOTE: *The "rhythm" theory for women is based on the facts presented above.*

CHAPTER 7

THE PERILOUS ROAD TO BIRTH

WE HAVE followed the first stage in Your Greatest Adventure—the remarkable coincidence by which you were conceived. But conception is a long way from birth. The beginnings of life, as science has now disclosed them, are beset with far more hazards than any one has ever imagined.

In the first days after fertilization, while all the cell division and activity has been going on inside the egg, it has been slowly making its way down a fallopian tube toward the mother's uterus. Within a few more days the egg finds itself at the entrance of what—to this tiny droplet of substance, smaller than a period on this page—must be a vast, foreboding universe. If you can think of YOURSELF at that stage, your life hung precariously in the balance. Innumerable adverse forces confronted you. At any moment you might be swept away to destruction. In short, the odds were most heavily against your survival.

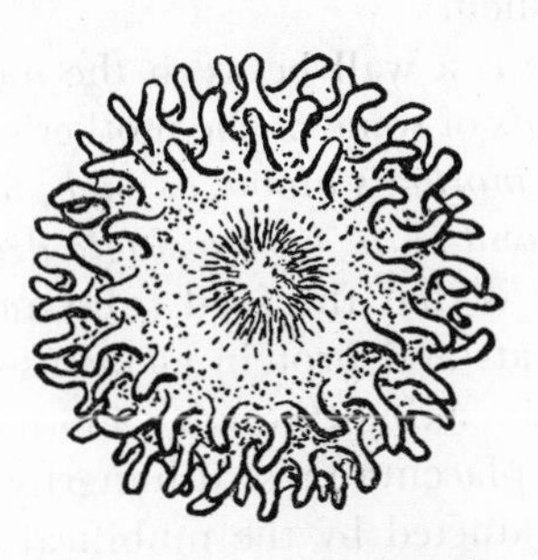

Exterior of HUMAN EGG (embryo) at time of implantation (about twelfth day)

Actual Size →

But to become impersonal once more, the immediate concern of the human egg at this stage is to take root somewhere. Already it has prepared itself for this by developing microscopic little "tendrils" from its outer surface, so that it somewhat resembles a tiny thistle. Thus it can attach itself to the mother's membrane, assuming —which is not always the case—that that membrance is receptive. If luck is with the egg, it is hospitably received—a hungry and thirsty little egg that has almost exhausted the store of food with which it started out. Immediately, with the maternal tissues cooperating, arrangements are begun for its food, oxygen and water supply through the development of a receiving surface—the *placenta* —which grows into the mother's membrane *but does not become part of it.* And so, about nine days from the start of its existence—the most perilous days in any person's life—the new individual becomes what is really a parasite on its mother.

And now we may ask, how far can the mother, from this point on, affect the development and future of the child? The answer, as revealed by the latest findings in embryology, should do much to dispel many popular misconceptions.

Skipping some of the early stages, we presently find the embryo encased in a fluid-filled sack, suspended from the placenta by the umbilical cord which acts as the conduit that brings in the food from the mother and carries out the waste products. But the umbilical cord is not, as is commonly supposed, a tube that goes directly into the mother's body. In fact, there is no direct connection anywhere, and at any time, between the mother and child. The child is from the earliest stage until birth as distinct an individual as if it were developing outside of the mother's body, like a chick within the eggshell.

There is a wall between the mother and child. On one side, the *open ends* of some of the mother's blood vessels empty into the wall. *But the mother's blood, as such, never reaches the child, nor do any mother and child have a single drop of blood in common.* For what happens is that the food substances in the mother's blood—chiefly sugars, fats and protein elements—are strained out by *osmosis,* like moisture soaking through a blotter. And it is these which are drawn into the placenta pressed hungrily on the other side of the wall, and then conducted by the umbilical cord to the embryo. As Professor C. H. Waddington has phrased it, if it were not for that wall or filter between mother and child, "the embryo would actually be killed by foreign proteins, since each animal is a chemical individual which has to be respected."

Science, by the way, has overruled the decision by the late great Justice Oliver Wendell Holmes, from a Massachusetts bench in

1884, that an unborn child is not an individual, but "part of its mother's bowels." In fact, acting on the new findings of science, a judge in Philadelphia ruled in 1940 during a contest over a will that "an unborn child is a life in being" and therefore entitled to share as a beneficiary.

Not only is there no direct blood connection between mother and child, but there is, moreover, no nerve connection, and hence no such mental or psychological relationship as mothers have always liked to believe exists between them and the little one they are

RELATIONSHIP BETWEEN MOTHER AND CHILD

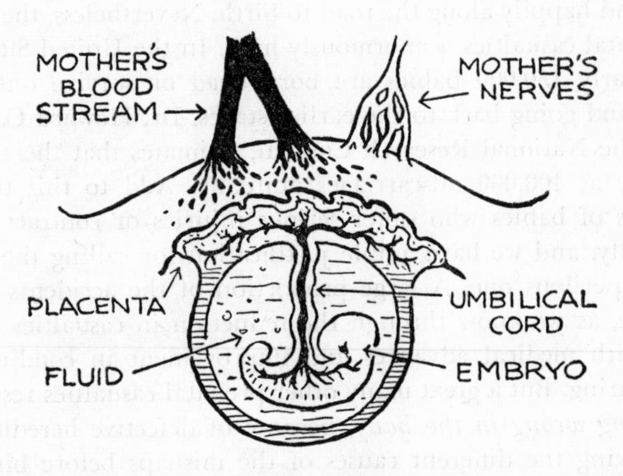

carrying. In the light of all this, another batch of myths, about prenatal influences and maternal impressions, about "strawberry marks" or other marks and deformities in the child resulting from the mother's having seen or done this or that, vanish into thin air. (We say "vanish" with reservations, for myths die hard, and even some of the most enlightened mothers still cherish a few of them.)

If the mother goes to concerts while she is carrying the child, that will not make it one whit more musical. Nor will thinking pure thoughts, reading elevating books or doing kind deeds during pregnancy improve the child's "character." Nonetheless, inasmuch as the mother's nervous system and her physical functioning work closely together, anything that will help her to relax and to feel happier may contribute toward making her physical condition better, and be to the child's advantage. By the same token, if the mother is unhappy and constantly upset, the child, too, may suffer.

We have proof of this in studies by Dr. L. W. Sontag, of the Fels Institute, showing that when a mother undergoes emotional stress there is a marked increase in the body movements of the child within her. (The fetus can also hear and react to sounds.) Prolonged maternal stress, Dr. Sontag reports, shows up in reduced birth weight of the baby, and may cause it to come into the world a "hyperactive, irritable, squirming, crying infant"—to all intents a "neurotic" infant when he is born.

There are many other ways in which the mother can adversely affect her child, but lest we sound too alarming as we recount the hazards, let us emphasize that the great majority of babies pass safely and happily along the road to birth. Nevertheless, the number of prenatal casualties is enormously high. In the United States each year nearly 150,000 babies are born dead or survive only a few weeks; and going back to the earlier stages, Dr. Howard C. Taylor, Jr., of the National Research Council, estimates that there may be as many as 400,000 miscarriages annually. Add to this the great numbers of babies who suffer serious injuries or contract diseases prenatally, and we have ample justification for calling the road to birth a perilous one. A large proportion of the accidents are preventable, as we know through the reduction in casualties that has come with medical advances and improvement in conditions for childbearing. But a great many other prenatal casualties result from *something wrong in the baby,* because of defective heredity. Only by knowing the different causes of the mishaps before birth, and especially, those which are avoidable, can we make much greater headway in reducing the prenatal mortality list.

First, there is the fact that the mother is the food provider, and if her supply is inadequate in any way, the fetus, being a voracious and exacting little parasite, will suffer malnutrition. Studies in Holland during the World War II hardships showed a marked decrease in the weights of infants at birth, and in Leningrad the food deprivations among mothers during the siege resulted not only in smaller sizes of the infants born to them, but in a much higher than average rate of defectiveness, prematurity and mortality. In London, on the other hand, where every effort was made to insure adequate nutrition to pregnant mothers during the war years, the infants born were as normal in size as ever before, and even healthier. It should be clear here that by "malnutrition" of the mother may be meant much less the quantity of the food she receives during pregnancy, than the *quality,* in terms of essential elements needed by the child. Lack of certain vitamins in the mother's diet might lead to rickets, scurvy or other defects in the unborn child, and may account for some of the stillbirths or deaths in early infancy. (Vitamin supplements during pregnancy may help to reduce these hazards.) Or if the mother's diet is too far overbalanced—with too much of certain proteins, for instance—*allergies* of various kinds may develop in the child before birth.

Again, in her rôle as nurse—a nurse inseparably linked with the child throughout the crucial prenatal period—the mother may unwittingly do it great injury. If her physical condition is very bad, or if she suffers any great shock, severe chill or strong emotional reaction, the life of the potential child may be snuffed out, often in its very earliest stages. Or the child may be propelled into the world so prematurely, or in so weak a condition, that it cannot survive.

In all this, the age of the mother may be an important factor, when it is related to an inferior physical condition. Thus, the hazards for babies in the prenatal stages are greatest among the "old" mothers—those close to or over 40, among whom the rate of miscarriages, premature births, or deaths of infants at birth or immediately thereafter, is far higher than the general average. The rate of stillbirths is about one in fifty for mothers up to age 30, and rises to one in thirteen for mothers aged 44 to 49. Especially bad is the situation for those having their first baby in their mid-forties. Very young mothers (those under 17) also have a higher than average rate of stillbirths and prematurity. At either age extreme, hormonal inadequacies or deficiencies in the mother may be chiefly to blame, the probability being that in the older mother the hormonal supply has begun to ebb out, whereas in the younger mother it may be incomplete. However, in any given instance, it is the mother's general physical state, and the conditions for her childbearing, rather than her age, that may be most important. Thus, the stillbirth rate among Negro mothers in the United States is far higher at all ages than among Whites, as Drs. H. H. Strandskov and Sara Einhorn have shown, and can be attributed primarily to poorer environments.

But some of the greatest hazards to the embryonic child come from the fact that the porous placental wall through which it gets its food *may also permit the passage through from the mother of many harmful substances,* especially in the later stages of pregnancy.

Most dramatic of the possibilities is that there may be an *incompatibility between the blood of a mother and her embryo child,* involving the "Rh" factor or other inherited differences in blood elements. (Many of you, especially those who have been mothers in the last few years, may already know about this.) Despite there being no direct blood connection between mother and child, as we said before, there still can be an interchange of certain chemical *substances* in their bloods, and if there is a clash between these substances, the child's blood cells may be seriously damaged, sometimes with death or severe injury resulting. In a later chapter we will give the full story of this amazing situation, of how in former years it cost the lives of thousands of infants, and of how discovery of the causes and precautionary measures have now greatly reduced the threats.

Offering further dangers to the embryonic child are various diseases in the mother which can be transmitted through germs or viruses penetrating the placenta. (We should note here—prior to our detailed discussions in later chapters—that a child *can not "inherit"* any germ disease, or acquire it at conception, for no sperm, and so far as we have record, no human egg, could carry a disease germ of any kind and still function.) Among the serious germ diseases that can be passed on to the child prenatally are diphtheria, typhoid, tuberculosis, influenza and syphilis, while other infections, such as gonorrhea, may be acquired during the final hours of birth. Moreover, whether through germs or her condition, where the mother suffers from typhoid fever, scarlet fever, cholera, malaria, smallpox, erysipelas or pneumonia, in a great many cases the child will be killed before birth. Other serious effects on the child may result if the pregnant mother has nephritis (kidney diseases), certain heart conditions or thyroid or other glandular deficiencies.

German measles (rubella) has been given special attention in recent years because of findings that if the disease is contracted by a mother during the first months of pregnancy, its effects may in some way, occasionally, cause her child to develop congenital cataracts and (or) other eye defects, or deafness, or heart defects, or any of a variety of malformations. Inasmuch as the disease in itself is not serious, some authorities suggest that as a safeguard all young girls should be exposed to German measles in order to develop an immunity which would prevent their having the disease in their childbearing years. In line with this, there have been findings that immunities which the mother may acquire to a number of virus infections, and to some diseases such as whooping cough, may in some instances be passed on to the child, fortifying it against these conditions after it is born.

Still another possibility is that various drugs may pass from the mother to the embryo, among them quinine and sleep-inducing drugs if used to excess. Most dangerous of all are the narcotics. If the mother is addicted to morphine or opium to the point where her tissues are saturated with the drug, *the child may actually come into the world as a drug addict.* One such case of a baby born to a morphine-addicted mother was reported in the *Journal* of the American Medical Association in 1947. A short time after birth the baby showed all the symptoms of an addict suddenly deprived of his drug, and might have died of convulsions if not given a standard treatment for drug addiction. Happily, in eight weeks the baby emerged safely from its morphine-addict state.

Less certain is the evidence of the effects of smoking or drinking by the pregnant mother. Some authorities believe that if the mother smokes *to excess,* the nicotine may get to the child and be harmful (Dr. Sontag having shown that the fetal heartbeat reacts to the mother's smoking just as does her own). There also is some indication that if the mother drinks heavily during pregnancy, the alcohol in her system may similarly reach the child with harmful effects (although the old belief that "monsters" may result in this way has now been discounted).

So far we have stressed all the perils on the road to birth, and it should be noted that with the exception of the blood incompatibilities, those we've dealt with are all *environmental.* In later chapters we'll have much more to say about the hereditary hazards. But at this point we can already see clearly that from the very first instant of the baby's life—we might say even before conception—both heredity and environment are at work.

An egg might start off with one or more defective chromosomes, or *bad heredity,* which might under average conditions destine it to be killed off. But if the mother's condition is unusually good—in other words, if the *environment* is extremely favorable—the "weak" egg may develop through to birth and the individual may survive.

On the other hand, an egg might start off with the finest of genes, the best of heredity. But through bad prenatal environment the individual might be killed off or permanently injured. However, where conditions are equally bad, or equally good, the chances for the egg with the better heredity will always be brighter than for the egg starting under a genetic handicap.

In the nine months before birth every human being faces the most severe test that he will ever undergo. With seeming ruthlessness Nature exercises her "Law of Selection," killing off the weak more relentlessly than ever the ancient Greeks ventured to do. In fact, so stringent is the initial ordeal that many experts believe the children who achieve birth represent only a *portion of the eggs fertilized*. In other words, in innumerable instances—perhaps a majority of the cases—women conceive and the egg is killed off without their even knowing it. What frequently are described as "false alarms" may have been actual conceptions.

Undoubtedly, and unfortunately, many worthy individuals are sacrificed in the initial weeding process. On the whole, however, most parents may have reason to be grateful for the rigid pre-selection, for without it the world might be overrun with some pretty bad specimens. As it is, plenty of them do survive, though these are in the great minority. Where birth is achieved, it can generally be taken as an indication that the individual is qualified to face life. From that point on, how he fares is up to his parents, to himself and to the environment created by society.

CHAPTER 8

"BOY OR GIRL?"

NEXT to being born, the most important single fact attending your coming into the world was whether you were to be a male or a female. Undoubtedly, that is the first question that occurs to prospective parents. Before you read this chapter, you may find it of interest to test your present knowledge as to what determines sex. Which of these statements would you say is right, which wrong?

1. The sex of an unborn child can be influenced before, during or after conception by (a) the stars, (b) the moon, (c) the climate, or (d) the mother's diet.

2. It can be much influenced before conception by the "acid-alkali" treatment, or other chemical means.

3. It is through the mother that the sex of a child is determined, because she produces two kinds of eggs, the right ovary forming "boy" eggs, the left ovary, "girl" eggs.

4. On an average, as many boys are conceived as girls, but more boys are born because they are stronger.

5. A mother's age or condition has no effect on her chances of giving birth to a boy or a girl.

Every one of the foregoing statements, you will presently find, is wrong!

The scene is a regally furnished bedchamber, in medieval times.

A beautiful young woman is lying in a luxurious, canopied bed. She is to become a mother, but although this will not occur for many months, already there is much to do.

A midwife carefully adjusts her so that she lies on her right side, her hands held with thumbs out. Over her now a bearded necromancer swings a tiny incense-burner with precise up-and-down motions. (Heaven forfend that it be allowed to describe a circle!) At the foot of the bed an abbot kneels in prayer. In one corner an astrologer mumbles incantations as he studies an almanac. In another corner an alchemist prepares a potion in which are boiled the wattles of a rooster, some heart blood of a lion, the head of an eagle and certain parts of a bull—the essence of all of which will be blended with thrice-blessed wine and given to the young woman to drink. And meanwhile, surrounded by high counselors, the young woman's noble spouse—none other than the mighty Sovereign of the Realm—looks anxiously on.

By this time you have probably guessed that all the ceremonial and hocus-pocus was for a single purpose: to make sure that the expected child would be a son and heir to the throne.

Synthetic as this particular scene might be, in effect it occurred many times in history. But if it were only a matter of dim history we would not be dealing with it here. The fact is, however, that to this very present day, throughout the world and in our own country, a fascinating variety of potions, prayers, midwives' formulas, "thought applications," diets, drugs or quasi-medical treatments is still being employed by expectant mothers to influence the sex of the future child. Most often, undoubtedly, the objective is a boy.* But an ample list could also be compiled of the "what-to-dos" to make it a girl.

Alas then, whatever the methods employed, primitive or supposedly enlightened, all are now equally dismissed by science with this definite and disillusioning answer:

The sex of every child is fixed at the instant of conception—and it is not through the mother, but through the father that sex is determined.

The moment that the father's sperm enters the mother's egg, the child is started on its way to being a boy or a girl. Subsequent events or influences may possibly affect the *degree* of "maleness" or "femaleness," or thwart normal development, but *nothing within our power from that first instant on can change what is to be a girl into a boy, or vice versa.*

The solution of the mystery of sex determination came about through this discovery:

* The general preference for a boy baby is a deeply rooted one in many parts of the world, for various reasons. Oriental men, and various primitives, are told by their religions that they must have a son to pray for their spirits, or they'll fare badly in the Hereafter. Kings and potentates want male heirs for their thrones. (The King of Egypt and the Shah of Iran secured divorces in 1948 for the official reason that their wives had borne them no sons.) Industrialists want sons to carry on their enterprises, and many men are deeply anxious to have sons to carry on their family names. But the stress on the importance of having sons has been steadily diminishing in the United States, many parents even preferring daughters. In fact, adoption agencies report a much greater demand for girl babies than for boy babies.

HOW SEX IS DETERMINED

This is what makes all the differences there are between a woman and a man:

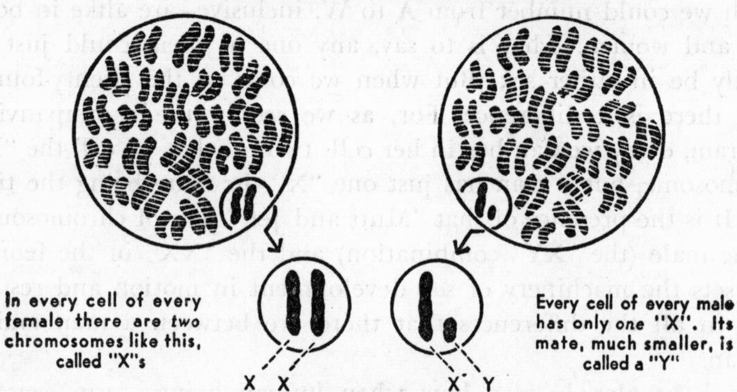

In every cell of every female there are *two* chromosomes like this, called "X"s

Every cell of every male has only *one* "X". Its mate, much smaller, is called a "Y"

For reproduction, a female forms *eggs*, a male *sperms*, to each of which they contribute only HALF their quota of chromosomes, or *just one from every pair*

Since a female has TWO "X"s, each egg gets one "X", so in this respect *every egg is the same:*

But as the male has only ONE "X", paired with a "Y", he forms TWO kinds of sperms:

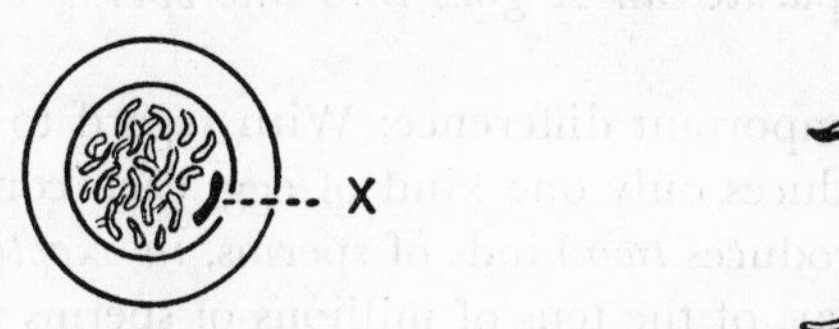

HALF WITH AN "X"

HALF WITH A "Y"

Thus: If an "X"-bearing sperm enters the egg, the result is an individual with TWO "X"s

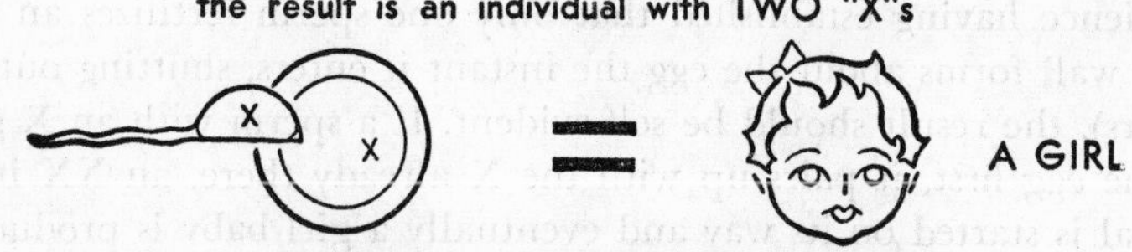

. . . If a "Y"-bearing sperm enters the egg, the result is an "XY" individual, or

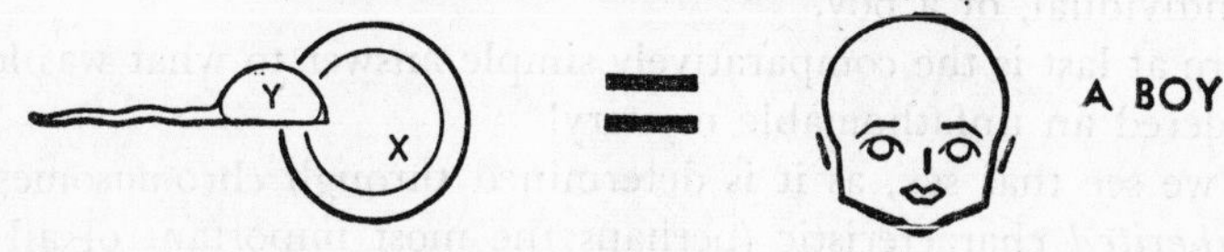

That the only difference between the chromosomes of a man and a woman lies in just one of the pairs—in fact, in a single chromosome of this pair.

Of the twenty-four pairs of chromosomes, twenty-three pairs—which we could number from A to W, inclusive—are alike in both men and women. That is to say, any one of them could just as readily be in either sex. But when we come to the twenty-fourth pair, there is a difference. For, as we see in the accompanying Diagram, every woman has in her cells two of what we call the "X" chromosome, but a man has just one "X"—its mate being the tiny "Y." It is the presence of that "Mutt and Jeff" pair of chromosomes in the male (the "XY" combination) and the "XX" in the female that sets the machinery of sex development in motion and results later in all the differences that there are between a man and a woman.

We have already seen how when human beings form eggs or sperms, each gets just *half* the respective parent's quota of chromosomes, or one of every pair. When the female, then, with her two Xs, forms eggs and gives to each egg one chromosome of every pair, *every egg gets an* X.

But when the male forms sperms, and his unevenly matched pair of sex chromosomes separate, *an X goes into one sperm, a Y into another.*

Thus, we have this important difference: With regard to the sex factor, the mother produces only one kind of egg, each containing an X. But the father produces *two* kinds of sperms, *in exactly equal numbers.* Which is to say, of the tens of millions of sperms released by a man each time, exactly half are X-bearers, half Y-bearers.

Science having established that only one sperm fertilizes an egg (as a wall forms about the egg the instant it enters, shutting out all others), the result should be self-evident. If a sperm with an X gets to the egg first, it pairs up with the X already there, an XX individual is started on its way and eventually a girl baby is produced. But should a Y-bearing sperm win the race, the result will be an XY individual, or a boy.

Here at last is the comparatively simple answer to what was long considered an unfathomable mystery!

So we see that sex, as it is determined through chromosomes, is an *inherited* characteristic (perhaps the most important of all inherited traits for the individual). But precisely how?

Do males get one kind of "sex" genes, females another? No. There are indeed "maleness" genes and "femaleness" genes, but each sex gets them both, *though in different proportions.* For sex development at conception and throughout life is governed by a *balance*

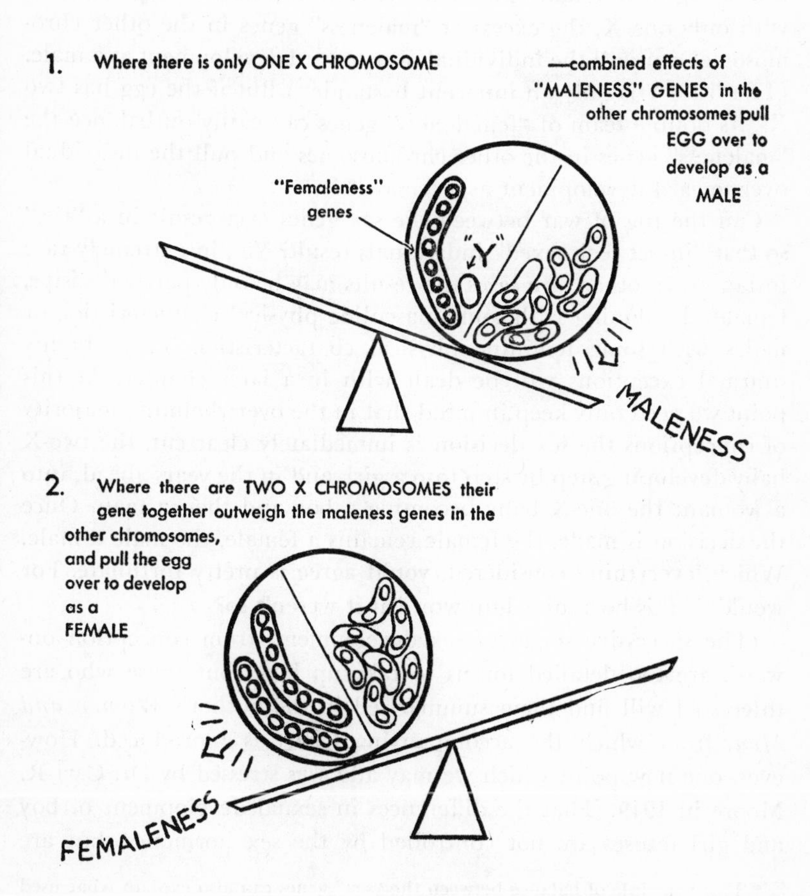
THE "SEX-GENE" BALANCE
1. Where there is only ONE X CHROMOSOME
—combined effects of "MALENESS" GENES in the other chromosomes pull EGG over to develop as a MALE
"Femaleness" genes
"Y"
MALENESS
2. Where there are TWO X CHROMOSOMES their gene together outweigh the maleness genes in the other chromosomes, and pull the egg over to develop as a FEMALE
FEMALENESS

between the two kinds of genes, which are carried not only in the X chromosomes, but in many of the other chromosomes. Excepting, strangely enough, the Y! Contrary to what you may have supposed, there is no evidence that this small chromosome contains any "maleness" genes or any "sex" genes at all. (In fact, in some species of animals there isn't any Y, males being produced by receiving merely one X, whereas the female gets two Xs.)

The key to the situation is held by the X chromosomes. These carry genes heavily slanted in the "femaleness" direction, whereas the "sex" genes distributed among the other twenty-three pairs of chromosomes are slanted in the "maleness" direction. So at conception a tug of war takes place. If the fertilized human egg starts off with only one X, the excess of "maleness" genes in the other chromosomes can pull the individual over toward development as a male. (The little Y is only an innocent bystander.) But if the egg has two Xs, its double team of "femaleness" genes can easily outbalance the "maleness" genes in the other chromosomes and pull the individual over toward development as a female.*

Can the tug of war between the sex genes ever result in a "tie," so that "in-between-sexed" individuals result? Yes, in extremely rare instances. In other rare cases the results may be only partly decisive, females developing with some masculine physical characteristics, or males with some feminine physical characteristics. These highly unusual exceptions will be dealt with in a later chapter. At this point we need only keep in mind that in the overwhelming majority of conceptions the sex decision is immediately clear cut, the two-X baby developing step by step into a girl, and in the years ahead, into a woman; the one-X baby becoming a boy and then a man. Once the decision is made, the female remains a female, the male a male. Which, everything considered, you'll agree is pretty fortunate. For wouldn't this be a mixed-up world if it weren't so?

(The successive stages of sex development, from conception onward, are too detailed for us to take up here, but those who are interested will find them summarized in the author's *Women and Men,* from which the accompanying Chart is reproduced. However, one new point which we may add was stressed by Dr. Carl R. Moore in 1949: That the differences in sexual development of boy and girl fetuses are not controlled by the sex hormones, but are

* This principle of balance between the "sex" genes can also explain what used to be a puzzling fact with respect to poultry, birds and certain insects: In these species the sex-determining mechanism is reversed, with the two-X combination producing a *male,* the XY combination producing a *female.* As we now know, in these species the arrangement of the "sex" genes is transposed, the X chromosomes being the ones that are overloaded with "maleness" genes, the other chromosomes carrying most of the "femaleness" genes, so that two Xs in the bird species pull the individual toward male development, whereas a single X permits it to be pulled toward female development.

HOW THE INTERNAL SEX MECHANISM DEVELOPS
(Shown Diagrammatically)

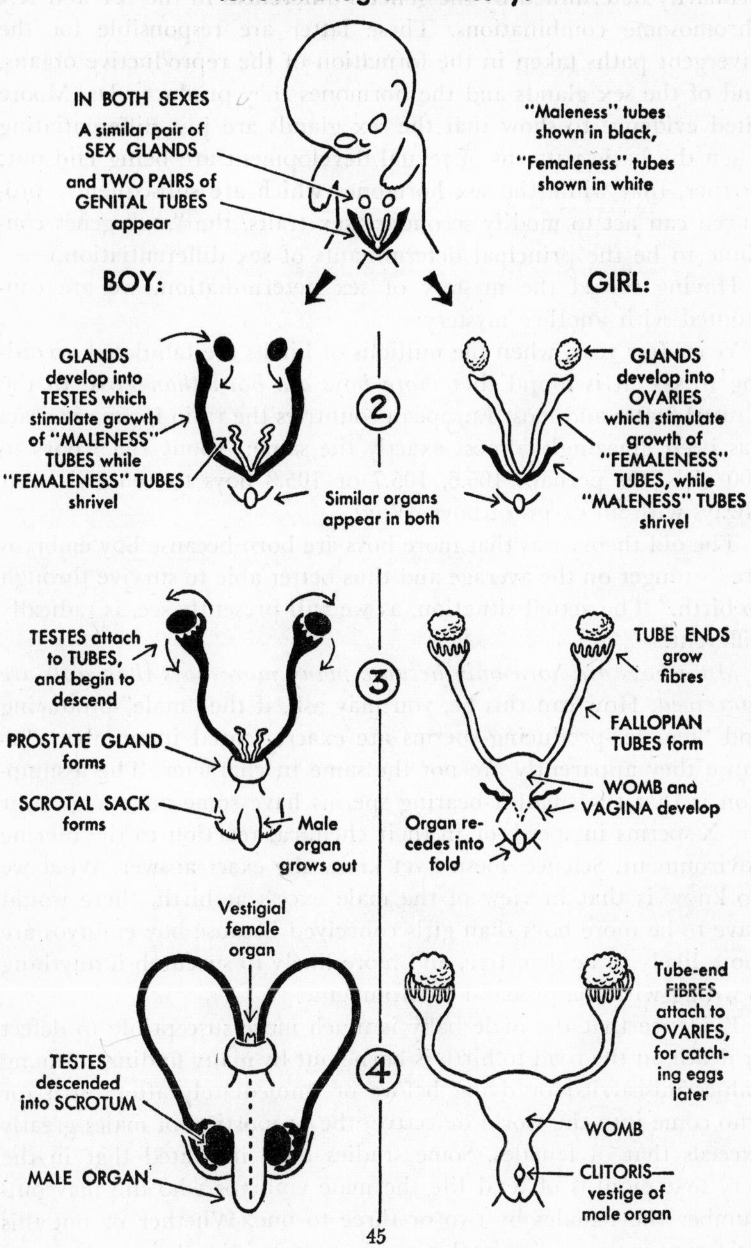

IN BOTH SEXES
A similar pair of SEX GLANDS and TWO PAIRS of GENITAL TUBES appear
"Maleness" tubes shown in black,
"Femaleness" tubes shown in white
BOY:
GIRL:
GLANDS develop into TESTES which stimulate growth of "MALENESS" TUBES while "FEMALENESS" TUBES shrivel
2
GLANDS develop into OVARIES which stimulate growth of "FEMALENESS" TUBES, while "MALENESS" TUBES shrivel
Similar organs appear in both
TESTES attach to TUBES, and begin to descend
PROSTATE GLAND forms
SCROTAL SACK forms
Male organ grows out
3
TUBE ENDS grow fibres
FALLOPIAN TUBES form
WOMB and VAGINA develop
Organ recedes into fold
Vestigial female organ
TESTES descended into SCROTUM
MALE ORGAN
4
Tube-end FIBRES attach to OVARIES, for catching eggs later
WOMB
CLITORIS—vestige of male organ

primarily determined by the genetic differences in the XY and XX chromosome combinations. These latter are responsible for the divergent paths taken in the formation of the reproductive organs, and of the sex glands and the hormones they produce. Dr. Moore cited evidence to show that the sex glands are just differentiating when the basic patterns of sexual development are being laid out; further, that while the sex hormones which are subsequently produced can act to modify secondary sex traits, the "sex" genes continue to be the principal determinants of sex differentiation.)

Having solved the mystery of sex determination, we are confronted with another mystery:

Year after year, when the millions of births are tabulated according to sex, it is found that *more boys are born than girls.* In the United States and most European countries the ratio for many years has been amazingly almost exactly the same: About 105.5 boys to 100 girls. Or perhaps 105.6, 105.7 or 105.8 boys to 100 girls. But always with an excess of boys. Why?

The old theory was that more boys are born because boy embryos are "stronger on the average and thus better able to survive through to birth." The actual situation, as we will presently see, is radically different.

More boys are born only because many more boys than girls are conceived. How can this be, you may ask, if the "male"-producing and "female"-producing sperms are exactly equal in number? Because they apparently are not the same in character. The assumption is that the small Y-bearing sperms have some advantage over the X-sperms in speed, or in their chemical reaction to the uterine environment. Science doesn't yet know the exact answer. What we do know is that in view of the male excess at birth, there would have to be more boys than girls conceived because boy embryos are more likely to be defective, and more likely to succumb if anything is wrong with the prenatal environment.

Evidence that the male baby is much more susceptible to defect or death on the road to birth is borne out by many findings. Among babies miscarried or dying before or immediately after birth (or who come into the world defective) the proportion of males greatly exceeds that of females. Some studies have indicated that in the very first months of fetal life the male embryos who die may outnumber the females by two or three to one. Whether or not this estimate for the earlier fetal stages is correct (it has been questioned in a recent study by Dr. Christopher Tietze), the fact is indisputable that among stillborn babies the average has steadily been about 125 boys to 100 girls. Nor is this higher early male mortality confined to human beings, for one finds also the same ratio of male to female prenatal deaths or stillbirths in many lower animals.

In short, *males—not females—are biologically the weaker sex, not only before birth, but in infancy, and always thereafter.* (All this we'll find brought out in more detail further along in our book.)*

Thus, if despite their greater weakness, and the greater toll taken of them on the road to birth, there still are more boys born than girls, it can only be because more boys are started off in the race—perhaps 20 per cent or even more at conception, in the belief of many authorities. And if we look ahead to the fact that at every stage of life males seem destined to die off at a higher rate, it can very well be that a canny Nature starts the sexes off with a surplus of males to partly provide for the greater drain upon their number later.

The explanations and theories as to *why* males are less able to survive will be presented in later chapters. For the moment, we might gather that where prenatal conditions are most favorable, the chances of a boy's achieving birth are greater; where prenatal conditions are less favorable, the chances of a son's being born are lessened.

There is much evidence to support this. Within each class or culture, the mother's physical condition at different ages and stages of her life affects her chance of producing a son. Young, healthy mothers on the average produce a considerably higher ratio of boys than do older mothers. In some groups the ratio among young mothers, 18 to 22, has been reported as high as 120 boys to 100 girls, while the ratio among mothers aged 38 to 42 has been reported as low as 90 boys to 100 girls. Further, an important class difference was noted in a study by Dr. Marianne E. Bernstein in 1948. She reported that among "upper class" families of Americans and Ger-

* A special point to be made here is that in prenatal life the male lags considerably behind the female fetus in skeletal development, and at birth may be as much as a month and a half behind the female in the process of bone-hardening (ossification). This may help to make the male baby a less sturdy individual in the early stages. Also of interest, there is some evidence that males take slightly longer in achieving birth. In fruit flies, the female is hatched some time before the male; in horses and cattle, it has been found that the period of gestation for male offspring is about 1½ days longer than for females; and in humans, also, several studies have suggested that girl babies, on the average, achieve birth several days before boys do. (*Women and Men*, pp. 27-28.)

mans there had been a continuous rise in the sex ratio of offspring for the past thirty years, with the sex ratio in these groups having now reached about 120 to 125 boys for every 100 girls.

Another striking comparison is in the sex ratio for Negroes and Whites, the ratio of boys born among Negro mothers being consistently below the White average, to the point where among Negroes of extreme poverty levels there are hardly any more boys born than girls. But race itself is not the factor, for among Negro mothers in more favorable circumstances the boy ratio reaches that of the White average. Also significant is a report by a Chinese sociologist, Ta Chen (1946), that in China more girls are born than boys, and that in India the sex ratio at birth is 98.7 boys to 100 girls. If these figures are correct, they would not be surprising in view of the generally bad prenatal conditions in both countries.

Taking other negative factors, in twins, triplets, etc., where the more crowded the womb, the more unfavorable is the environment for each embryo and the higher the stillbirth rate, the ratio of males to females drops according to the number of multiples. Among twins born in the United States, the average is 103.5 boys to 100 girls; among triplets, fewer than 98 boys to 100 girls; among quadruplets, as low as 70 boys to 100 girls. (For Negroes the prenatal mortality for multiples, and for boy twins, triplets, etc., as compared with girls, is much higher than among Whites, as Drs. H. H. Strandskov and Doris Ondina have shown.)

In "illegitimate" births, a much lower than average male ratio was formerly reported, which could well have been explained by the unfavorable conditions that usually went with these births. However, a study made by the author (1944) in five New York homes for unmarried mothers, where the best of care is provided, showed that among the more than 3,000 children born to these mothers the ratio was 108.6 boys to 100 girls.

Another belief of long standing is that the ratio of boys born goes up in wartime through some mysterious influence of "Nature," presumably an attempt to make up for the men killed. Statistically, there may seem to be some support for this. After World War I, there was a reported advance of from 1 to 2.5 per cent in the ratio of male births in the principal war countries, the largest increase being in Germany, where the ratio rose to 108.5 males to 100 females. The figures for World War II and its aftermath available to date seem less significant, with only slight increases having been reported in the boy to girl ratio in the United States and Great Britain.* However, granted that somewhat more than average ratios of boys are born during war time, scientists don't believe there need be anything supernatural about it. The reason might be chiefly that during or following wars there is a large increase in childbearing among the younger, healthier or more favored mothers, who normally produce a higher ratio of boys.

A popular question is whether a tendency to bear sons may not run in certain families or individuals. Quite possibly, yes. Ordinarily, a "run" of either sons or daughters in a given family may be as much a matter of chance as a succession of heads or of tails when tossing coins. Yet the strikingly high disproportion of either sons or daughters in some large families for successive generations suggests other possibilities. In lower animals, it has been shown that variations in the sex ratio do often have an hereditary basis, some breeds consistently producing more males than others. For example, mice can be bred with the sex ratio shifted in either direction, from an average of 25 per cent more males to 25 per cent more females, and in the fruit fly a 100 per cent ratio of either sex can be achieved by breeding strains in which those of one or the other sex are killed off at conception. So in humans, too, it is possible that hereditary factors may be operating in some families to influence the sex ratios, perhaps directly through the genes, or indirectly through making the uterine environments of mothers either more or less favorable for sons, or else making the male-producing sperms of fathers either more or less active and potent than in average cases. Another theory is that fathers (or mothers) who come of sturdy and long-lived strains, and who themselves are genetically superior in vigor, may tend to sire sturdier boy babies with a better chance of prenatal survival.

There are other questions which may have occurred to you. Can the weather or climate of where you happen to live influence the chances of conceiving, or bearing, a son or daughter? Apparently not, for studies in the United States over a ten-year period show that the sex ratios average up to about the same in one part of the country as compared with another, despite marked differences in climate.

* Among births in the United States during the war years, from 1942 to 1946 inclusive, the ratio was 106.1 boys to 100 girls, as compared with a ratio of 105.8 for the preceding five years. (Reported in the Metropolitan Life Ins. Co. Bulletin, June, 1949.)

POSSIBLE FUTURE METHODS OF "SEX CONTROL"

DIFFERENCES MAY EXIST, CHEMICALLY, STRUCTURALLY, IN ELECTRICAL REACTION OR IN SIZE OR SPEED, BETWEEN THE

FEMALE-PRODUCING SPERM

MALE-PRODUCING SPERM

ACCORDINGLY, THESE METHODS MAY POSSIBLY LEAD TO PRODUCING OFFSPRING OF THE SEX DESIRED:

(1) A. Before introducing the father's sperms into the mother, it may be possible to separate the "male-producing" sperms from the "female-producing" sperms, by "centrifuging" or by chemical or electrical action:

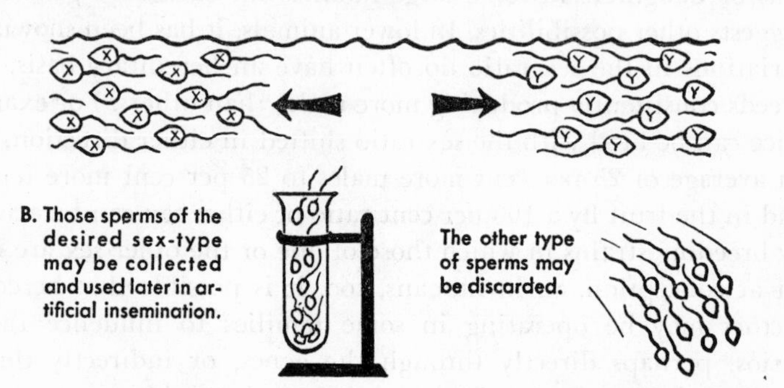

B. Those sperms of the desired sex-type may be collected and used later in artificial insemination.

The other type of sperms may be discarded.

(2) Some chemical solution may be found in which the sperms of one type can swim faster than the other, so that when injected into the mother, only one type of sperms will reach the egg.

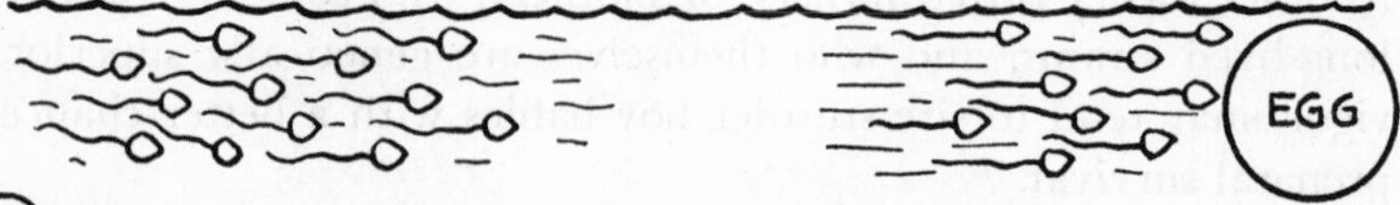

(3) —Or some chemical may be injected, or some technique employed, by which only one type of sperms will survive in the womb, leaving the field exclusively to the other type:

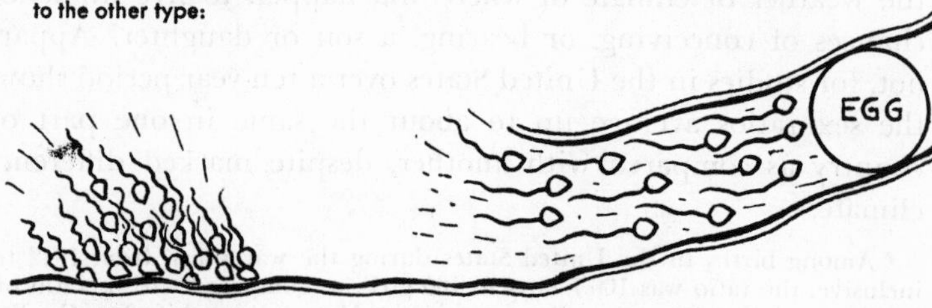

Can the "acid-alkali" treatment before conception ("acid" for a girl—"alkali" for a boy) influence sex determination? Again, apparently not. Despite the wide publicity given to this "method" in recent years, careful follow-up studies by scientists have produced no corroborative results. Nor has any other kind of drug, or any kind of diet, been found effective in this respect. (More recently, in 1949, it was reported that the time of conception—earlier or later in the woman's fertile period—might have an influence on whether a boy or girl was conceived, with the earlier conception presumably favoring a female birth. But this is regarded as dubious by a number of authorities, and at best, remains to be proved.)

All of which isn't to say that some method may not eventually be found which will give parents some power with regard to having a child of the sex they desire. The strongest possibility, many scientists believe, may lie in finding a way to separate the Y-bearing from the X-bearing sperms, and then, through artificial insemination, using either kind of sperms as desired. Or, if chemical differences can be found in the two types of sperms, a way may be devised to give one or the other a marked advantage in the race for conception. No doubt if parents can have a boy or girl baby, as they wish, it will bring happiness in many individual cases. But for society at large, it may open up a Pandora's box of new headaches and troubles.

So perhaps the genetic process of sex determination, whatever its shortcomings, may still be the best. For the time being, anyway, it remains for parents a matter of chance, with this qualification, as we have seen: The better prepared a woman is for motherhood, the slightly greater will be the odds that as the anxious father paces the hospital corridor, the nurse will report,

"It's a boy!"

CHAPTER 9

PEAS, FLIES AND PEOPLE

YOUR sex is only one of the myriad of characteristics potentially determined by your genes at the instant of conception.

But before we go into details about all the other inherited traits, let us turn back the pages of genetic history to learn something of how the mysteries of the genes and chromosomes were unravelled.

Whatever we know about heredity is based largely on the original findings of two men:

One, an obscure Austrian monk of the past century, Gregor Mendel, who cultivated garden peas.

The other, an American scientist, Thomas Hunt Morgan, who, until his death in 1945, cultivated fruit flies.

How, you might ask, could ordinary garden peas (the same peas that you get at any club luncheon with your chicken and candied sweets), and fruit flies (the tiny kind that buzz around bunches of bananas—and not the best bananas, either), how could these have any bearing on what you or other humans are? They could, because, as we know now, the mechanism of heredity in peas and flies, as in all other living things, is basically the same as it is in man. This is one of the amazing facts that may be hardest to accept for those who think of human beings as completely unique.

When in 1857 the plump Abbot Gregor Mendel, waddling about in the garden of the monastery at Brno (in what is now Czechoslovakia), set out to clarify his mind about the heredity of peas, he himself did not dream that he was at the same time about to throw lasting light on the heredity of human beings. Mendel had a brilliant mind, but it was simple and direct. And this is why he succeeded where others failed. He resolved to confine his studies to his own little thirty-by-seven-foot patch and not to wander afield (possibly because he was too fat to travel comfortably). In his garden were plants with many different characteristics. Mendel decided to concentrate on just one character at a time. So, as one instance, he

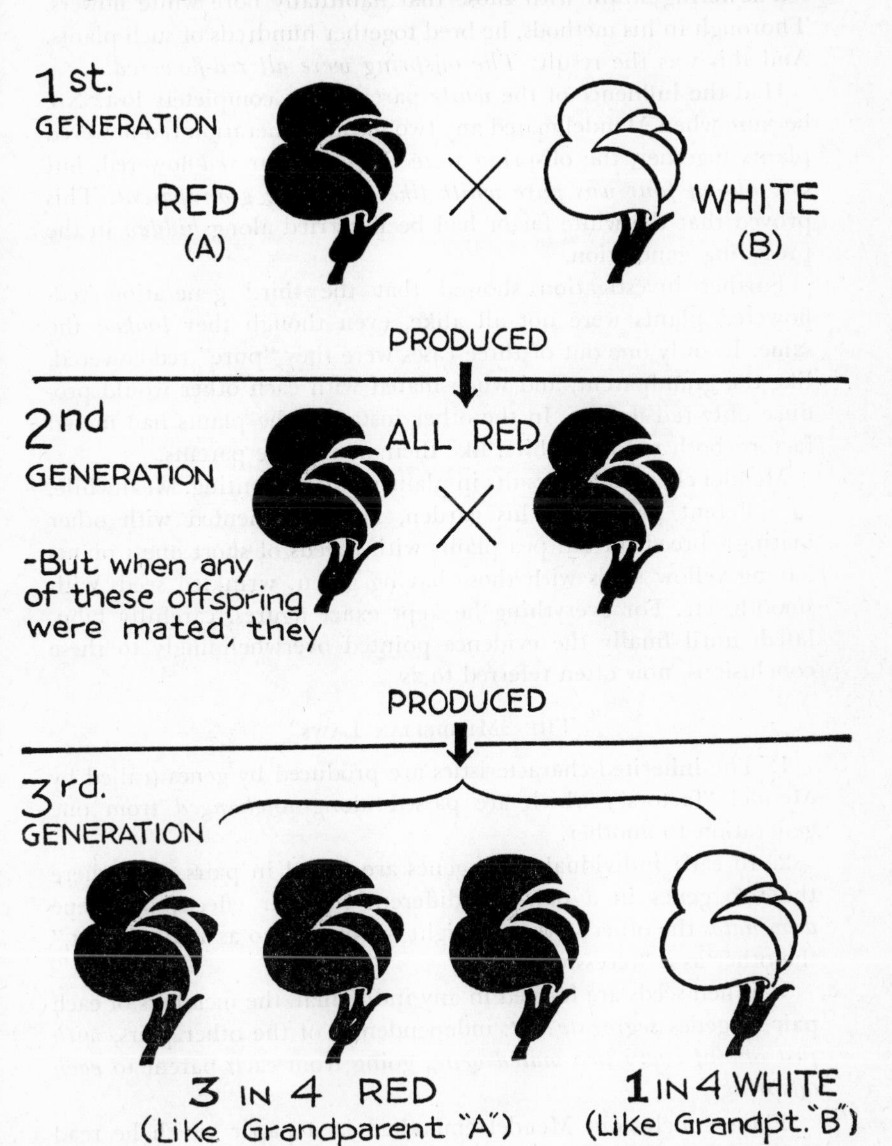
ONE OF MENDEL'S EXPERIMENTS WITH PEAS
1st.
GENERATION
RED
(A)
WHITE
(B)
PRODUCED
2nd
GENERATION
ALL RED
-But when any
of these offspring
were mated, they
PRODUCED
3rd.
GENERATION
3 IN 4 RED
(LiKe Grandparent "A")
1 IN 4 WHITE
(LiKe Grandp't. "B")

set out to see what would happen when he mated peas of a pure red-flowering strain with those that habitually bore white flowers. Thorough in his methods, he bred together hundreds of such plants. And this was the result: *The offspring were all red-flowered.*

Had the influence of the *white* parent been completely lost? No, because when Mendel mated any two second-generation red-flowered plants together, the offspring were three in four *red*-flowered, but *one out of four was pure white like the white grandparent.* This proved that the white factor had been carried along *hidden* in the preceding generation.

Further investigation showed that the third generation red-flowered plants were not all alike, even though they *looked* the same. In only one out of three cases were they "pure" red-flowered, like the grandparent, and when mated with each other would produce only red flowers. In the other instances the plants had mixed factors, both red and white, like their immediate parents.

Mendel checked the results in planting after planting. Meanwhile, in different patches of his garden, he experimented with other matings—breeds of tall pea plants with breeds of short ones; plants having yellow seeds with those having green; wrinkled seeds with smooth, etc. For everything he kept exact figures, carefully tabulated, until finally the evidence pointed overwhelmingly to these conclusions, now often referred to as

The "Mendelian Laws"

1. The inherited characteristics are produced by genes (called by Mendel "factors") which are passed along *unchanged* from one generation to another.

2. In each individual these genes are found in pairs, and where the two genes in a pair are different in their effects, one gene *dominates* the other so that it might be referred to as a "dominant," the other as a "recessive."

3. When seeds are formed in any individual, the members of each pair of genes *segregate out,* independently of the other pairs, *with just one of every two mated genes* going from each parent to *each offspring.*

These conclusions Mendel embodied in a paper which he read before his local scientific society in 1865 and which was published in 1866. But almost no attention was paid to it. The scientific world of the time was in a turmoil over Darwin's theory of evolution. The few who saw Abbot Mendel's paper ignored it. And so Mendel, little aware of the scientific treasure he had unearthed, turned to other things and passed on in 1884, at the age of sixty-two.*

But recognition did come—sixteen years too late. In 1900, three biologists, almost at the same time (although they were working independently) chanced on Mendel's paper and quickly realized its importance.† Their reports set the world of biology feverishly experimenting to see whether the Mendelian findings applied to other living things—including man. Yes, in many cases Mendel's "laws" did seem to operate. But in other instances the results were either inconclusive or flatly contradictory. Biologists were floundering about in confusion, and might still have been had not the very large man named Thomas Hunt Morgan happened to become intensely interested in the very little fly named *Drosophila melanogaster*.

The drama which might be called "Man Meets Fly" began in 1907. Professor Morgan, then at Columbia University, found the fruit fly an ideal subject for his experiments. For one thing, the Drosophilæ, mère and père, do not believe in birth control. At the age of twelve days they are ready to breed and within another twelve days each female produces some three hundred offspring. Starting from scratch, within two years one can get sixty generations of flies, as many as there have been generations of mankind from the time of Christ. Moreover, the fly has many easily distinguished variations and the cost of boarding it is trifling. The reward for all this is that the Drosophila has today become the most famous

* Even in Mendel's own community "not a soul believed that the experiments of the kindly cleric were anything more than a pastime, and his theories anything more than the maunderings of a charming putterer." This was reported a few years ago by C. W. Eichling, Sr., of New Orleans, Louisiana, who as a youth, representing a French botanical firm, had visited Mendel in 1878. When asked about his work with peas, Mendel (Mr. Eichling said) deliberately changed the subject, as if it were a sore spot with him. Others have reported that biology was only one of Mendel's interests, which included playing chess, organizing fire brigades, running banks and fighting government taxes. During World War II, the Mendel "shrine" in the monastery at Brno was struck by a shell, and many of the priceless mementos kept there were destroyed. However, the little plot where he worked with his peas was unharmed.

† The three "discoverers" of Mendel were Hugo de Vries (Dutch), C. Correns (German) and Erich von Tschermak (Austrian), the latter of whom was still alive and active in 1949. The claim has been made, however, that an American, Dr. L. H. Bailey, founder of the Cornell University Hortorium bearing his name, referred to Mendel's work in one of his papers in 1892, and that it was this reference which caused De Vries to look up Mendel's work. But while other scientists, too, may have taken some note of Mendel's publication well before 1900, the real implications were not seen, nor applied, until that year by the three "discoverers" mentioned.

experimental animal in science, and is assured immortality, even though individually it might prefer a speckled banana.

With the Drosophila, then, Morgan was able to prove that while the basic Mendelian principles held firmly, the mechanism of heredity was not nearly so simple as Mendel had suggested. There were many complicated forms of gene operation, Morgan showed, and many environmental factors that influenced the genes. All this he was able to make clear with the aid of a brilliant corps of his student-collaborators—Herman J. Muller, Calvin B. Bridges, A. H. Sturtevant and others. They identified hundreds of special genes in the Drosophila, even constructing "maps" showing at exactly what points on the flies' chromosomes these genes were located. They actually bred flies of almost any kind specified as easily as a pharmacist would compound a prescription. And later Professor Muller showed how, with X-rays, innumerable changes in the genes of these flies could be produced. (Both Professor Morgan and Professor Muller were in turn awarded Nobel prizes for their contributions.)

All this time, everything learned about the gene workings in flies was being applied to the study of other living things, up the scale from the most elemental creatures to man himself. There were Jennings with the paramecium, Goldschmidt with moths, Castle with rabbits, Wright with guinea pigs, Stockard with dogs, Crew with livestock, Cuénot and, later, Little with mice. With studies of humans, there were Davenport, Haldane, Hogben, Penrose, Snyder. And these are but a handful of the hundreds of brilliant researchers who pyramided the facts on which our present knowledge of the genes so firmly rests.

So it was by way of Mendel with his peas, and Morgan with his flies, that we have finally arrived at an understanding of the complexities of human heredity.

CHAPTER 10

OUR SUPER "CHAIN-GANGS"

IN THIS Atomic Age when we've gotten used to the idea of fantastically big things resulting from fantastically tiny things, it may no longer seem so miraculous that a single gene, millions of times smaller than the smallest speck you can see with your naked eye, should be capable of producing the difference between a blond and a redhead, a dwarf and a six-footer, or, in rare instances, a sane person and an insane one.

But how, and by what processes, do the genes do their work—not merely in the interval between conception and birth, but throughout one's life?

What, to begin with, *is* a gene?

Here we have to talk a bit about atoms and molecules, taking it for granted that you know that all substances in the universe—air, water, earth, vegetables, your cat, your hat, and you yourself—are composed of minute little molecules, which in turn are made up of many immeasurably tinier atoms. Each gene, then, is also a molecule, made up of a great many atoms. But a gene is a very special kind of molecule, different from almost all others in that it is a *living* thing—the ultimate unit of life, so far as we know—with the power to reproduce itself endlessly.

More definitely, scientists believe, genes are highly complex protein molecules, composed chiefly of nucleic acid, which is the basic material of all protoplasm, or living substance.* Further, to explain the countless differences in genes, among all the many living animals and plants, and within each individual, we have only to remember that every gene is made up of millions of atoms, and that variations in the nature, number and arrangement of the atoms within each gene could result in an infinite variety of properties.

* For the technically-minded: One constituent of genes has been identified as *desoxyribonucleic* acid, the quantity of which is identical for each cell in a given animal species, but may vary from species to species.

In its workings, each gene individually acts like a chemist—or rather, scientifically speaking—like an enzyme or catalyst: a substance which can produce a certain change in the material around it without itself being affected. You yourself often employ enzymes. You do so when you put yeast in dough to make it rise, or when, with a pellet of rennet, you turn milk into junket. Home brewers in the old prohibition days depended on enzyme-action when they put a few raisins in their jug of mash. And any of you engaged in manufacturing may be familiar with hundreds of catalytic substances (small pieces of platinum, for instance) used in various processes to bring about desired chemical changes.

In creating an individual, the genes work first upon the raw material in the egg, then upon the materials which are sent in by the mother, converting these into various products. The products, in turn, react again with the genes, leading to the formation of new products. So the process goes on, with specific materials being sorted out meanwhile to go into and to construct the various cells of the body.

But as the genes are *living* units, we cannot quite regard them as mere chemical substances. Considering the amazing things they do, we may well think of them as workers endowed with personalities. No factory, no industrial organization, has so varied an aggregation of workers and specialists as the genes in a single individual, and no army of workers can do more remarkable jobs. Architects, engineers, plumbers, decorators, chemists, artists, sculptors, doctors, dieticians, masons, carpenters, common laborers—all these and many others will be found among the genes. In their linked-together forms (the chromosomes) we can think of them as "chain-gangs"—twenty-four of these gangs of workers sent along by each parent to begin the construction of a new human being—and each chain-gang capable of reproducing itself endless times.

Turn back to the moment of conception. The chain-gangs contributed by your mother are packed together closely in a shell (the nucleus) suspended in the sea of nutrient material which constitutes the egg. Suddenly, into that sea, is plunged a similar shell (the sperm) filled with the chain-gangs sent by your father. Almost immediately both shells open up and out come the thousands of gene-workers, stirred to activity.

The first impulse of the tiny workers, after their long confinement, is to eat (which seems natural enough). So they gorge themselves on the sea of materials around them in the egg. Then they reproduce, as we noted in a previous chapter, by dividing and forming two of themselves. The one-cell egg becomes two cells, the two become four, the four become eight, etc.—a replica of *each original chain-gang going into each cell.*

However, the cells as they multiply to hundreds, thousands, then millions and billions, do not all remain the same. In the initial stages the genes have been doing mostly ordinary construction work, or concerning themselves largely with producing basic body materials. But more and more, as the process of multiplying themselves and the body cells continues, the specialists get into action and begin constructing *different kinds of cells at different locations.*

The details of how this is done—such details as are known or surmised—fills tens of thousands of pages in scientific treatises. Briefly stated, we can assume that on set cues the different genes step out for their special tasks, snatching at this bit of material or element, combining it with other stuffs, fashioning a product, setting it in place, etc., all the time working in cooperation with the other genes.

Throughout one's lifetime the genes are in a constant ferment of activity, carrying on and directing one's life processes at every stage. Everything seems to be done according to plan, as if the most detailed blueprints were being followed. The step-by-step process has been explained as a sequence of reactions, the workers being motivated to each step by the effects of the preceding one. By observing the process in lower experimental animals we can see how first the broad general construction of the body is worked out; then how certain cells are marked off for the organs, certain ones for the respiratory and digestive systems, certain ones for the muscles, others for the skin, features, etc.

The generalized cells now begin to develop into special ones. In those marked off for the circulatory system the rudiments of hearts, veins and arteries begin to be formed (here is where the "plumber" genes step in to construct the great chain of pumps and pipe-lines); from the generalized bone cells the skeleton begins to be shaped; from the skin cells, the rudiments of features, etc. With each stage the specialization is carried further along in the developing embryo. The amazing way in which the development of every human being parallels that of every other proves how infinitely exact and predetermined are the genes in their workings.

Another remarkable feature of the process is this: Despite the growing differences in the various specialized cells, *into every cell, as it is being created and constructed, go exact replicas of all the chromosomes with their genes.* Thus, the same gene which produced eye color in your eye cells will also be found in your big toe cells, and the same gene which directed the fashioning of your big toe will also be found in your eye cells—or in your ear and liver cells, for that matter. Probably, then, in addition to every special task that each gene performs, it also takes part in general activities which make its presence required everywhere.

("Some genes," as Professor J. B. S. Haldane puts it, "are pretty lazy on the average. They only get an assignment of work if they happen to find themselves in a cell concerned with making pigments, forming bone or transmitting messages. But the majority seem to have some work to do in almost every kind of cell, even though it may be a more vital job in a gland cell than in a skin cell.")

To go on, we may recall that a person starts life with two chromosomes of every kind, which means also two genes of every kind. If, in terms of chain-gangs, we designate the chromosomes by letter, there would be two A chains, two B chains, two C chains, and so on up to the last pair—where in the case of a girl, as noted in the preceding chapters, there would be two X chains, but in the case of a boy, only one X chain, the other being a Y chain. With this latter exception, the corresponding chain-gangs (AA, BB, CC, etc.) would be exactly alike in the number of workers each contained, and in the *type* of worker at each point in the chain.

If the No. 1 gene in the A chain contributed to you by your father was an architect, so would be the No. 1 gene in the A chain from your mother. The No. 2 genes next in line might be carpenters, the No. 3s decorators, etc. All the way from the A chain to the X or Y chain, the genes at each point on matching chromosomes in *all human beings* are exactly the same in the *type* of work to which they are assigned. In other words, every individual starts life with *two* workers for each job, one sent by the mother, one by the father.

But here is a vitally important point: The two paired genes, or workers, delegated to the same job, very often do not work at all in the same way. The two "A-4" "carpenter" genes, one coming from your father, the other from your mother, may be as different in

OUR "CHAIN-GANGS"

he CHROMOSOMES may be thought of as Chain-Gangs," twenty-four of which are sent long by each parent to create the child. Every gang" consists of many linked-together workrs, each assigned to given tasks.

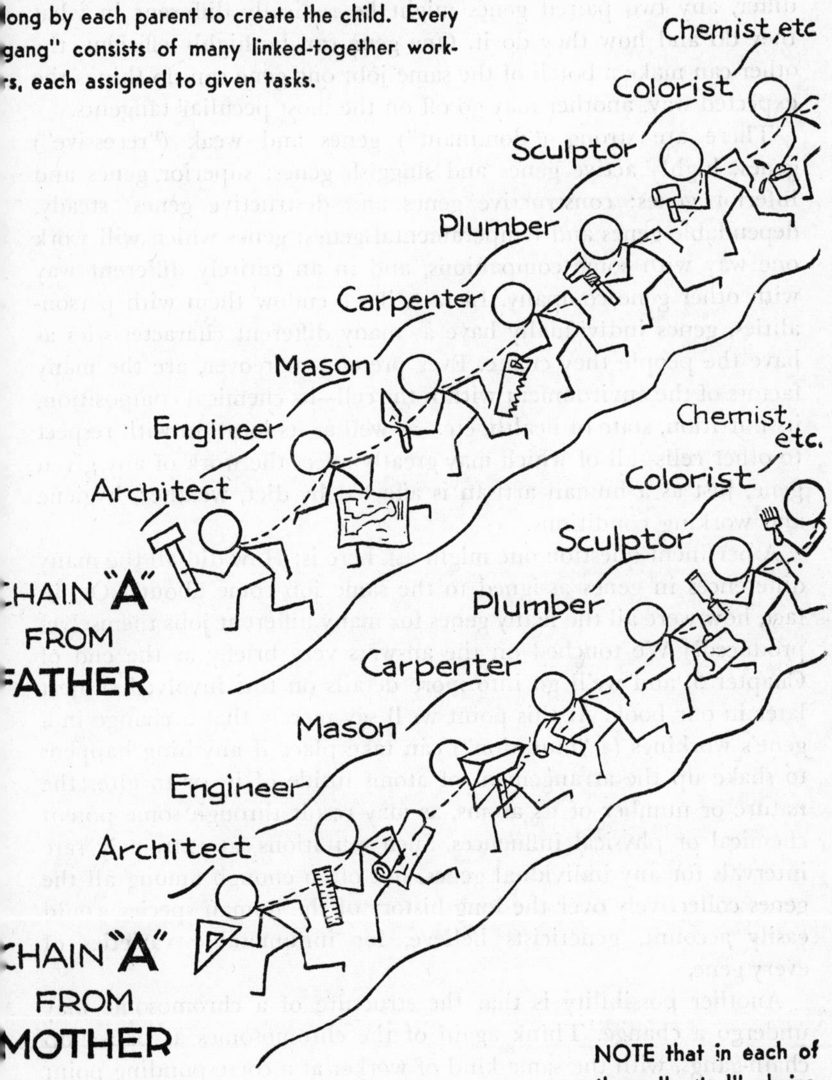

Chemist, etc
Colorist
Sculptor
Plumber
Carpenter
Mason
Engineer
Architect

HAIN "A"
FROM
FATHER

Chemist, etc.
Colorist
Sculptor
Plumber
Carpenter
Mason
Engineer
Architect

HAIN "A"
FROM
MOTHER

NOTE that in each of these "mated" chains, the workers ("genes") at corresponding points, are assigned to exactly the same type of work.

their characters and abilities as any two human carpenters. So, too, just as any two plumbers might differ (even though they belonged to the same union), or any two architects, artists or chemists might differ, any two paired genes might be radically different in what they do and how they do it. One gene can be highly efficient, the other can make a botch of the same job; one gene can do things the expected way, another may go off on the most peculiar tangents.

There are strong ("dominant") genes and weak ("recessive") genes; highly active genes and sluggish genes; superior genes and inferior genes; constructive genes and destructive genes; steady, dependable genes and temperamental genes; genes which will work one way with some companions, and in an entirely different way with other gene company. In fact, if we endow them with personalities, genes individually have as many different characteristics as have the people they create. Ever present, moreover, are the many factors of the environment within the cell—its chemical composition, its nutrition, state of health, etc.—as well as its location with respect to other cells—all of which may greatly affect the work of any given gene, just as a human artisan is affected by diet, weather, hygiene and working conditions.

A pertinent question one might ask here is: How did all the many differences in genes assigned to the same job come about? (Or, in fact, how were all the many genes for many different jobs themselves produced?) We touched on the answers very briefly at the end of Chapter 3, and we'll go into more details on this involved subject later in our book. At this point we'll say merely that a change in a gene's workings (a "mutation") can take place if anything happens to shake up the arrangement of atoms inside of it, or to alter the nature or number of its atoms, as may result through some potent chemical or physical influences. Such mutations, at extremely rare intervals for any individual genes, but often enough among all the genes collectively over the long history of the human species, could easily account, geneticists believe, for innumerable varieties of every gene.

Another possibility is that the structure of a chromosome may undergo a change. Think again of the chromosomes as paired-up chain-gangs, with the same kind of worker at a corresponding point on each chain. One phenomenon during the process of forming egg or sperm cells is that two matching chromosomes, or chains, may get twisted about one another, and in breaking away, the two chains may interchange sections. Thus, some of the workers (or genes) may find themselves in entirely new company, and this may often cause a change in their workings. In even rarer instances, a chromosome chain may lose some of its genes, while another chromosome may hook on a few extra ones.

There are many other complexities in the structure and functioning of our genes and chromosomes which are highly meaningful for the specialist, but which the general reader shouldn't have to worry about—at least, not at this stage in our book.

What is most important to know for the present is that with the countless shades of difference possible among all the human genes in circulation and the infinite number of gene combinations, and their constant interplay with environment, a limitless variety of human beings can be produced.

The best way of illustrating this is to tell what the genes do in specific instances with regard to our features, organs, minds, and all other individual characteristics.

CHAPTER 11

COLORING: EYES

ALTHOUGH there are no statistics on the subject, we dare say that millions of husbands since the world began, and a not inconsiderable number of mothers, noting that one of their children looked very different from themselves, have had the cold suspicion creep up that it wasn't actually theirs. And a great many children, in turn, having noted how little they resembled others in their family, may have felt that they actually had had different parents.

Sometimes the suspicions may have been justified. But in the great majority of cases, the doubts have been groundless, for today we know that the process of heredity can act in many peculiar ways, to produce not only resemblances, but marked *differences,* between parents and their offspring.

Among the traits which often are most puzzling and unexpected are the coloring of eyes, hair and skin. These warrant special, and detailed attention because of all the social significance attached to them, first, with regard to the attitude of whole peoples toward their color, and second, with regard to individual preferences and prejudices.

Where a person's coloring is identified with race, and there is hostility or conflict for whatever reason between this race and another, we can easily see why inherited color differences may have much meaning. But where race is not at issue, why are individuals still so much swayed by the tints of each other's faces? Why do you, personally, "go" much more strongly for a member of the opposite sex with one kind of eye or hair color rather than another? Or why, if you are a prospective parent, are you so likely to be concerned about what the coloring of your baby will be? Some of the reasons may be sociological—bound up with general preferences or prejudices in certain groups or countries. But for many of the individual attitudes toward color, only a psychoanalyst could dig out the reasons.

What we can explain more easily is how human-color differences are produced, and even more, what kind of coloring you can or can not expect in a baby, if you happen to be awaiting one.

Being on the surface, color differences can quite easily be perceived and graded, and therefore offer us some of the simplest means of studying and analyzing the action of genes. In fact, eye color was the first normal trait in human beings for which genetic mechanisms were worked out.

The first point to clarify is that any color, as we know it, is not a substance, but an *effect* produced by the reflection of light on different materials. "Blue" eyes, for example, have no blue substance in them, but merely look blue to us (as we'll explain later). When we speak, then, of different genes "producing" different colors, what we actually mean is that they take part in producing different amounts or kinds of substances which give the various color *effects*.

Have the pigment substances any practical value? Yes. Among many lower animals coloration may make possible concealment from enemies or victims, may enhance natural attractiveness to mates, etc. Among human beings, one's coloring may also have importance in relationship to other people, but only in a social way. *There is no "natural" attraction or repulsion between people because of their coloring,* so far as science can establish. The practical value of pigmentation in human beings, however, is mainly in insuring protection from the sun. In the eyes, the pigment deposited in the otherwise translucent iris shades the retina within. The pigment in the skin protects the raw flesh underneath. Even the pigment in the hair affords some protection to the hair cells and the scalp.

Although we recognize many different kinds of coloring in human beings, all of the color effects, in the eyes, skin and hair, are produced by virtually the same pigments. In fact, one basic brown pigment, *melanin,* accounts for most of our color differences, as determined by its strength, particle-size, degree of concentration and the way in which it is distributed. Supplementing melanin are a few other pigments which lead to special color effects.

Taking the eyes, specifically, the wide range of human eye colors, from black to light blue, all are results of the way different "eye-color" genes produce and distribute melanin, plus one or two other pigments. Geneticists believe that the original "eye-color" genes in the human species were the highly active ones producing in all the first humans heavily pigmented eyes, dark brown or "black"; and that by subsequent mutations through the ages, weaker variations of these genes developed which now provide us with all the many lighter shades.

Where eye color is determined is in the cells of the *iris,* which, as you probably know, is the small disk around the pupil (or rather, one should say, the pupil is the hole in the iris). Without any pigment the iris would look something like a tiny, transparent doughnut. It has, however, two clearly defined parts, as if it had been slit in half and pasted together again. Thus we speak of the part facing out as the "front" of the iris and the other half as the "rear." And it is in the way that pigment is produced both in the front and in the rear of the iris—in some cases separately—that eye-color differences result.

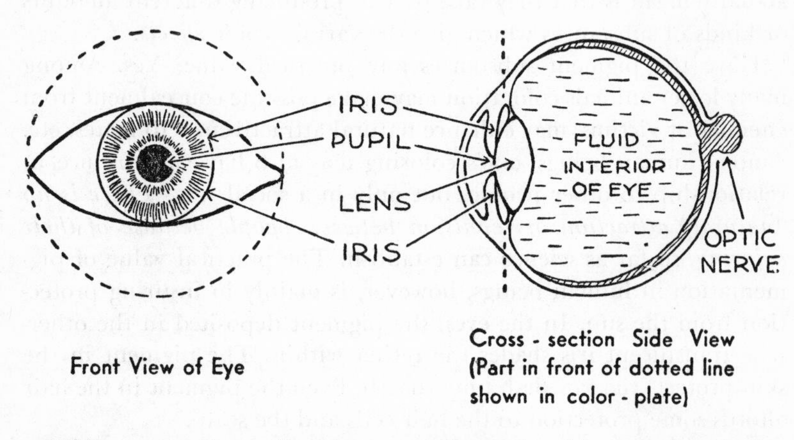

Front View of Eye

Cross - section Side View (Part in front of dotted line shown in color - plate)

While a number of genes participate in this eye-pigmenting process, it is a single "key" gene which usually determines the main outcome.

In Blue Eyes (of various types) the genes are weaklings which produce little or no pigment in the front of the iris (as you can see if you look at a light blue-eyed person sideways), but manages to produce a certain amount in the rear. But this pigment itself, remember, is *not blue.* What is present in the "blue" eyes is merely a scattering of the brownish melanin particles, which produce the *optical effect* of blue, through the reflection and dispersion of light rays. It is precisely in this way that dust particles make the sky look blue. The other eye colors are due mostly to the addition of pigment in the front of the iris.

In Gray Eyes the gene action produces a somewhat heavier con-

WHAT MAKES YOUR EYE COLOR—

—BLUE

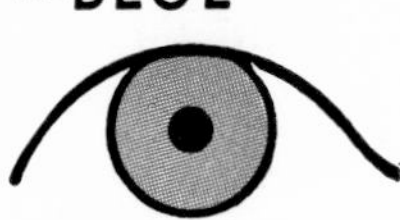

An optical illusion

(There is no blue pigment in the eye)

Effect is due to reflection of light from tiny dark pigment granules in REAR OF IRIS

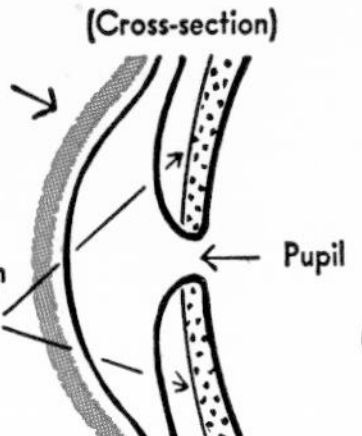

GENES

If "true" blue-eyed you carry two "blue-eye" genes

(One alone is recessive to all others except Albino)

—GREEN

Effect is due to scattered yellow pigment in FRONT OF IRIS acting with the blue reflection (yellow + blue = green)

(Gene action of green and gray eyes not yet clearly established)

—GRAY

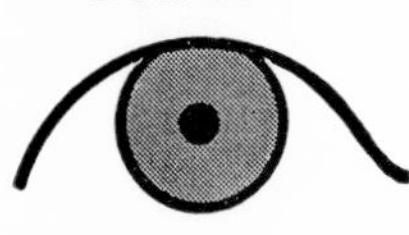

Effect is due to scattered dark pigment in FRONT OF IRIS screening blue reflection from behind

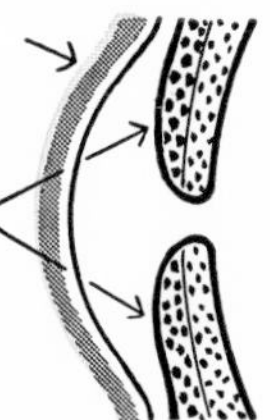

—BROWN

or Black

Effect is due to concentrated dark pigment in FRONT OF IRIS masking blue reflection (The heavier the pigmentation, the darker the eye)

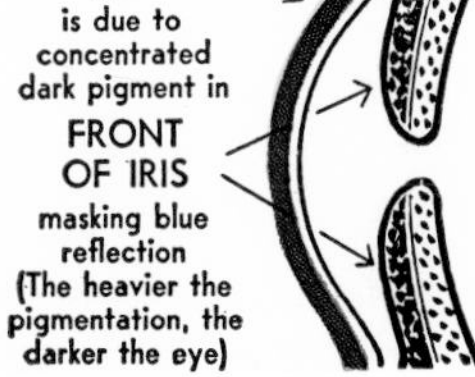

Two brown-eye genes

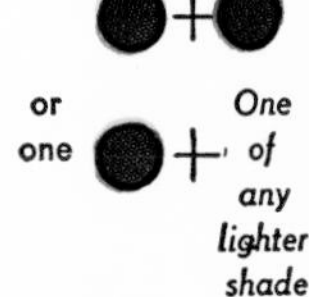

or one + *One of any lighter shade*

—PINK

(Albino)

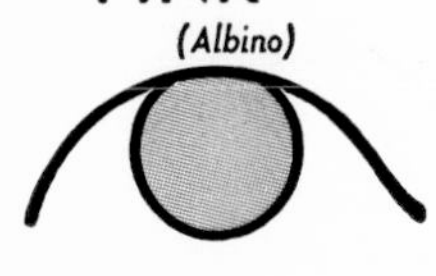

Effect is due to reflection from pink blood vessels in and through the unpigmented iris

An albino carries two albino genes

But persons of any other eye color including blue may be carrying a hidden albino gene

centration of the pigment in the rear of the iris, plus a scattering of dark pigment in the front, enough to give a gray or grayish-blue effect, depending on the depth of the pigmentation. (Color from muscle-fibres behind may contribute to, or modify the gray effects, as also the blue.)

In GREEN EYES the rear of the iris has the same kind of pigmentation as in blue or gray eyes, but in addition there is a special gene which lays down a certain amount of dilute brown or yellow pigment in the front of the iris. Superimposed on the "blue" background, this produces the effect of green (just as you might make any blue surface look green by stippling it with yellow dots). With a little more pigment in the front and rear of the iris one may have grayish-yellow or grayish-brown eyes.

In BROWN EYES the "key" gene is active enough to so fill up the front of the iris with pigment that no reflection can be seen.

And, finally, in "BLACK" EYES (or very dark brown) the gene is of the most vigorous type, which lays down an intense deposit of pigment in the front of the iris, and perhaps also in the rear, making it completely opaque.

In addition to these main eye-color types, various other color effects can be produced by the patterns in which the pigment in the iris is distributed. (Altogether, if we tried to get down to the finer shadings, the problems of tracing eye-color inheritance would be very complex. In blue eyes alone it has been estimated there are nine color classes which can be inherited in forty-five possible combinations!)

ALBINO EYES should be dealt with separately because they are not due to any "eye-color" gene but to a defective "general" gene which interferes with all pigmentation processes. Thus, the true albino eyes have *no pigment whatsoever,* in either the front or rear of the iris. The *pink* effect results from the tiny blood vessels in the otherwise colorless iris, and the reflection from other blood vessels behind.

Let us see now what happens when an individual receives one kind of "eye-color" gene from one parent, a different gene from the other parent.

In eye color, as in most other processes, some genes can do the same work singly quite as well as if there were two. The blackest, or darkest "eye-color" gene, generally works this way. That is to say, if a child should receive just one dark "eye-color" gene from one parent, no matter what other gene it received from the other parent—

green, gray, blue or even albino—that child would have dark brown eyes.

This follows the principle of *dominance* and *recessiveness* which Mendel discovered. Just as the gene for red flower dominated that for white flower in his garden peas, in human beings the gene for black (or brown) eyes dominates that for blue eyes (or any other of the lighter shades).* But, you might ask, doesn't the "blue-eye" or other recessive gene do *anything* when coupled with the dominant "brown-eye" gene?

Possibly you may recall having gone to a party planning to sing, or to play the piano or exhibit some other accomplishment, and just as you were preparing to perform, some one else got up and did the same sort of thing, much more forcefully than you could do it. If you were an ordinarily shy person, the chances are that you kept your performance to yourself for the rest of the evening.

That is about what happens when a little Blue-Eye gene arrives and finds a big domineering Brown-Eye gene on the scene. Little Blue-Eye may sit back with never a move out of it through all the long lifetime of the individual in which it finds itself. (Perhaps it does do some work, though if so, the effects are obscure.) But there is always "another time." Just as you might go to the next party and, in the absence of the menacing competitor, perform handsomely, so the Blue-Eye gene need not be permanently squelched. To a gene, the "next time" means the next individual to which it is sent—that is, to some future child. Again little Blue-Eye gene goes forth hopefully (and if necessary again and again, generation after generation) until in some child it finds itself coupled, not with a "bully" Brown-Eye gene, but with a kindred Blue-Eye gene. And this time, glory be, the two Blue-Eye genes happily fall to work, and the result is a blue-eyed baby!

In all mixed matings the "blue-eye" genes have a hard time of it, for they are also dominated in whole or part by the "light brown-," "green-" and "gray-eye" genes; by all the rest, in fact, except the "albino" gene, which all normal genes dominate. As for the other

* Some authorities believe that the "black-eye" or "dark-brown-eye" genes of Negroes and Mongolians may be of different types, or at least more intense in their workings, than the "black-eye" gene found among Whites. It is possible, then, that the former types of "dark-eye" genes may be more completely dominant over lighter "eye-color" genes in some cases than is the "dark-eye" gene of Whites.

"contests," the general rule is that the genes for darker colors dominate those for the lighter shades. When a "green-eye" gene and a "gray-eye," both of apparently equal potency, get together, the result may be grayish-green.

Always to be kept in mind is that eye colors are not simple effects, such as might be produced by painting little discs with flat colors from a palette or paintbox. In addition to the actual pigment, there are many structural details of the eye which contribute to the impression of color it gives, leading to many varieties of each basic eye color. Thus, the specialist may distinguish among numerous shades and types of blue eyes genetically determined through many combinations. Nevertheless, while the finer details of eye-color inheritance are very complex, and there still are many points to be worked out, the general facts are well established.

In short, you may make these *guesses* about the "eye-color" genes you are carrying:

If you have black or brown eyes:

(1) Where both your parents, all your brothers and sisters and all your near relatives also have dark eyes, in all probability you carry *two* "black" (or "brown-eye") genes.

(2) Where both your parents have dark eyes, but one or more of your brothers and sisters or other near relatives have eyes of a lighter shade (gray, green, blue) you may be carrying, in addition to the "dark-eye" gene, a "hidden" gene for the lighter shade. The greater the number in your family who have light-colored eyes, the greater the chance that you carry such a gene.

(3) Where one of your parents has black or brown eyes and the other light-colored eyes, you definitely carry one "dark-eye" gene and one for a lighter shade. If the light-eyed parent has gray or green eyes, your "hidden" gene may be either a gray, green, or blue one. If the parent has blue eyes, then you almost certainly carry a "hidden" "blue-eye" gene.

If you have gray or green eyes:

Regardless of what eye colors your parents have, in all probability you carry no "dark," but only "light-colored" genes, which may be gray, green or blue. If *one* parent has blue eyes, however, you may be quite sure you carry at least one "hidden" "blue-eye" gene.

If you have blue eyes:

Regardless of the eye colors of your parents, you are almost certain to be carrying *two* "blue-eye" genes of one type or another.

If you have albino eyes:

In all probability you are carrying two "albino" genes. (In rare instances in men there is a special "sex-linked" single gene which may prevent color production.)

To all the foregoing deductions there may be occasional exceptions. Once in a blue moon a freak gene in a person with blue eyes may rear up and dominate a freak "brown-eye" gene, in which case the usual eye-color forecasts would be upset. More often, though still with great infrequency, environmental factors may swerve a gene from its normal course. For example, one cannot always be positive that a person whose eyes are, or appear to be blue, really is carrying two "blue-eye" genes, there being a one to two per cent chance of error. Cases occur from time to time where an individual receives at conception one, or even both genes for some darker eye color, and at some stage thereafter something happens to inhibit or modify the usual "eye-color" gene workings, so that blue or blue-appearing eyes result. Diseases (or dietary deficiencies) which upset the body chemistry and affect pigment production may be among these modifying influences. In another way, cataracts, or some other eye defects, may rob dark eyes of their color and make them look watery blue. In still other instances eye-pigment production may be speeded up abnormally, so that, despite there being genes for blue eyes, dark eyes may result.

Age is the most important modifier of eye color throughout life. Generally, eyes darken from birth to maturity, and thereafter begin to lighten up a bit with aging. Among Whites (and in some cases among Negroes), most babies at birth have slate-blue eyes, which may in time either become more heavily pigmented, turning to brown, or in other cases may become clear blue, depending on the genes carried. As any mother knows, it may take a number of years before the true eye color of her child is revealed. Borderline blue and gray eyes may turn to green or brown, or brownish eyes may become green or gray, but "pure" blue or gray eyes usually remain fairly constant in color. In old age, brown eyes may again become bluish-slate.

There is an interesting sex difference in that the time and manner in which age affects eye color is different in females and males. The development toward physical maturity of girls is more rapid than of boys (their full maturity being reached about two or three years earlier), so as eyes tend to darken at puberty, girls and young women on the average may have somewhat darker eyes than males of the same ages.* In addition, throughout life sex differences in body chemistry may affect eye-pigment production in variable ways.

Iris-pattern differences among individuals may also modify the coloring or appearance of eyes. Such patterns of pigment distribution, with the pigment in rings, in "clouds," in flecks or patches, in radial stripes, or even spread evenly over the whole iris, are inherited in various ways. Predictions can be given for some of the "pattern" genes, but it is doubtful whether the average reader would be much concerned with them. (Do you know what your own iris pattern is?) However, these patterns may be important in that if a child has a different inherited iris pattern from that of a given parent, even though the color genes are the same, their eyes may look somewhat different.

One peculiar phenomenon, which occurs about once in every six hundred persons, is that of unmatched eyes (*heterochromia iridis*)—where each eye of an individual is of a different color. Most commonly one eye is brown, the other blue. This may occur in several ways: A person may inherit one "brown-eye" gene and one "blue-eye" gene, which normally would make both eyes brown. But in the very earliest stage something may happen to the "brown-eye" gene in one of the rudimentary cells, leaving the field clear for a blue eye to develop on that side, whereas on the other side the "brown-eye" gene may be doing its work normally. Or, starting with two "blue-eye" genes, some disease may increase pigment production in one of

* The technical reader may be interested in some recent findings by Dr. Alice M. Brues, supplementing the facts given about eye-color inheritance. Dr. Brues reported (1946) that, with respect to the thickness and surface of the iris, there are two genetically distinct types:

In one, usually characterizing the darker eyes, the iris is full and smooth, and partially or entirely brown. In the contrasting type (recessive to the other), usually characterizing the lighter eyes, the front of the iris is shrunken to a greater or lesser extent, and as a rule has little or no pigment. The exception, in rare cases, is when a special gene may cause the "atrophied-iris" type of eye to become heavily pigmented. (This may account for some of the infrequent cases where a dark-eyed child is born to two blue-eyed parents.) Dr. Brues also makes note of the possibility that the special "dark-eye" gene may be present on the X-chromosome, and, if dominant, could therefore result in a slightly higher ratio of dark-eyed females to males (inasmuch as females have a double chance of getting this gene).

the eyes, making it brown. Conversely, a person starting with two brown eyes may develop glaucoma, or a cataract in one of the eyes, which will make that eye bluish.

While most unmatched eyes are believed due to environmental factors, the condition might also be *inherited* as the result of a one-sided nerve defect which can be transmitted through a certain gene (dominant or recessive). On record are a number of families where unmatched eyes of the same type have appeared for several generations. The condition, by the way, is quite prevalent among many domestic animals, including dogs, cats, rabbits and horses.

Although the range of human eye color is ordinarily confined to variations of brown, blue, green and gray eyes, rare instances have been reported of persons with "tortoise-shell" eyes (mottled yellow and black), and also, of persons with ruby-colored eyes. But we may eventually see eyes of other new colors. One way may be through spontaneous gene changes such as have occurred in our past, and as geneticists see popping out from time to time in flies, mice and other laboratory creatures.

Another remote possibility is that humans who want new eye colors may not have to wait for their genes to oblige them. One leading geneticist, the late Professor H. S. Jennings, seriously suggested that new eye colors in people might conceivably be produced by means of chemicals. So the time may come when women may be able to change the color of their eyes just as they now change their hair color. When that day arrives, and a man says to a girl, "Where did you get those big blue eyes?" she may reply, "At Antoine's, corner of De Peyster Avenue and Thirty-second Street!"

CHAPTER 12

HAIR COLOR

GENTLEMEN, we are told, prefer blondes.

There must still be some truth to this—or at least, many women must think so—for how otherwise account for the large numbers of dark-haired damsels who go to beauty parlors for a bleaching? Is there any record of *blondes* converting themselves into *brunettes* (unless the police are after them)?

Red hair, too, has a certain social significance, as the brisk demand for henna rinses and other hair-reddening alchemies will bear out.

Which might lead to this question, assuming that you are a prospective parent:

"What are the chances of a child of yours being a natural blonde or a redhead?"

As you already have gathered, looking at your own hair and that of your mate may not in itself provide the answers. You must try to ascertain what *genes* for hair color you both carry.

Pigmentation of the hair follows the same general principle as that of the eyes. Often, in fact, but not always, the two are related. Where the general pigmenting process of the body is very intense, as in "pure" Negroes, black hair and black eyes (and also dark skin) almost invariably go together; while among Mongolians the black hair is almost invariably accompanied by dark brown eyes. In most White stocks, too, one finds darker hair going as a rule with darker eyes, and lighter hair going with lighter eyes. But as evidence that the "hair-color" genes and "eye-color" genes may work independently, one frequently finds black hair with blue eyes (most often among the Irish), or *natural* blond hair with dark brown eyes.

One's hair color is determined chiefly by the way genes work to produce pigment in the hair cells, although, as in eyes, the basic actions of the "hair-color" genes may be modified or changed by a variety of factors, some inherent and some environmental. Also, as with eyes, the distinction between one hair color and another is not always clearly marked. You know what difficulty there often is in deciding whether a person's hair is blond or brown, or brown or red. (Among women, this hasn't been made any easier by the use of bleaches, dyes, "rinses," etc.) So what we are dealing with here, mostly, are the quite definitely distinguishable shades of hair color.

In structure your hair is a tube (somewhat like the twig of a tree), with an inner section through which pigment granules and tiny air bubbles are distributed, and an outer cover which may also contain pigment granules. The same pigment found in eyes, melanin, is also the principal element in our hair coloring. And this is the way the "hair-color" genes work:

If the key "hair-color" gene works to produce a heavy deposit of melanin in and among the hair cells, the result is black hair; a little less melanin, dark brown hair; still less, light brown; very dilute, blond hair. The shade of hair color is further influenced by the gradations of melanin produced, by the way the hair cells are constructed, by their air content and by their amount of natural oil or greasiness. But keep in mind that hair color, as you see it, is an *effect,* governed by the way the pigment reflects light. You need hardly be told that your hair looks different under different lights.

Red hair is due to a supplementary gene which produces a diffuse red pigment. The "red-hair" gene is often present with the key "melanin" gene. If this key gene is very active, making the hair black or dark brown, the effect of the "red" gene will be completely obscured. (The claim has been made, however, that a hidden "red" gene may betray its presence in black-haired persons by a special *glossiness* of the hair.) Where the "melanin" gene is weaker, the "red-hair" gene can manifest itself, and the result will be a reddish brown, or chestnut shade. If the "brown-hair" gene is an utter weakling, or if it is absent, distinctive red hair will be produced.

That the "red-hair" gene is an independent little cuss is shown by the fact that red hair may be present with almost any eye color, whereas brown or black hair usually goes with brown or black eyes, and blond hair usually goes with blue or gray eyes. However, red eyelashes seldom go with anything but very red head hair.

How the "red-hair" gene works in relation to a "blond" gene is not yet completely clear. Theoretically, it should dominate the blond, but we have cases, nevertheless, where blond parents have

WHAT MAKES YOUR HAIR COLOR—

	DUE TO		GENES YOU CARRY
—WHITE *(Natural)* 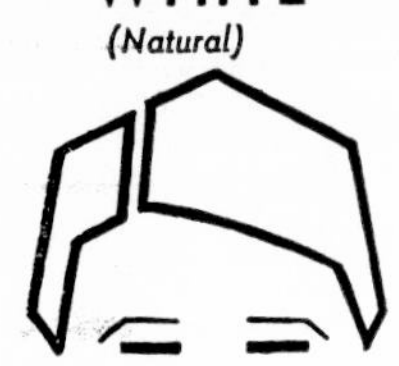	No pigment granules among hair cells	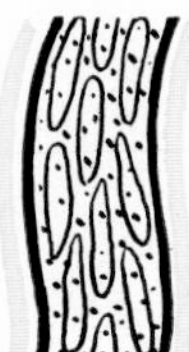	(If white hair is not due to age or disease) 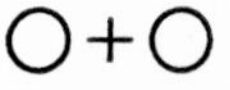 (But all hair color types may be carrying one hidden White-Hair Gene)
—BLOND 	Yellow effect produced by dilute pigment	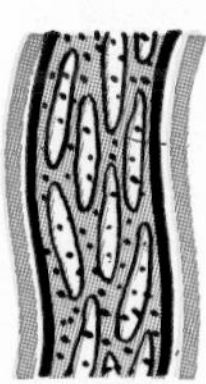	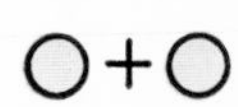
—RED 	Effect produced by dissolved red pigment diffused with the scattered pigment granules	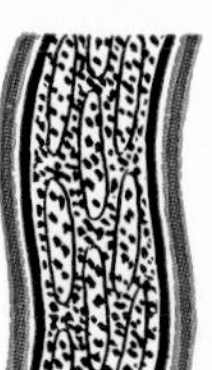	+ ? *(The "Red-Hair" Gene is a special one which shows its effect if not masked by very "Dark-Hair" Genes)*
—BROWN 	Effect produced by heavy deposit of pigment granules (The heavier the deposit, the darker the brown)		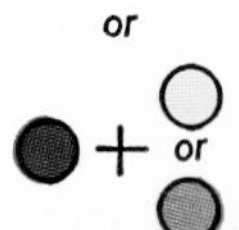 (Red Gene may make hair reddish-brown)
—BLACK 	Intense deposit of pigment granules	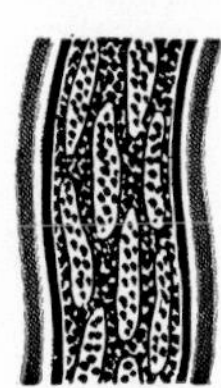	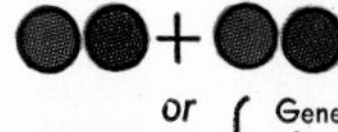 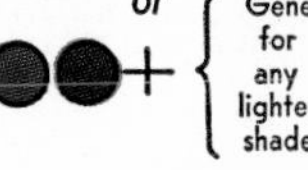

NOTE: ANY GENE SYMBOL USED HERE MAY REFER TO MORE THAN ONE GENE

a red-haired child. With rare exceptions, however, the "blond" gene is definitely recessive to those for all darker hair shades.

This leads to these general conclusions:

If you have dark hair, you are carrying either two "dark-hair" genes, or one dark and one for any other shade.*

If you have blond hair, you carry two "blond" genes.

If you have red hair, you are carrying either one or two "red" genes, supplementing "blond" or "brown" genes.

The basic "hair-color" genes are found among all peoples, although not by any means in the same proportions. Redheads are found even among Negroes and are quite frequent among the usually black-haired Latins. (The highest proportion of redheads—11 per cent—is among the Scotch Highlanders.) While blonds are also not uncommon among Latins and other black-haired peoples, we have no way of knowing to what extent the "blond" gene may have arisen among them by mutation, or to what extent it was introduced through interbreeding. The mutation theory seems to be the most plausible one in the case of blond Indians found among certain black-haired tribes, notably in Panama.

White hair can be due to various factors, genetic and otherwise. In its most striking form it is caused by the "albino" genes, which, as we have already seen, also rob the eye of color. White hair might also be due to extremely weak "blond" genes, or to some "inhibiting" genes or conditions which would interfere only with the hair-pigmenting process. White-haired persons of this type, quite common among Norwegians, Swedes, etc., differ from albinos in that they are normal in eye and skin pigmentation. And finally, there is the white hair due to age, disease, etc. In fact, in all hair colors there is the constant possibility that other factors may alter the effects of the key genes.

Age plays a much more important part in hair color than it does in eye color. The "hair-color" genes may be slow in expressing themselves, and also, the structure of the hair changes with age, which may affect its coloring. Light hair as a rule has a tendency to turn darker from childhood on through maturity, as may also

* The black hair of Negroes and Mongolians, however, may be due to stronger genes, producing a more intense dark pigmentation than in the black hair of Whites. Thus, while a Negro or Mongolian "black-hair" gene completely dominates any "light-hair" gene, there is some indication that the "black-hair" gene of Whites is not always completely dominant over the "blond" gene, and that in some cases when these are paired, an in-between shade of hair color may result.

be true of red hair. (How often have mothers wailed as they have seen the golden or auburn locks of a young child turn later into an indefinite murky brown!)

Among Whites, babies are frequently born with a temporary growth of dark hair which in a few weeks is replaced by light hair. But if the dark hair remains, only rarely does it become lighter in color as a child grows up. Constant exposure to the sun, or bleaching by salt water, drugs, or some other artificial means, can of course easily lighten or change hair color, and climate can also be an influence. But regardless of surface changes, the pigment particles will still be there, so that under a microscope a scientific Sherlock Holmes could easily tell whether a blond was natural or artificial.

The hair-color change that comes with age is one of *decolorization.* Not merely the pigment, but the air content, oil content and structure of the hair are affected. The time at which hair pigmentation begins to slow down often seems to be governed by heredity. Where a parent has grayed prematurely, in many cases a child will begin to gray at about the same time. The exact cause of "natural" and normal graying, though, has not at this writing been established, nor has any medically approved way been found of preventing it or of restoring hair color once it is lost. (Incidentally, when gray hair comes naturally, it has no necessary connection with health or physical fitness, and need not be related to aging in other ways.)

Nerve or gland disorders, diseases, peculiarities of the body chemistry and other physiological factors have been shown to affect the hair-forming cells and the hair-pigmenting process. Thus, occasionally, persons during a long illness or as a result of some harrowing experience may have their hair *gradually* turn gray or white. But this is far from supporting the popular belief that a person's hair can turn white "overnight." While a sudden nerve upset might cause the *new hair* to grow out white, a little study of the hair structure will show that no nervous shock could instantaneously knock out all the pigment particles in the hair already grown out. For lack of authenticated cases the "turning white overnight" stories will have to be lumped with the myths about children being born with white hair because their mothers were frightened by white horses during pregnancy.

Another point of interest is that discrepancies in color or shade between the hair on the head and that elsewhere might be caused by localized conditions in different parts of the body. Contributing factors may be differences in the various hair areas and the structure and nature of their hair cells, gland-action, degree of exposure to air and sunlight, etc. Whatever the reasons may be, we sometimes find men with brown or black head hair having red mustaches and beards, and fair or reddish *pubic* hair, while others with light head hair have dark pubic hair.

We have dealt with environmental influences in hair coloring at some length because it is important for parents to consider them before drawing conclusions as to what "hair-color" genes they carry and can transmit to their children. However, in the great majority of cases a person's hair coloring during maturity offers some pretty accurate clues as to the genes he is carrying, for hair color is among the traits most definitely determined by heredity. This is unquestionably proved by the fact that all types of hair color are found among humans in many different environments; and also by the fact that among lower animals which are bred for their color—dogs and cats, and especially fur-bearing animals—a great variety of hair colors down to the most minute shades, can be accurately produced through carefully controlled breeding along genetic principles.

If there was any point in breeding human beings in this way, and we did so, we could also most certainly produce redheads, blonds and brunettes, of every shade, at will. But for the sake of the beauty parlors, anyway, let's be glad we aren't doing it—as yet!

CHAPTER 13

SKIN COLOR

JUDY O'GRADY and the Colonel's lady, both being White, might very well be "sisters under their skins." But whether the "Black" man, "Yellow" man and "White" man are brothers under their skins is a question that has long agitated the world and continues to cause strife and bitterness.

If skin color itself were the only point at issue, modern scientists would say there is little or nothing to justify the prejudices associated with it, or even to warrant making clear-cut distinctions among peoples on the basis solely of their skin pigmentation. For the old notion that each race has a pigment peculiar to itself—that Negroes have special "black" pigments in their skins, Chinese "yellow" pigments, Indians "red" pigments, etc., which are not found in Whites—is all wrong!

What is now established is that *exactly the same skin-coloring elements are present in all human beings, of all races.* The only differences are in the degrees and amounts in which these elements are produced and blended, *chiefly through inheritance.*

Depicting flesh color always has been a headache to artists, although they may come close to the desired results by using mixtures of brown, red, yellow and blue. This, too, is the "palette" of colors and effects used by Nature in tinting human skins.

Whatever your own skin coloring may be, it is produced by a combination of these five pigments:

1 and 2. Our old friend *melanin*—the same sturdy brownish pigment found in eyes and hair—and a junior relative, *melanoid,* which two are mainly responsible for the degree of darkness of your skin. (Melanin is present in granule form, melanoid in diffuse form.)

3. Possibly *carotene,* a yellowish or yellowish-red pigment, chemically very much like one found in carrots (hence its name).

4 and 5. Two blood pigments in the two forms of hemoglobin—the bright red one in the arteries and a darker kind in the veins—

which, as they shine up through the skin give it its pinkish flesh tint.

Finally, not involving a pigment, a bluish tinge is contributed to the general skin color by the deep, opaque, underlying layers of the skin. Without this bluish effect, produced through light-scattering (in the same way that eyes or the sky are made to appear blue), "the normal skin would appear much like a piece of Cellophane-wrapped, raw beefsteak" (to quote Drs. Edward A. Edwards and S. Quimby Duntley, leaders in the field of skin-color research).

In individual cases, the effects of skin pigmentation are also influenced by the structure of the skin, its thickness, translucency, oiliness, etc., and pigmentation itself may be speeded up or decreased by hormonal action, sunlight and other factors which we'll deal with later. But all important differences in human skin colors, racial and individual, can be attributed to the way the basic pigments mentioned are produced and distributed through gene action.

The "key" genes in the whole process are those which govern the production of the varying amounts of melanin and melanoid. Differences in concentration of these brownish pigments alone can produce grades of color from yellow, in dilute form, through orange, orange-red, dark brown and almost black. The most active "melanin" and "melanoid" genes are found in Negroes, with decreasingly active genes, in order, being present in Mulattos, Hindus, Japanese and Whites. Where the darkest skins are produced, there is probably a special "intensifying" gene which causes an extra speeding-up of the whole pigmenting process, not only in the skin, but in the eyes and hair. This may account for the fact that whereas in the lighter shades of eyes, hair and skin, colors of various kinds may go together, "black" skin is almost invariably linked with very dark eyes and hair.

For *carotene* there quite likely may be another gene. Inasmuch as this pigment is yellowish or yellowish-red, we might suspect (as a theory, for there is as yet no proof) that the most active "carotene" genes are in the Chinese and other Mongolians, and in their offshoot-relatives, American Indians. (Incidentally, Indians don't have "red" skins: at best they're bronze, or copper-colored.) However, many authorities believe there is actually no difference in carotene among the races, and that "yellow" skin is probably due to fine melanin particles, plus effects produced by the small blood vessels in the way (or depth) that they lie beneath the skin.

As for the blood pigments, these have no racial connections, the blood of all peoples being the same in coloring. (The exceptions are

SKIN PIGMENTATION

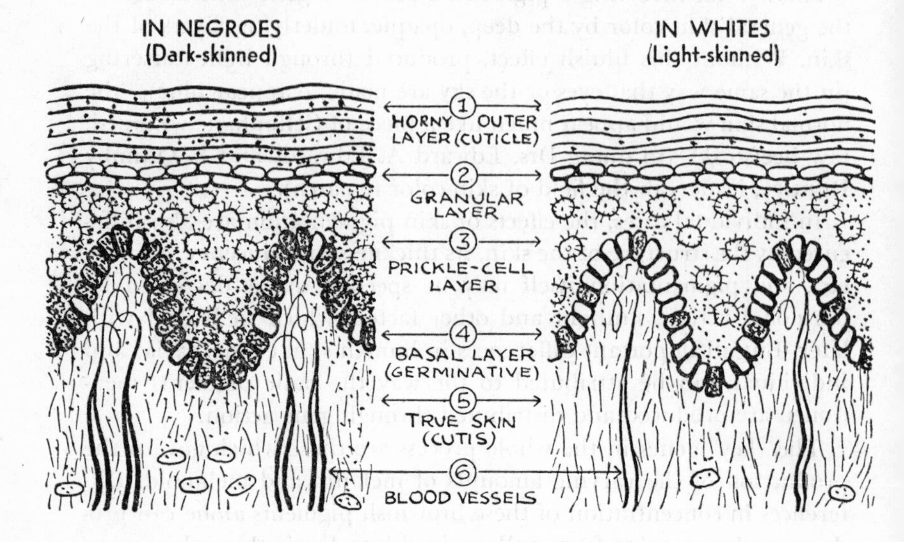

Notes to Above.*

1. The outer layer (cuticle) tends to be slightly thicker in Negroes, and contains considerable more scattered pigment.

2. The granular layer (same in both races) is made up of clouded (opaque) cells, which screen the flesh beneath. (Otherwise skin would look like raw meat.)

3. In the prickle-cell layer pigment is much more heavily distributed in Negroes.

4. Basal or germinative cells: It is among these that the skin pigment is produced. Not all the cells produce pigment, but in Negroes a much higher proportion of these cells are active, and to much greater degree, than in Whites (even when the latter undergo tanning). The term "germinative" is applied because it is from these cells that the skin cells above them arise: First, the prickle cells (3), which move up to become the granular cells (2), these latter, in turn, as they dry out, becoming the horny-layer cells (1)—actually semi-dead or dead cells which peel off as they reach the surface.

5. The "true" skin: Some pigment (more in Negroes) descends here from the layer above and may be taken up by certain cells (shown near bottom of diagram). The true skin also contains the skin nerves, and (6), the small blood vessels, which are somewhat more abundant and thicker in Negroes, and contribute to their skin color.

*Diagrams and notes prepared with aid of Dr. George H. Kostant.

only in individual cases where some persons are more anemic than others.)

Thus, all the important differences in skin color among human beings—ranging all the way from the darkest Negroes to the whitest Whites—can be related mainly to the graded action of a few separate genes governing the production, in varying degrees, of melanin and melanoid. Further, with this simplified understanding of how much more limited are the actual differences in skin colors than we used to think, and how much overlapping there is among races and sub-groups even in these differences, it becomes clear now why we can't make any accurate classification of the world's peoples merely on a color basis. (You yourself probably know Whites who are darker than many Negroes, or "yellower" than many Chinese, or "redder" than many Indians.) Indeed, modern anthropologists no longer speak of "Black," "Brown," "Yellow," "Red," or "White" races, but refer instead to "Negroids," "Mongoloids," "Australoids," "Caucasoids," etc., and to various divisions of each race, basing their classifications on composites of many physical traits in addition to skin color.

Also a lot clearer is our knowledge of what happens in matings between persons of markedly different complexions. The old notions were that skin colors were "blended" in the offspring of such matings, much as colors are blended by mixing different pigments. True, this seemed the case when a Negro mated with a White and they had Mulatto children of an in-between shade. But always baffling was the result of matings between one Mulatto and another, for instead of their offspring continuing to be all of the same blended shade, it was found that they could be of all different colors, ranging from the darkest black of any Negro grandparent, to the very light skin of the fairest White grandparent.

This mystery is ended now by proof that in matings between persons with different-colored skins, there is no mixing of colors, but merely a recombination of pigment-producing *genes*. Further, following the Mendelian laws, these genes remain separate and distinct in their workings, and only in their effects is there any blending. In subsequent matings the genes segregate out again, and may form new combinations and produce new effects.

How this sorting-out and recombination of the "skin-color" genes may work in Negro-White and Mulatto matings is shown in our accompanying Plate. To simplify the process, we have depicted the

"Negro" genes and "White" genes as each of two kinds (which might refer, theoretically, to their different "melanin" and "melanoid" genes) *although there probably are a number of other genes involved.* With these multiple genes we introduce a new genetic principle. In the case of eye and hair color, you will remember that a "dark" gene dominates a "light" one: Where a "brown-eye" gene is coupled with a "blue-eye" one, brown eyes result quite as well as if there are two "brown-eye" genes, and blue eyes result only with two "blue-eye" genes. With the multiple "skin-color" genes, however, *each gene* can assert itself and can add to the production of pigment. Individually, a "dark-skin" gene is stronger than a "light-skin" gene, but it is not nearly as strong as *two* "dark-skin" genes together. Thus, as you will see by our Plate, if at least two pairs of different "dark" genes are required to produce the full Negro color, one pair alone coupled with a "White" pair will produce the in-between Mulatto shade, and still other shades will result when three "Negro" genes are linked with one "White," or one "Negro" gene is linked with three "White" ones. Should additional types of genes be involved in producing Negro skin color as compared with White, the possible graded color combinations would be even more complex.

Anyway, we can see now why a truly black-skinned child can result only if *both* parents carry some "Negro" "skin-color" genes. This should dispose of a still widespread superstition that a woman with a little "hidden Negro blood," "passing" as White, and married to a White man, might give birth to a coal-black baby. One such "case," repeatedly reported to geneticist Curt Stern, was thoroughly investigated by him in 1947, and found—as always with such "cases"—to be groundless. Where a black baby does unexpectedly turn up, it can be taken for granted that (a) both parents have Negro ancestry, or (b) the parentage is doubtful. In reverse, it would be equally impossible for a Negress with "hidden White blood," mated to a full-blooded Negro, to give birth to a White child (unless it were an albino, which abnormality we'll deal with at another point).

One important question with respect to Negroes in the United States is whether their average skin color hasn't been becoming steadily lighter through the infiltration of "White" genes. No accurate scientific studies have been made on this point, nor could they be made easily. For one thing, while a great many "White" genes were mixed into the Negro population in the past (some authorities estimating that not more than 10 per cent of the Negroes are free of

SKIN COLOR

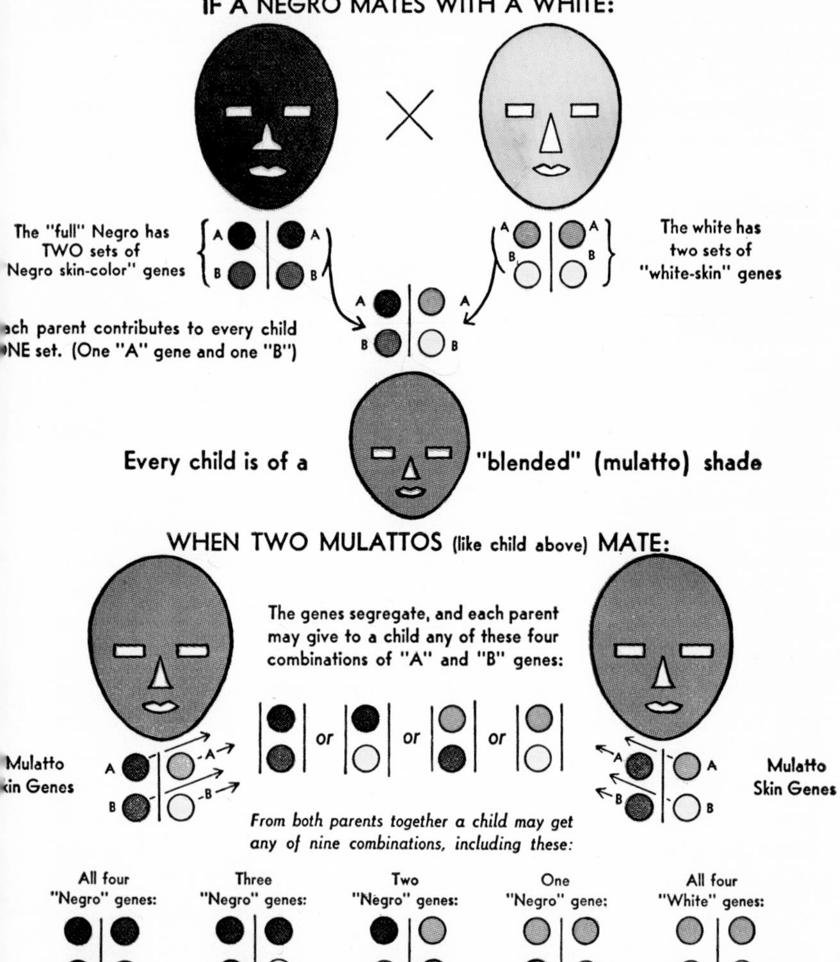

IF A NEGRO MATES WITH A WHITE:
The "full" Negro has TWO sets of Negro skin-color" genes
A
B
The white has two sets of "white-skin" genes
ach parent contributes to every child
NE set. (One "A" gene and one "B")
Every child is of a "blended" (mulatto) shade
WHEN TWO MULATTOS (like child above) MATE:
The genes segregate, and each parent may give to a child any of these four combinations of "A" and "B" genes:
or
or
or
Mulatto
kin Genes
Mulatto Skin Genes
From both parents together a child may get any of nine combinations, including these:

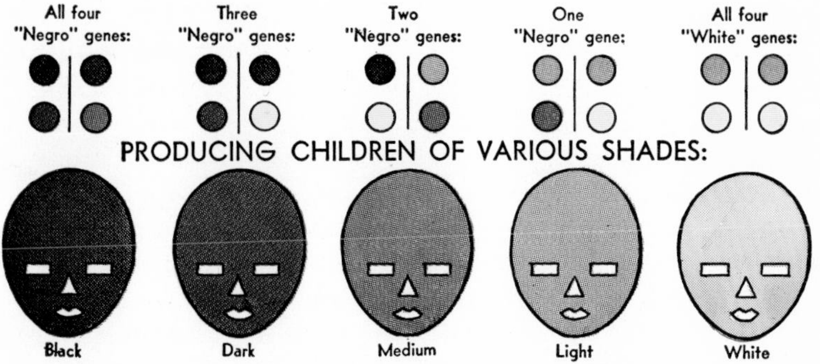

All four "Negro" genes:
Three "Negro" genes:
Two "Negro" genes:
One "Negro" gene:
All four "White" genes:
PRODUCING CHILDREN OF VARIOUS SHADES:
Black
Dark
Medium
Light
White

(NOTE: *Only two types of skin color genes are shown, but there probably are more*)

them), there is little evidence of any increase in interbreeding in recent years, with the probability being greater that there has been a decline. On the other hand, the lighter-skinned Negroes, who tend to be economically more favored, are reported as having a lower birth rate than the darker-skinned ones; and further decreasing the pool of "lighter" genes would be the fact that a certain number of those with the fewest "Negro" genes "pass over" into the White population each year. Taking together all these factors (and others which we'll touch on in our "Race" chapter later), the answer might be that our Negro population is not at present turning genetically lighter to any great average extent.

But, you may ask, haven't we overlooked the possibility that living in a temperate climate for generations has made Negroes much lighter-skinned than their African ancestors? Before we answer this specifically, let's go on to the general subject of environment in relation to skin color.

First, it can be said that pigment production in the skin is much more responsive to outward and inward influences than is eye coloring or hair coloring. (Perhaps you don't have to be reminded that you may look like a boiled lobster after your first day at the seashore, and that at other times your mirror may have told you you look "positively black," or "green," or "yellow," or "pasty white.") Most often, skin color is affected by sun and climate. One of the principal purposes of the skin (aside from its "breathing" and excretory functions) is to serve as a protective wrapping, and where the pigment has its special value is in shading the delicate blood vessels from strong sun or light rays. Because human beings may live in many different climates and under different conditions, the mechanism of skin-pigment production is so adjusted that it can be governed to some extent by the needs of the individual. Thus, under some conditions the pigment genes step up their production, and a darkening of the skin results; under other conditions they lazy along, and there is less pigmentation.

However, the way that different skins react to outer influences—for instance, the sun's rays—may also be governed by genetic differences, both in the way the skin is constructed and in the way the pigment genes work within it. Take the familiar examples of stenographers on their vacations. In Gertie's case, the more she basks on a blazing beach, the more her genes will rally to increase pigmentation, with a beautiful deep tan resulting. In poor Flossie's case (as is usually true of very fair-skinned people, and often of redheads), the pigment genes may be unequal to the task. Unless she properly protects herself, her flesh may actually be *broiled,* sometimes with serious consequences.

There are White persons who through constant exposure to a hot sun can become almost as dark as Negroes. But a heavily tanned White man never has quite the same skin color as a "full-blooded" Negro, for even with the same degree of darkness, other factors contributing to their coloration, would differ. Also to be stressed is that if a normally fair White man does become dark-skinned, it is only an *acquired* characteristic which can have no effect on his children. White families can live in the tropics for generations, and yet their children will continue to be born as fair-skinned as if their forebears hadn't ever strayed from Hoboken, New Jersey.

What of the differences in complexions between the very light-skinned Nordics of the cold climates and the swarthy southern Italians, or the very dark Arabs? These are only in part due to degrees of exposure to the sun, for one can find light-skinned Whites and swarthy Whites of native stocks in every climate. Most Mediterranean peoples have a heavy admixture of "dark-skin" pigment genes, whose effects would persist regardless of the climates in which they lived. (We need hardly point out that in the United States offspring of peoples of many stocks living side by side reflect in their skin colors all shades of their ancestral differences.)

Which brings us back again for a moment to Negroes. By now it should be apparent that it wasn't "the shadow'd livery of the burnish'd sun" which accounted for the skin color of their ancestors—regardless of how many generations they had lived in Africa—but certain genes which they happened to have to start with (and which may have become more concentrated through selective breeding). Nor has the lack of any such burnished sun made too much difference in the skin color of their descendants living in New York, or Minneapolis, although it is true that Negroes living in cool climates will, like Whites, be less heavily pigmented than those of their race in the tropics.* We might also add that among themselves Negroes of different ancestral stocks have almost as many genetic variations in skin color as have Whites, and that they, too, react differently on exposure to hot suns. Not only do some Negroes sunburn more easily than

* Bleaching of Negro skin by means of certain chemicals is possible, but is dangerous and also impractical, as it results in a "dead" white and spotty skin.

others, but many Negroes run almost the same risk of sunstroke as do Whites.

We are not offering much data about other racial aspects of skin-color inheritance, or the pigmenting results of crossbreedings between Chinese or Japanese and Whites, Indians and Whites, etc., because they have not been given much detailed study, which in turn is largely because they do not have as much social significance or interest as do those relating to Negro skin color. However, the same principles for skin-color inheritance that were set forth with respect to Negro-White and Mulatto-Mulatto matings also have been proved to apply to inter-racial matings of all kinds, and to a less marked extent to matings between persons of the same race with very different skin colors. For instance, where a Caucasian of swarthy stock (southern Italian, Arab, East Indian, etc.) mates with one of the fair-skinned stock, the offspring would be of in-between shades, and in matings of Whites of mixed stock, the offspring may be of a variety of skin colors, ranging from dark to light-skinned. In some instances, though, the "darker" genes appear to dominate the "lighter" ones.

Of special interest are the cases where a remote Mongol ancestor or sometimes a Negro ancestor may reveal himself in a White European or American infant through the *"Mongolian spot."* This is a temporary bluish patch in the skin near the base of the spine which is present through heredity in almost all infants of the Mongolian races (Chinese, Japanese, Eskimos, American Indians, etc.), in many infants of some Negro stocks, and occasionally among White infants of Armenian, Italian or other darker-skinned Caucasian stocks. It disappears by the end of the first year. The Mongolian spot appears to be produced by dominant genes in some cases and by recessive genes in others, but is not reported in blonds, indicating that generally active pigment genes are needed to bring it out.

Freckles provide a more familiar example of spotting with an hereditary basis, a dominant gene being reported as the usual cause. Freckling is often transitory, appearing in childhood and disappearing in maturity. Frequently it is associated with red hair and white skin, indicating that where there is such a combination, the "freckling" gene may have some special opportunity to assert itself.

Albinism, which deprives eyes and hair of their natural coloring, also greatly reduces the pigmentation of the skin, most strikingly so in the case of Negro albinos (two of whom are shown in the photo opposite page 193). But this condition belongs with other skin oddities and abnormalities to be dealt with in a later chapter (23).

In the general skin-pigmenting process, the genes do not assert themselves in full strength until after infancy. Characteristic pigmentation, however, begins during the embryonic stages and is quite well advanced at birth. Newborn Negro babies are usually of light chocolate or brick-red color but darken steadily, so that by the end of the first month they are quite fully colored. Mulatto babies may look white for a time, but if both parents are Mulattos, their babies, as we've previously indicated, may be of almost any color at birth and thereafter. As for White babies, any mother knows they're anything but "white" at birth, their flaming redness being due to their very thin and sparsely pigmented skin allowing the actively charged blood vessels beneath to shine through.

Changes in skin color in later years may be due to various influences other than those already mentioned. Many diseases, especially the ones arising from glandular upsets, may affect the pigmenting processes, leading to either darkening or lightening effects. As examples, Addison's disease gives the sufferer a bronzed skin, jaundice produces a yellowish skin, and tuberculosis may give a person very white skin with very red cheeks. Pregnancy tends to darken the skin for a while, though normally a woman's skin is somewhat lighter in color than that of a man of the same stock, for female skins have somewhat less of the melanin pigment, and somewhat more of the carotene, and tan less deeply than do male skins. These sex differences are due largely to hormonal influences on the pigmenting process, as well as on the development of the blood vessels, which in individuals of either sex may modify skin color (over the body as a whole or in specific areas) all the way from infancy through old age.

But, as we must constantly keep in mind, whatever the varying states or environmental conditions of individuals may be, and whatever effects these may have on their skin pigmentation, they can in no way change the "skin-color" *genes* which persons transmit to their children.

CHAPTER 14

THE FEATURES

IF YOU'RE among those who believe that "your face is your fortune," you might want to know how much of that "fortune" is inherited.

Making faces happens to be one of the most interesting jobs done by genes, though in the plastic details such as nose, eye shapes, ears, lips, etc., examples of gene dominance and recessiveness are not quite as clear-cut as occur in our coloring processes. This isn't because the "sculptor" genes are necessarily less definite in their workings than the "color" genes, but because many more of them may be involved in producing any given feature, and so many more things can happen to modify and alter what these genes set out to do. Added to all this is the difficulty of classification.

In eye color, for instance, "blue" is blue, applied to anyone the world over. We know quite clearly what is meant by "blue" when we say a child or a man of sixty has blue eyes, a girl or a boy has blue eyes. But in describing features or body forms we can use such terms as "large," "small," "broad," "narrow," etc., only relatively. A nose that would be large on a child would be small on an adult; a nose that would look handsome on a Gary Cooper would be a whopper on a Hedy Lamarr. Moreover, in appraising the features of persons of the same age, sex and stock, when you say this one has a "long" nose, that one a "small" nose, you might be surprised to find that the actual differences in length of the noses are perhaps no more than three-sixteenths or a quarter of an inch. (The famed "schnozzola" of the comedian Jimmy Durante may be no more than half an inch longer than average.) Similarly, "enormous" eyes, or a "wide" mouth, may represent only a fraction of an inch more in width than the average (although this might significantly affect the total area of the feature).

In general, most of the feature differences considered important among persons of the same family or stock are so small as to require very detailed and minute measurements to be reduced to statistical terms. For this reason, geneticists and anthropologists who have studied feature inheritance have so far confined themselves largely to the very marked racial differences—as between Negroes and Whites, or Whites and Mongolians—and the results of crosses among them. However, these inter-racial studies have been checked sufficiently with observations of matings of people of similar stocks to lead to some fairly definite conclusions as to how features are inherited.

Let's start with the face as a whole, not only because it's the way you ordinarily see a person at first, but because each individual feature may be much influenced in its appearance by the sum total of all the features (or what the psychologists call the "gestalt"). This goes much further than mere looks, however. In the actual process of facial construction, during prenatal life and in all the developmental stages thereafter, the molding of the face in its entirety can affect the shaping of each separate feature, and each feature can individually affect its neighbors.

Have you ever modeled a head out of clay or soft wax, and then, for fun (or out of disappointment), squashed it? You've laughed as you've seen how every feature is altered, and how different are the effects if you push in the clay head from the sides, or from top to bottom. There are much the same results when you stand in front of the distorted mirrors in the "laughing galleries," or look at your reflection in bowls or vases, some of which widen the face, or others narrow and lengthen it to exaggerated degrees.

This illustrates a basic principle in facial construction. First, there are genes which govern the structure of the skull as a whole, as you can see most clearly in the case of dogs, ranging all the way from the pulled-out, lengthened faces of wolfhounds and dachshunds, to the squashed-together faces of bulldogs and Pekingese. Humans, fortunately, have not been bred for any such extremes, but nonetheless there are abnormal cases, as in certain kinds of dwarfs (*achondroplastic*), where a gene or two can radically change the structure of the whole face and affect every feature. There are many other cases, to be dealt with in later chapters, where a few abnormal genes, or glandular abnormalities in whole or in part hereditary, may shape the face as a unit in characteristic ways, or greatly distort individual features. (In certain pituitary disorders the face of a White person may be so transformed that he or she will appear to be Negroid, with broad nostrils, thick lips and a darkening of the skin as well.) In normal persons, however, no gene is known which singly can do much to affect the features in unison, although a few genes together may act to broaden or lengthen the face.

As a general rule, wider heads and stronger jaws (which can be much influenced by chewing habits) tend to make for broader faces. Longer or deeper jaws contribute to face lengthening, particularly so in the case of men, who, on the average, have longer faces than women (and not only when the bills come in at the end of the month). Either in the sex differences or otherwise, hormonal influences may also have much to do with the broadening or lengthening of the face. (Professor Hooton believes that most very long-faced persons probably have overactive pituitary glands.) Thus, so many factors are involved in face-shaping, that it is quite impossible to speak of inheriting such or such a type of face as a whole.

For the most part, the construction of every feature individually is governed by special genes. While these usually work together with the genes for the neighboring features, they can also go off on tangents of their own. The ears and the nose, which grow away from the face, may be most independent in their development, whereas the mouth, as we shall see, is much influenced by its surroundings.

But the best evidence of how closely "feature" genes follow their basic blueprints is presented by something which we've taken too lightly for granted: the precision and symmetry with which opposite sides of the face, and particularly paired features—eyes, ears, teeth, nostrils, etc.—are constructed. If the genes did not construct the features in specified ways, down to the most minute details, or if environment were the major factor, one eye would be radically different from another, one ear from another ear, etc. As it is, minor differences do exist between corresponding features and sides of the face, but except in some abnormal instances, these result from the slightly different conditions encountered by the duplicate genes as the body develops.

Now let's consider each of the features in detail.

The Nose. The "nose" genes are among those that can be most clearly analyzed. Some studies might indicate that there is one "key" gene producing the general shape of the nose, but most authorities agree that three, and possibly four genes are at work, each on a different part. That is, there would be separate genes for the bridge (its shape, height and length); the nostrils (breadth, shape and size of apertures); the root of the nose and its juncture with the upper lip; and the "bulb," or point of the nose.

Often, it is true, the nose as an entire unit appears to be "inherited" from one parent. Where such resemblance occurs it could be assumed that the different genes involved were passed over in combination and were almost all of them dominant over those of the other parent.

Very often, on the other hand, a child has a nose which seems to be a cross between that of both parents. This would bear out the theory that several or many unit factors are involved. At any rate, it is clear that distinctive genes are at work, and that they sort out independently. If this were not so, the nose of every child would be a "blend" of its parents' noses. But we know, of course, that this is not so. Even in the most inbred peoples noses of every shape and size appear, proving the Mendelian segregation and sorting out of the "nose" genes.

In the *bridge*—the most important part of the nose—shape and size are dependent on how far out from the skull and at what angle, the "bridge" gene works until it stops. At the same time other "nose" genes are acting to determine the *breadth* of the nose, ranging from the thin bridge found among "Nordics" to the broad bridge found among Negroes; and these, or still other genes, are at work on the nostrils and on the "bulb" or tip of the nose.

What happens in children when parents with very different noses mate is suggested in our accompanying illustration. In general, *the more active "nose" genes*—those for larger, more prominent or more accentuated noses—*tend to dominate the more conservative ones.* Thus, in most cases the genes for prominent and convex noses, or for hooked and pug-noses, dominate those for moderate and straight; the genes for high and narrow bridges dominate those for low and broad bridges; the genes for broad nostrils, of the Negro type, dominate those for narrow nostrils (although in White-White matings, the reverse may be true in some cases). The "potato" nose of Dutch families seems to result from a dominant gene, as apparently does also the "bulbous tip" which in other strains continues to enlarge with old age.

However, with the various "nose" genes sorting out independently, we can see how persons may have a large nose with small nostrils, a small nose with a wide bridge and large nostrils, or any other combination. The full effects of the "nose" genes do not assert themselves until maturity; in fact, these genes may keep on working throughout life producing increases in both length and breadth. As many readers have learned to their regret, the pertest, daintiest little noses of childhood may blossom after adolescence into veritable monstrosities. Moreover, during and after middle age, there may be

"DOMINANCE" AND "RECESSIVENESS" IN NOSE-SHAPES

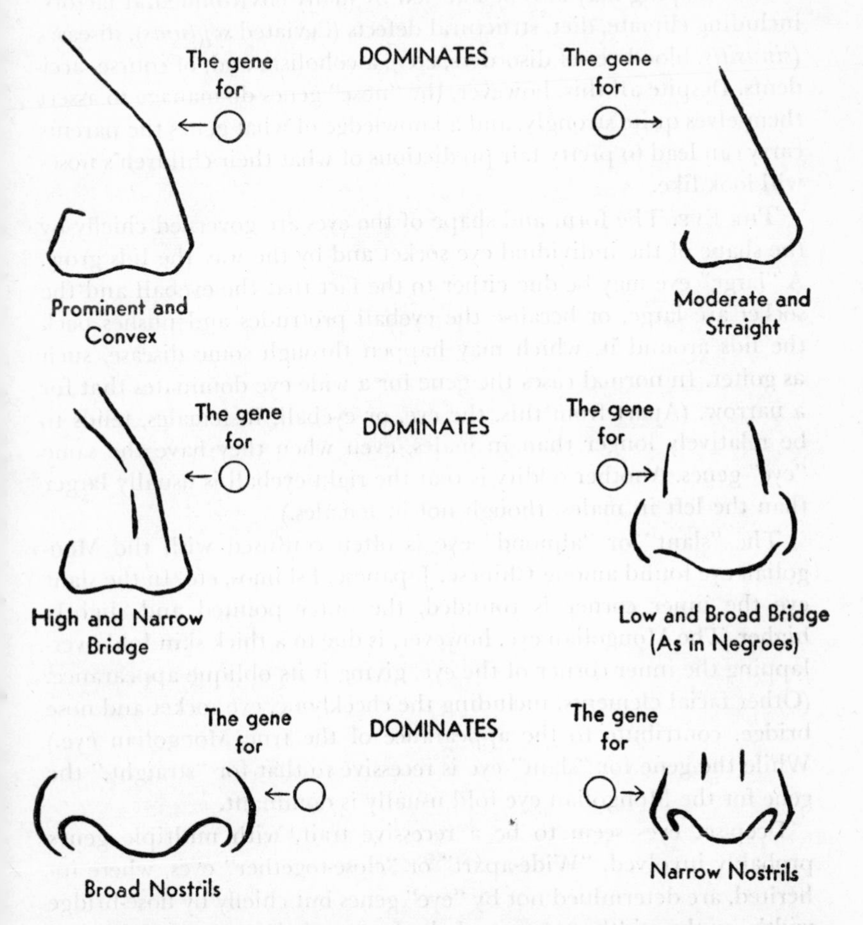

NOTE: *It should be clear that it is not any type of nose itself that "dominates" another nose, but the genes producing the nose-effects that dominate the other genes. Also, for certain exceptions to the dominance relationships illustrated, and for some other types of "nose-matings," see the text.*

a final spurt in nose development, or a putting on of "finishing touches," so that often, in later years, racial or familial characteristics become most apparent.

As a rule, the general growth of the individual affects nose form and size, with tall people tending to have longer noses than short people. Sex differences, too, play an important part, the male ("androgenic") hormones acting to make the noses of males somewhat relatively larger than those of females.

Nose-shaping may also be affected by many environmental factors, including climate, diet, structural defects (deviated *septums*), diseases (*sinusitis,* blood-vessel disorders, etc.), alcoholism and, of course, accidents. Despite all this, however, the "nose" genes do manage to assert themselves quite strongly, and a knowledge of what genes the parents carry can lead to pretty fair predictions of what their children's noses will look like.

THE EYE. The form and shape of the eyes are governed chiefly by the shape of the individual eye socket and by the way the lids grow. A "large" eye may be due either to the fact that the eyeball and the socket are large, or because the eyeball protrudes and pushes back the lids around it, which may happen through some disease, such as goiter. In normal cases the gene for a wide eye dominates that for a narrow. (Apart from this, the eye, or eyeball, in females, tends to be relatively longer than in males, even when they have the same "eye" genes. Another oddity is that the right eyeball is usually larger than the left in males, though not in females.)

The "slant" or "almond" eye is often confused with the Mongolian eye found among Chinese, Japanese, Eskimos, etc. In the slant eye the inner corner is rounded, the outer pointed and slightly higher. The Mongolian eye, however, is due to a thick skin fold overlapping the inner corner of the eye, giving it its oblique appearance. (Other facial elements, including the cheekbone, eye socket and nose bridge, contribute to the appearance of the true Mongolian eye.) While the gene for "slant" eye is recessive to that for "straight," the gene for the Mongolian eye fold usually is dominant.

Deep-set eyes seem to be a recessive trait, with multiple genes probably involved. "Wide-apart" or "close-together" eyes, where inherited, are determined not by "eye" genes but chiefly by nose-bridge width, or the width-structure of the face, and the genes for these.

Unusually long eyelashes are inherited through a dominant gene (fortunately for the ladies). Where a mother has very long lashes she can count on an average of one in every two children inheriting them.

THE EAR. In ear shape the inheritance of several characteristics has been noted:

The gene for long ear seems to dominate that for short.

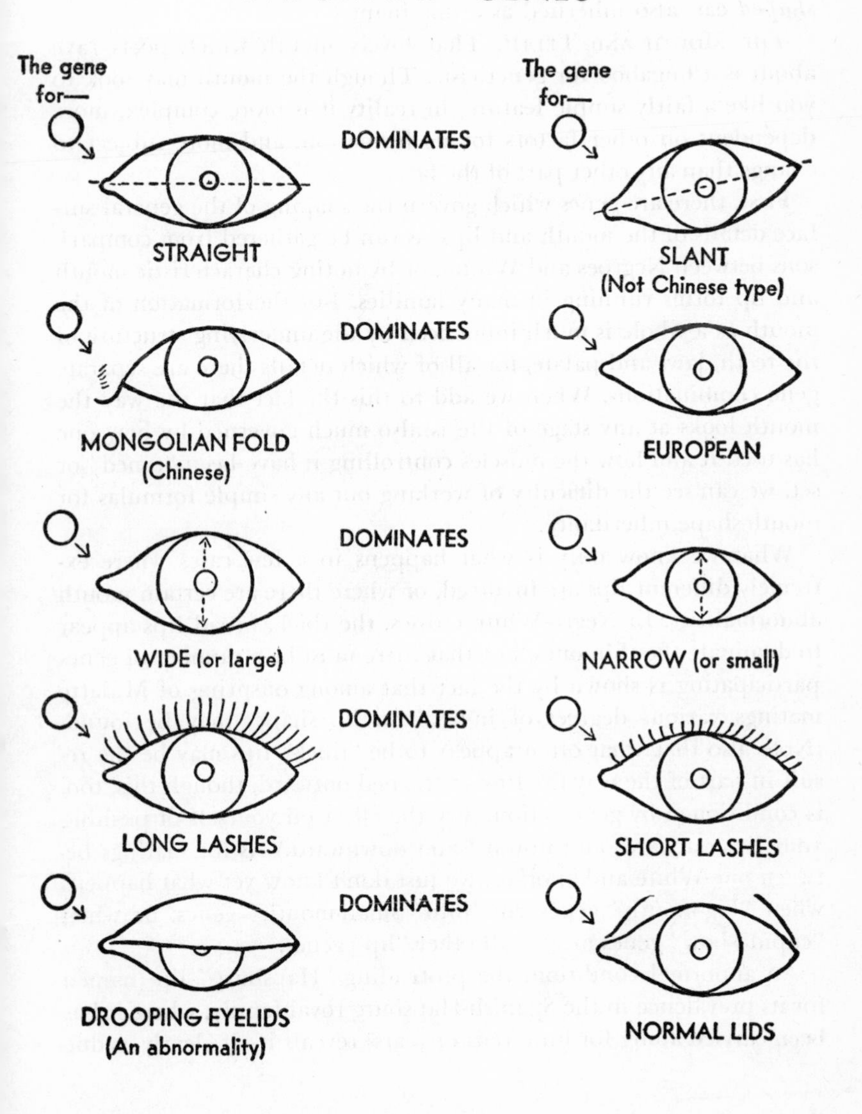

The gene for wide ear dominates that for narrow ear.

The gene for full and free lobe usually dominates that for affixed (women with the latter type being at a disadvantage when they wish to wear earrings).

A minor peculiarity in some ears is a "pit," or small hole about the size of a pinhead, on the inner flange where the ear meets the temple. It is usually dominant in inheritance. A rarer oddity is the small *cup-shaped* ear, also inherited as a dominant.

THE MOUTH AND TEETH. That lovely mouth which poets rave about is a bugaboo for geneticists. Though the mouth may look to you like a fairly simple feature, in reality it is more complex, more dependent on other factors for its formation, and more subject to change than any other part of the face.

First, there are genes which govern the shaping of the general surface details of the mouth and lips, as can be gathered from comparisons between Negroes and Whites, or by noting characteristic mouth and lip forms running in many families. But the formation of the mouth as a whole is much influenced by the underlying structure of the teeth, jaws and palate, for all of which details there are separate gene combinations. When we add to this the fact that the way the mouth looks at any stage of life is also much governed by how one has used it and how the muscles controlling it have been "toned" or set, we can see the difficulty of working out any simple formulas for mouth-shape inheritance.

What we know only is what happens in a few cases where extremely different lips are involved, or where there are certain mouth abnormalities. In Negro-White crosses, the thick, broad lips appear to dominate the thin ones, but that there must be a number of genes participating is shown by the fact that among offspring of Mulatto matings various degrees of in-between lip shapes may be found. (Note also that what often appear to be "thick" lips may be the result in part of the way the lips are turned outward, though this, too, is conditioned by gene action. Try the effect on yourself of pushing your lips outward, and upward and downward.) As for matings between one White and another, we just don't know yet what happens when "big-mouth" genes run into "small-mouth" genes, or when "cupid's-bow" genes meet with other "lip" genes.

An abnormal condition, the protruding "Hapsburg" lip (named for its prevalence in the Spanish-Hapsburg royal family, where it has been carried along for hundreds of years) reveals itself clearly as due to a dominant gene. The narrow, undershot Hapsburg jaw also goes with the lip as a rule. Dimpled, or "cleft" chins may be inherited either through dominant or recessive genes. (Cheek dimples may also be inherited, as a rule through dominant genes.) The receding chin is generally recessive in inheritance to the straight chin, and narrow or pointed chins also seem to be recessive to the wide one. However, the appearance of the chin is much dependent on how the lower jaw is set against the upper jaw, and in this the whole structure of the head may be involved.

In teeth, genes are at work to produce many of the variations noted among individuals, but attention has been given by geneticists chiefly to abnormalities and defects, which we'll deal with in a later chapter. One special item: A space between the upper center teeth—much valued by some little boys (though hardly by adults)—appears to be inherited as a dominant.

Hair Form. The hair has been subjected in times past and present to more artificial changes than probably any other human feature. But of all hairdressers, the greatest are the "hairdresser" genes with which a person starts life. They determine whether one's hair is to be as straight as a poker, naturally curly, or so kinky "you can't do a thing with it." Whatever one may do to alter the surface effects of the genes' workings, we may see that under the microscope the different forms of hair are actually different in their basic construction.

In cross section, straight hair generally tends to be almost round; wavy hair more oval and curly hair still more so; and kinky hair a flattened oval. However, this refers to *averages*. As Dr. Stanley M. Garn of Harvard, and others, report, all forms of hair may be found with all forms of cross sections. Even on the same head the forms of individual hairs may differ considerably. Thus, the cross-section shape of the hair would appear to be only one of the factors associated with the form it takes, another factor perhaps, being the shape of the follicles out of which hair grows. (In curly hair the follicles tend to be curved; in straight hair, straight.) Yet as Professor Earnest A. Hooton suggests (in his book, *Up from the Ape*), the more circular cross-section form in hair may make for greater rigidity and straightness, while the flattened-oval cross section may permit of greater curliness or kinkiness. "I should doubt," he says, "that it would be possible to put a 'permanent wave' into really straight, coarse Mongoloid hair, or to make permanently straight the flattened oval, twisted Negroid hair."

THE "HAIRDRESSER" GENES

They Account for These Characteristics:

1.* In cross section, hairs show different shapes:

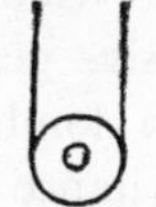

Round Oval Flat Three-cornered

2.** While hairs on any one head may vary, in general a given clump of hair will tend to be like this in cross section:

Straight Hair: Round

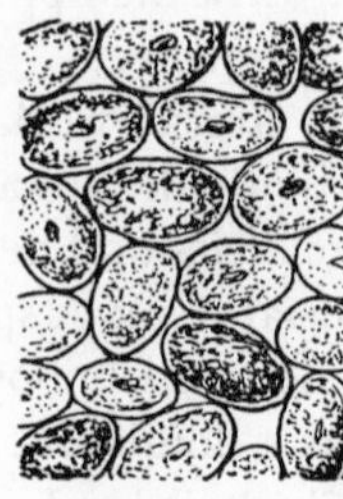

Wavy Hair: More Oval

Kinky (or Woolly) Hair: Flat Oval

3. Lengthwise, wavy or curly hairs are twisted (A). Where curvature is extreme or kinks appear, there are pinched places (B).

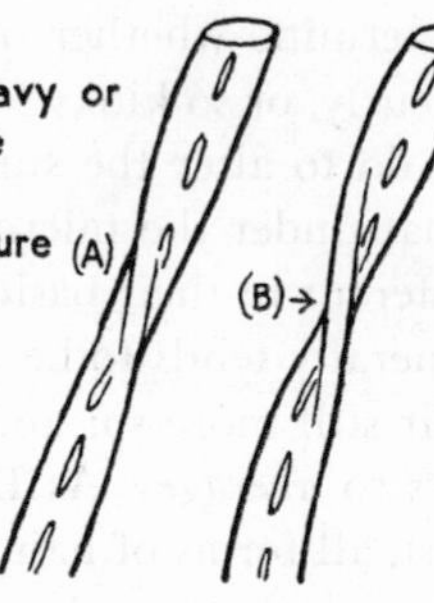

4. Also, wavy or curly hairs grow out curved from follicle, and root is tipped

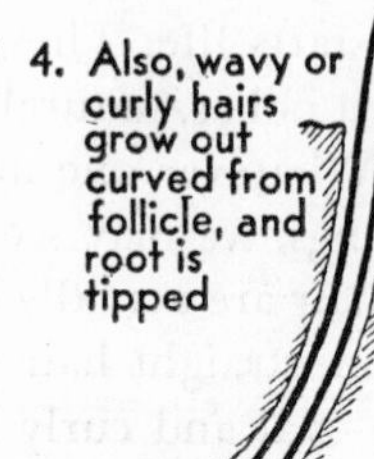

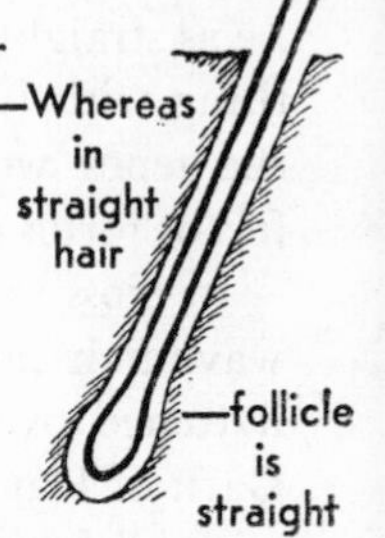

5. Where a different "hair" gene is received from each parent (particularly if parents are of similar racial stocks), the effect generally is as follows:

*Figures 1, 3 and 4 after sketches and data by Dr. Stanley M. Garn.

**Figure 2 after micro-photographs by Dr. Morris Steggerda.

In the manner of growth, kinky hair is characterized by "bunching" (or "matting") in spirally twisted locks. In woolly hair, the extreme form of kinky, these spiral twists are very small and clumped together close to the scalp. This is most accentuated in the "peppercorn" hair of some Negro stocks, where the bare skin may show between the tightly twisted clumps. (Added to the genes producing the form of the individual's hair, there may be other genes governing the way it grows.) Although the matted woolly or kinky hair occurs chiefly among the Negroid peoples, the gene for it seems to have arisen independently among Whites, for occasionally woolly hair is found in White families—some very fair-skinned and blond—where there can be no presumption of Negro blood. Also, Dr. Garn reports, some kinky hairs may occur here and there on the head and body of most Whites.

As will have been gathered, the most marked genetic differences in hair form are racial. While there may be some overlapping in hair types among all races, the Mongoloid peoples (Chinese, American Indian, Eskimo, etc.) have, almost all, straight and coarse hair; the Negroid peoples, chiefly curved, woolly or kinky hair; and the Whites, the in-between forms of wavy, curly or *fine* straight hair. The latter type of straight hair, it is important to note, is genetically and in structure quite different from the Mongolian straight hair, which is very much thicker, heavier and coarser.

Now what happens when different "hair-form" genes come together? With respect to *dominance* and *recessiveness* their workings are on the whole fairly distinct, the potency of the genes appearing to be graded by the degree of curliness they produce. The "woolly" gene is the most potent, and seems to dominate all the others. The "kinky" gene, in turn, dominates the "curly"; the "curly" dominates the "wavy"; and the "wavy" dominates the "straight."* An exception is in the case of the Mongolian "straight-hair" gene, which may be dominant over that for woolly hair (the thickness and stiffness of the Mongolian hair being here probably the determining factor). There may also be other occasional exceptions in the interaction of the "hair-form" genes, due to various qualifying factors. But in matings among Whites, it appears quite certain that the "straight-

* A sex difference has been reported in a number of studies, with findings that the male hair often tends to be wavier than the female hair in the same families (to the distress of many girls who view their brothers' hair with envy). This may lead to the fact that some apparently straight-haired parents may have boys with some degree of wavy hair.

hair" gene is recessive to all the rest. As a rule, then, *two straight-haired parents can expect to have all straight-haired children.* Where the parents have other types of hair the results for their children cannot be so easily predicted, unless we have a fair idea as to which two genes each is carrying.

Also, in attempting genetic forecasts, or in comparing hair of parents and children, it should be kept in mind that hair form and structure undergo changes with aging. Wavy or curly hair may become straighter, and the diameter of the hair in the same individual may vary from very fine in childhood to its maximum thickness in adult life, then thinning again in old age. Apart from this there undoubtedly are genes governing degrees of hair thickness (as is evident in comparing the hair of Mongolians and Whites), but how these genes work in people of the same stock to produce finer or coarser hair hasn't yet been established.

Environmental factors have not been shown to have much influence on hair form. (We are excepting, of course, what beauty parlors or home treatments may do. But these cannot alter the way the new hair grows out.) Whether in the tropics or in Alaska, the hair of Negroes is equally kinky or woolly, and the hair of Mongoloid peoples is equally straight. Nor, among Whites, does curly hair, wavy hair or straight hair undergo any change in different climates. Also, contrary to popular notions, hair doesn't grow thicker or coarser if it is cut repeatedly, or, in the case of men's facial hair, if it is shaved. (Of special interest to the ladies, this also applies to hair on the legs, as Dr. Mildred Trotter of St. Louis showed in experiments with a number of women.) Likewise, Dr. Hooton cites various studies as evidence that nutrition, sunlight or the covering of hair with clothing have little effect on hair growth. In short, hair form must be set down as one of the traits most directly determined by heredity and least influenced by environment.

An interesting hair characteristic is the *whorl,* the manner in which the hair grows wheel-like around the point at the top-center of the head. Some people tend to inherit a clockwise whorl, others a counter-clockwise, though which dominates which seems to vary in different families, and may also be influenced by chance factors in prenatal development. About 5 per cent of the people have double whorls. (What kind do you have?—though you probably won't care much one way or another!)

The distribution and arrangement of body and head hair—the

forms and density of beard and mustache, the shapes and thickness of eyebrows, the growth of hair on arms, legs and chest, etc.—all are determined or strongly influenced by genes. (This is indicated when we look at the characteristic patterns of hair growth in lower animals.) Hormonal influences, in turn, account in large measure for the sex differences in hair growth, for differences in amount of hair at various ages, and for some of the abnormalities in hair loss or excessive hairiness.

Where the hereditary differences in hair distribution and density appear most strongly are again in comparisons between racial groups. Facial and body hair is most sparse in the Mongolians (particularly full-blooded American Indians), is more abundant in Negroes, and tends to be heaviest in Whites. The hairiest of all peoples are the Ainus, a primitive group who, while inhabiting the northern parts of Japan, basically are of White stock. (It is believed that they are the remnants of a White people who very long ago lived in Asia.) "Coalescent" eyebrows—heavy ones growing together—are most common among Mediterranean peoples (Greeks, Turks, Armenians, etc.). There also are inherited racial differences in baldness, which we'll discuss in a later chapter. However, the individual differences in hair distribution found in persons and families within each race and group have as yet been little studied with respect to the genetic mechanisms responsible. So if you're much concerned as to whether or not your child will have bushy eyebrows, or a low hairline, or a "widow's peak," or a hairy chest, we can't tell you now.

"LOOKS" AND ENVIRONMENT. In discussing the separate features, we have given some attention to the effects of environment on each. However, environmental changes or modifications in the structure of any given feature, barring accidents, are apt to be much less marked, and certainly much less sudden, than can be such changes in the appearance of the face as a whole, especially in its fleshy formation. Throughout life the face as a unit is constantly influenced by habits of eating, sleeping and speaking, by thinking, emotions and various eccentricities of behavior, and, of course, by disease and aging. Where these influences are consistently the same for members of families, or even for large groups of people, many of the similarities in looks which we think of as hereditary may actually be in large part environmental. It is only when individual differences in features develop in the very same environments that we can be pretty sure they are hereditary.

But also to keep in mind is that when we speak of environmental effects on the "feature" genes we must include not only outside influences, but those, too, of the *internal* environment of the individual—all the glandular and other bodily workings which can shift the courses taken by the genes. Where these internal environmental factors differ from the outer ones is that they may be *hereditary* in part or whole. This is most clearly shown in comparisons between the features of women and men. We know that they carry the same "feature" genes, and yet the differences in their internal environments (started off initially by the XX- and XY-chromosome mechanisms) are sufficient to cause their features to develop differently in a number of ways and degrees.

In general, the bony foundations and frameworks of male faces are more rugged, and thus their features are more pronounced than those of females, given the same genes. Males within a given ethnic group tend to have heavier brows, higher cheekbones, more prominent noses, squarer and heavier chins, somewhat larger teeth, and heavier facial muscles. And need we mention beards and mustaches? All of these distinctions arise mainly through different glandular influences in the two sexes, but it is important to remember that in individuals of the same sex any degree of difference in the workings of the glands which control or modify growth—especially before or during puberty—can similarly affect the formation of individual features or the face as a whole. *Eunuchs,* for instance (if castrated before puberty), will develop "feminized" features, and girls and women in whom the glandular balance is radically upset will tend to develop "masculinized" features (including, sometimes, beard and mustaches).

And now let's see how heredity and environment work with respect to the broader details of the body.

CHAPTER 15

YOUR SIZE AND SHAPE

As A human being, your size and shape are pretty closely determined by your genes (as are the sizes and shapes of other animals). Otherwise you might have developed with the dimensions of an elephant or a rabbit, or what not.

But we take the general proportions of humans for granted. What concerns us are the relatively small differences—the few inches more or less in height, the ten pounds either way in weight, which may cause you to be considered "tall" or "short," "plump" or "scrawny." Not to mention the little bulges here and there, or the lack of them, which may classify your figure as "gorgeous" or "terrible"—depending on the viewpoints of the people among whom you live. (For what rates as an "enviable" shape varies considerably according to group, place and period.)

Accepting the fact that the little differences in human form may mean a lot, to what extent are they inherited? As in the case of the features our answers will have to take note of various environmental influences, and these we will find to be very great with respect to whatever genes there are for body shape and stature. In fact, many of the characteristics of figure or size in yourself or other people which you've thought of as inherited may be largely environmental. On the other hand, it has also become clear that hereditary factors, working directly or indirectly, account for most of the *major* differences.

Comparing individuals rather than groups, the greatest differences in body size and formation may arise through their *internal* environments, chiefly glandular, which may be in part or whole hereditary. The most striking examples, of course, are provided by comparisons between women and men. Here we have the fact that two physically distinct groups of humans are produced not through differences in specific "body-form" or "stature" genes, but through over-all developmental differences, set in motion by the sex-chromosome balances, which cause the same genes to work in radically different ways. As one example, with the same "stature" genes and under the same outward conditions, a man will grow to an average height of about one-sixteenth greater than a woman, or somewhat over three-quarters of an inch more to every foot of her size. (The present averages in the United States are, for men, just over 5 feet 8 inches [174 cm.], for women 5 feet 4 inches [164 cm.], with an increase for both in sight.) And with the same "shape" genes, we also know that the results can be in the two sexes. But on all these general points we'll have more to say as we go along.

STATURE. In the matter of human sizes we are indeed speaking for the most part of relatively small differences, for as a species we present no such extremes in variability as are found among many other animals: a giant St. Bernard dog, for instance, alongside a pint-sized Mexican Chihuahua. Taking the extremes in normal human breeds (we'll touch on abnormal cases presently) the very tallest humans, the Lake Chad Negroes of Africa, average 6 feet 1 inch in height (for males), whereas the very smallest, the pigmy Negrillos, average 4 feet 6 inches. This is a difference of little more than 25 per cent. While it may be considered for the most part hereditary it involves two small, isolated groups of people who for thousands of years have been inbred among themselves.

Between and among larger groups of humans—whole races or nationalities—where there has been a constant intermingling and dispersal of "stature" genes, there are no such marked contrasts. Though Americans may consider themselves very tall in comparison with the Chinese and Japanese, the average differences in height are somewhat over three inches, but, as many of our soldiers discovered during the Pacific campaigns, there are some pretty strapping specimens among the Orientals, too. The tallest of European nationalities, the Norwegians, Swedes and Montenegrins, may now average over 5 feet 8 inches (for males), and the "short" Italians slightly under 5 feet 6 inches.

What would happen if we deliberately tried to breed humans for size we can only guess. Two such attempts of which we have record can hardly be called "scientific." The Prussian king, Friedrich Wilhelm I, set out to produce a race of tall soldiers by marrying his towering grenadiers to tall women. His death stopped the experiment. (We may assume that left to their own devices, his grenadiers probably picked out the shortest and most petite Gretchens they could find.)

Catherine de' Medici, who had many cute ideas, took the opposite tack by setting out to breed a race of midgets. She did promote quite a number of midget-matches, but these unfortunately (or perhaps fortunately) proved sterile, as such matches usually do. However, if she had chosen for her experiment the type of larger dwarfs known as *achondroplastic*—the ones with stubby limbs and large heads—she could have produced as many as she wanted. (These abnormal individuals, and also the "pituitary" giants who would be useless for breeding, will be dealt with in a later chapter.)

Much more significant are the informal "experiments" which people themselves have carried out where they have chosen mates to match them for size. In one Canadian family which went in for tall matings—started off by a man 6 feet 6 inches who married, in succession, three wives each 6 feet or over—there were thirteen male descendants, all between 6 feet and 6 feet 4 inches in height, and ten females all between 5 feet 8 inches and 6 feet, with one exception. In the opposite direction, several Canadian families of "shorties" have produced successions of sons ranging between 5 feet 2 and 5 feet 4 inches.

These facts, coupled with much other evidence, have led to the conclusion that, conditions being equal, there are definite "key" genes for tall stature and short stature, and that they may work in fairly simple ways. But how these genes operate when they are mixed together is not yet too clear. The prevailing theory is that the "tallness" genes tend to be recessive, the "shortness" genes dominant. What this means, specifically, is that *a tall person is probably not carrying "shortness" genes, whereas a short person may very well be carrying hidden "tallness" genes.*

Whatever the "stature" genes may be in an individual, they can be greatly speeded up or slowed down by environment. And we've needed no scientific experiment to prove this. Right under our very eyes in the United States we have been observing, during the past few decades, one of the most remarkable biological phenomena in human history: an increase in stature as well as various other changes in bodily development, more marked than any which in previous epochs came only through many centuries of slow evolution. In little more than three or four decades average heights of males have gone up almost two inches, with an even greater gain being registered in the youngest groups, and the largest gains occurring in many of the groups of foreign stock. In innumerable families over the country there are sons taller by four inches or more than their fathers or any male relatives of previous generations.*

This upshooting of our youth has made six-footers commonplace, six-foot-sixers no longer objects of pop-eyed staring, and even close to seven-footers a familiar sight in basketball games. Moreover, as practical proof of the changes in both sexes, the whole range of sizes in shoes, hats, suits and other wearing apparel has been markedly increased. The phenomenon isn't confined to the United States, either, for in most European countries, and also in Japan and Hawaii, people have been growing steadily bigger. When we look much further back in history, we find that the redoubtable ancient Greeks and the brave knights of old were veritable "shrimps" compared with their modern descendants.

What has caused this change? We know there can hardly have been any mass mutations in our genes, so the most obvious reason for at least a good part of the increase must be the great improvements in diet, living conditions and medical care. Nevertheless, some scientists are not convinced this is the whole explanation, advancing the possibility that our growth genes may have been further speeded up by changes in world climatic conditions, and even by "cosmic rays" or other still unknown meteorological effects.

Thus, Dr. Harry L. Shapiro, who has made many studies in this field, said in 1945, "The phenomenon has been too world-wide to attribute it solely to nutritional factors or living conditions. Some of the tallest statures in the United States are found in some of the most backward regions, such as the Ozark areas and the *Tobacco Road* sections of the South, where the poorest nutrition and the worst living conditions prevail. Even though it may be claimed that these people come of tall stock by inheritance, the fact is that they are still taller than their European ancestors, despite very bad conditions. Likewise, we find very tall stature in many other areas of the world where nutrition is poorest."

How far can the present stature increases go? If you're visualizing future humans as story-book giants, scientists offer no encourage-

* That the increase in size begins at a very early age is indicated in these findings (1950) by Dr. Lawrence B. Slobody: Where a generation ago American babies doubled their birth weight in their fifth or sixth month, today a majority achieve this weight in their fourth month and a great many by the third month.

ment. Some authorities believe that, at best, in two hundred years the average male American stature might reach an average of 6 feet. A few believe that it might go on to 6 feet 6 inches, or slightly more. But, to again quote Dr. Shapiro, "Man is a more efficient organism if he isn't excessively tall, so it's hardly likely he'll ever reach dinosauric proportions."

What we do know to date is that the few giants in the 8 feet or over class have all been pretty weak and defective individuals, and that few have survived much beyond maturity. In any case, no change in outward conditions could carry our heights much further than the potential limits fixed by our genes.

So we come back to our main fact that while *external* environments may direct human stature upward or downward by a certain number of inches, the big differences appear to be largely dictated by heredity. But this, as suggested before, refers not only to the "stature" genes, but to the general genetic makeup of the individual (as, for instance, one's sex), and to a variety of genes that may be involved in the growth processes. Important differences have been found in the "rhythm" or rate of growth in different individuals which may be in considerable part genetic (although, obviously, various diseases or dietary deficiencies can affect the growth rates). Thus, some children who grow much faster than the average during one period may grow less than the average during another period. In estimating the future height of a child from his or her stature at any given age before puberty, one should therefore not be too hasty about deciding whether "tallness" or "shortness" lies ahead.

Also important is that heights in different peoples are not achieved in the same way. Some growth genes affect body development uniformly, whereas others specialize with respect to certain segments—limbs, torso, neck, etc. For example, in the very tall Nile Negroes a good part of the height derives from their stork-like legs, whereas among some short strains heights may be cut down sharply by stubby legs and short necks, although torso lengths are average. In some families there are special characteristics in the sizes and shapes of chests, necks, legs, hips, etc., any or all of which may be gene-influenced, and where body segments of different kinds are combined, there may be considerable variations in heights among members of a family even though their key "stature" genes may be the same.

Taking into consideration, then, all the many genetic and environmental factors we've discussed, it is evident why stature inheritance is considerably more complicated than earlier authorities thought. Nonetheless, these general conclusions are justified:

Any two normally tall parents are probably both carrying "tallness" genes, and can usually count on having *all* tall children. (As in the Franklin D. Roosevelt family, and the royal family of Sweden.)

Short parents may be of several genetic types: (1) Where both are of consistently short ancestry, and carrying predominantly "short-stature" genes, in which case all their children will probably be short; (2) where both parents are of ancestry with mixed "stature" genes, in which case they may have children of various heights, grading up to quite tall; (3) where parents are short not because of their genes, but because their growth was suppressed by various environmental factors, in which case all their children will tend to be taller than they.

Where one parent is tall and the other (particularly the father) is short, there is a greater probability that any given offspring will be short rather than tall. But from what has been brought out about the trend toward increased stature in recent years, there is more and more likelihood of short parents having children considerably taller than themselves, especially if the parents were foreign-born or had been reared under adverse conditions.

In any parent-child comparisons or forecasts, it also should be kept in mind that stature may increase in young men up to their twenty-seventh year, and in women up to their twenty-fifth year, after which there may be a gradual *decrease* at the rate of about one-thirtieth of an inch annually. (Which is to say, when you near 60, you'll have lost an inch of your maximum height, and when you near 90, you'll have lost 2 inches.)

THE FORM DIVINE, OR OTHERWISE. Here's where we *really* have a job in establishing heredity, for even much more than in the case of stature, innumerable environmental influences are all mixed up with the workings of the many genes involved in shaping human figures. How unpredictable human shapes may be is apparent when we see Miss Americas and bathing beauties spring from parents with contours like well-filled sacks of potatoes. Moreover, while stature is virtually set after puberty, you know how inconstant may be your figure at any stage of life.

Despite this, attempts have been made to classify human figures according to "basic" types (the emphasis being rather more on the structure than the upholstery). The most familiar are the Kretschmer classifications:

The *"asthenic"*—tall and slender, somewhat flat-chested, with narrow, drooping shoulders.

The *"pyknic"*—short and fat, thick neck, protruding abdomen, barrel-shaped thorax.

The *"athletic"*—the intermediate type, with broad, square shoulders, muscular limbs, large hands and feet.

The assumption is that while environmental factors may modify or alter human shapes, as a rule persons tend by inheritance to be of one or another of these body types, or of the gradations in between.* Moreover, there has been the theory that the "asthenic" type is characteristic of the "Nordics," the "pyknic" type of the Alpine peoples, and the "athletic" type of the Dinaric peoples (southeastern Europeans). This becomes rather dubious when we see that all the types are liberally represented in all races and nationalities, and that where a particular body form does seem to characterize the members of one large group, similarities in environment may often explain these differences just as easily as might genetic factors.

However, applied to individuals living under the same conditions, there does seem to be evidence that the body types as classified, or degrees of slenderness or obesity, tend to run in given families through genetic influences. (This is quite consistent with what we find in different strains of domestic and experimental animals.) In some cases it even appears that slenderness may be caused by recessive genes, obesity by dominant genes. For, as in tall and short statures, slender parents as a rule have slender children, whereas fat parents—presumably those with hidden "slenderness" genes—while tending to have children who are fat, as a rule, also may have others who are slender.

One way in which obesity might be inherited, as Dr. G. E. Dickerson and J. W. Gowen suggested in 1947 (after breeding strains of experimental animals ranging from fat to lean), is through gene action which reduces the amount of food required per pound of gain and increases the proportion of gain that is fatty tissue. Normally, there is a balance between the intake of food and the amount of it that is

* More recently Dr. William H. Sheldon, Dr. George Draper and others, have carried body-type classifications into various detailed subgroups of "endomorphs, ectomorphs, mesomorphs, leptomorphs," etc., and have related these to different types of behavior (which we'll discuss later).

utilized by the body, but in "constitutionally" fat people it appears that the body's regulating devices are out of order, so that a good part of the food is converted into fat products which accumulate in the tissues. Glandular disorders (sometimes present at birth), faulty diet or emotional factors are involved in many cases of obesity, but whether through heredity or not, it is quite clear that certain persons are predisposed to excessive plumpness, and others not, regardless of what they do and what they eat.

(Just in case you think *you* are fat—or for others interested: The fattest human being on record was a Florida woman, Mrs. Ruth Pontico, who weighed 772 pounds, with a height of 5 feet 5½ inches. She was a circus "fat lady" like her mother, who had weighed 720 pounds. Mrs. Pontico, who died in 1942, aged 38, had started her career by weighing 16 pounds at birth and 50 pounds at the age of one. The heaviest human on record—not the fattest, because he was 7 feet 6 inches tall—was Miles Darden of Tennessee, who weighed 1,000 pounds. He died in 1857.)

But whether you are fat or lean, the most important elements of your shape—as any bright child of three could tell you—are determined by your being a man or a woman. For in constructing and upholstering bodies, Nature is ever mindful of the sex of the individual. First, there are the general differences, with the male skeletal and muscular structure larger and heavier throughout. Then there are all the differences in the fleshy formations, such as the breasts, and those in the hip region, thighs, legs, etc., with the female tending to have more fatty tissue everywhere. Not only are there genes governing all the detailed sex characteristics, but the degrees in which these are pronounced may also be influenced by heredity. As in lower animals, the "sex" genes in one human strain may be more potent than in another, and may send the sexes further apart in their development.

As examples, there are certain African tribes where the females have quite small breasts and narrow hips, bringing them closer to the male form, while in other tribes (as well as in most White strains) the females have much larger breasts and hips, differentiating them much more from their males. (Shapes of breasts may also vary considerably, as a result of genetic factors.) Environmental influences—living habits, occupations, the extent of childbearing, etc.—may help to exaggerate or reduce the basic bodily sex differences, but degrees of civilization have little to do with this, inasmuch as primitive peoples the world over have every range of sex differentiation. If anything, civilization seems to have reduced the differences, for anthropologists report that in all the prehistoric races the sex differences in body structure and size were much more marked than they are in modern men and women.

In establishing the sex of skeletons, the "bone" experts go principally by these clues: the hip structure of females is wider, shallower, smoother and more forward tilted than that of males, while in males the bones of the limbs are relatively longer, thicker and heavier, and the "knobs" are bigger. Also the chests of males are larger, the shoulders broader; their hands and feet are relatively longer, and the finger and toe bones are heavier and blunter; and there are various differences in the skulls (as we noted in the last chapter).

One interesting *average* difference (for it doesn't always apply) is in the *angle* at which the upper and lower arm are set together at the elbow, and the thigh and leg are set together at the knee. You

SEX CHARACTERISTICS IN LIMBS

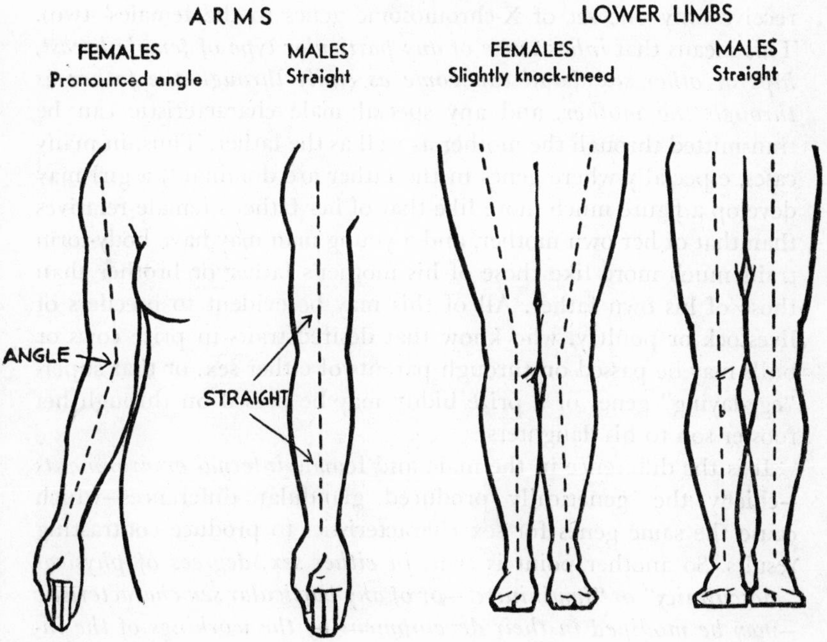

ARMS
FEMALES
Pronounced angle
MALES
Straight
ANGLE
STRAIGHT

LOWER LIMBS
FEMALES
Slightly knock-kneed
MALES
Straight

can test this for yourself by standing alongside a person of the opposite sex (with both of you preferably in bathing suits), in front of a full-length mirror. When you hold your arms straight down with palms facing front (as shown in the illustration), you will find as a rule that the female arm has a much more definite bend at the elbow whereas the male arm is much straighter. Similarly, when the thighs are placed together, you will see that the female tends to be much more "knock-kneed."

Another difference in body contour is in what has been called "the more pronounced southern exposure" of the female, due both to the greater angle made by her pelvis and the incurve of the back, and to the proportionately greater amount of fat and muscle distributed there. The degree of this protuberance can be determined by heredity, and where it occurs in an extreme form is known as *steatopygia.* This condition is highly prevalent among women of Hottentot and Bushman tribes (where it is greatly admired), and is occasionally found among American Negro women.

In noting all the many special sex characteristics in body form we must continually keep in mind that any genes involved in producing them can be carried equally by both sexes (except insofar as males receive only one set of X-chromosome genes to the females' two). This means that *inheritance of any particular type of female breast, hips or other sex detail can come as easily through the father as through the mother,* and any special male characteristic can be transmitted through the mother as well as the father. Thus, in many cases, especially where genes in the father are dominant, a girl may develop a figure much more like that of her father's female relatives than that of her own mother, and a young man may have body-form traits much more like those of his mother's father or brother than those of his own father. All of this may be evident to breeders of livestock or poultry, who know that desired traits in prize cows or bulls may be passed on through parents of either sex, or that super-"egg-laying" genes of a prize biddy may be passed on through her rooster son to his daughters.

It is the difference in the male and female *internal environments* —chiefly the genetically produced glandular differences—which cause the same genes for sex characteristics to produce contrasting results. So another point is that, *in either sex, degrees of physical "masculinity" or "femininity"—or of any particular sex characteristic —may be modified in their development by the workings of the in-*

dividual's sex glands. Where something happens in an individual to radically upset the hormonal balance proper for his or her sex—particularly if this occurs before puberty—"feminization" of the male's figure, or "masculinization" of the female's figure, may result, with in either case, an approach toward the "neuter" type. (The abnormal cases will be dealt with more fully in a later chapter.) Lesser shifts in the hormonal balance may lead only to some underdevelopment of the breasts or hips in females, or some overdevelopment of these parts in males. During old age there is often some degree of "masculinization" or "feminization" in the physical sex characteristics.

HEAD TO TOE. The shapes of heads may not have too much importance for average readers, except when they go into hat stores. But to anthropologists this has long been a fascinating subject for research, one thought being that head shapes might prove useful in the classification of races and subgroups. This objective has been somewhat dimmed by findings in recent years that in every race and in almost every large group of people there are many forms of heads, and that to some extent head shapes may be modified by environment. Nonetheless, the most important details are determined by genes.

Roughly speaking, people are identified as "round-headed" or "long-headed" (as viewed from the top). Your hat-store man might say, "broad oval" or "long oval." The scientist would say *"brachycephalic"* or *"dolichocephalic,"* and with very detailed measurements would give you your exact "index" down to several decimal points. On a racial basis, the broad oval ("round") head is predominant among the Mongoloids, the long head being rare among them, while among Negroes it is the long head which is common, the round head rare. Whites, taken as a whole, have among them every type of head shape in about equal proportions, although in different stocks there are strong tendencies toward one type of head shape or another.

Quite a number of genes are involved in determining head shapes, some genes working toward roundness, some toward length, some toward size, and some toward special shaping. The complexity of the factors makes difficult any accurate predictions of what children's head shapes will be. But in general, the genes for round head tend to dominate those for long head.

The inherited tendencies to one type of head shape or another assert themselves quite strongly from birth onward (although, with the same genes, boys' heads start off by being somewhat rounder than those of girls, and end up by being somewhat longer). Among certain primitive peoples, heads are artificially shaped by various appliances, but in less marked ways head-shaping may be somewhat influenced in our own world by prenatal factors, and later by diet and habits of sleeping, eating and talking. The principal head-shape change in the United States has been a certain degree of lengthening which has come largely with the increase in stature.

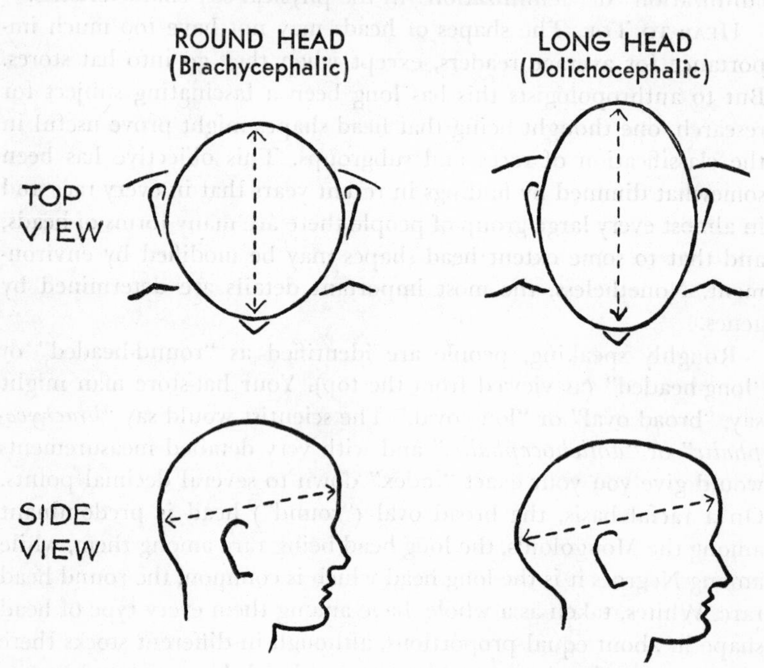

Differences in head *sizes,* grading from fairly large to fairly small within the normal range, also result from an interplay of heredity and environment. Where head size has special importance is in extreme deviations from the average in young children, which may sometimes indicate glandular or mental abnormalities. However, Drs. Henry K. Silver and William C. Deamer, who worked out scales of head-size "norms" for babies, reported that in most cases what appears to be an abnormally large or small head may be simply a hereditary characteristic, and if the head continues to grow at a normal rate, there need be no cause for alarm. (They also reported —which should be no surprise to mothers—that boy babies have somewhat larger heads than girl babies, averaging about 1/4 inch more in circumference at birth, and about 1/2 inch more at the age of two.)

From the head down to the toes, there are innumerable other details throughout the body whose sizes and shapes are governed by heredity—hips, chest, thighs, legs and arms, fingers and toes, muscle formations, etc. Each of these characteristics may have social importance, where they are judged in terms of attractiveness. They may also have much practical importance, where they affect the capacities for various kinds of physical performance. It is with the latter thought that geneticists have given most of their attention so far to inherited defects or abnormalities in these structural details, which we'll discuss in another chapter. Otherwise, questions regarding the inheritance of beautiful legs or other points of interest to beauty judges (professional or amateur) must for the time being go unanswered.

We may emphasize again, however, that occupations and living habits can account for at least some of the difference in bodily details which we see among individuals. If the son of a blacksmith has brawny arms like his father, it doesn't necessarily follow that these arms were "inherited," for they may just as well have been developed by working in the smithy. So, too, when we take note of certain physical characteristics common to families of tailors, policemen, farmers, miners, etc., we must not confuse the results of similar working and living habits with those of heredity.

In your own case, then, you may find that many of your bodily characteristics which may have seemed an integral and inevitable part of you, can likewise be ascribed to "conditioning." On the other hand, the possibility that heredity is involved becomes of interest when you try to guess whether these traits will also appear in your children. And this is now what we're about to help you find out.

CHAPTER 16

WHAT WILL YOUR CHILD LOOK LIKE?

WE HAVE gone far enough in identifying genes linked with various characteristics so that, given certain facts about you and your mate, we could make some fairly accurate predictions as to what your children would look like.

Were we able to breed people as the geneticist breeds flies, we could make many more predictions, with greater accuracy. By constant breeding and inbreeding, geneticists have established strains of Drosophila, ranged in rows of bottles in their laboratories, whose genes they know almost as well as the chemist knows the makeup of his various compounds. In fact, with almost the same precision that the chemist mixes compounds, the geneticist can "mix," by mating, two flies of any strains and predict the types of offspring that will result.

We cannot, of course, ever expect to do anything like that with human beings. Pure strains of humans cannot be produced, like flies (or like horses, dogs or cats), by long inbreeding of parents with children, brothers with sisters, etc. And where flies can have three hundred offspring at a time and more than two generations to a month, human couples do not average more than four offspring to a marriage, and only three or four generations to a century.

So, genetically, in most respects we humans are unknown quantities. With regard to your own genes, you can only make guesses, but in this you will be helped considerably not merely by the characteristics which you yourself reveal, but by those which appear in your parents, grandparents, brothers, sisters and other close relatives. As was noted in the "Eye Color" chapter, if you are dark eyed, the chances of your carrying a hidden "blue-eye" gene increase according to the number of your relatives who have blue eyes, and their closeness to you. Going further, if you marry a blue-eyed person and have a blue-eyed child, then you know definitely that you carry a "blue-eye" gene. On the other hand, if two, three, four children in a row are all dark-eyed, the presumption grows that you haven't a "blue-eye" gene.

Likewise, where both parents are dark-eyed, the appearance of a blue-eyed baby is good proof that both carry hidden "blue-eye" genes. But if all the children are dark-eyed, it still might mean only that *one* of the parents has no "blue-eye" gene.

These qualifications hold for every case where persons have some characteristic due to a *dominant* gene (dark hair, curly or kinky hair, a Hapsburg lip, etc.) and wish to know what chance they have of carrying a hidden gene which might produce a different trait in their child.

But before we try to make any predictions these facts should be clear:

All forecasts as to the types of children people will have are based on *averages determined by the laws of chance.*

Wherever *dominant* and *recessive* genes are involved, it is like tossing up coins with heads and tails. Toss up coins long enough, and the number of heads and tails will come out even. So if you are carrying one dominant and one recessive gene for any characteristic, were it possible for you to have an unlimited number of children, you'd find that *exactly half* would get the dominant, half the recessive gene.

With *two* parents involved, the results will be like those obtained in "matching" coins. This, of course, conforms with Mendel's laws.

When we think in terms of the *characteristic* produced, the result in "mixed" matings will be that the dominant characteristic (dark eyes, dark hair, etc.) will show up *three out of four times,* the recessive only *one in four,* as it requires a *matching* of the recessive genes.

Of course, where one parent carries *two* dominant genes, all the children will show the dominant trait. Where one parent carries a dominant and a recessive, and the other parent *two* recessives, *half* the children will show the dominant trait, half the recessive.

But here is something else to bear in mind:

Wherever it is a question of a child's getting one gene or another, or having such and such a characteristic, *the odds for every child are exactly the same.*

Some gamblers might dispute this, but if you toss up a coin one time, and it comes up heads, that does not mean that the next time there is any better chance of its coming up tails. *There is the same*

THE LAWS OF CHANCE

IF YOU TOSS A COIN WITH TWO DIFFERENT SIDES, ONE "HEAD", ONE "TAIL" –

The odds are exactly even that it will land

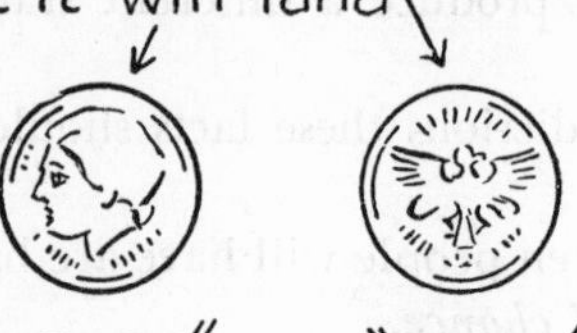

"HEADS" 1 in 2 times

"TAILS" 1 in 2 times

– SIMILARLY, IF YOU CARRY A MIXED PAIR OF ANY GENE, ONE "DOMINANT", ONE "RECESSIVE"

When you mate, the odds are exactly even that any child will receive

THE DOMINANT GENE 1 in 2 times

THE RECESSIVE GENE 1 in 2 times

IF YOU AND ANOTHER PERSON EACH TOSS A COIN

-The odds are exactly

1 in 4 times BOTH HEADS

1 in 4 times BOTH TAILS

2 in 4 times ONE "HEADS" ONE "TAILS"

-SIMILARLY, IF YOU AND YOUR MATE EACH CARRY A MIXED PAIR OF GENES FOR SOME TRAIT

You:

Your Mate:

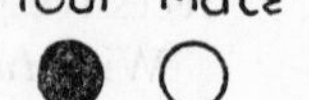

Every time you have a child the odds are exacty

1 in 4 times Child will receive BOTH DOMINANTS

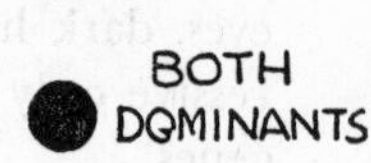

1 in 4 times Child will receive BOTH RECESSIVES

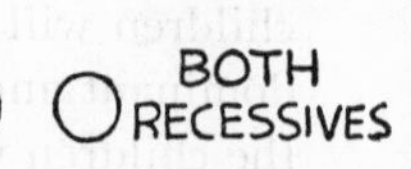

2 in 4 times child will receive ONE DOMINANT ONE RECESSIVE

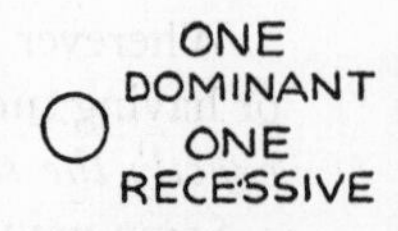

No matter how many times coins are tossed, the odds will always be exactly the same for the next toss

No matter how many children you have or how many "in a row" are the same type, the odds will be exactly the same for the next

---

fifty-fifty chance on each toss-up. Even, if through an unusual "run," there would be ten heads in succession, on the eleventh toss there would still be an exactly even chance for either heads or tails. (This applies to dice, roulette or any other game of chance. Many a gentleman has lost a fortune trying to disprove it.)

So, let us say, if the odds are even for your having a blue-eyed child, and your first one is brown-eyed, that doesn't mean that the odds are any better that the next will be blue-eyed. Even if four or five children in a row are born with brown eyes, there is still that same fifty-fifty chance, no more and no less, that the next child will have either brown or blue eyes.

But perhaps we need not have gone into all this. In the "boy or girl?" question we say that there is a 106 to 100 chance that the child will be a boy. And yet, authorities like Eddie Cantor will tell you that the fact of their having had three or four girls in a row in no way bettered the odds that the next one would *not* be a girl!

In "boy or girl?", however, it is a simple question of one or the other. But in the case of features or form—in fact, of any detail of the body—we must contend with innumerable variations, often involving many complex gene combinations, plus, always, the possible influences of environment. Thus, the degree of preciseness in forecasting any given trait depends, first, on how directly it is produced by heredity; second, on how many genes are involved in producing it; and third, on whether any of these genes are "eccentric" ones which do not always work in the same way.

By these principles, you will find that the forecasts for eye and hair color, and for hair form, will come closer to the mark than those for the shapes of nose, ears, eyes, mouth, etc., or for stature or body build. On the whole, however, if you and your mate conform to the averages, the forecasts here presented will prove fairly dependable. Where there seem to be exceptions, these need in no way represent upsets to genetic theories, for the expert might easily be able to account for them.

Anyway, do make allowances for the exceptions and, whatever happens, don't blame us (or the geneticists on whose studies these Tables are based) if the baby does not turn out the way the forecast indicated.

And now to Sir Oracle!

HOW TO USE THESE "CHILD FORECAST" TABLES

(1). If this is to be your first child, find out as much as possible about what genes you and your mate may be carrying by consulting the detailed treatments of each feature in preceding chapters, and by studying other members of your families.* Make allowances for all characteristics influenced by *environment*.

(2). If you have already had one or more children, also study each child for additional clues as to your genes.

(3). Remember that no matter how many children you have had, or what they look like, the *odds* that your next child will receive a given characteristic are exactly the same as if it had been the first.

(4). In consulting the tables, look for your own characteristic in *either* of the "parent's" columns. (They each apply equally to father or mother.) If you and your mate are of different types, look first for the type *most pronounced*—the darkest coloring, the most extreme hair form, etc.

(5). Remember that these "forecasts" are based on averages in large numbers of matings. With just one child, that child might be the *exception*.

(6). Wherever age is a factor, make due allowances for its future effects or changes that may be expected to take place. (This applies particularly to hair color, hair form, eye color and nose shapes.)

* In the following pages, "family" refers not only to parents, brothers, brothers and sisters, but to grandparents and other close relatives.

EYE-COLOR FORECAST

IF EYES OF ONE PARENT ARE:	IF EYES OF OTHER PARENT ARE:	*Child's Eyes Will Be:*
BROWN (or **BLACK**)		
Type 1. If all this parent's family were dark eyed	× **No Matter What Color**	Almost certainly *dark*
Type 2. Where some in this parent's family have lighter-colored eyes (gray, green or blue)	× **Brown,** Type 2	Probably *brown,* but possibly some other color
	× **Gray, Green or Blue**	Even chance *brown* or lighter color (most likely like that of lighter-eyed parent)
GRAY or **GREEN**	× **Gray, Green or Blue**	Probably *gray* or *green,* but possibly *blue.* (Rarely brown)
BLUE	× **Blue**	Almost certainly *blue.* (Rarely a darker shade, the possibility being less if parents' eyes are light blue)
ALBINO (Colorless)	× **Normal**-eyed parent of any eye color	*Normal,* leaning to shade of normal parent's eyes, *unless* this parent carries "hidden" "albino" gene, when 1 in 2 chance of child being albino
	× **Albino**	Definitely *albino*

EYE-SHAPE FORECAST

Width: If just one parent has *wide* eyes, child is quite likely to have them, too; if both parents, the chance is much greater.

Slant: If one parent has slant eyes (but *not of Chinese type*), child will not be likely to have them unless slant eyes also appear in the family of other parent. If, however, a parent's eyes are of the Chinese, or Mongolian *(epicanthic-fold)* type, there is great likelihood the child will have them.

Lashes: Where just one parent has *very long* lashes, child has a more than fifty-fifty chance of "inheriting" them.

HAIR-COLOR FORECAST*

IF ONE PARENT'S HAIR-COLOR IS:	OTHER PARENT'S HAIR-COLOR:	*Child's Hair-Color Will Be:*
DARK (Brown or Black)		
Type 1. Where all in this parent's family had dark hair	× **No Matter What**	Almost certainly *dark*
Type 2. Where there are lighter shades among others in this parent's family	× **Dark, Type 2**	Probably *dark,* but possibly some lighter shade
	× **Red**	About equal chance (a) *dark* or (b) *red-brown* or *red,* with (c) some slight possibility of *blond*
	× **Blond**	Probably *dark,* but possibly *blond*—rarely *red*
RED	× **Red**	Most probably *red,* and occasionally light brown or blond
	× **Blond**	Even chances (a) *red* or (b) *light brown* or *blond*
BLOND		
Type 1. If medium shade	× **Blond**	Fairly certain *blond,* with rarely *brown.* (*Red* possibly if this shade is present in either parent's family)
Type 2. If flaxen or white	× **Blond**—Flaxen or white	Certainly blond, but with shade of darker parent apt to prevail

* In forecasting hair color of a child, remember to be guided by what the hair color of you and your mate was *originally,* in your earlier years. Refer to Chapter 12.

HAIR-FORM FORECAST

IF ONE PARENT'S HAIR IS:	OTHER PARENT'S HAIR:	*Child's Hair Will Be:*
CURLY		
Type 1. If all in this parent's family are curly haired	× **Any Form,** except kinky or woolly	Almost certainly *curly* (rarely any other)
Type 2. If some wavy or straight in this parent's family	× **Curly,** Type 2	Probably *curly,* possibly *wavy* or *straight*
	× **Wavy**	Even chance (a) *curly* or (b) possibly *wavy* or occasionally *straight*
	× **Straight**	Probably *curly* or *wavy,* possibly *straight*
WAVY		
Type 1. If no straight-haired persons in this parent's family	× **Wavy or Straight**	Most probably *wavy,* seldom *straight*
Type 2. If there are some with straight hair in this parent's family	× **Straight**	Even chance *wavy* or *straight.* (Rarely anything else)
STRAIGHT*	× **Straight**	Almost certainly *straight*
KINKY		
Type 1. Where all in this parent's family are kinky haired	× **No Matter What Hair Form**	Almost certainly *kinky*
Type 2. Where other hair forms appear in this parent's family	× **Curly or Wavy**	Even chance (a) *kinky* or (b) *curly* or *wavy;* rarely *straight*
	× **Straight**	Almost same as above, but with greater possibility of *straight*

Woolly: While fairly frequent among Negroes, it is rare among Whites. Where, however, it appears in even one parent, there is a fifty-fifty chance any child will have woolly hair.

* If the parent with straight hair is Mongolian (Chinese, Japanese, full-blooded Indian, etc.) *all* the children will probably be straight-haired, regardless of the hair form of other parent.

FORECAST OF FACIAL DETAILS

Nose

(Nose shape is not "inherited" as a unit. Different characteristics of the nose may be "inherited" separately, from either or both parents. Environmental factors also have great influence.)

Generally: Where both parents have about the same type of nose, a child in maturity will have a similar type.

But: If just one parent has a *pronounced* type of nose—very *broad,* or very *long,* or very *high* and *narrow-bridged,* or *hooked,* or *"pug"*-shaped, or *bulbous-tipped,* etc.—while the other parent has a *moderate* nose, there is a greater than even chance that the child's nose will eventually resemble that of the parent with the more extreme type. This applies especially where a marked nose form has appeared in several generations of a parent's family.

Ears

Large: If just one parent has large ears (very long, or very wide) the child will be quite likely to have similar ears.

Cup-shaped: If in one parent, about a fifty-fifty chance for the child.

Affixed Lobes: If only one parent has *affixed* ear lobes, or *absence* of lobes, and the condition does not appear in the other parent's family, there is not too much likelihood that the child's ear lobes will be of these types.

Mouth

Lips: If just one parent has *thick* lips, the child will probably have them, or at least thicker than average lips.

Hapsburg (protruding) lip and jaw: If one parent has this, child has an even chance of "inheriting" it.

Chin: If one parent has a *receding* chin, a child is not likely to have it unless a similar-type chin has appeared in the family of the other parent. This is also true if only one parent has a very *narrow* or *pointed* chin. But if one parent has a dimpled or "cleft" chin, there is quite a strong chance a child will have the same.

Dimples in cheek: If one parent is dimpled, the child is very likely to be, also.

Teeth: If either parent has unusually shaped teeth, there is considerable chance they will appear in a child. (Inheritance of normal teeth shapes hasn't yet been worked out, but forecasts for dental abnormalities are given in the Summary Tables, end of Chapter 31.)

STATURE FORECAST

Both parents **tall.** The child on maturity will almost certainly be tall, or taller than average.

Both parents **short.** The child will probably be inclined to shortness, but may possibly be taller than the parents, and even very tall.

One parent **tall,** one **short.** The child will probably incline toward the *shorter* parent.

BUILD

If both parents are **slender,** the child will be more likely to be like them than if both parents are **fleshy.** But build is a highly variable characteristic, dependent on so many conditions and genes that it can hardly be predicted.

(For the inheritance of "abnormal" conditions and characteristics of all kinds, in features, form and appearance, see later chapters.)

HOW TWO HOMELY PARENTS MAY HAVE A BEAUTIFUL CHILD

FATHER
Bald
Murky-green eyes
Long-lashes lost through disease
Misshapen mouth due to bad teeth
Bad nose due to accident

MOTHER
Black, straight hair
Dull-brown eyes
Drooping eyelids
Bad skin (local disorder)
Protruding under-lip

BUT they may carry and pass on to their child hidden genes for
—Blond, curly hair
Blue eyes
Long lashes
Pretty nose
Cupid's-bow mouth
Lovely complexion

RESULT: A "BEAUTY CONTEST" WINNER

HOW TWO HANDSOME PARENTS MAY HAVE A HOMELY CHILD

FATHER
Curly, black hair
Large, black eyes, long lashes
Well-shaped mouth and chin

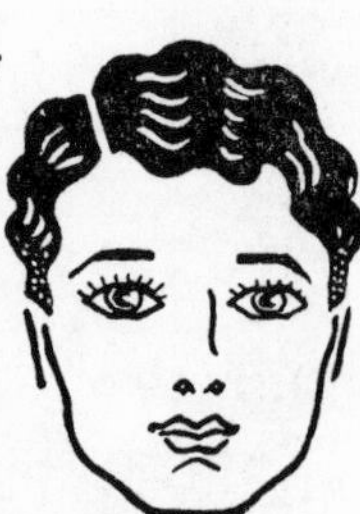

MOTHER
Wavy Blond hair
Blue eyes
Long lashes
Regular teeth
Pretty mouth

BUT they may carry and pass on to their child hidden genes for
—Dull-brown, straight hair
Murky-green, small eyes with short lashes
Protruding jaw and teeth (and, alas, other irregularities)

RESULT: AN "UGLY DUCKLING"

CHAPTER 17

WHAT MAKES US TICK

You have seen what produces your external appearance. But you are much more than a hollow doll with such and such kind of eyes, hair, skin, etc. While your "looks" may be extremely important, your real importance as an individual lies in what is within your shell: your organs—brain, nerves, heart, lungs, glands and other functional parts. These are "what make you tick" and they are what account for the greatest differences between individuals.

In fashioning and constructing every one of our organs our genes are constantly at work, and we know that individual differences in these organs are often inherited. But the task of identifying them is vastly more complicated than it was in the case of features, for we are here dealing not with easily recognizable characteristics but with *functions and effects*. In that regard, mere appearances are of very little help to us, for in very few cases have we yet been able to establish by mere surface inspection the nature of the important organs and their hereditary aspects.

The glands, for instance, form a group of organs which hold special interest because almost every peculiarity in humans is being ascribed to them these days. When people talk of "glands" they do not mean such old standbys as the liver and kidneys, or the gastric and salivary glands, etc. They refer to the "ductless" (endocrine) glands—the pituitary, thyroid, parathyroids, pancreas (one part), adrenals, suprarenals, pineal, thymus, and the testes or ovaries. These introduce into the blood certain all-powerful substances called "hormones," the effects of which are often confused with the direct action of genes. (See Chart, "The Ductless Glands," p. 195.)

Comparing our glands with those of lower animals, we can see quite clearly that general glandular construction and functioning are determined by heredity; and also, that in given cases of individuals or of humans of different strains, a vast number of glandular characteristics show distinct hereditary influences, such as rates of growth and development, age and onset of menstruation, of puberty and of "change of life," and of many continuing processes of the body. But glandular differences among individuals may also be conditioned by environment. It is only, as a rule, when there are marked abnormalities in the *effects* of the glands, repeatedly following the same pattern, that the hereditary differences may reveal themselves.

Then there is the brain, the most important single organ in the body. We can again assume that if the enormous differences between the human brain and those of lower animals are inherited, as we know, then smaller differences or variations in brain structure between one human being and another are probably also inherited. Thus, Professor K. S. Lashley of Harvard said, in 1947, "Even the limited evidence at hand shows that individuals start life with brains differing enormously in structure . . . unlike in number, size and arrangement of neurons as well as in grosser features. Some of the more conspicuous structural differences can be shown to be hereditary, and there can be little question that some of the lesser variants in cerebral structure are likewise hereditary."

So, too, it may be possible to show that differences in form and structure of other organs—heart, liver, lungs, stomach, etc.—are inherited, as we can prove with lower animals. But little has been done as yet to identify and classify any of these inherited differences in *normal* humans—not even as between such distinct types as tall, White, American intellectuals and primitive, pigmy Hottentots. Only, as we said, in the case of easily recognized *abnormalities,* or defects in functioning, have we much knowledge regarding inherited individual differences in given organs, or clues as to the specific genes involved.

"Normal" and "abnormal," by the way, are vague words wholly inadequate to express what we mean. "Abnormal" means "not normal"; but "normal" cannot be defined except in relation to some standard that in itself is usually highly variable. For instance, if a man eats three pounds of meat at a sitting, we'd say he has an "abnormal" appetite; but suppose that man were seven feet tall and weighed three hundred pounds? An appetite abnormal for others would be normal for him. Four feet 6 inches would be an abnormal height for a man in northern Scotland and 5 feet 8 would be normal; but 5 feet 8 inches would be an abnormal height among Pigmies, whereas 4 feet 6 would be normal. In other words, an abnormality is a deviation from some arbitrary standard which may vary according to the point of view. It should not be confused with a "defect," for an abnormality may be favorable or unfavorable. An idiot is abnormal; so also is a *genius*. (All of this will be dealt with in much greater detail presently.)

But the question which looms largest with regard to human differences in what makes us tick is the one which inevitably pops up, like a heckler, in any discussion of heredity:

"Which is more important, heredity or environment?"

We have tried to bring out that both forces go hand in hand in shaping anyone's life, and that consideration of one without the other is impossible. You will understand, therefore, why the geneticist counters with, "Which is more important, the fish or the water in which it swims?"

However, when a person says, "I don't believe in heredity. I believe in environment!" he is being downright silly.

Perhaps you are familiar with this old chestnut: "What do elephants have that no other animals have?" The answer (not "trunks"!) is, "Baby elephants."

Obviously, where humans are also most unique is in their having human babies. Even more obviously, this is not because of anything special in their environments which is not accorded to other animals. No amount of similarity in environments, prenatally or otherwise, could cause a chimpanzee to develop into a human being (although a man may sometimes make a monkey out of himself).

First and foremost, what causes us to develop as human beings, different from all other animals, is heredity. All that environment can do is only to enable our hereditary *potentialities* to assert themselves or to modify or to prevent their development. But once our genes are allowed to go their course, there is not too much that environment can do to alter the general *physical* directions taken by members of our species. Under infinitely varied conditions, all the way from cave men down to modern men, the physical and organic makeup of human beings has remained remarkably constant, with their similarities far overshadowing their differences.

Thus, what we really have in mind when we argue about "heredity versus environment" are always the relatively small differences between one person and another within special areas. As biological mechanisms, which all human beings are primarily (regardless of what spiritual qualities they may have), it is apparent by now that they are constructed by their genes in an infinite variety of ways, with many minute shades of difference. Our problem is to find out how important are these differences with respect to specific functions—especially those which cause one individual to be much more efficient and successful in life than another. For it is only when we concentrate on specific points that we can begin to identify the relative influences of the two forces of heredity and environment.

For instance, between 1939 and 1945, millions of young men were killed in battle. Which factor was more important in bringing on early death, heredity or environment? You need hardly think twice about that.

On the other hand, there are conditions due to simple recessive genes (as we shall see in later chapters) which will cause a baby to die before it is 3 years old, no matter what care can be given it. Which is more important here, heredity or environment? That, too, can be answered easily.

Many physical defects in people—facial disfigurements, bodily distortions, crippling conditions, loss of eyes, etc.—can be attributed solely to accidents or other environmental mishaps. Many others, as you will presently be reading, can be blamed entirely on defective heredity. In such clear-cut cases we are quite justified in speaking of *either* heredity *or* environment.

But still other conditions, both advantageous and disadvantageous ones, can be seen as the result of special hereditary factors in combination with special environments. And, finally, when we begin to deal with the composite of many traits and circumstances—with the *sum total* of any person's life—the constant interplay of heredity and environment becomes increasingly apparent. Here truly, like the fish and the water, you cannot ever disassociate your biological mechanism, or that of anyone else, from the surroundings in which it operates, and from all the forces which control or influence its workings throughout its existence.

So, in seeking to find out why people tick the way they do, we are required, first, to concentrate on one trait or function at a time (which is how old Mendel proceeded). And, second, to make sure that with respect to this trait or function individuals either have *exactly the same heredity,* in which case we can attribute any differences to environment, or that they have *exactly the same environment,* in which case we can attribute their differences to heredity.

But with some individuals we can go even further. Instead of applying these principles to only a few traits, we can apply them to their total makeup, and their lives as a whole. For, with these individuals, to whom we will now turn, Nature has provided teammates who can offer innumerable fascinating comparisons.

CHAPTER 18

DUPLICATED HUMANS

THERE are few of us so blasé that we will not turn automatically for a second look when identical twins pass by.

But we are not nearly so impressed by the phenomenon as we should be. For if it is at all amazing that in the tiny speck of substance with which a human life begins there should be the blueprints and capacities to construct a human being with myriads of unique and complicated details, it is much more amazing that the same bit of substance should be capable of developing into two, three or even more separate individuals of exactly the same pattern. If anything else were needed to prove the remarkably orderly way in which our genes follow the most precise and intricate paths conceivable, through thousands of successive stages, it would be provided by these replicas of one another which we see in our midst. What concerns us here, however, is not so much the wonder of twin production, but what twins can teach us. For to the geneticists they offer bountiful material with which to study many of the most detailed aspects of human heredity.

In your own case, you may often have thought, how would you with your given heredity have turned out under different conditions? Or, under the same conditions, to what extent might you have been different with a slightly different heredity?

The only way it could be answered—or, at least, partly answered—is this:

1. If there were *two* of you to start with and each were exposed to different conditions; or

2. If you started life with somebody else at the same time *within the same mother,* and after you were both born, developed under approximately the same conditions.

Is either of these situations at all possible?

Yes, for Nature has most thoughtfully provided us with *twins,* who, willy-nilly, are human guinea pigs for such experiments.

For the first experiment we have "identical" twins; for the second, "fraternal" twins. The two types differ in this way:

Identical twins are the product of a single fertilized egg which, shortly after it begins to grow, splits in half to form two individuals. Each has exactly the same hereditary factors, so among other things, identical twins *must always be of the same sex.*

Fraternal twins, on the other hand, are the product of *two entirely different* eggs which happen to have been simultaneously matured by the mother and fertilized, approximately at the same time, by *two entirely different sperms.** They may, therefore, each carry quite different genes, and need be no more alike than any other two non-twin children in the same family, as often as not, in fact, being of opposite sex.

In other words, *identical* twins are, from the standpoint of heredity, *exactly the same individual in duplicate.*

Fraternal twins are *two entirely different individuals* who merely through chance were born together.

The important distinction between the two types of twins was not known nor fully realized until recently. In earlier years, twins were considered "identical" if they were of the same sex or resembled each other fairly closely. Even when the "one-egg" and "two-egg" distinctions became known and when biological facts of their birth were considered, mistakes in diagnosing them were frequently made. It was believed that the "one-egg" (identical) twins were always encased in a single fetal sac, with one placenta, whereas the two-egg (fraternal) twins invariably had separate fetal sacs and separate placentas. While generally true, it has now been found that this is not an invariable rule. Sometimes the sacs and placentas of fraternal twins are fused; and sometimes in identical twins each may grow a separate placenta and become encased in a separate sac.

Today, in classifying twins as "identical" or "fraternal," geneticists no longer consider midwives' or even doctors' reports. They have much more certain evidence in the form of "correlation" tests. By comparing the twins with regard to many characteristics known to be definitely inherited or influenced by heredity, they can tell

* In rare instances a woman already pregnant may conceive again some time after the first pregnancy is under way. A number of cases are on record of twins with two different fathers. In another unique case, in 1944, a school teacher in Philadelphia had two girl babies who, while born at the same time, were found not to be twins, inasmuch as one was a full-term baby, the other was a month premature. Subsequent examination of the mother showed that she had two separate wombs, a very rare condition.

HOW TWINS ARE PRODUCED

IDENTICAL TWINS

Are products of

A single sperm and A single egg

In an early stage the embryo divides

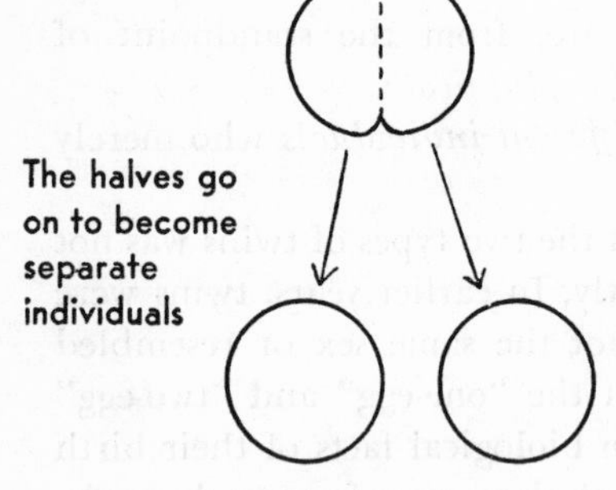

The halves go on to become separate individuals

Usually — but not always — identical twins share the same placenta and fetal sac

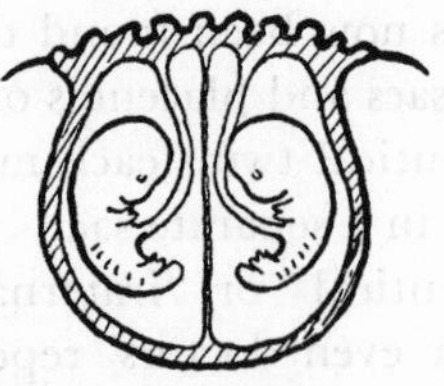

But regardless of how they develop, they carry the same genes and are therefore

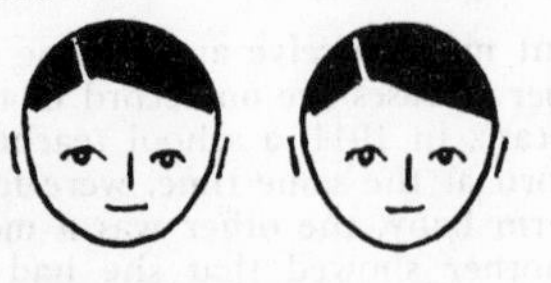

Always of the same sex — two boys or two girls

FRATERNAL TWINS

Are products of TWO different eggs fertilized by TWO different sperms

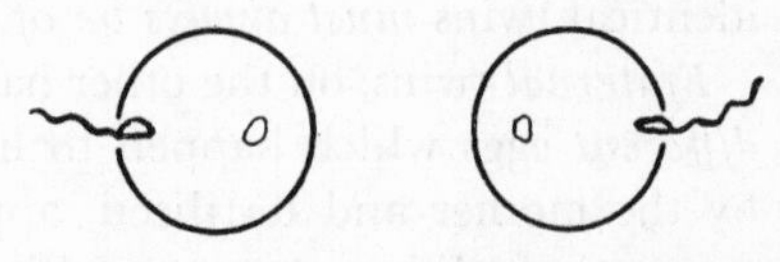

They have different genes and may develop in different ways, usually—but not always — having separate placentas and separate fetal sacs

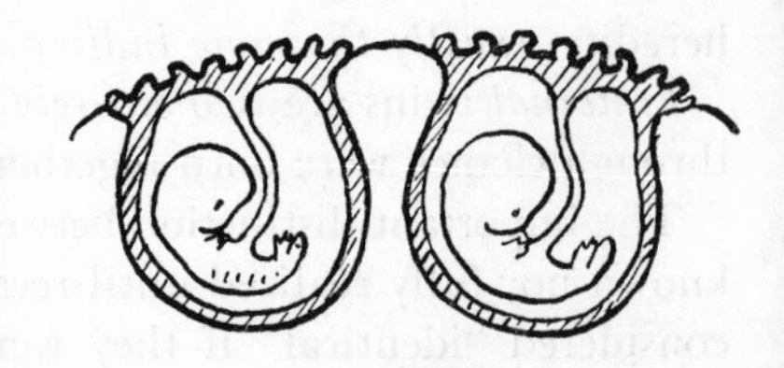

Also, as they are totally different individuals, they may be

whether or not the degree of resemblance, or "correlation," is high enough to stamp them as "identicals." Among the characteristics used for comparison are blood groups, blood pressure, pulse, respiration, and brain-wave patterns; eye color and vision; palm, sole and finger patterns; skin color, hair color, hair form and hair whorls; and various minor hereditary abnormalities where present. The correlation in these characteristics is so much greater between any two identical twins than between any two fraternal twins that there is virtually no possibility of confusing their relationship.

Now why are geneticists so concerned about this distinction? Because on it depends whatever conclusions may be drawn from studying twins. (For example, one much-publicized psychological study, some years ago, of a pair of twin boys given different training, came to grief when it was discovered that they were not identical, as had been assumed, but fraternal.)

Inasmuch as identical twins have exactly the same heredity, whatever differences there are between them must be due to *environment,* (whether in prenatal life or thereafter). But when identical twins are reared in different environments—there being instances of such separation in infancy—and nonetheless develop marked similarities of many kinds, these might be ascribed to heredity.

The study of fraternal twins takes a different direction. In their case, as they have a much more similar environment in prenatal life and often thereafter than singly born individuals, the question is how much more alike this will tend to make them.

If heredity were everything, then identical twins would be exactly the same in all respects, even if reared apart. But a number of studies show that they are never *exactly* alike, even though they do have remarkable similarities in most respects.

On the other hand, if *environment were everything,* then fraternal twins, reared under the same conditions, would also be alike, regardless of how different were their genes. But here we find that although they show a closer resemblance to each other than do non-twin brothers and sisters, "fraternals" even when of the same sex are less alike than are "identicals" reared apart.

Thus, the various studies of twins have comprised an important source of evidence for geneticists, and some of the conclusions will be presented in succeeding chapters. You will always have to keep in mind, however, that these conclusions can never be absolute. No identical twins are really *identical* because they cannot possibly have had identical environments, even before birth. If their prenatal environments were always identical there would never be any instances, as there frequently are, of one identical twin being born alive while the other is dead, or of one born normal and the other defective.

Differences between identical twins may also be due to the manner and stage in which the halves of the embryo from which they spring are separated. If the separation takes place in the very earliest embryonic stage, before any body differentiation has begun, twins may be as identical as possible. But if the division takes place later, when the potential two sides of the body have already begun to be laid out, the twin from one side might develop differently in a number of ways from the opposite twin. (This is hardly surprising in view of the fact that the two sides of your own face or body show differences in development.) Sometimes, also, one twin might be at a slight disadvantage in receiving nutrition, or might suffer some minor accident or upset in development, so that the other twin might be born slightly heavier or healthier. This slight initial lead may be carried on throughout life, and may be productive of other differences, both physical and psychological.

"Mirror-imaging," or reverse-patterning, in about one-fourth of the identical twins, is an interesting phenomenon that often results when their division takes place after the embryo has begun to differentiate, as Dr. H. H. Newman discovered. (See illustration.) Thus, in the hair whorls, the whorl of one may be clockwise, of the other counter-clockwise. Dental irregularities, dominance of one eye over the other, birthmarks, freckle patterns, and other details may occur on reverse sides in the paired identical twins. Also, in rare instances, there may be in one of them a reversal of the usual position of the internal organs—heart, liver, pancreas, intestines, etc. (Transposed organs are likewise found occasionally in non-twin individuals. Dr. Newman believes these may be survivors of original twin pairs. Other authorities attribute some of these cases to heredity, through recessive genes.)

Differences in *handedness* between identical twins—where one is left-handed and the other right-handed—were also formerly linked with the same factors that cause "mirror-imaging," but while this may hold for some of the cases, it is probably not so for most others. Left-handedness occurs in about 15 to 20 per cent of the identical twins, at least twice the incidence in the general population. But the

Photograph under direction of the author by M. Lasser, 1950

A REMARKABLE "TWIN" FAMILY

This unusual and charming family group comprises the identical-twin Rubin brothers, married to identical-twin sisters (neé Reisman), with one couple parents of identical-twin daughters, the other of a son born four days earlier. The twin couples have shared the same home in New York since their marriage in 1937, and have raised their children as *sisters and brother, which genetically they are*. For, while legally the girls and the boy are "double" first-cousins, the fact that their parents are genetic duplicates makes them biologically as much sisters and brothers as any children of the same parents. Actually, the children until they were eight years old did not differentiate between the two sets of parents, and at this writing (at age ten), while knowing which are their "true" parents, still refer impartially to either woman as "mother" and either man as "father."

(Identification: Standing, rear, at left, Benjamin and Sylvia Rubin, parents of Carol and Linda, seated. Rear, right, Ruth and Hyman Rubin, parents of Edward, center.)

THE DIONNE QUINTUPLETS AT "SWEET SIXTEEN"

The famed identical-quintuplet sisters, born May 28, 1934, photographed a few months after their sixteenth birthday at their home, Callander, Ontario. Left to right: Cecile, Emilie, Marie, Annette, Yvonne. (Note that Marie, center, the frailest and smallest at birth, still appears to be the most delicate.) See text, page 140.

fact that this trait is also more than ordinarily high in *fraternal* twins (in whom there could not be any "mirror-imaging") has led one of the experts, Dr. D. C. Rife, to the conclusion that in all probability conditions before birth which are peculiar to twins, such as crowding and position in the womb, must be in large measure responsible for the higher incidence of left-handedness among them.

However, there is also evidence that in twins of either kind, as well as in non-twins, special hereditary factors may produce a *tendency* toward left-handedness. Thus, Dr. Rife reports that where both

HOW "MIRROR-IMAGING" MAY BE PRODUCED IN TWINS

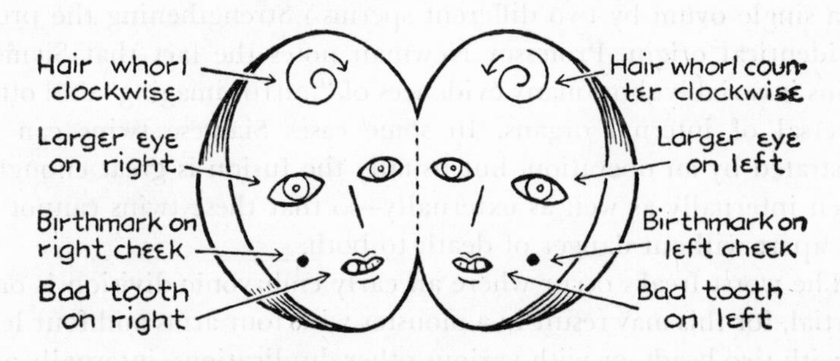

Think of the early human embryo as a solid sphere with a design running straight through. Cut in half (like an apple) the halves would show the parts of the design in reverse.

parents are left-handed, the chance is almost fifty-fifty that any given child also will be a "leftie," whether a twin or not; where both parents are right-handed, the chance is only one in sixteen of a child's being a "leftie"; and where one parent is left-handed, the other right-handed, the chance is about one in six that a child will be a "leftie." To explain this, Dr. Rife offers the theory that there are "handedness" genes which work in this way: Two "leftie" genes will cause a person to be left-handed, two "rightie" genes will make him right-handed; and a mixed pair, one of each gene, will incline a person to be ambidextrous though, in a right-handed world, in most instances he will be right-handed. However, should identical twins be carrying mixed genes, "mirror-imaging" in handedness will occur.

In fraternal twins, also, the prenatal conditions previously mentioned will increase the chance that one of them will be left-handed where the tendency is present.*

Freak twins of various kinds occur when there is an incomplete separation of the halves of the original embryo. In *Siamese* twins (so-named because the most famous pair of these came from Siam), the continued linkage of the two individuals may be slight, with a fusion at only one point in their bodies, as at the hips, heads or sides. While there is no clear evidence that any Siamese twins are anything but identical—they being always of the same sex, for one thing—some authorities believe that fusion might also take place in rare instances between fraternal twins if the embryos from which they derive are pressed close together in the earliest stages. (Another rather far-fetched theory is that Siamese twins may result from the fertilization of a single ovum by two different sperms.) Strengthening the proof of identical origin, Professor Newman notes the fact that Siamese twins invariably show many evidences of "mirror-imaging" and often reversal of internal organs. In some cases Siamese twins can be separated by an operation, but usually the fusion is great enough—often internally as well as externally—so that these twins cannot be cut apart without danger of death to both.

The worst freaks occur where an early embryonic division is only partial, for this may result in a monster with four arms and four legs, or with two heads, or with various other duplications, internally and externally. The most spectacular example was that of the Russian coalescent twins who had two heads, one torso, four arms and two legs, and—if that weren't enough—a rudimentary tail as well. Born in 1937, they lived for a year. Fortunately, all but a few of such monstrosities perish before birth, and are of little interest to us here because no one has shown that they can in any way be blamed on heredity.

Normal twinning, however, does have some hereditary basis. Numerous studies reveal that twinning is consistently more frequent in some families and human strains than in others. (Among certain breeds of cattle, sheep and goats the incidence of twinning is also much higher than in other breeds.) Often the same mother may have

* There are also theories that left-handedness may be linked with psychological factors, but little proof has been offered in support. One formerly common belief, that stuttering and left-handedness are in some way related, has been refuted by studies showing the incidence of "lefties" among stutterers is no higher than in the general population.

a succession of multiple births,* but there is evidence that the mother's influence is not the only factor, because many cases are on record where the tendency toward twinning has been shown to have been running through the male side of families. In one instance a man who was married twice sired profusions of twins and triplets by each wife.

The causes of twinning are nonetheless complex, with environmental factors most certainly being also involved. To the extent that heredity is a factor, it would appear that there are different genes for producing either identical or fraternal twins, and differences in their manner of working. The production of "identicals" may depend on some faculty in the original fertilized egg which causes it to split apart at an early stage. In this case the twinning tendency could come through the father as well as the mother. But some outside influence might also cause such a division, in which case the prenatal environment provided by the mother would be the determining factor.

For fraternal twins, a definite initial requirement is that the mother must produce two or more eggs simultaneously (one from each ovary, or two from the same ovary); or, in rare instances, she may produce a "double-yolked" egg—one with two nucleii.† In any of these cases the mother would be the prime agent in producing "fraternals." But there also is some evidence that once two eggs are present, certain fathers have more than the average probability of siring fraternal twins, presumably because their sperms are more active and more virile.

There are many other curious and as yet not fully explained aspects of twin production. The age of the parents is one of the factors, for older mothers—those in their late thirties or early forties—are more than twice as likely to have twins as are much younger women (particularly in the case of first births and of fraternal twins). Here there is the possibility that the "older" or "more experienced" womb is best adjusted to multiple pregnancies. But it is odd that where fathers are older, too—regardless of the age of their wives—the chances of there being twins are likewise increased.

Another question relates to the great variation in the proportion

* The world's record mother was reported to have been an Austrian woman, Mrs. Bernard Scheinberg, who bore sixty-nine children; quadruplets four times, triplets seven, twins sixteen times.

† There is a theory, as yet unproved, that in the case of an egg which has doubled before fertilization, each identical half might be fertilized by a different sperm, resulting in twins who would be half-identical—each with the same genes from the mother. but with different sets of genes from the father.

of twins born among different peoples in the world. Among Whites in the United States and in Europe, the general average is about one pair of twins in every 90 births. Among the Mongolian peoples—Japanese, Chinese and American Indians—twins occur no more than half as often. On the other hand, Negroes in the United States have a higher ratio of twin pregnancies than Whites (one twin in every 70 births), due either to some unknown environmental factors (though certainly not better prenatal conditions), or to some genetic factors. Also, in the United States and Europe, people of taller strains, such as those of Scandinavian descent, tend to have more twins than those of shorter stocks, such as Italians and Greeks, which, taken with the very low incidence of twinning among Japanese, might suggest at first thought that the size of the mother is the determining factor. This is open to doubt, as we shall presently see.

A highly important fact is that the marked racial or ethnic differences in twin incidence apply chiefly to *fraternal* twins. For example, where in the United States and Europe the average has been almost three fraternal-twin pairs to each identical-twin pair (though in recent years it has been coming closer to two to one), in Japan the ratio is hardly more than one fraternal to each identical pair. In other words, the incidence of identical twins among the Japanese, as among most other peoples, is almost the same as it is in the United States, so where there is a low twinning rate it is generally due only to a much smaller production of "fraternals." This, then, would becloud the theory that the smallness of Japanese or other women can account for the fewer twins among them, inasmuch as any adverse effect of the mother's size would be the same for either "identicals" or "fraternals." So it is not unlikely that there are hereditary differences which in some human strains reduce the chances of conceiving fraternal twins (perhaps by making multiple-egg production less frequent), or that there may be some environmental influences, still obscure, which account for the discrepancies in the ratios of fraternal to identical twins.

As a rule, though, it follows that because twins have a harder time on the road to birth, a favorable prenatal environment is even more essential for them than for singly developing babies. The prenatal casualty rate for twins is extraordinarily high, some authorities estimating that about three or four times as many twins are conceived as manage to achieve birth, either one or both of the pair being killed off along the way. In infancy, too, the death rate for twins is much higher than average, due principally to the fact that so many of them are prematurely born. But once twins pull through safely, they are usually quite as hardy as singly born individuals.

Unquestionably, many of us who are undistinguished singletons started off as twins and lost our other halves without even knowing it. Which seems a pity, when we think of all the advantages of being a twin, such as being able to be a member of a twin dancing act, or always having someone else around whose hats, shoes and clothing we can wear, or (if female), being glorified by manufacturers of home permanent-wave outfits. Not to mention the even greater advantages that come with being a member of the three, four and five multiple sets, with whom we'll deal next.

CHAPTER 19

"TRIPS," "QUADS" AND "QUINTS"

ON A night in May, 1934, Nature poured into the lap of science a lavish gift—the Dionne quintuplets.

While the birth of five children simultaneously to one mother had occurred about ten times in each century, never before, in the history of medical science, had all members of a set of quintuplets survived.*

But that was hardly the major reason for all the scientific excitement. What made the Dionnes so important was that all five were *"identicals,"* the product of a single egg, and therefore all carrying exactly the same hereditary factors—*to the very last of their thousands of genes.*

That the Dionnes were a "one-egg" set was definitely established soon after they were born, by means of the "twin" tests we've previously discussed. But before going into details about them, let's consider the simpler multiples—triplets and quadruplets—for the way these are produced gives us the clue to how the quintuplets also developed. In fact, the production of any multiple set of babies follows the same basic principles as those which we have seen applied to twins: The members may be all identical, all fraternal, or partly each. In other words, all can develop from a single egg (as with the Dionnes), or they can develop from two or more eggs.

In *triplets* (as our Chart shows), it is possible to have:

1. A "one-egg" set: all three "identicals" (either all boys or all girls).

2. A "two-egg" set: a pair of "identicals," developed from the same egg, and both either boys or girls; and a single "fraternal," developed from a second egg, and either a boy or a girl.

* One other *reported* set of living quintuplets are the Diligentis of Argentina, born in 1943, and consisting of three girls and two boys. They have not been available for study and, inasmuch as there is some doubt regarding them (one report gives them as a "four-egg" set), they have not been of great scientific interest.

HOW TRIPLETS MAY BE PRODUCED

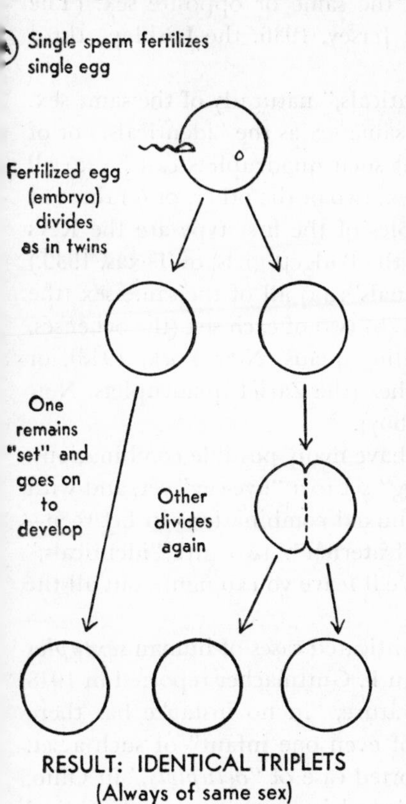
(A) Single sperm fertilizes single egg
Fertilized egg (embryo) divides as in twins
One remains "set" and goes on to develop
Other divides again
RESULT: IDENTICAL TRIPLETS (Always of same sex)

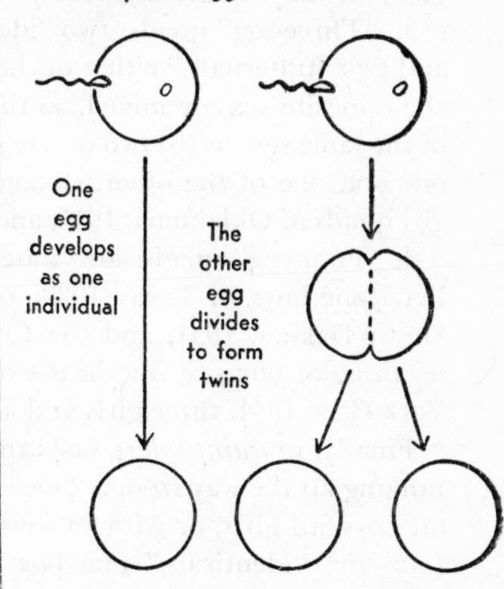
(B) Two separate sperms fertilize two separate eggs
One egg develops as one individual
The other egg divides to form twins

RESULT: Triplets, two of whom are really identical twins, the other a fraternal twin of theirs, of the same or opposite sex.

(C) A third type, of "unmatched" triplets, can result from the union of three separate sperms and three separate eggs.

3. A "three-egg" set: all "fraternals," and either all of the same sex, or two of one sex, the third of the opposite sex.

A noted example of the "two-egg" set of triplets is provided by the Brodes, three well-known American scientists: Robert, physicist, and Wallace, chemist, who in relation to each other are identical twins; and Malcolm, the zoologist, who is a "fraternal."

Among *quadruplets,* there are these possibilities:

1. "One-egg" quads: all four "identicals." (The Morlok girls, born in Michigan, 1930; the Hargreave girls, Ontario, Canada, 1949.)

2. "Two-egg" quads: (a) two pairs of one-egg twins (no case re-

ported, and doubtful if can occur), or (b) three "identicals," of the same sex, and one "fraternal," of the same or opposite sex. (The Kaspers, three boys, one girl, New Jersey, 1936; the Lashleys, three girls, one boy, Kentucky, 1941.)

3. "Three-egg" quads: two "identicals," naturally of the same sex, and two "fraternals," either of the same sex as the "identicals," or of the opposite sex, or mixed, so that such quadruplets can be (a) all of the same sex, or (b) two of one sex, two of the other, or (c) three of one sex, one of the other. (Examples of the first type are the Keys girl quads of Oklahoma, 1915, and the Badgett girls, of Texas, 1939.)

4. "Four-egg" quads: all "fraternals": (a) all of the same sex (the Perricone boys, of Texas, 1929), or (b) two of each sex (the Schenses, South Dakota, 1931, and the Collins quads, New York, 1948), or (c) three of one sex, one of the other (the Zarief quadruplets, New York City, 1944, three girls and a boy).

Finally, in *quintuplets,* one can have many possible combinations, ranging all the way from a "one-egg" set to a "five-egg" set, and with all boys, all girls, or with various mixed combinations in between—four girl "identicals," one boy "fraternal"; two girl "identicals," three boy "identicals"; etc., etc. (We'll leave you to figure out all the possibilities, if you're interested.)

There also have been four authenticated cases of human *sextuplet* births in past years, but, as Dr. Alan F. Guttmacher reported in 1948 after appraising the medical literature, "in no instance has there been proved temporary survival of even one infant" of such a set. He also pointed out that one reported case of *"octuplets,"* in Ohio, in 1872 (an account of which appeared in newspapers and medical journals of the time), turned out to be a complete fabrication, emanating from a malicious former suitor of the alleged mother.

Among lower animals, it may be noted, the kittens or puppies in a litter are usually "fraternals"—all products of different eggs (and sometimes of several fathers). However, it is quite possible that in any litter two or more might be "identicals." One mammal, the nine-banded armadillo, habitually gives birth to four "identicals," at a time, suggesting the possibility that in humans, too, a tendency to produce such higher multiples may also have some hereditary basis.

An amazing fact with regard to the incidence of human multiple births, ranging from twins to quadruplets, is the mathematical relationship which apparently governs the order of their frequencies. Back in 1895, a German scientist, D. Hellin, discovered the strange mathematical progression in these ratios: if the frequency of twins is once in 90 live births, for example, that of triplets will approximate the square of 90 (90 x 90) or one triplet set in every 8,100 births; that of quadruplets will approximate this sum multiplied again by 90, or once in about every 729,000 births; and that of quintuplets, the foregoing sum multiplied by another 90, or about once in every 65,610,000 live births.* (Where the twin incidence is 88, 92 or any other figure, the progressive ratios are governed accordingly.) What accounts for this phenomenon is not known, but over the years the formula has worked pretty closely, if slight modifications are made (as Dr. Sigismund Peller has shown) to allow for the reproductive ages of women and the repetition of twin births to the same mother. But also, the formula must be applied to the incidence of "multiples" at birth, not to those alive in any population, for the chances of survival decrease as the numbers in multiple sets increase. In twins, the chance of survival following birth is twelve to one; in triplets, six to one; in quadruplets, four to one; and in quintuplets, the odds are greatly against survival as a set following birth. However, once safely launched through infancy and childhood, individual members of a multiple set may look forward to a quite average life expectancy.

In all probability, we will be seeing more and more twins, trips and quads—possibly even quints—in the coming years, not because any more of them will be conceived, but because more of them will be enabled to achieve birth and to survive. The steady improvements being made in prenatal care, the ingenious methods now possible for finding out when "multiples" are on their way, the steps that can be taken to pull them through the critical hours and days following birth, all these factors should help to increase the proportions of "multiples" among us.

Now we come back to the Dionnes. Even though we know they're "identicals," they still could have been produced, theoretically, in

* The actual incidence of multiple births in the United States, during the years 1934 to 1947 (inclusive), was as follows: per million confinements, *twins,* 10,889; *triplets,* 106; *quadruplets,* 1.6. Specifically, in the period given, there were 392,000 twins reported out of 36,000,000 maternity cases, or one twin pair in every 92 confinements; triplets, one set in every 9,400 confinements; quadruplets, one set in about every 620,000 confinements (Metropolitan Life *Bulletin,* April, 1950).

THE DIONNE QUINTUPLETS

(A) SIMILARITIES

—And all five have the same "Webbed Toes" (2nd and 3rd)—on each foot.

All have same:

- Blood group "O"
- Medium-brown eyes mixed with gray
- Same eye pattern, same eyelashes, same light-brown eyebrows
- Same hair-color (dark, slightly reddish-brown)
- Same hair-form: Wavy
- Same feet pattern
- Same complexion: Light and fair

(B) DIFFERENCES (At age of three)

YVONNE	ANNETTE	CECILE	EMILIE	MARIE
HAIR WHORL				
				✓
HANDEDNESS:				
Right	Right	Right	LEFT ✓	Right
VISION:				
+.75	+.75	+.75	+1. ✓ (Slightly far-sighted)	+1.25 ✓ (Most far-sighted)
EYE FOCUS				
Normal	Normal	Normal	Lingering ✓ trace of cross-eyes	Still slight ✓ cross-eyes
MANNER OF HOLDING OBJECT				
			✓	✓

several ways. Starting with the single egg (or embryo), they first would have had to divide into two. But from that point on:

1. One-half might have doubled and then redoubled, forming *four* individuals, while the second half went on to develop by itself, intact.

2. Or the two halves might have each doubled, forming four individuals, and then one of these four could have divided again to make the required five. *This, it is believed, is the way the Dionnes were produced.*

It also would have been theoretically possible for even more divisions to have taken place, with six, seven or eight individuals created, of whom only the five survived. Dr. Allan Dafoe, who brought them into the world, did believe that there were six and that one of these failed to develop.

There was, however, interesting evidence to support our theory that the Dionnes were in the early stage *four* individuals, and that one of these divided again to make the fifth child. The clue was provided by the *differences* which the experts who studied the children in their first few years found among them.

As our Chart shows, *three* of the Dionnes—Cecile, Annette and Yvonne, were similar in all the characteristics noted. But both Emilie and Marie differed from the others in these respects: They were more far-sighted (Marie the most) than the other three; they were mildly cross-eyed long after this condition, found in all infants, disappeared in their sisters; they had slenderer faces and more sloping palates; and, as infants, Marie and Emilie displayed a special mannerism in grasping things—holding a spoon, for instance, as illustrated on the Chart. These, and several other minor differences noted by the experts indicated that Marie and Emilie were in some way paired and set apart from the others. As this could not possibly have been due to any differences in heredity, here is the most logical explanation:

When the embryo reached the four-division stage, three of the divisions were "set" and went on to form Cecile, Annette and Yvonne. But the *fourth part divided again,* one-half going to form Emilie and the other, Marie. Going further, if their division occurred at a later stage, it could produce some "mirror-imaging" in these two (as we explained with respect to identical twins in the last chapter). And this is just what was found: Marie's hair whorl was clockwise, that of Emilie, counter-clockwise. The further fact that Emilie

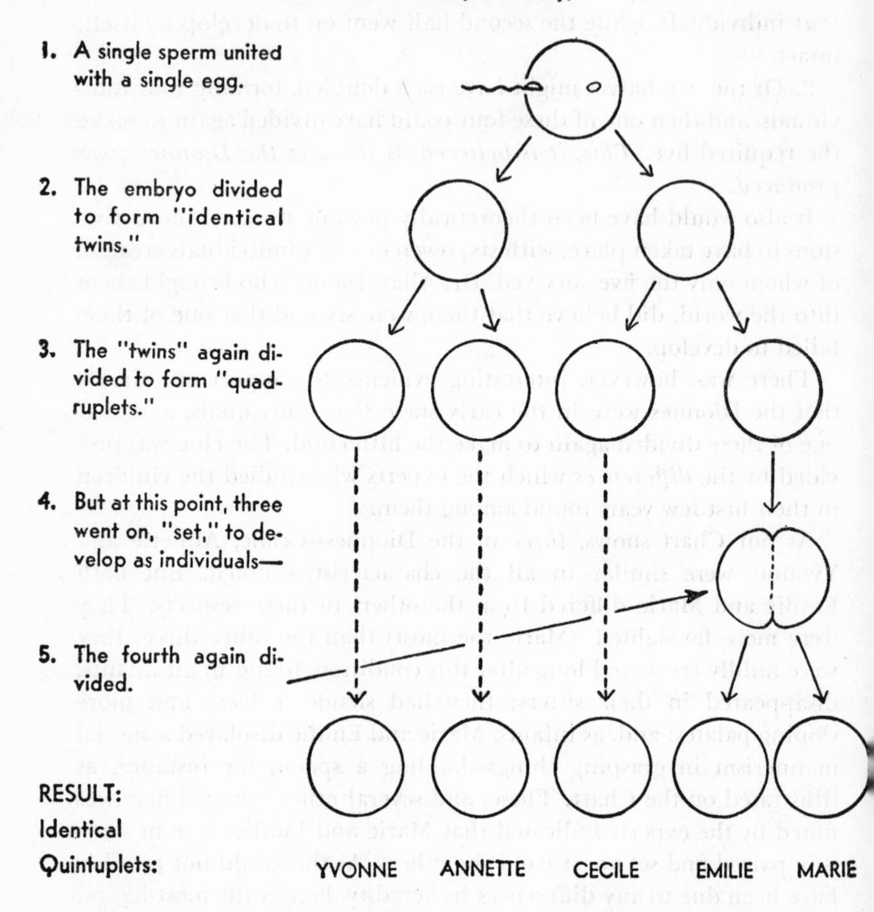
HOW THE DIONNE QUINTUPLETS WERE PRODUCED
(Theoretical probability)
1. A single sperm united with a single egg.
2. The embryo divided to form "identical twins."
3. The "twins" again divided to form "quadruplets."
4. But at this point, three went on, "set," to develop as individuals—
5. The fourth again divided.
RESULT: Identical Quintuplets:
YVONNE
ANNETTE
CECILE
EMILIE
MARIE

was left-handed, whereas Marie, like the others, was right-handed, might or might not have been due to "mirror-imaging," as we also pointed out with respect to twins.

The assumption that Emilie and Marie were the last to develop is given added weight by the fact that they were the smallest and lightest at birth and for some time thereafter, Marie being the "baby" of the whole set (which might further suggest that her development came slightly behind Emilie's). When Marie was six she was still the smallest and most delicate, and was treated for a minor muscular ailment in one leg and a minor blood-vessel condition.

Yet all the differences noted are rather unimportant when compared with the multitude of amazing similarities that continued to show themselves in the Dionnes. When the Dionnes were four and a half, all five had tonsillitis simultaneously, and had their tonsils removed. As their teeth developed, it was found (by Drs. Norma Ford and Arnold D. Mason) that all five had the same mild kind of "malocclusion" (where the upper and lower teeth do not fit together quite properly); that their lower first molars had erupted after the upper ones, which is the reverse of what happens in most children; and that there were a number of other distinctive differences in dental development common to all of them.

Again, in their general bodily development, including height and weight, the initial differences among the Dionnes were gradually reduced as they grew (although Marie still lagged a bit behind). Thus, when they were five, Drs. Dafoe and John MacArthur concluded that inequalities in the prenatal environment had "restricted the fullest expression of their hereditary growth factors," but that, following birth, with similar environments and care (the most uniform ever provided for any group of children) the workings of their identical genes caused the growth and development of the Dionnes to become more and more equalized.

We have spoken so far merely of the physical makeup of the Dionnes. Differences in degrees of thinking, achievement and personality also began to appear in their early childhood, and these we will deal with in a later chapter. But unfortunately for the scientists who were avidly interested, the Dionne family, not unnaturally, refused permission for further study of the quints after the first few years. So, even though the girls at this writing have passed the age of 16, we can add very little to what was known about them scientifically ten years ago. (See photograph, page 135.)

Secretly, of course, many a geneticist might have wished that a set of quintuplets like these had been available for a "controlled" experiment. Instead of being reared with the calculated uniformity of the Dionne set, such an experimental set would be separated immediately after birth and placed each in an environment radically different from that of the others: One quint to be reared with a millionaire socialite family, another in the worst slums, a third in the home of a college president, a fourth with the most backward tribe in the jungles of Africa, and perhaps the fifth in just an average middle-class home of average Americans. The parents of any quints would hardly fancy such an idea, alas. Yet only in that way might we really get to know how much environment could do to produce differences among five individuals having exactly the same heredity.

Nevertheless, the Dionnes already have taught us a great deal, and can be expected to teach us much more through whatever they do and whatever happens to them. With maturity, their paths will have to diverge, either in their careers or their marriages, or in both (unless they all enter a convent). If they do marry, their husbands will have to be quite different—there being no quintuplet males for them, as, on occasions, there have been identical-twin husbands for identical-twin girls. Their homes, their children, their lives in many details will be different. And so, in time (and the world hopes they will all live to a ripe old age), we will see how environment will write out each of the five stories which began with the same genetic plot. What we need not wait to know is that even in the case of the Dionnes, the substance and nature of an individual is never exactly repeated. We can say to each—to Annette, Cecile, Emilie, Marie and Yvonne—what we said with regard to anyone else in the very first lines of our first chapter:

"Stop and think about yourself: In all the history of the world, there was never anyone else exactly like you, and in all the infinity of time to come, there will never be another."

CHAPTER 20

THE "BLACK" GENES

MR. ROLLS-ROYCE, Mr. Ford or Mr. General-Motors could hardly be blamed if they didn't think highly of Mother Nature as a producer of mechanisms.

No self-respecting modern industrialist would think of turning out one of his products unless it had been rigidly inspected and found as free from flaws as he could make it. But Nature exercises no such care with regard to many of the human machines. We see, alas, that she creates individuals with every conceivable kind of defect or abnormality. In many cases this is the result of accident, or of being given bad materials to work with or bad conditions to work under. In other cases the abnormalities seem to be deliberately produced, perhaps as by-products of a constant process of experimentation in some vast scheme which we little mortals are not privileged to understand.

Actually, it is futile to compare the human body with any machine which we ourselves have constructed, for the finest automobile, airplane or scientific instrument is but the crudest of mechanisms compared with the human body and what it can do. Moreover, while some human beings do have serious flaws, what should never cease to impress us is how amazingly free of them are the great majority of us. Nor should we forget that many human ills which in former times were blamed on Nature—or on bad heredity—have now been found due wholly or in large measure to bad environment, and are being steadily reduced by improvements in living conditions and medical care. Even where heredity is to blame in one degree or another, these environmental improvements have done much to lessen the threats of many conditions, as we will show.

This having been said on the brighter side, we turn to the distressing fact that there are a great many inherent human defects which assert themselves regardless of what we can do about the environment. In addition, there are many other defects and diseases which, under the same conditions, will afflict some individuals more readily and more seriously than others because of inherited weakness or susceptibility. No human being is completely without hereditary imperfections. Fortunately, the great majority of these are so slight as to cause little damage or inconvenience. Some of them, however, are serious enough to interfere with important functions, to produce abnormal appearance which may make social adjustment difficult, or, in rare cases, to cause premature death.

To all of those genes responsible for some harmful or detrimental condition, we have given the name of *"black" genes.* And only when one or more of these "black" genes is involved in producing a defect, disease or abnormality can such a condition be considered, in the scientific sense, as *hereditary.*

This latter fact cannot be stressed too strongly. One of the greatest mistakes in the past—one still commonly made, even by some doctors—is to confuse "congenital" or "familial" with "hereditary." Sometimes these terms may be synonymous. Often they are not. In other words, the mere fact that a condition is congenital (present at birth) or that it is familial ("running" in a family) is no proof that it is hereditary, for there are many environmental effects that "run" in families, too, and that can be overcome with proper attention. Contrariwise, a condition may be hereditary and yet not show itself at birth or for many years thereafter, and, also, may never before have appeared in the individual's family (this latter being so when rare recessive genes are brought together or new "black" genes are created).

As an example of one of the commonest of the errors, there is that of speaking of congenital syphilis as "hereditary." But—*syphilis is not, never was, and never can be inherited.*

A dramatic episode from the writer's experiences bears on this point. Some years ago we were conducting a "baby" contest in a Midwestern state, the ostensible purpose of which was to select the most "perfect" babies. A more important objective was to have babies brought in for careful medical checkups. With a first prize of $1,000 and other awards as lures, thousands of babies were entered, and after weeks of examinations and re-examinations the field was narrowed down to a dozen or so little ones, every one of whom was already in line for a prize.

The writer was inside the final examining room as an observer with the jury of leading pediatricians. Suddenly one of the specialists who was examining a 2-year-old baby whispered excitedly to his colleagues, *"Look at this."*

The others crowded around. And then came the gruesome pronouncement, "Congenital syphilis!"

No one else had previously detected the almost imperceptible symptoms. The child already had been publicly proclaimed as among the prize-winning finalists. Nothing could be done now but to award it the last major prize. A shudder still runs through us as we recall how the mother glowingly received the token for her baby as "one of the most perfect in the state"—and was then quietly taken aside and told that her beautiful little offspring had syphilis. But that wasn't all. As she and the baby returned to their home town for an exuberant welcome by proud relatives and neighbors, the mother carried with her the knowledge that the child had *acquired* the disease from her.

For the only way that a child can be born with syphilis is through prior *infection by the mother.* The mother herself may have had the disease to begin with, or she may have been infected by her husband during conception or later. But the germs had to be present in her if her child was born with syphilis. All this is also true of gonorrhea or any other infectious disease.

A father, no matter how diseased, could not possibly transmit syphilis or gonorrhea to his child through inheritance—that is, through his sperm cells. For no sperm cell could carry a venereal disease germ (or any other germ known today) and function. However, germs could easily be carried with the sperms in the seminal fluid, so that infection of the mother could take place simultaneously with a child's conception. Then, in subsequent stages of prenatal development or during the birth process, the child might acquire the disease from the mother. Happily, under modern methods of prenatal care and treatment, it is possible to prevent syphilitic infection of an unborn child in almost every case.*

We have dealt at such length with syphilis because ever since Ibsen's *Ghosts* startled the world, the belief has been widespread that the disease can be inherited, and that a "syphilitic" taint may persist in a family for generations. Attending this was the theory, called "blastophthoria," that syphilis, as well as drunkenness, drug addic-

* Drs. H. F. Johnson and C. N. Frazier of Texas reported in 1948 that of sixty syphilitic pregnant women treated with penicillin, only one gave birth to a syphilitic infant.

tion, depravity, etc., might in some way permanently effect the germ cells in a family strain, leading to increasing degeneracy and *progressive* weakening from generation to generation. But as we have seen in previous chapters, no disease or evil habit can alter the *genes* in the germ cells, and therefore there can be no such thing as an "acquired" hereditary taint.

When a child comes into the world with syphilis, or some terrible defect resulting from it, the question as to whether the condition should be termed "congenital" or "inherited" may seem to be mere quibbling. But this is emphatically not so. For if a condition is congenital but *not hereditary* the afflicted individual can grow up and marry with no fear that his children will inherit his defect. If it is a disease which has been cured (as syphilis can now be cured) he will certainly not pass it along. But where a condition is hereditary, *no matter whether the parent has been cured of it or not,* and no matter how healthy he or she may be, there is always the possibility that the "black" genes involved will be passed along and reproduce the condition in some of the offspring. Thus syphilis and many other acquired diseases, congenital or otherwise, may be wiped from the earth in a few generations merely by modern methods of treatment and prevention. Inherited conditions may persist forever, for they could be eliminated only by preventing all carriers of the "black" genes from breeding, an almost impossible eventuality.

In the case of *familial* conditions, it is equally important to distinguish between those which are *genetic*—running in families because the same genes are passed along in successive generations—and those which are purely *environmental*—recurring in a given strain merely because the same bad conditions or harmful influences continue to prevail. This latter applies to many infectious diseases, many physical defects, and certain types of mental abnormality and abnormal behavior which once were thought to be hereditary. We know also that dietary deficiencies—the lack of needed foods and vitamins—can explain repeated occurrences in some underprivileged strains of a great many diseases, disorders and physical defects; or that the presence or absence of certain chemicals in the drinking water may produce teeth defects or glandular abnormalities of the same kind in successive generations. (For example, excessive fluorine may lead to pitted and mottled teeth, and the absence of iodine may lead to goiter, especially in adolescent girls.)

But there is another side to the picture. For just as grave mistakes

HOW GENETIC PEDIGREES ARE ILLUSTRATED

SQUARE: MALE

CIRCLE: FEMALE

Plain outline square or circle indicates individual who does not have the trait in question.

OR — Solid black indicates individual with the trait in question.

OR — Heavy dot indicates person who carries the gene for given trait but does not show trait.

1. SIMPLE DOMINANT PEDIGREE*

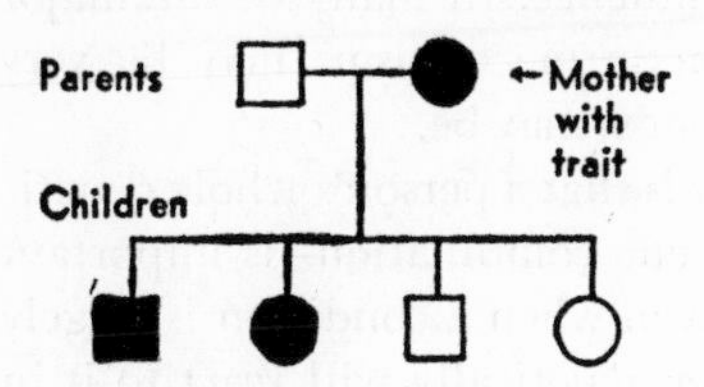

Any parent carrying dominant gene shows the trait, and average of one in two children will receive the gene and also show the trait. If parent has two of the dominant genes, every child will show trait.

2. SIMPLE RECESSIVE PEDIGREE*

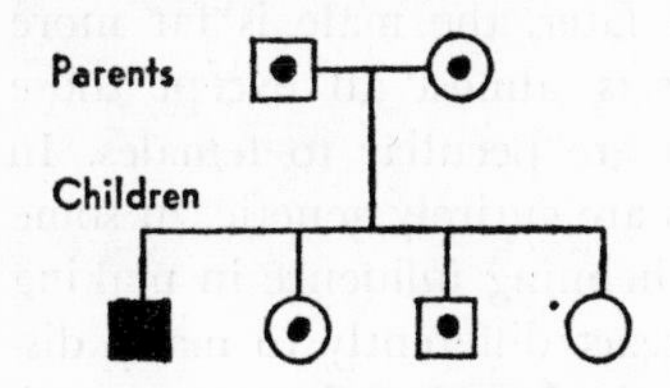

Both parents here carry same recessive gene. Average of one in four children will receive both genes and have the trait. One in two children will receive only one gene and be carriers, but without the trait. One in four children will be entirely free of the gene.

3. SIMPLE "SEX-LINKED" PEDIGREE*
(Gene carried on "X" chromosome)

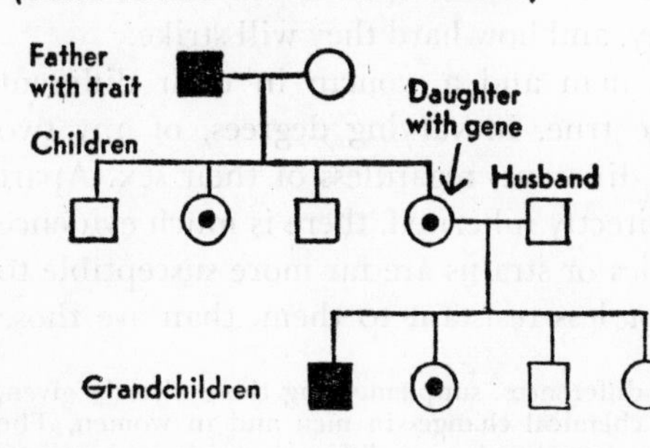

Father with trait passes on gene to all daughters. Each is a carrier, and if she has children chances are one-in-two any son will receive gene and have trait, like his grandfather; and one-in-two any daughter of hers will be a carrier, like herself.

* Details regarding other types of dominant, recessive and sex-linked genes will be found in "Black Gene" Forecast Tables, p. 307.

were made in the past in designating conditions as "hereditary" when they were wholly or chiefly environmental, so mistakes were and still are being made in dismissing conditions as purely environmental when heredity may have much to do with their causation or development. The extreme "environmentalists" of today (including those who see almost every disease as "psychosomatic") tend to ignore the fact that the line between heredity and environment in disease is not always clearly drawn. Many conditions depend for their expression upon adverse heredity *plus* adverse environment, nor does failure to pin down a condition to a simple gene formula mean there is no evidence of hereditary influence. In many of the major conditions, as we shall see, the genetic mechanisms may be very involved, just as environmental influences may be.

What has become increasingly clear is that a person's whole genetic makeup—and not merely a specific gene combination—is important in relation to almost every disease. Even when a condition is largely environmental, individuals who differ genetically will react to it in different ways. The most striking distinction in this respect is that between *males* and *females.* As we have seen in an earlier chapter, and as will be brought out in detail later, the male is far more vulnerable to most diseases and defects—almost all except those which are chiefly glandular or which are peculiar to females. In some instances the determining factors are entirely genetic, in some entirely environmental, but the overwhelming influence in making boys and girls, or men and women, react differently to many diseases (including syphilis!) derives from the fact that they are *genetically different,* that their bodies are constructed differently in many ways, and function differently.* Throughout your life, on whether you are a male or a female may often depend what diseases will strike at you, and in what way, and how hard they will strike.

What is true, then, of a man and a woman in their different reactions to disease, may be true, in varying degrees, of any two persons who are genetically different, regardless of their sex. Apart from conditions which are directly inherited, there is much evidence that members of some families or strains are far more susceptible to certain infectious diseases, or less resistant to them, than are those

* Among newer findings of sex differences, supplementing those already given, are that old age brings different chemical changes in men and in women. The blood of an aging woman has been found to have a different *amino-acid* content from that of an aging man. The effects of this chemical difference now are being studied.

of other families and strains. This may apply to a wide variety of germ diseases—smallpox, tuberculosis, pneumonia, etc., and perhaps also to dietary-deficiency diseases, such as pellagra.

In fact, as studies in this field progress, we will probably learn that there is almost no disease or affliction in which heredity does not play some part. These finer distinctions, however, must await clarification. In the succeeding chapters, our major interest will be focused on those conditions where inheritance is fairly clear-cut and where we know, or suspect, the "black" genes responsible.

But before going on, let's ask, "How, generally, do the 'black' genes do their work?"

Not so differently from the way normal genes work—except that the "black" ones don't follow the usual blueprints. Sometimes they "overwork" (as when a gene produces six or seven fingers instead of five). Sometimes they "underwork" (as when a gene constructs only part of a hand, or leaves some organ incomplete, or doesn't produce enough of some important chemical). And sometimes a gene delegated to a really important key job falls down so badly, or goes on the rampage to such an extent, as to kill the individual who is host to it.

In most cases a single "black" gene produces only one special effect. But often a whole cluster or series of defects (a *"syndrome"*) can result directly from the action of a single gene or pair of the same genes. (Consider the unfortunates who get blindness, deafness, deformity and mental defect, all in one genetic package—as in *amaurotic idiocy*, or some forms of *retinitis pigmentosa*.) Contrariwise, some single conditions result only through a combination of many genes or the presence of a certain environment.

In many ways, "black" genes may be as capricious as human wrongdoers. They may act abnormally and do bad things only under special circumstances, or if linked with certain other genes which are bad influences or with which they can't get along; they may be only a little bit bad, or very, very bad; and they may go wrong in early life—as "juvenile delinquents" or not until later life, or sometimes, unexpectedly, they may not go bad at all. Even in members of one family the same "black" gene or genes may produce a certain effect in one individual and a different effect in another, or may act at different ages.

All of this will become clearer as we take up specific diseases and defects. But prepare yourself not to become too upset. Though the list of "black" genes is a long and formidable one, always keep in mind that the great majority of them—particularly those most serious—affect only a small number of individuals, and that most of mankind's ills are not due to their influence. Also, not all of the conditions discussed may be of personal interest to you, so if you are inclined to skip lightly through the next several chapters, in search of items that may touch you, your relatives or your friends, you can locate the facts and subjects under easily found headings. Finally, all of the "black" genes dealt with, and additional ones of minor interest, together with "predictions" for their inheritance, will be summarized in a later chapter.

CHAPTER 21

THE BIG KILLERS

ALMOST every day you read that such-and-such a disease is the "No. 1 Killer" or the "No. 2 Killer"—or some other rank—among the disease enemies of human beings. What interests us here is the part that heredity may play in these most menacing conditions. Of first significance, then, is the fact that the ranking order of the "killers" has undergone a striking change within two generations—*and this would not have been so if the chief causes of death had been mainly hereditary.*

Let's look at the "box score" of deaths from the principal diseases in the United States in 1948:

Cause of Death	*Death Rate per 100,000 Population**
Diseases of the heart	322.7
Cancer (all malignant tumors)	135
Cerebral hemorrhages and other blood-vessel conditions	89.7
Nephritis (kidney disease) all forms	53
Pneumonia and influenza	38.7
Tuberculosis, all forms	30
Premature birth	26.7
Diabetes mellitus	26.4

* Figures from National Office of Vital Statistics.

But a half-century earlier—in 1900—the listing was radically different. Then tuberculosis was far at the top, with a death rate *almost six times that of 1948.* (195 per 100,000 compared with 30.) Pneumonia came a close second with a death rate of 176 per 100,000; next diarrhea and other digestive diseases in infancy and early childhood, with a rate well over 150. But *heart diseases were only fourth on the list,* infectious diseases of childhood next, nephritis next and *cancer no more than seventh* with a total death rate of 64 per 100,000—less than half that in 1948. (All of the foregoing estimates and comparisons are approximate, because diagnoses and census death records in 1900 were not always on the same basis as in later decades.)

The sharp change in the order of the "killers" has been due principally to two related factors. One is the vast improvement in living conditions and in medical care, especially with regard to the prevention and treatment of infectious diseases. This, with its greatest benefit to infants and children, has permitted ever-greater numbers of people to live well into the mature years. And that, in turn, accounts for the second factor: With the numbers of older persons steadily increasing, there has been a proportionate increase in deaths through diseases which come mainly in the later ages, such as heart conditions, cerebral hemorrhage, cancer and diabetes.

Can we see any meaning with respect to heredity in all this? Obviously, the hereditary makeup of our population hasn't changed in any important way. Only the environment has changed. But the more we eliminate the worst hazards of environment, and the more we equalize conditions for all persons, the more the *inherent differences in individuals assert themselves* and the more important becomes the role of heredity in creating distinctions, large and small, between individuals with respect to what diseases and defects afflict them, and how serious these turn out to be.

In short, we are beginning more and more to see not only where heredity is directly responsible for given conditions but where and how it exerts varying degrees of influence on many others, including some of the major diseases in which the role of heredity was previously obscured. As an introduction to what will follow, we can make these classifications:

Directly inherited (with environment playing only a small part in causation) are perhaps most cases of diabetes, some of the less prevalent forms of heart disease, and some of the very rare forms of cancer.

Indirectly inherited (where, with the given "black" genes a person will develop the condition under certain adverse circumstances) are rheumatic heart disease, and some other forms of heart and arterial diseases.

Influenced by heredity, in some degree or another, may be virtually all of the other major diseases. But there are important qualifications. In the major heart and arterial conditions the evidence for some probable hereditary rôle is very strong, whereas in common cancer the *possible* rôle of heredity is still very uncertain. Or, taking the infectious diseases, while there certainly aren't and couldn't be any "genes" for tuberculosis, pneumonia, syphilis or any other germ disease, it is very possible that inherited constitutional weaknesses may make some individuals an easier prey than others to given infections.*

All of this will be clarified when we take up the specific diseases in detail. But let us note, first, that we are confining ourselves in this chapter to the major diseases which are "killers" and are rating them in terms of how many lives they claim each year. If we were to rank diseases as enemies, according to how much unhappiness they cause, or what their effect is on society, the order of importance might well be different. Topmost among our "principal enemies," with heredity playing an important part, we might have to place mental diseases and defects. (These we'll discuss in a later chapter.) Also, in evaluating diseases as "major" or otherwise, we might have to consider not only how many people they kill, but *when* they strike and what damage they do, even if they do not kill. By this standard, rheumatic fever, which strikes at the very young, disabling many of them for life and killing others, might have to be regarded in a different light from a heart condition which carries off a person in the twilight of life; and a disease which brings death suddenly and painlessly might have to be weighed differently from one which is attended by years of suffering.

So it is that, as we discuss the various diseases from the standpoint of heredity, you, the reader, may have to evaluate them in your own way, according to their meaning to you and to those close to you.

Heart and Blood Vessels. There is hardly a family in which some member or immediate relative isn't afflicted by, or hasn't been carried off by one or another of the heart or blood-vessel diseases. Most common and serious of these are hypertension (high blood pressure), arteriosclerosis (hardening and thickening of the arteries), and rheumatic heart disease. In all of these conditions heredity, directly or indirectly, may play some part. Even when a non-hereditary condition such as syphilis is involved, the general genetic makeup of the individual may be a factor in the way the heart or other organs are affected.

Hypertension, when not a product of other diseases, is more likely to occur in persons with a family history of the condition than in

* The reason that physicians and insurance companies ask questions regarding these conditions in a family is not, however, because of any proved heredity, but because the information may be helpful in recognizing obscure symptoms and with respect to taking preventive measures.

those without one. Although no specific genes for this disease have been identified, the probability is that a predisposition may be hereditary.* (Aggravating influences may be nervous strain, "stepped-up" living, or personality factors.) Where hypertension is most serious is in the threat that it may lead to (1) heart disease (enlarged heart and heart failure), or coronary artery disease, with blood clots; (2) kidney diseases; (3) apopletic stroke or brain hemorrhage. (This latter was the cause of President Franklin D. Roosevelt's death.)

Arteriosclerosis, which is responsible for from 25 to 40 per cent of the heart deaths, involves the thickening and hardening of the arteries, with a loss of elasticity, and a narrowing of the passages. There may be impairment of the blood supply to the heart muscle, resulting in a certain type of constricting heart pain *(angina pectoris)* or damage to the heart muscle when an artery becomes closed *(coronary thrombosis).* Often, also, the arteries of the brain are affected, particularly in older people.

While many authorities cite a high familial incidence of arteriosclerosis—but possibly only because it occurs so frequently—no satisfactory evidence of its inheritance has yet been produced. However, in the common types of arteriosclerosis where a fatty deposit is present in the arteries (a condition known as *atherosclerosis*), resulting from a disordered metabolism of the fatty element *cholesterol,* the evidence of hereditary influence appears to be clearer. (Recent findings to this effect have come from Drs. Ernst P. Boas, David Adlersberg, Albert D. Parets, and others.)

Childhood rheumatism (or rheumatic fever, as it is now generally known), which strikes down mostly children and younger adults, presents a picture of inheritance different from that of the other heart ailments. One of the most puzzling of diseases, it is characterized by joint swelling and pains, chorea (St. Vitus dance), fever and inflammation of the heart. It claims as its victims one in every fifty children, and causes four-fifths of the heart illnesses under forty. Added to its often fatal consequences, rheumatic fever every year makes thousands of children invalids for life in greater or lesser degree.

Long known to run in families, childhood rheumatism has been

* The "cold pressor" test, in the belief of some authorities, may be helpful in identifying individuals who have the predisposition toward eventual development of hypertension. (In this test the hands are placed in a dish of ice water for two minutes, and the time is measured for the blood pressure to return to normal.)

identified as one of those conditions where a *susceptibility,* rather than the disease itself, is inherited. Evidence now points to the fact that a single pair of recessive genes—one gene received from each parent—may lead to the development of the disease *under certain conditions.* But medical science is still far from clear as to precisely what these conditions are. We know, for example, that the disease is very widespread among the poor and much less common among the rich. Why? We can only guess. That diet and living conditions may be involved was suggested by evidence from England during World War II, where a decline in rheumatic heart disease coincided with a decrease in poverty, the evacuation of many children from slum areas to the country, and the making of more milk available to them. (However, some authorities believe that the lessened danger of respiratory infections, in the move from city to country, was the main factor in this.)

Another peculiarity of childhood rheumatism, according to various reports, is that its serious effects manifest themselves more in temperate climates than in hot zones, cases in the tropics being uncommon. Within the United States, the highest death rates from this disease are in the Middle Atlantic and Rocky Mountain states; the lowest rates (less than half), in the South Atlantic and Gulf states, and in California. But, again, why? No one knows.

Despite these uncertainties, the evidence is clear enough so that where rheumatic fever has previously appeared in a family, parents and doctors should be watchful of any suspicious symptoms in children.*

Varicose veins, a condition which involves a weakening of the walls of the veins, leading to their enlargement, appears only in *some* cases to be linked with heredity. The condition is quite common, especially in women after childbirth and in persons of either sex whose occupation requires continued standing. The predominant causes as a rule are external, but in certain families varicose veins have been found hereditary, transmitted through an *irregular dominant* gene.

CANCER. The greatest of all disease mysteries is presented by cancer. Thousands of medical and scientific detectives have been at work throughout the world trying to throw light on this disease, or group of diseases, and to track down any hereditary factors that may be

* At this writing high hopes are being held out that the new drug, cortisone, may prove very effective in the treatment of rheumatic fever.

involved. As yet we know only that heredity is directly responsible for just a very few rare types of cancer—not necessarily related to the others—and plays a part in certain additional types that are more prevalent. But in the common cancers the rôle of heredity is still a matter of conjecture. Such evidence as there is rests mainly on statistics showing a considerably higher than average incidence of cancers in certain families; on twin studies which show that where one of a pair of identical twins has cancer, the other is much more likely to develop the same type of cancer, and within a much shorter interval of time, than is true of fraternal twins; and perhaps most significant, on findings of "cancer-susceptible" strains in experimental animals. But while most authorities now believe that there are some hereditary factors common in cancer among humans, no one has yet identified them, and it is obvious that any "black" genes there may be for such factors must be very complex in their workings.

Why it should be so difficult to clarify the rôle of heredity in cancer, when in every community large numbers of people are afflicted by it or die of it annually, becomes clear when we consider its many baffling aspects. Cancer is not a specific disease. It is a general term for malignant areas of growth which occur in organs or tissues of the body and go from bad to worse. There are a great many different types of cancer, each with its special peculiarities and its particular sphere of action, but all cancerous growths have this in common: They consist of cells which behave abnormally, and do not cooperate with the surrounding cells in the orderly processes of the body. As they grow, multiply, and become malignant "evil-doers" they starve and invade and eventually destroy their neighboring cells and tissues in which they are located. Eventually they may break loose, like outlaws, and by way of the blood stream range through the body, and ultimately cause the death of the host individual.

How do these cancer cells originate? Not so differently, it appears, from the way that human outlaws and killers are launched into criminal careers. There may be some gradual or sudden bad influence in the environment—a strong irritant or other force which upsets the normal workings of cells. (Some 500 cancer-inducing substances already are known, ranging through nitrogen mustard gas, abrasive dusts, a great variety of chemicals and up to radiation set loose by atomic bombs.) But, as with humans who go wrong, there may be something initially *unstable* or deranged in the cells which become cancerous. This is where heredity enters the picture. (And it also explains why the advanced study of cancer is today so closely interwoven with the study of cell-genetics, because most cancer scientists believe that the mystery of the disease may be solved when we fully lay bare the essential mechanism of the human cell and find out just what happens in cancer to throw chromosomes and their genes out of gear, or what makes cytoplasm—or cell substance—abnormal.)

Theoretically, cancer or the susceptibility to it could be inherited in one of several ways: (1) certain "black" genes might produce an instability in the cell workings, so that at a certain stage of life—particularly when the cells had begun to weaken and wear down—some of them could go "haywire," either spontaneously or through sudden adverse influences; (2) some individuals might inherit peculiarities in their body chemistry (hormonal or otherwise), which could irritate their cells into becoming cancerous; (3) faulty construction, through defective genes, of a specific part of the body might result among other things in causing cancer cells to develop at that location (which apparently is the case in certain very rare forms of cancer that appear in early life); (4) cells might inherit unusual susceptibility to invasion by a virus or some other outside agent.

But applying these theories to any specific person or condition is another matter. For example, take breast cancer. A grandmother, a mother and a daughter all had or have cancer of the breast. Is this not proof of inheritance? Not necessarily. As we've learned, an unfortunate property of cancer cells is that they may break loose from where they originate and settle down almost anywhere. Thus, in the three women, while they themselves were related, their cancers need not have been, for their cancer cells may have had widely different points of origin, or may have developed at different times and under different influences; and even if located in the breast, the cancers could have been quite different in their action, virulence and susceptibility to treatment. Similarly, lung cancer, or throat cancer or some other cancer, originating in different ways in two members of the same family may be of different types, with no genetic relationship.* Moreover, various environmental factors which may "run" in certain families—for example, continued exposure to coal dust among miners, or to abrasive dusts among quarryworkers and

* The cancer that killed Babe Ruth, American baseball idol, in 1948, originated in the throat, but death was due in large part to the spread of the cancer cells to the lungs and liver.

pottery-makers, or to other irritants, both external and internal, in different occupations—may influence related persons for successive generations to develop similar types of cancer.

Nevertheless, one must be equally cautious not to attribute a succession of cancer cases in a given family merely to coincidence or to environments. Breast cancer, as it happens, is one of the types where there is strong suspicion of *some* hereditary influence. It may or may not mean that in the women of some families the breast tissues are particularly susceptible to the development of cancers, wherever and however the cancer cells may originate. We know only that when we study the backgrounds of women with breast cancer, we find many more with mothers or other close relatives who have been similarly afflicted than is true of women in general. This evidence is sufficiently strong to suggest that wherever there have been previous cases of breast cancer in a woman's immediate family, she should have periodic medical checkups on reaching the age when this condition may begin to develop.

How significant with respect to humans are studies of cancer inheritance in certain *highly inbred strains of mice* (as revealed in notable studies by Dr. C. C. Little, Dr. John Bittner and others) remains to be seen. One must be particularly cautious at this stage of research about applying to human beings the evidence that susceptibility to breast cancer *in mice* may be transmitted by way of the mother's milk, perhaps through a virus or some other irritant.

In certain other specific types of cancer heredity has been claimed, but of this we cannot be sure. *Cancer of the intestines, and cancer of the rectum,* have been said to be much influenced by heredity, although the only clear evidence is in the case of *multiple rectal polyps* (smooth growths). This latter condition occurs in early adult life, and the presence of one case in a family should put all other younger members on special guard. In *cancer of the stomach* heredity is possibly a factor, but unfavorable diet has much to do with bringing on the condition. *Cancer of the liver* is even more likely to be influenced by diet, living habits and environment.*

Where the origin of cancer is often most puzzling is in its appearance in very young people—for cancer is not exclusively a disease of maturity or old age. It is now the second highest cause of death

* Some very rare types of cancer where heredity is definite will be discussed in later chapters. These conditions include malignant freckles, epiloia, polyposis of the colon, glioma retina, retinal angioma and neurofibromatosis.

among children. Among cancers afflicting those from 1 to 14 years of age are included each year hundreds of cases of cancers of the blood (leukemia), bone cancers, and cancers of the skin, eyes and kidneys. Sometimes the cancers are found to have started long before birth, and may or may not be influenced by heredity. Growing awareness that children may be victimized by cancer already has led to the establishment of cancer-prevention clinics in some cities.

Further suggestive evidence that genetic factors, in interoperation with environmental factors, are involved in the development of cancers—and of particular types of cancers—comes from comparison of the cancer rates for women and men. In every type of cancer the incidences for the two sexes differ considerably, with the male rate higher for every type except the cancers specific to women, such as cancers of the breast and the womb. Although occupational hazards may account for part of the higher rate among men in cancers of the skin, lungs and throat, there seems to be little question but that the greater inherent susceptibility of males to most diseases also applies to cancers. Findings that the "male" sex hormone may stimulate development of cancer of the prostate and that a "female" hormone may help to suppress it, suggest that various sex differences in internal chemistry may heighten the susceptibility of men to other cancers which afflict them to a markedly greater extent (such as cancers of the digestive tract).* In women, on the other hand, the high incidences of cancers of the breast and uterus, *together with the fact* that many more women than men survive into the "cancer" ages, have lifted the total cancer rate for females beyond that of males. But it is important to note that with improved methods of detection, prevention, control and cure, the cancer death rate is being steadily cut down proportionately more among women than among men.

Much less clear are reports of inherent cancer differences among people of different races or ethnic stocks. For instance, statistics may show that the general cancer rate for Negroes in the United States is much lower than for Whites, but this doesn't mean that Negroes

* According to Dr. Frank E. Adair, in women under the menopausal age (under age 46, generally), it has been shown that the ovarian hormones tend to stimulate the development of breast cancer where the tendency is present. Administration of *testosterone,* the "male" hormone, temporarily suppresses the ovarian action in these younger women and has markedly beneficial effects in reducing the breast-cancer threat. On the other hand, in women well beyond the menopausal age (60 and over), there is a reverse situation. In these older women, in whom ovarian action has already greatly diminished, the administration of *estrogen,* the "female" hormone, has been found to produce remedial effects with respect to breast cancer.

are any less resistant to cancer. Proportionately fewer Negroes may die of cancer because fewer among them live into the older ages when cancer is most likely to develop. As life spans of Negroes have lengthened, their cancer rate has gone up. So also, the much higher cancer mortality for those of some nationalities (Irish, German, English, etc.) as compared with others (Italians having the lowest rate) must be viewed in the light of a great many complicated factors before any conclusions can be drawn. (We shall deal with this again in our chapter on "Longevity", and in the "Race" chapters.)

Unless we have evidence to the contrary, we must assume that cancer is almost equally common to human beings of all races and nationalities. Given a prolonged enough exposure to cancer-producing factors, internal and external, it is believed that most persons would eventually succumb to the disease. Some indication of this already is given by the fact, previously noted, that with continued increases in life spans and reductions in other causes of death, there has been a steady increase in the number of cancer cases and of cancer deaths.

If there is any brighter side to this picture, it lies in the hope that better cures or more effective treatments for cancer will be discovered. Even as matters now are, there has been increasing success in preventing or staving off the worst effects of the disease, in a great many cases, by *early detection* and treatment. *This is precisely why it is so important to clarify the rôle of heredity.* When cancer was a "hopeless" condition, it may have served no purpose to alarm individuals about the chances of their having inherited the disease. But as the possibility grows that early detection of cancer symptoms may lead to prevention or cure—already in perhaps as high as 40 per cent of the cases, according to some authorities—it may be of the utmost value to give warning to individuals wherever their family histories would so justify. This, to repeat, has particular meaning with regard to cancers of the breast, stomach, intestines and rectum, though we may also find eventually that it applies in some measure to all common cancers.

Another important point is that a clear distinction no longer is always being made between *"benign"* tumors (presumably not harmful) and *"malignant"* (or "evil") ones. Evidence is mounting that many "benign" tumors may be merely arrested or incipient forms of "malignant" tumors which ultimately could become cancerous. (For example, a large majority of older men are now believed to have tumors of the prostate in one stage or another, which, mostly, never create serious trouble but eventually would if the men lived long enough.) In many cases, however, the tumors are indeed "benign." But "benign" or "malignant," many authorities believe that the tumors arise through the same causes: *irritation* or *upsets* of the originally affected cells by either internal or external means.

As we have noted, a great many different substances have been identified as *"carcinogenic,"* or cancer-inducing, most of them being external irritants, but some being chemicals manufactured in the body. (An unbalanced production of hormones might be one cause. A *virus* infection, according to a recent theory, might be another cause.) There also is little doubt that undue and sustained irritation of the delicate mucuous membranes of the mouth, throat, lungs, alimentary tract or sex organs, may contribute to the production of cancers.* Long ago it was found that chimney sweeps in England had an unusually high incidence of cancer. Special cancer hazards also go with such occupations as mining, quarrying, sandblasting or glass-blowing, where precautions are needed to protect workers from abrasive substances. In any instances where successive generations of individuals have been exposed to the same irritants (through occupation or living conditions), the appearance of the same types of cancer among them might be much more due to environment than to heredity.

Finally, we have a new cancer threat—*radiation.* The first warnings of this were given many years ago, when radium and X-rays began to be used to destroy or check the growth of cancer cells. While countless individuals have been saved and helped by radiation treatment, it also was found that, if not properly controlled, radiation could unbalance and injure normal cells, inducing cancer. An unfortunate few among doctors and radiologists of the earlier years who did not protect themselves against X-rays subsequently became cancer victims, and even today, the death rate from *leukemia,* a serious type of blood-cell cancer, is about 75 per cent higher than

* The question of the influence of *smoking* on cancer of the lungs, lips and mouth has been given considerable study. Some evidence has been recently offered that habitual smokers are more likely to have these cancers than are non-smokers. Dr. Bernard Pierre of Philadelphia reported (1950) that in one group of male lip-cancer cases, 40 per cent were apparently due to pipe smoking. That lung cancer is also much more prevalent among smokers than non-smokers was reported from two sources in the *Journal* of the American Medical Association, May 27, 1950. Cited as especially susceptible to lung cancer were heavy cigarette smokers who inhale, which may explain why lung cancer is far more prevalent among cigarette smokers than among pipe or cigar smokers.

average among physicians, apparently because of their exposure to X-rays. Many readers also will remember the tragic case of a group of girls in a New Jersey watch factory who worked at painting luminous dials (pointing the brushes with their lips) and who all developed malignant cancer and died within a space of twenty years.

Today, with the development of the atomic bomb and the vast exploitation of atomic energy, the radiation threat looms as a potential new Colossus of cancer danger. No expert doubts that among the deadliest effects of atomic radiation, indiscriminately set loose, would be inevitably the induction of cancers in a great many individuals. (And as we shall see in a later chapter, on "Evolution," this would be only one of the consequences of shaking up human cells.) We might well give thought to the dangerous possibility that while our medical scientists are making headway against cancer on one front, with the hope of victory growing ever stronger, we do not open ourselves to a new threat from this other direction.

DIABETES. Playing and living in a special camp in the Catskills each summer are more than 150 children with diabetes. They are some of the 500 children in New York City, and of the thousands of others throughout the country, similarly afflicted. Half of the children in the camp (maintained by the New York Diabetes Association) come from underprivileged homes, where the means are not available to give them the special care that they require. But the disease is just as likely to afflict children in wealthy homes. There is nothing in the early diet or living conditions of a child to account for the onset of diabetes. Nor, according to Dr. Edmund L. Shlevin, is there evidence that the children in the camp have previously had any undue emotional stresses or other unusual experience.

"In the absence of contrary evidence," says Dr. Shlevin, "we must conclude that these children are victims of diabetic heredity. If there are any emotional or psychic symptoms, these presumably are the results, rather than the cause, of their condition, for once diabetes gets under way in a child, it may well create psychic problems."

What applies to these children also applies in large measure to older diabetics. Although with increasing age it is more likely that unfavorable diets or other factors may bring on or worsen the disease, diabetes in most cases is primarily the result of an inherited predisposition. Specifically, this "sugar sickness" is caused by the failure of the pancreas to secrete sufficient *insulin*, vitally necessary for the conversion of sugar in the body processes. This is why large amounts of sugar accumulate in the blood, leading to degeneration in the kidneys and also producing poisons that may cause death.

Studies by Dr. Elliott P. Joslin and his associates of Boston have shown that diabetic inheritance usually comes through a pair of simple *recessive genes*—one received from each of the individual's parents. Other types of transmission have been reported, but in any case, inheritance of "diabetic" genes does not necessarily portend the certain development of the disease. Diabetes may develop in some individuals (most commonly not until the middle years or later) only if they have unfavorable "fatty" diets, overeat, and become obese, or undergo excessive strains or (in occasional instances) suffer from certain diseases. It also is claimed that even without any hereditary predisposition diabetes develops in some individuals under such adverse circumstances, but there is no clear evidence as to just what proportion of diabetic cases are thus "acquired." Overweight people unquestionably have increased hazards in diabetes, but whether obesity goes with the diabetic constitution or tends to produce it, is another question.

What is certain is that under equal conditions heredity singles out some individuals and families far more than others for the development of the disease. Of the diabetics in the United States one in four has diabetic relatives, a far higher proportion than in the general population. Twin studies further support the evidence for heredity. In identical twins, where one has diabetes, the other almost invariably has the disease or shows a tendency toward it.*

Also to be noted is that diabetes is one of the few major diseases in which women are more vulnerable than men, deaths from diabetes claiming about 65 per cent more women. But in this case any inherent differences are heightened by other factors, including adversities of childbearing, the general greater susceptibility of women to glandular diseases, and the markedly longer life spans of women which puts more of them into the "diabetic" ages.

In fact, as with cancer and heart ailments, a growing diabetic incidence has attended the general increase in life spans for both men and women. In addition, insulin and other treatments have been

* A recent theory is that what diabetics may inherit, specifically, is a metabolic abnormality in which the tissues utilize or inactivate insulin in amounts greater than normal, putting an undue and damaging strain on the pancreas. (Dr. B. A. Houssay, 1947.)

keeping more diabetics alive, and for longer years. Studies at the Joslin Clinic show that before the discovery and use of insulin, in 1922, most children who developed diabetes died within a year, and few survived for very long thereafter. By 1945, the death rate among diabetic children at the age of 10 had been cut to 1 per cent of what it formerly was, and their average expectation of life had been raised to 45 years. Smaller but still substantial gains have been registered among diabetics at every age, although the expectation of life of diabetics at most ages remains about one-fourth less than for the general population.

At this writing there are a million known diabetics in the United States, and about 50,000 new cases are being added annually. But the indications that many more persons—perhaps another million—are diabetic without being aware of the fact, came from nationwide studies in 1947 and 1948. One survey, made in a "test town" in Massachusetts, revealed that for every four known diabetic cases there were three more which previously had been undetected and unsuspected. In more than a third of these cases there were family histories of the disease.

Incidentally, referring back to the diabetic cases in children, there may be a unique reversal of the usual procedure of forecasting inheritance of a disease. In most cases, where diabetes (or any other inherited diseases) has occurred among parents, doctors are on guard for its appearance in children. But, as Drs. R. T. Woodyatt and Marseille Spetz showed in their studies (1942), in some cases where there is a child with diabetes, careful examination of the presumably unaffected parents may reveal in one or the other, or both, either the disease itself or symptoms of its oncoming. However, the fact that diabetes usually is caused by recessive genes means that in most cases neither parent is afflicted, although each carries a "hidden" "diabetic" gene.

Thus, as in cancer and heart disease, a knowledge of hereditary threats in diabetes may aid in the early detection, prevention and treatment of the disease, and in helping to ease and prolong the lives of affected individuals. The "glucose tolerance" test, now in use, has proved highly valuable in identifying individuals who are "prediabetic" or have a susceptibility to developing diabetes. Among women having children, a special clue may be offered if babies are born unusually large—ten pounds or over. It has been found that in a great many cases women having extremely oversize babies tend to be pre-diabetic, with the likelihood of developing diabetes within twenty years.

But the continuing dangers of diabetes should not be minimized, nor is undue optimism regarding its control warranted. As Dr. Henry Dolger reported in 1947, while immediate dangers of diabetes can be reduced through insulin treatment, the victims "with few exceptions cannot escape progressive damage to the blood vessels, especially in the eyes." Unless means are found not merely to treat diabetes, but to *cure* it, this disease will continue to be—and ever-increasingly as the numbers of those afflicted increase—one of the worst of those which can be blamed on "black" genes.

We have been speaking thus far of *diabetes mellitus,* or true diabetes. Several unrelated hereditary conditions, some of whose symptoms approximate those of diabetes, are often confused with it and cause unnecessary fear.

Diabetes insipidus is related to true diabetes only in name and in the fact that, as in diabetes mellitus, there may be abnormal thirst and frequent urination. Aside from the possible inconvenience, it need have no harmful effects. There is no abnormal production of sugar in the blood or urine, and there is no danger that the condition will develop into true diabetes. This condition also is different in that it is believed to be a pituitary gland disorder and is almost always inherited through a *simple dominant gene.*

Sugar urine (renal glycosuria) is the condition in which there is an excessive amount of sugar in the urine, but with none of the harmful effects which attend a similar symptom in diabetes. It is inherited, probably, as a dominant.

TUBERCULOSIS. Here is a disease regarding which almost all the facts are now on the optimistic side. Fifty years ago the "No. 1 Killer" among diseases, particularly among younger people, tuberculosis deaths have been dropping so precipitately that by the end of this century the disease may be all but wiped out in the United States.

What is most significant is that for a long time tuberculosis was thought of as in large measure "hereditary." But as it became known that the disease was caused by a germ (the *tubercle bacillus*), that it was most prevalent in slum areas or wherever living conditions were the worst, and that it was spread by direct personal contacts, the factor of "heredity" began to be minimized. Nevertheless, there is still the question of whether or not, where the germs flourish and the same bad conditions are present, some individuals may be more susceptible to the development of the disease than others because of *inherited constitutional differences.*

Evidence on the latter point has been offered in a number of studies. Drs. Franz J. Kallmann and David Reisner, on the basis of extensive studies of tuberculous twins, concluded (1943) that the chances of developing tuberculosis or of resisting it were much influenced by one's inherited constitution, although any gene mechanism involved was probably a complex one. Studies by Dr. Ruth Puffer in Tennessee (1946) also stressed possible familial susceptibility to tuberculosis. Earlier, studies of lower animals (chiefly mice and rabbits) established that some strains were genetically more susceptible to the disease than others, but in these cases the experimenters were dealing with highly inbred strains for which there are no counterparts in human beings.

While it is more than likely that individual human beings differ in their reaction to tuberculosis (as to almost any disease), it is quite another matter to prove that there are such inherent differences among human *races.* For example, a common belief is that Negroes are much more susceptible than Whites to tuberculosis because—allegedly—they have "weaker respiratory systems." Unquestionably, the Negro tuberculosis death rate is vastly higher—fifteen times as much in some localities. But also without question, the general living conditions of Negroes are vastly worse. Equalize the conditions for Negroes and Whites and it is likely that their tuberculosis rates also would be equalized. For example, a personal check made by the author in Milwaukee in 1940 revealed these surprising facts: The tuberculosis mortality rate among Negroes living in a slum area was fifteen times as high as for Whites of the city. But a generation before (in 1915), the rate among Whites, mostly foreign-born, who lived in the same depressed environment *had been almost exactly the same as it now was among the Negroes who succeeded them there.* And among descendants of those same Whites, now living elsewhere and under much better conditions than their forebears, *the tuberculosis mortality rate had dropped to one-fifteenth*—to the same rate current for other Whites in the city. The rule that the tuberculosis rate goes precisely down or up like a seesaw as living conditions rise or drop has been grimly illustrated by the situation in Europe. In the aftermath of World War II, the rampant poverty and starvation in Germany, Poland, Roumania and other countries jumped the tuberculosis rate to the point where the disease once again became the "No. 1 Killer."

The one unquestioned fact, then, is that whatever hereditary differences there conceivably might be among human beings with regard to tuberculosis resistance or susceptibility, the incidence of the disease is overwhelmingly dictated by the conditions under which they live. And if these conditions improve to what they should be, while at the same time cures for the disease grow in effectiveness, the question of what rôle heredity plays in tuberculosis will become purely academic. For there won't be any more "T.B."

Pneumonia has even less to be said about it from the hereditary angle than has tuberculosis. In only a few studies has there been any suggestion that the onset or course of this disease (or of influenza) is in any way affected by specific hereditary factors, and evidence on this score is extremely flimsy. What we know is that pneumonia and influenza are purely environmental in their causation, and with new preventives and methods of treatment (penicillin, sulfa and other antibiotics, etc.) their hazards are being steadily reduced

GOITER. In the common, simple form of this disease, which is attended by a swelling of the thyroid gland in the throat, the possible rôle of heredity is still open to doubt. This is because development of the disease is so largely dependent on a specific environmental factor: lack of sufficient iodine in the food or drinking water, with a resultant strain on the thyroid gland whose function it is to abstract and utilize this chemical.

But there is also the possibility that some inherent weakness in the thyroid gland of certain individuals prevents them from making full use of the iodine supply that is available. Thus, in regions where there is an iodine insufficiency, as in places far from the sea, only some of the persons—often only certain members in a given family—develop the disease; and in regions where iodine is plentiful, there still are some individuals who develop the condition. It is on this premise that the theory of goiter inheritance rests. Some studies have suggested a "qualified" dominant gene, others, recessive genes, as responsible for goiter susceptibility. But the evidence is inconclusive.

On the other hand, there is no question but that the major threats of goiter can be overcome easily by insuring sufficient iodine in diets. In one experiment made some years ago among schoolgirls at Akron, Ohio, in the so-called "goiter belt" of the Great Lakes region, it was shown that of 2,100 who were given supplementary iodine for three years, only five developed goiter, as compared with 495 goiter cases which developed among 2,305 of their schoolmates whose diet was not so supplemented.

What is most striking about goiter is its far higher incidence among females—at least four women being afflicted to every man. Apparently, the proper functioning of the female system requires more iodine than does that of the male, and as a result, if there is an iodine insufficiency, or—theoretically—if there is any inherent thyroid weakness in a family, the females are much more likely to develop goiter. One of the most unfortunate consequences of thyroid deficiency in a mother, in some cases, may be the birth of a *cretin* (a type of mentally defective child which will be discussed at more length in the "Slow Minds" chapter).

Exophthalmic goiter (or Graves' disease) differs from common goiter in a number of respects, chiefly in that it results from an overactivity of the thyroid for which the cause is not known, and has more serious consequences, taking the lives of close to 3,000 women and 600 men in the United States annually. Protruding eyes are a characteristic symptom, in addition to the glandular swelling. The disease occurs most frequently among young adults—chiefly female—of highly nervous temperament and of narrow, light build (which constitutional factors may be either cause or effect). As in common, or simple, goiter, inheritance of the disease has been claimed by way of "qualified" dominant genes, or of recessive genes, but again adequate proof is lacking.

DIGESTIVE DISEASES. There are a great many diseases associated with the digestive organs and processes, some high up on the list of "killers," but with the exception of diabetes, none of the common ones can be conclusively blamed on "black" genes.

Ulcers of the stomach and intestines, growing in incidence and as causes of death, have been regarded in many quarters as almost entirely due to excessive nervous strain, but this may be too sweeping a conclusion. One authority, Dr. Andrew C. Ivy of Chicago, reported (1946) that nearly half of the stomach ulcers can *not* be attributed to worry, anxiety or any particular "personality" type. Among the reasons for suspecting some constitutional factors (related to the internal environment) as at least influencing the condition, is the fact that the incidence of the disease is so much higher among men—with deaths four times as great—as among women. It also has been claimed that ulcers go with certain types of body build. But while some investigators report a higher than average incidence of ulcers in certain families, the "inheritance" of ulcers remains doubtful.

Among the kidney diseases, *nephritis,* the most common one and a leading cause of death, offers little evidence of direct heredity. In women it often is one of the adverse aftereffects of pregnancy, but nonetheless, the incidence of the disease is higher among men. *Polycystic* disease of the kidneys, a rare disorder which is especially serious in pregnant women, is considered hereditary. While the manner of transmission is uncertain, it has been recently reported as dominant in some pedigrees.

Appendicitis offers little evidence of any direct heredity, but some suspicion of an hereditary influence may arise from the fact that the condition occurs with much more than average frequency in some families. One theory is that a "predisposition" to inflammation of the appendix may be involved.

Deaths from *premature birth* are undoubtedly in many cases associated with genetic defects in the children, but what proportion of these fatalities can be blamed on heredity is not known—the probability being, however, that the great majority are due primarily to prenatal mishaps or other environmental factors.

This, then, completes our discussion of inheritance in the major *"killers"* (although we still have much more ground to cover on the "black" genes). What we have found so far is that direct and simple inheritance is the chief factor in only one of these major conditions—diabetes, and a contributing factor in one of the principal heart afflictions, rheumatic heart disease. Also, that heredity is probably an *influence* (but certainly not a simple or direct cause) in other of the major heart and arterial conditions, and to a lesser degree may be an influence in the common cancers. What rôle heredity may have in common goiter, nephritis, ulcers, appendicitis, etc., remains to be established. Least certain is the influence of heredity on any of the major infectious diseases (pneumonia, tuberculosis, syphilis, etc.), where its part can be only that of making some individuals more vulnerable than others to given infections because of general differences in biological makeup. This latter fact, however, applies to almost any disease, and is most clearly revealed in further comparisons between the two sexes, to which we now turn.

CHAPTER 22

THE POOR MALES

"IT's a man's world!" Women have been saying this, and flattered men have believed it, no doubt from the beginning of time.

But in one important respect it's all wrong. In health and physical well-being—not only as applied to the major conditions we've discussed, but also to the great majority of other afflictions—the human female, from *before* birth and throughout life, is favored far above the male.

The reasons for much of this discrimination are now clear. First, there are the general sex differences in the makeup and functioning of the body, which endow the female with many advantages in resisting or overcoming most diseases. Second, the male is much more vulnerable to many directly hereditary diseases and defects, as we'll presently explain. Third, there are environmental factors, such as differences in occupations, habits and behavior, which expose the male to greater hazards. But these differences in the paths taken by the two sexes are in themselves, to a considerable extent, outgrowths of inherent sex differences.* In short, the margin of advantage which women have over men with regard to physical defectiveness or mortality is much less due to environmental factors than is generally supposed.

Long before anyone can talk of males leading "rougher and faster" lives the discrimination is apparent. Even in prenatal life, as we've seen, the male is more vulnerable to almost every adversity, a much higher proportion of males than females being carried off before birth. Further, more males die a-borning, more come into the world with congenital abnormalities, and in the first year of life, the average death rate among boy infants is 30 per cent higher than

* Detailed discussions of the sex differences in disease, defect and longevity, and of the biological and environmental factors contributing to these differences, will be found in the author's *"Women and Men,"* particularly on pp. 58-71 and 162-67.

among girls. Even if a boy baby and a girl baby should both tumble down the steps—or have any other accident of exactly the same kind—the chances of fatality are markedly greater for the boy.

As childhood proceeds, and as the chief hazards are reduced for a while, the differences between the sexes in mortality diminish considerably, but with male casualties still always in the lead. Then with maturity the curve goes sharply up again, becoming more marked in the middle and older ages, where in almost every major affliction, except in diabetes, cancers peculiar to women (breast, womb and ovary) and goiter, the male death rate is much higher. (By an excess of 40 per cent for males in diseases of the heart, 130 per cent in diseases of the arteries and angina pectoris, 100 per cent in cirrhosis of the liver, 400 per cent in ulcers, etc.) Further, the more that environmental factors for the two sexes have been improved and equalized, the proportionately greater has been the advantage to women, and *the more apparent it has become that females are genetically better constructed, have a more efficient internal chemical system, and in various other ways are biologically better adapted to resist most of the modern human afflictions.*

But in addition to all their general disadvantages, males from the beginning have one special handicap in the fact that Nature has *short-changed* them in some of their genes. You will recall from the "Boy or Girl?" chapter that at conception the female is started off with *two* X chromosomes (one from each parent), while the male gets only the single X from his mother, plus the very small Y from his father. And if any "black" genes are in the male's X chromosome, it's usually far more dangerous for him than it would be for his sister even if she got the very same X. This is always so when the defective gene is recessive, as it most often is. Here's why:

Where a female gets a recessive "black" gene in one of her X chromosomes, the chances are there will be a normal gene for the job in her other X. (Like a motorist with a spare tire when there's a blow-out.)

But if a male gets such a black gene in his single X, he's in a bad spot, because most often there is no corresponding gene in his very small Y chromosome to do the job. (So he's like a motorist who hasn't any spare tire.) Inasmuch, then, as there are a great many recessive genes in the X chromosome which every so often are defective, males, by and large, are directly exposed at conception to many more special defects and afflictions than are females.* At the same time, in the fact that the male's X can come only from his mother, we have the explanation for a long-standing mystery as to why certain diseases are transmitted *only by way of mothers to their sons.*

HEMOPHILIA. Most famous of the "sex-linked" conditions is this bleeding disease, which results when the "blood-coagulating" gene, located on the X chromosome, is defective. Usually it means death in early life, but if the afflicted male survives to manhood (never much beyond) he often becomes crippled by bleeding into the joints. While hemophilia is comparatively rare, it has been given much prominence in recent decades by this dramatic fact:

A single gene for hemophilia, passed on through Queen Victoria to one of her great-grandsons, the last little Czarevitch, may well have been a motivating factor in bringing on the Russian Revolution and in changing the course of the world's history.

As the world knows, it was because of their son's affliction that the credulous Czar and Czarina became victims of the designing Rasputin, who held out hopes of a cure through supernatural powers. From Rasputin, as from a spider, spread a web of intrigue, cruelty, debauchery, demoralization and mass indignation which helped to bring on the collapse of the empire and all the subsequent political developments. *If* the Czarevitch hadn't had hemophilia, *if* his parents hadn't become the prey of Rasputin, *if* Rasputin hadn't demoralized the court. . . . Thus a momentous structure of "ifs" can be built up, like an inverted pyramid, resting on that infinitesimal bit of substance, constituting a single gene, which found its way to one sad little boy.

In all, ten of Victoria's male descendants have suffered from hemophilia, and seven of her female descendants were carriers of the gene. Prince Leopold, one of Victoria's four sons, was definitely hemophiliac, and another son, who died young, also may have been. Of Victoria's five daughters, three—Victoria, Alice and Beatrice—were carriers, as were two granddaughters, the last Czarina, who bore one hemophiliac son, and the last Queen of Spain, who bore

* That there is a greater prenatal hazard in having only a single X chromosome seems to be borne out by this fact: In poultry, where the sex-determination mechanism is the reverse of what it is in human beings and other mammals (as we reported in Chapter 8), and it is the *females* who have only one X whereas the males have two Xs, the embryonic deaths are much higher among the females. (The facts with respect to chicks were summarized by Dr. F. A. Hays in *Science,* Nov. 18, 1949.)

two. (Of the latter, one died from bleeding as a child, the other died following an automobile accident in Florida in 1938.)

What of the present British royal family? Prior to the birth of a son in 1948 to Princess Elizabeth and her husband, *both* descendants of Queen Victoria, many were concerned about the possibility of its

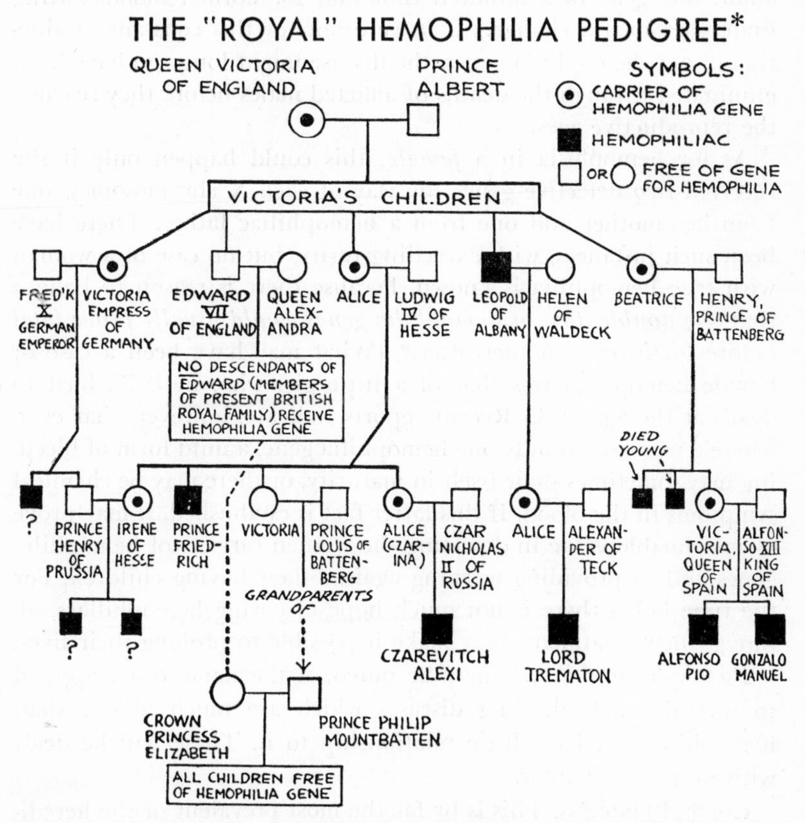

***Only some of the members of each of the families represented are shown here. The Chart is based on a diagram and data compiled by Dr. Hugo Iltis. (*Journal of Heredity*, April, 1948.)**

being a hemophiliac. Happily, geneticists were able to give assurance that there was no fear whatsoever of this occurring. Inasmuch as the great-grandfather of Princesses Elizabeth and Rose, King Edward VII, definitely did not receive the dread gene, there is no possibility that they could be carrying it; and the fact that Princess Elizabeth's husband, Philip Mountbatten, is not a hemophiliac, is proof that he is also free of the gene.

Of special interest to geneticists is the fact that the particular hemophilia gene passed on by Queen Victoria appears to have arisen through a *mutation* (a sudden change), either in her or her mother. It is precisely in this way that many other cases of hemophilia are known to arise. (Professor J. B. S. Haldane estimates that about one gene in a hundred thousand for normal blood-clotting undergoes such a change.) If it were not for this constant production of new hemophilia genes, the disease might long ago have been eliminated through the deaths of afflicted males before they reached the reproductive ages.

As for hemophilia in a *female,* this could happen only if she received *two* defective genes (by way of each X chromosome), one from her mother and one from a hemophiliac father. There have been such instances, with exceeding rarity, but no case of a woman with true hemophilia is known, because there is reason to believe that *any double dose of hemophilia genes would usually prove fatal before birth* or soon thereafter.* (What may have been a case of female hemophilia was that of a little girl who, in 1947, bled to death at the age of 3.) Recent reports indicate, however, that even where a woman has only one hemophilia gene, a mild form of bleeding may sometimes show itself in maturity, or there may be chemical symptoms in the blood. If this latter fact is established, it may prove of inestimable value in detecting the women carriers of hemophilia genes and in providing warning against their having children. For the time being there is not much hope of curing hemophiliacs, although new treatments may make it possible to prolong their lives.

Pseudo-hemophilia, it may be noted, is the name often applied to several other bleeding diseases which are much milder than hemophilia and have little relationship to it. These will be dealt with in a later chapter.

Color Blindness. This is by far the most prevalent of the hereditary sex-linked conditions afflicting chiefly males. As most everyone knows, color blindness in its common form is the inability to distinguish between red and green as *colors.* This does not mean—to answer a frequent question—that color-blind persons can't tell the

* In dogs, where hemophilia occurs as it does in humans, females with true hemophilia have now been produced by the process of mating hemophiliac males with female carriers. (Drs. Kenneth M. Brinkhous and John B. Graham, *Science,* June 30, 1950.) The findings suggested that the lack of female hemophilia cases in humans is mainly due to the extreme rarity, if not unlikelihood, of similar matings.

difference between a red traffic light and a green one, because the one appears to them different in intensity from the other. Nevertheless, the flat colors of red and green may not be so distinguished, and it is for this reason that so many color-blind men during World War II were barred from the Air Force and certain other branches of service where good color vision was essential.

About 4 per cent of the American males are definitely red-green color blind, and another 4 per cent are partially deficient with regard to red-green or some other type of color vision. This is at least eight times the incidence in women. (American Indians are reported as having only a fourth as much color blindness as Whites, and Negroes only half as much.)

Explaining the sex difference in color blindness is the same hereditary mechanism found in hemophilia. The "color-blindness" gene is also carried in the X chromosome, and if the one X that a male receives has that gene, he will be color blind. The man's X chromosome, remember, can come only from his mother, so, as with hemophilia, it is only through mothers that color blindness is transmitted to sons.

Where a woman carries one X with a defective color-vision gene, and her second X has a normal gene, there is a fifty-fifty chance that any son will be color blind. But if the mother herself is color blind, because she carries two defective genes—which happens to about one woman in 200—every one of her sons is almost certain to be color blind.

What about the daughters? Only if the father is color blind and the mother is a carrier of the gene, or is herself color blind, will a daughter be color blind. But there is a possibility that even with one defective gene a woman may be slightly red-green color blind, recent studies showing that in some cases the "normal" gene does not quite overcome the influence of the defective one. This has significance because in these cases the women who are carriers of the "color-blindness" gene may be identified.

Can environmental factors, as well as heredity, produce color blindness? Various theories to this effect have been advanced, among them that a vitamin A deficiency can cause defective color vision, or that dietary treatment can overcome it. But this has not been proved. Moreover, while color-blind individuals may be trained to more sharply discriminate between red and white on the basis of shade differences, there is little evidence at this writing that their

"SEX-LINKED" INHERITANCE

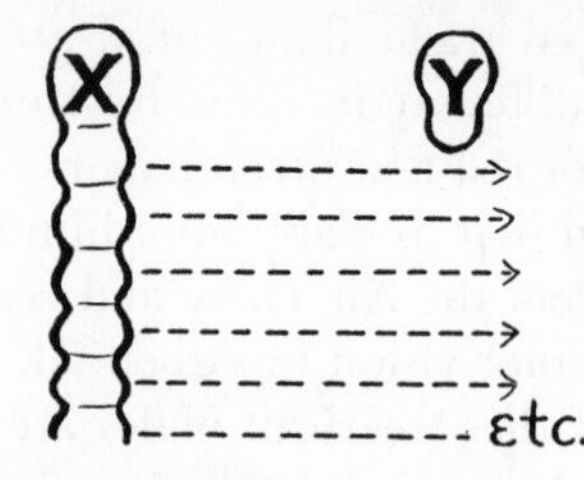
X
Y
etc.

The "X" chromosome is many times larger than the "Y."

The "Y" chromosome lacks duplicates of almost all the "X" genes.

If a recessive "black-X" gene is circulating in a family,
(A) for COLOR-BLINDNESS

DAUGHTER
Receiving one "color-blindness" gene usually has in her second "X" a normal gene to block it.

SON
Receiving a "color-blindness" gene in his single "X" has no normal gene to block it.

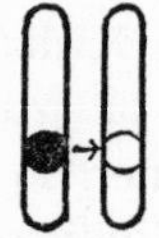

Result: Perfectly NORMAL (but a carrier)

Result: COLOR-BLIND

(B) "CRISS-CROSS" TRANSMISSION
As in Hemophilia

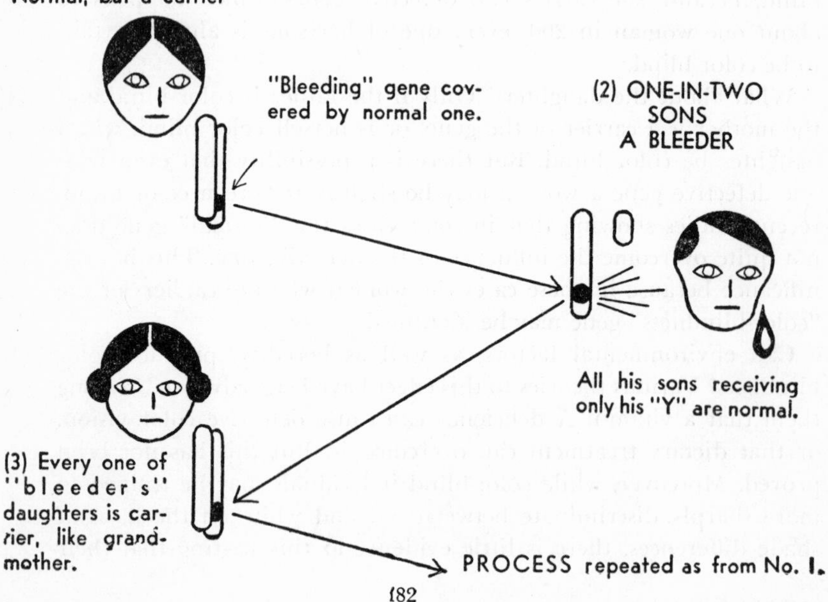
(1) WOMAN
Normal, but a carrier
"Bleeding" gene covered by normal one.
(2) ONE-IN-TWO SONS A BLEEDER
All his sons receiving only his "Y" are normal.
(3) Every one of "bleeder's" daughters is carrier, like grandmother.
PROCESS repeated as from No. I.

actual color vision can be permanently improved, not to say cured, by any known treatment. Apparently, color blindness results from a basic defect in the construction of the color-seeing mechanism in the eye.

Many other eye defects which strike particularly at males have been tracked down to "sex-linked" genes. Included are certain, but not all forms of extreme near-sightedness, oscillating eyes *(nystagmus)*, eye-muscle paralysis, enlarged cornea, defective iris, optic atrophy, and *retinitis pigmentosa* (in which the retina fills with pigment).

Altogether, eye defectiveness, *including blindness,* is far more prevalent among males than females. While only a few of the known sex-linked conditions directly produce blindness, some hereditary influences certainly contribute considerably to the much higher incidence of blindness among males. Making full allowances for the more frequent loss of eyesight among men through injuries and accidents, it is significant that the blind population in the United States starts off with about one-third more blind boys than girls, *three-fourths of these childhood cases originating before the fifth year, and more than half being of prenatal origin.* When we remember that the male in early life is inherently more vulnerable to almost every disease and defect, there is no reason to doubt that this applies also to blindness, even where there is no inheritance, as in congenital blindness due to syphilis or some other infectious disease.

OTHER SEX-LINKED CONDITIONS. *Speech disorders* provide another category in which males are overwhelmingly in the majority, but in this case there is as yet no clear proof that heredity is involved. We know only that stuttering is from five to ten times more common in little boys than in girls, the ratio increasing with age. *Reading difficulties* in school are also much more common among boys. While psychologists are inclined to attribute many cases of both speech and reading defects to early emotional disturbances or personality disorders, it is open to question whether environmental factors alone can explain away all the cases and the whole big difference between boys and girls in the incidence of these defects. Some inherent male weakness may well be involved. (There will be more on this in the chapter on "Functional Defects.")

We haven't by any means presented all of the hereditary conditions which afflict chiefly or exclusively males. For instance, the peculiar sweat-gland defect which makes the victim pant as dogs do, and a form of muscular atrophy where the man can't stand properly and appears to have a drunken gait. Many other known sex-linked conditions are too rare to warrant listing here, and there is every certainty that further research will lengthen the list of anti-male discriminators.

When we look for conditions that discriminate against women, we find very few, indeed, other than those related to the specifically female organs and functions. In all organic breakdowns (circulatory, respiratory, digestive, nervous system, etc.) male casualties are in the lead. The exception is only in glandular disorders (including diabetes, goiter, etc.), from which women suffer somewhat more. In childhood, there is only a single important disease which takes a higher toll of girls—whooping cough—where the year-in-and-out mortality excess of about 7 per cent more girls than boys remains a mystery.

But coming back to "sex-linked" genes, there are several of these which strike *particularly at women* for a very interesting reason:

In most of the other sex-linked conditions—hemophilia, color blindness, etc., the defective gene is recessive to the "normal" one. It is only because a male getting such a gene has *no "normal" one* to counteract it, as a woman usually has, that it asserts itself. But there are a few conditions which are caused by a *dominant* "black" gene in the X chromosome to which the "normal" gene is recessive. In such cases, women, therefore, would be particularly vulnerable because their *two* Xs open them to a double chance of getting the gene: If a father is affected, every daughter (but no son) will receive his single X with the defective gene, although if the mother is affected, there is the same fifty-fifty chance for either a son or a daughter to get the X with the gene. This explains the much higher incidence in women of one type of hereditary nosebleed, *thrombasthenia* (see Table III-B, p. 325) and another sex-linked condition which produces defective enamel in the teeth. Apart from these, no clearly established dominant X-gene condition of importance in human beings is now on record.

The genes in the little Y chromosome are still largely unknown. But it is apparent that any "black" genes occurring in this chromosome, and not duplicated in the X, would make matters still worse for the males, inasmuch as only a male can carry a Y. So far, the few identified Y-gene conditions are very rare ones, among them being one which causes an odd, bark-like skin on the body. All conditions thus produced by genes on the Y are passed on directly from fathers to sons.

In still another category are a number of conditions due to genes which occur *both in the Y chromosome and the X*. Such conditions can therefore afflict women equally with men. One of the most interesting examples is *total color blindness,* in which the color-discriminating cones in the retina are absent (leading also to in-

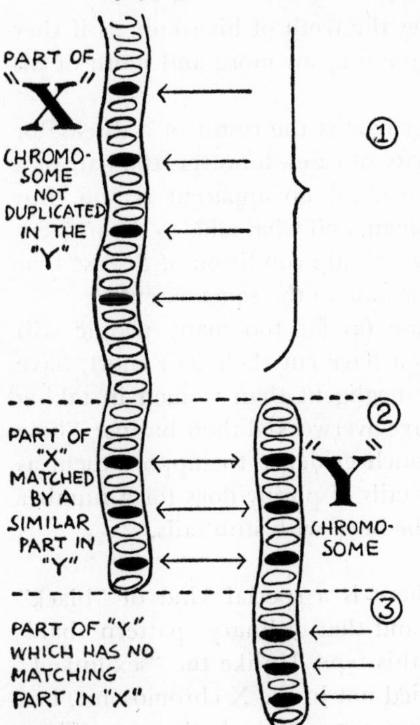

1. Genes found only in the "X." Any "black" gene here singly produces a defect in the MALE, but two of these genes (one in each "X") are required to produce the defect in the FEMALE.

2. "NEUTRAL" ("incompletely" sex-linked) genes, on the matching parts of the "X" and "Y." If any of these genes are defective, MALES and FEMALES are equally affected.

3. Exclusively "MALE" genes, found only in the "Y." Only MALES can be affected by these genes.

ability to see in bright daylight). In this defect, the afflicted person sees all colors only in shades of black and gray, as is the case with dogs and many other animals other than apes and human beings, so far as is known.

In all, about ten conditions have been found so far in which the same genes occur on either the Y or X chromosomes. Among them are a few other serious visual defects (*Oguchi's disease*—a form of night blindness—and several types of *retinitis pigmentosa*), and a skin disease *(xeroderma)*.

Finally, there is a special type of gene which offers one more genetic disadvantage to the male. The condition is not too serious—no man gets sick or dies of it—but it nonetheless causes much worry, leads to the wasted spending of millions of dollars annually, and otherwise is sufficiently important to many men to warrant considerable discussion. We refer to:

BALDNESS. Comes a time when the hair on the head of the rugged male begins to loose its hold like the seeds of an autumn dandelion, presently to be gone with the wind.

Dejectedly, fearfully, he watches the teeth of his comb, as if they were some devouring monster, gobbling up more and more of his precious locks. What to do?

In some cases, it is true, falling hair is the result of a disease or scalp disorder. In the great majority of cases, however, the hair of a man healthy in every way falls out for no apparent reason. But this almost never happens to a woman, and what adds to the mystery is that even if a woman has the same scalp condition or disease that a man has, rarely does she lose her hair to the same extent.

How explain this? Is it because (as far too many people still believe) that through the ages men have cut their hair short, have worn tight hats, have been more negligent than women in taking care of their hair and scalps—or have overworked their brains? These and similar statements have as much evidence to support them as the theory that if you cut off the tails of puppy dogs for a number of generations, the offspring will be born with stub tails.

What, then, is the explanation?

Geneticists have found that there is a special kind of "black" gene called a *"sex-limited"* gene, and that ordinary "pattern" baldness is inherited through one of this type. Unlike the "sex-linked" genes, a "sex-limited" gene is carried not in the X chromosome, but in one of the general chromosomes common to both sexes. Thus, the "baldness" gene can be inherited equally by a man or a woman. But it doesn't *act* the same way in both. It behaves like a *dominant* in a man, only *one* gene being required to produce baldness. In a woman, however, the gene acts as a *limited recessive:*

She must receive *two* "baldness" genes before she will be affected, and even then, only partial baldness or merely a thinning of the hair may result. Again, why?

The best theory is that the glandular makeup of the two sexes governs the way in which the gene expresses itself or doesn't. Apparently, in a woman the lack of an excess of "male" hormones (*androgens*) and the absence of their effects keeps the hair from falling out even where the baldness tendency is present, while, in a man, the excess of "male" hormones makes the hair follicles particularly vulnerable to the action of the "baldness" genes. Some remarkable evidence to support this assumption has been given in studies and experiments by Dr. James B. Hamilton. Following up previous reports that *eunuchs* were not known to develop baldness, he administered "male" hormones to a large group of men who had been demasculinized through accident or injury, or who for biological reasons had failed to mature sexually. Where previously not one case of baldness had appeared among these men, the addition of "male" hormones resulted in the loss of hair among many of them—particularly those from families in which baldness was common. On the other hand, Dr. Hamilton found evidence that no amount of "male" hormones will produce baldness in men who lack the hereditary tendency to it.

The foregoing makes hash of the popular notion, perhaps derived incorrectly from the Samson episode in the Bible, that a large amount of head hair is correlated with virility. Actually, we have the contrary: Once the "baldness" gene is present, the most "feminine" man—with a deficiency of "male" hormones—is most likely to retain his hair; the most "masculine" man—with an excess of "male" hormones—is most likely to lose his hair. However, without knowledge of the hereditary tendencies, the presence or absence of hair on a mature man can have no meaning in this sense. Similarly, there is little basis to the belief that "grass doesn't grow on busy streets," although if recent theories hold up—that thin scalps grow bald sooner than plump ones, and that nervous strain may hasten hair fall—intellectual men, tending to be both leaner and more worrisome, might lose their hair more quickly. But always, only if the "baldness" gene is present.

Degrees and specific types of pattern baldness are probably also inherited. (Precisely how hasn't yet been worked out.) Dr. Hamilton has made eight classifications (as shown on our Chart) ranging from Type I, where there is no hair loss at all, through to Type VIII, in which virtually all the hair is lost as time goes on. Intermediate is Type IV, with hair receding at the temples and a small bald spot in the center of the crown. This represents about the extreme of the baldness reached in women who have inherited the suscepti-

THE HEREDITARY "BALDNESS" TYPES

WHICH ONE ARE YOU?

TYPE **(A) NORMAL (NON-BALD)**

1

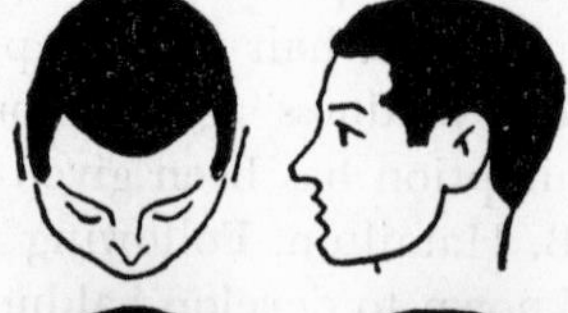

Hair retained throughout life. (In only about 4 per cent of adult White males, but in much higher proportion of Mongolians.)

2 AND 3

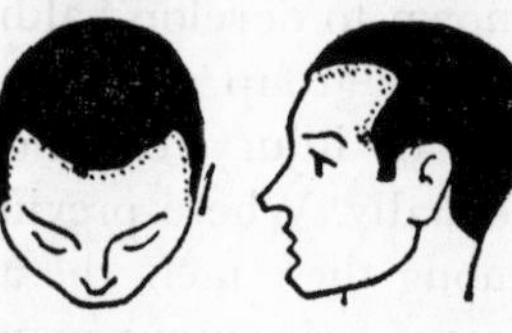

Slight hair loss at forehead and temples (not classified as baldness).

Type 3: Uncertain cases (with causes of hair loss in doubt) and borderline cases between Types 2 and 4.

(B) TRUE BALDNESS TYPES

4

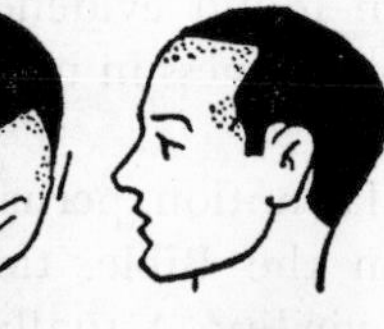

Marked loss of hair at forehead, temples and sides (and in older men also small bald spot at crown). Women very rarely pass further than this type of baldness.

5

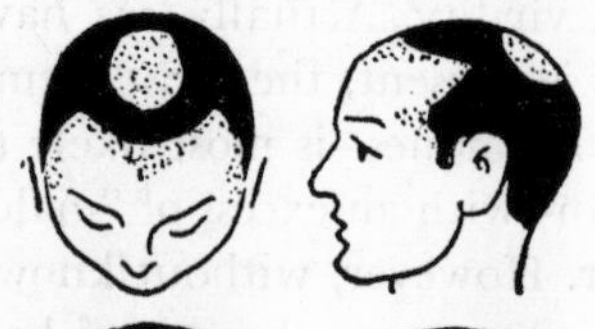

Extensive bald spot at crown, with considerable hair loss at forehead and sides (usually in older men). Types 5 to 8, inclusive, occur in about 60 per cent of males after age 50.

6

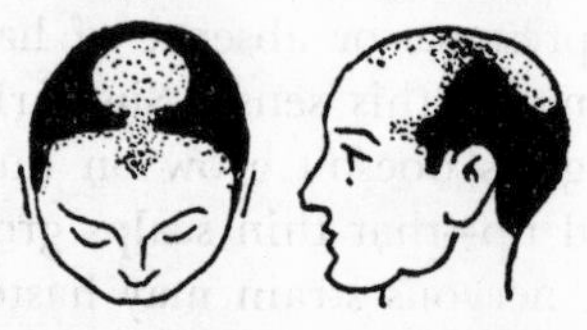

Baldness all the way from forehead to crown.

7

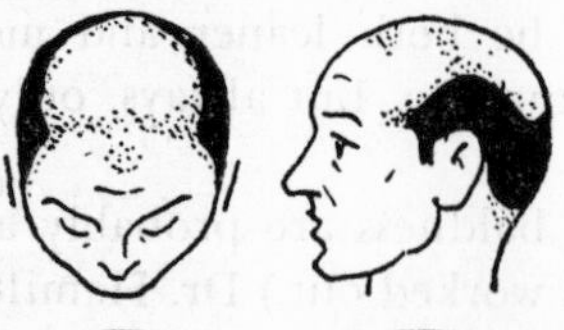

"Shiny" spot all the way across crown, but with bridge of sparse hair.

8

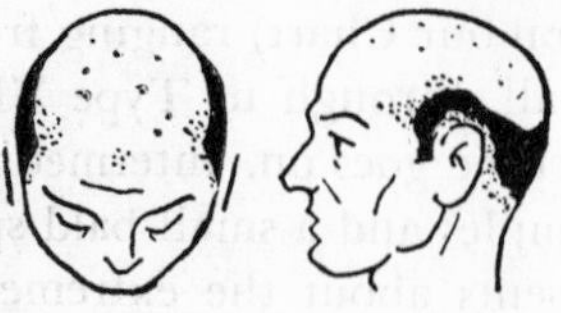

Almost completely bald, with only sparse hair over ears and around in back.

Prepared from data and sketches by Dr. James B. Hamilton.

bility. In general, Dr. Hamilton estimates that only about 4 per cent of the men in the White population are lucky enough to be of Type I (with no hair loss at all in maturity), as compared with 20 per cent of the women who are of this type.

The reference to the White population is made because there are important hereditary differences among racial groups with respect to balding tendencies. Whites are the most susceptible to baldness (those of eastern Mediterranean stock most of all). There is less baldness among Negroes, and still less among the Mongolians. This is exactly the reverse of the race differences with respect to the degree of facial and body hair, for, as was brought out in our "Feature" chapter, it is the Whites, generally, who have the most hair on their faces and bodies, the Mongolians the least, with Negroes intermediate. How account for this inverse *racial* correlation between the tendency to lose hair on the head and to grow it elsewhere? It doesn't apply to individuals within a race, because studies show that men who retain their hair may be as likely as balding men to have heavy beards and hairy chests. (The exception is in the case of eunuchs, previously discussed.) Nor have hormonal tests of Whites in comparisons with Mongolians or Chinese shown any special differences in amounts of the "male" hormones, which bring out the balding tendency. The indications are, therefore, that the "baldness" genes are inherited independently from those governing facial- or body-hair growth, and that it is merely a coincidence that both types of genes are present in different proportions among the racial groups.

At any rate, can we predict whether a given man will become bald? Within reasonable limits, yes. If a man's father was bald, there is at least a fifty-fifty chance that he also will become bald eventually. This chance is increased if baldness has been common among men in his mother's family (her father, brothers, etc.). Specifically, chances of baldness inheritance depend on whether a man's parents are of the "*two* baldness-gene," "*one* baldness-gene," or "*no* baldness-gene" types, which may be roughly guessed at by observance of his close male relatives on both sides, including older brothers, if he has them. Where either father or mother carry *two* "baldness" genes—and particularly, in infrequent cases, where both do—a son reaching maturity had better plan on having a shiny pate or wearing a toupee.

In addition to the ordinary "pattern" baldness, there are a num-

HOW BALDNESS IS INHERITED

. . . "BALDNESS" GENE (Symbol).

In *Men*—Dominant. One produces baldness.

In *Women*—Recessive or completely suppressed. Two genes required to produce any degree of baldness in a woman.

. . . "NORMAL HAIR" GENE (Symbol).

MEN

Type A

TWO "BALDNESS" GENES

(All of this man's sons will be bald, and if wife is Type A, daughters also)

Type B

SINGLE "BALDNESS" GENE

(Same effect as two genes, but only one-in-two sons of this man will be bald)

Type C

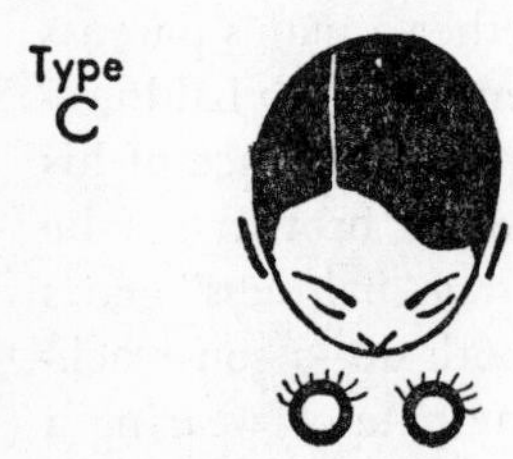

TWO "NORMAL" GENES

No baldness in this man's sons unless his wife is Type A or Type B

WOMEN

Type A

TWO "BALDNESS" GENES

Produces thin hair or partial baldness in women. (All sons will be bald)

Type B

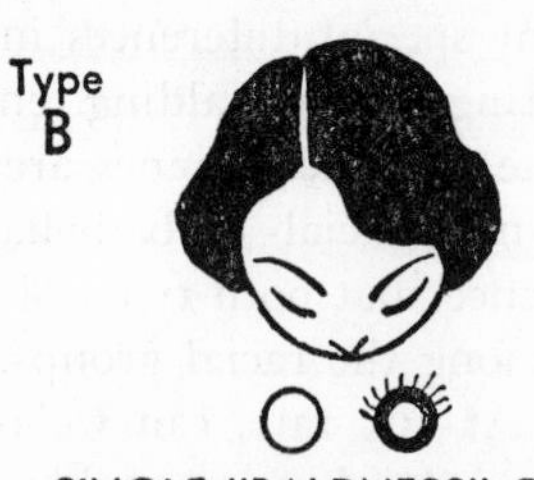

SINGLE "BALDNESS" GENE

No effect on woman herself, but one-in-two sons will be bald

Type C

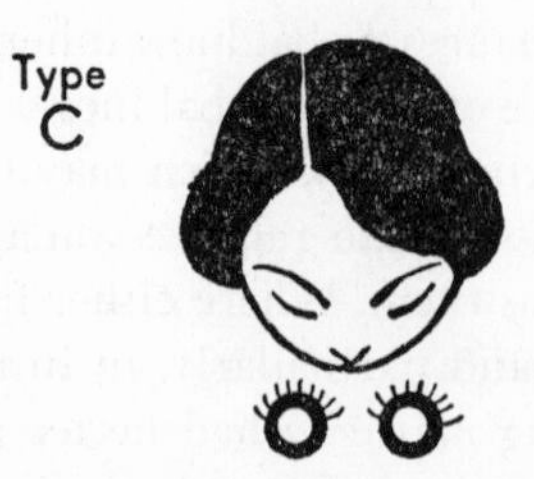

TWO "NORMAL" GENES

No baldness in this woman's sons unless her husband is bald

ber of less common types of baldness, whole or partial, which have an hereditary basis. These, however, are not due to "sex-limited" genes, and affect females as well as males. (Complete hairlessness and congenital hairlessness are discussed in the chapter following.) But always keep in mind that there are a number of non-hereditary causes of baldness, which include various infectious diseases, fevers, diabetes, certain glandular and nervous ailments, local scalp disorders, etc. Some of these conditions produce only temporary hair fall; in others, the resulting hair loss may be permanent. (However, ordinary *dandruff* or even *seborrhea*, a disorder of the oil glands in the scalp, have not been proved to be causes of baldness, whatever the "baldness" institutes or hair-drug advertisements may imply.)

The whole situation with respect to baldness was thoroughly analyzed at a conference of leading hair specialists at the New York Academy of Sciences in February, 1950. The conclusions were that hereditary "pattern" baldness is the result of a natural process in many individuals (perhaps, as Dr. Marion Sulzberger said, a step in evolutionary development, like losing our tails). *No cure was reported,* and many of the specialists doubted that any cure is in sight. (Advertising of any baldness "cure" is now forbidden by the government.)

To emphasize the foregoing, the author might cite a story from his own experience. Some years ago, while living in Paris, I grew concerned about my undue hair fall, and went to see one of the outstanding hair specialists of France. First, an assistant made a thorough examination, took a careful case history and wrote out a report. Then I was ushered into the inner sanctum of *le Professeur* himself. The great man glanced at the report, looked at me, then smilingly bent over. In the center of his head was a very large bald spot!

"Voilà," he said. There was an eloquent silence. The writer sadly asked, *"Il n'y a rien à faire?"* ("Is there nothing one can do?")

"Oui," answered the great specialist. *"Il faut choisir vos parents!"*

Which means, simply, "The one thing you can do is to pick your parents." (He might have added, "—and your sex.")

We can joke about hereditary baldness because, as we said, it has no relationship to a man's health. But as we think back to all the other evidence about the male's greater inherent disadvantages, the facts have very serious implications. Further, peculiar as it may seem, we have the situation mentioned earlier that as environments have improved, the genetic disadvantages of males have become even more marked in comparison with females. Why? Because where conditions are very bad, the female's extra margin of resistance isn't sufficient to make much difference. But the more conditions improve, the more that slight advantage of the female may count in preventing a disease from developing, or in permitting her to pull through in a serious illness or accident where a male might succumb.

All of this (which will be amplified in our later chapter on "Longevity") should prompt us to give decent burial to the age-old fallacy that men are hardier than women, and, particularly, that little boys are "sturdier" and require less attention than their (presumably) "more delicate" little sisters. Where this fallacy may have arisen is in the notion that bigger bones and heavier muscles must necessarily mean greater resistance to disease and death. But as the author has pointed out elsewhere, people might do well to recall the parable of the sturdy oak and the frail reed, and what happened to each in the thunderstorm.

Photographed under direction of the author by M. Lasser (1950). Courtesy of Ringling Brothers

THE "UNDERSIZED" AND "OVERSIZED"

Two types of "little people," with a "giant" and a "fat lady."

Shown here are, front row (first four), a rare family of midgets or "Lilliputians," the "Dolls" (neé Schneider), three sisters and a brother, aged respectively (reading from left), 38, 50, 34 and 48. All were born in Dresden, Germany, of normal-sized parents, and have four normal-sized sisters.

Alongside the "Dolls" are two unrelated *achondroplastics,* Frankie Saluto (42, born in Boston), and Jimmy Armstrong (31, born in Oklahoma).

The "giant," Jacob Nacken, 7 feet 4 inches ("small" for a circus giant), is 44 years old, vigorous, and apparently of the hereditary, non-pathological type. A "displaced person" from Germany, he was in active service in the German army for five years. Extreme tallness runs in his family. Maternal grandfather, 6 feet 7 inches; father, 6 feet 4 inches; mother, 6 feet; two brothers, 6 feet 10 inches and 6 feet 3 inches, respectively, and a sister (now aged 55), 6 feet 4 inches.

The "fat lady," Irene Perry, 540 pounds (apparently glandular, non-hereditary) was born in Detroit. All members of her immediate family were or are of normal weight.

1938:

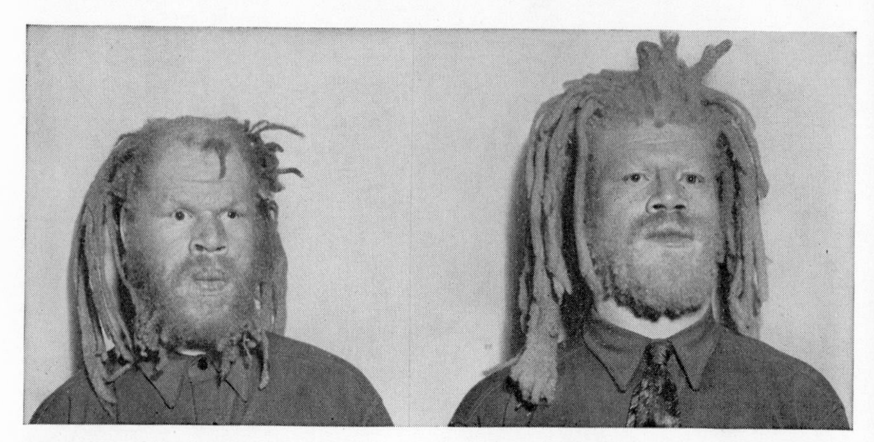

1950:

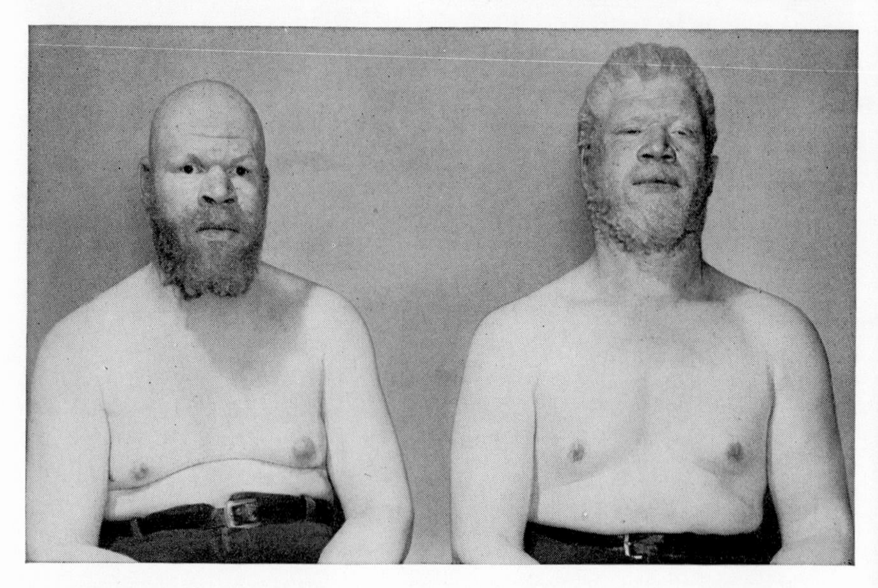

These Negro albino brothers are shown as they looked in 1938 (above) when photographed for the first edition of this book, and in 1950 (below, at left, "Iko," aged 56, and right, "Eko," 57). Born of black parents in Roanoke, Va., and otherwise Negroid, the brothers are typical albinos. They have very white skins, pale blue eyes and yellowish hair (the odd effects being produced by letting their woolly strands grow out for exhibition purposes, although one of the brothers, as may be seen, is now almost completely bald). Both have *nystagmus* (oscillating eyeballs), and defective teeth, characteristic of many albinos.

(Upper photograph arranged through courtesy of Ringling Brothers' circus; lower photograph arranged by Rex D. Billings, Belmont Amusement Park, Montreal.)

CHAPTER 23

FAULTY CONSTRUCTION

WE ARE so accustomed to seeing human beings almost uniform in their construction that we can hardly help staring (unless we're very polite and mature) at anyone who deviates noticeably from the expected pattern.

The surface abnormalities, being most easily detected and classified, have been most intensively studied from the standpoint of inheritance. In fact, the very first condition in humans for which Mendelian inheritance was established was *brachyphalangy* (stub fingers), which, back in 1904, a few years after the science of genetics was born, was proved to be a dominant condition. Not long after, *polydactylism* (extra fingers and toes) was also shown to be due to a dominant gene. But almost two thousand years before, Pliny, the Roman author, had reported the case of a nobleman with six fingers and six toes, "and his daughters likewise, whereupon they were named *Sedigitae*." (C. Plinius Secundus, in his *Natural History*.)*

At circus or carnival sideshows you can see some of the more startling examples of "black" gene caprice—midgets, freaks with distorted bodies or features, Negro albinos, "India-rubber" men, and other types we shall deal with. A great many of the freak individuals result not from heredity but from abnormal conditions before birth or after. However, many hundreds of inherited structural abnormalities have now been identified. We shall confine ourselves here to those which are most common, conspicuous or otherwise important.

STATURE. Midgets, or "Lilliputians," always have been of engrossing interest. Technically known as *ateleiotic* dwarfs, they stop growing early in childhood because of an inherited deficiency in the pituitary, or "growth" gland, and do not reach beyond 3 feet

* An earlier reference to this condition, though not linked with heredity, will be found in the Bible (II Samuel, 21:20), which speaks of a six-fingered-and-toed warrior.

6 inches in height.* (One of the smallest midgets, Martina de la Cruz, 21 inches tall, died in Georgia in 1949 at the age of 74.) Where they differ markedly from other dwarfs is in their having normal proportions, which gives them their appealing doll-like appearance. In contrast are the misshapen *achondroplastic* dwarfs (the funny little bow-legged men of the circuses) who have normally sized torsos but are dwarfed because they have stunted arms and legs. (Also, usually, oversized heads and pug noses.) Moreover, where midgets generally are sexually underdeveloped or sterile, the achondroplastic dwarfs are normal in all respects except body form, their abnormality being caused, apparently, not by any basic glandular disorder but merely by peculiar workings of their "structural" genes. (While in prenatal life achondroplastics have a high mortality state, once they survive infancy they are as sturdy and as long-lived as normal persons.)†

In manner of inheritance, also, there are marked differences between the two dwarf types. The genetic mechanism responsible for midgets probably involves two separate rare dominant genes, although in some families inheritance seems to have been simple recessive. However, in the infrequent instances where midgets are able to have children they are not likely to reproduce their type, their offspring tending to be normal, and so it is from normal parents that midgets almost always derive. In achondroplastic dwarfs, however, inheritance usually is more direct and may be due to a single dominant gene. The fact that in many cases there are no previous achondroplastics in a family might indicate that the gene for this condition often arises through a sudden mutation. Whatever the causes, achondroplastic dwarfs are much more common than midgets, whole families of them occurring here and there.

Pygmies are in a different category from either of the dwarf types mentioned. These undersized peoples, found largely in Negroid groups of Africa, and in New Guinea, the Philippines and Malay (but also reported among South African Indians), average about 4 feet 6 inches in height. They are generally regarded as merely products of "small stature" genes, the theory that some pygmies are achondroplastic dwarfs having been questioned.

* In a milder form of pituitary dwarfism, individuals may grow to 4 feet 6 inches, putting them out of the midget class.

† The Orthodox Hebrew prayer book takes note of dwarfs and giants. On seeing one of these, the pious Jew is urged to say, "Blessed art thou, O Lord, who variest the forms of Thy creatures." (*Standard Prayer Book,* p. 432.)

THE DUCTLESS GLANDS

	NORMAL FUNCTION:	IF DERANGED MAY PRODUCE:
Pituitary	—"Pacemaker." Regulates growth and development; stimulates sex-functioning.	—Structural defects such as gigantism, dwarfism, acromegaly and sexual disorders.
Thyroid	—"Thermostat." Regulates metabolism.	—Goitre, cretinism, myxedema.
Parathyroids	—Govern bone-formation and "tone" nervous system.	—Bone softening. Also, spasms (tetany).
Pancreas	—"Sugar" gland. Produces insulin, regulating sugar-conversion.	—Diabetes.
Adrenals	—"Emotional" glands. Affect nervous, emotional and sex processes.	—Addison's disease. Also, in females, secondary male characteristics; in boys, premature growth.
Gonads	—Sex glands (Ovaries in women, testes in men). Affect sex processes and characteristics.	—Sterility. "Maleness" in females, "femaleness" in males. Various sexual disorders.

Before taking leave of the undersized people, it is worth noting that parallels to all these human types are found throughout the lower animal kingdom. In dogs, bulldogs and dachshunds are achondroplastics (with the characteristic stunted and bowed limbs), and Pekingese, Chihuahuas and other "toy" types are midgets. Achondroplastic sheep—the Ancon short-legged breed—were in favor many years ago among canny New England farmers because they couldn't jump fences. Other dwarf species have been bred or pop up spontaneously in almost all species of domestic animals, and occur regularly among birds and fish.

At the extreme opposite pole of stature abnormalities are *giants.* Although seven-footers may be direct results of "tall stature" genes, the cases where men reach heights approaching or over 8 feet can be ascribed almost invariably to some early derangement of the glandular system, usually extreme overactivity of the pituitary. Of this type was Robert Wadlow (the Alton, Pennsylvania, giant) tallest of all humans known to medical science, who reached a height of 8 feet 10 inches and was still growing when he died in 1940, aged 22. Gigantism in dogs, such as Great Danes and St. Bernards, is not an analogous condition, because while unusually active glands probably contribute to their growth, this gland action is hereditary, and is linked with other genetic factors for bigness.

Extreme obesity, of the circus "fat lady" kind (distinguished from ordinary obesity which we discussed in an earlier chapter), also is a glandular disorder, but whether heredity plays any rôle in this is uncertain. Although cases are on record of mother-and-daughter circus fat ladies, the prenatal glandular influence of the mother on the child might have been involved. (This is especially true where the mother is diabetic.) *Myxedema,* a milder type of obesity, with thick dry skin and sluggishness, is the result of a thyroid deficiency and may be associated with goiter. Usually it comes on in adult life (most frequently among women), but it also may occur in children. Here, too, the possible rôle of heredity is in doubt.

Hands and Feet. Just about every conceivable type of hand and foot abnormality may be hereditary. We already have spoken of "stub" fingers and extra fingers, but dozens of other hereditary hand abnormalities have been established—"claw" hands, "spider" hand, fused finger joints, webbed fingers, crooked fingers, paddle-shaped thumbs, missing fingers or thumbs, double joints, etc. (Some of these are depicted on the next page.) In many instances the abnormality is duplicated in the feet. What is most significant is that *in almost every one of these cases the condition is due to a dominant gene,* providing for direct transmission from parent to a child. However, genes causing these abnormalities may vary in their action in

HAND ABNORMALITIES
(All inherited through dominant genes)

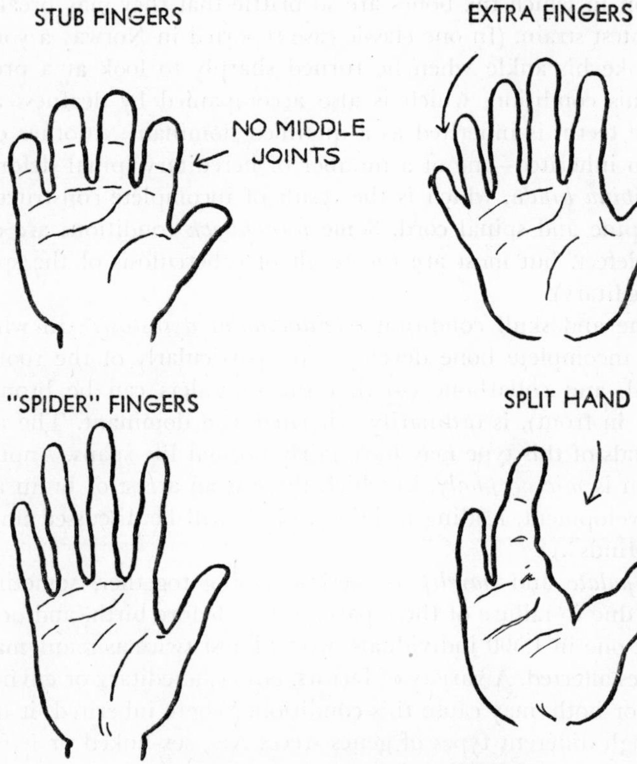

STUB FINGERS
NO MIDDLE JOINTS
EXTRA FINGERS
"SPIDER" FINGERS
SPLIT HAND

(All conditions above may be repeated in the feet and toes of the same individual)

different individuals, possibly influenced by other genes or external factors, so that in the same family varied forms of hand or foot abnormalities may occur. In rare instances, there may be complete absence of hands or feet, or of arms and legs, or absence of some important bone. Ordinarily, these latter defects appear to result from some prenatal mishap, but in some cases they may be due to seriously defective genes.

Still doubtful is the extent to which *congenital clubfoot* is hereditary. The term applies to a number of conditions which, if and when inherited, probably are caused by recessive genes. In other cases various prenatal upsets may be involved.

SKELETAL. "Brittle bones" (*blue sclerotic,* so called because one of its attendant effects is bluish eye-whites) is a not uncommon condition in which the bones are so brittle that they may break at the slightest strain. (In one classic case reported in Norway a young man broke his ankle when he turned sharply to look at a pretty girl.) This condition, which is also accompanied by deafness and defective teeth, is inherited as a qualified dominant. Another condition so inherited—one of a number of hereditary spinal deformities—is *spina bifida,* which is the result of incomplete construction of the spine and spinal cord. Some *hunchback* conditions are due to this defect, but most are the result of tuberculosis of the spine (nonhereditary).

A bone and skull condition *(cleidocranial dysostosis),* in which there is incomplete bone development, particularly of the roof of the skull, and collarbone (so that the shoulders can be brought together in front), is ordinarily inherited as a dominant. The rare individuals of this type may have fairly normal life spans. Another condition is *microcephaly,* in which there is an arrest of brain and skull development, leading to idiocy. (This will be discussed under "Slow Minds".)

Cleft palate and *harelip* (sometimes going together, sometimes not) are due to failure of these parts to fuse before birth, and occur in about one in 1,500 individuals, with almost twice as many males as females affected. A variety of factors, either hereditary or environmental, or both, may cause this condition. Where inherited, it may be through different types of genes—recessives, sex-linked or irregularly dominant, the expression of the genes often depending on adversities in the prenatal environment. How important even minor environmental differences before birth may be in causing these defects to develop or be suppressed is proved by the fact that among identical twins, where one has harelip and/or cleft palate, in about a quarter of the cases the other has not, or shows only slight symptoms of the condition.

TEETH. While most teeth defects are clearly due to environmental factors, some individuals are nonetheless predestined by their genes to run up greater dental bills than others. For example, following a study in a community where fluoride had been added to the drinking water to combat tooth decay, Dr. Henry Klein reported in 1948 that dental disease was still considerably greater among children from parents with bad teeth than among those from "good-teeth" families, leading to the inference that some hereditary factor was involved. In addition to the general hereditary differences in teeth construction, many specific inherited teeth defects or peculiarities have been identified. Some of the serious ones are by-products of other conditions, previously discussed, such as "brittle bones," cleft palate, albinism, etc. But there also are many teeth defects which are inherited independently.

Absence of certain teeth may be inherited. In some cases, none of the *incisors,* or only the upper incisors, appear, while in still other cases the *molars* may not appear, or the roots of some teeth may be absent. But *extra* teeth may also be inherited, and so may a hastening of tooth development which gives some babies teeth at birth. (For the manner of inheritance of these teeth abnormalities, see Summary Tables.) A rare gum condition, in which the gums grow over the teeth, is also hereditary.

Malocclusion (the improper fitting-together of the upper and lower teeth, endangering healthy dental development) may be partly due to faulty chewing habits, but heredity also may be involved. (A mild example of malocclusion is found in all five of the Dionne quintuplets.) Dr. J. H. Sillman, following a study of progressive dental development in many children, reports that the pattern for malocclusion may be present at birth—definitely at 1½ years of age —and suggests that it is hereditary. (Dr. S. E. Stoddard attributes some cases to an "incompletely" dominant gene.)

Several defective *enamel* conditions are hereditary. In some the enamel is soon lost or pitted, in others it is discolored. One condition producing brown teeth—through a dominant "sex-linked gene" carried in the X chromosome—was discussed in the preceding chapter. Another rare condition, *porphyria* (recessive) produces reddish teeth. *Opalescent dentin,* in which the teeth are almost as transparent as plastics, and break or wear away easily, has been reported as due to a dominant gene. It should be borne in mind, however, that many cases of defective dentin or enamel, especially where they are prevalent in a community, are due to such extraneous causes as harmful chemicals in the water, or faulty diet. Attention to these factors has greatly reduced the incidence of teeth defects in many places.

SKIN. Abnormalities in the outer wrappings of people are so easily recognized that, like eye defects, they have been intensively studied, and a great many of them have been established as hereditary. Most of these inherited skin disorders or abnormalities are not functionally serious, but derive their importance from their effect on the social and economic life of the individual. Such conditions as "scaly skin," "shedding skin," "elephant skin" or "blotched face" (large birthmarks) may greatly interfere with the victim's chance of employment, social adjustment and marriage. Some skin conditions, however, may go with serious constitutional effects, and a few may even prove fatal.

Among the "oddities" is *"rubber skin."* The sideshow "India-rubber" men may have skin so elastic that it can be pulled out five or six inches on the chest or forearms and snapped back. This is possible because of an increased amount of elastic tissue, a condition produced by a rare "qualified" dominant gene. In still another odd condition afflicting mostly males, there is perpetual "goose-flesh," due to pinhead-sized gatherings of skin at the mouths of the hair follicles. Inheritance is apparently through sex-influenced recessives.

Birthmarks are, of course, the most familiar of skin peculiarities, but only in the rarer instances do they deserve special attention. Everyone has some type of birthmark, and most people have many. Often these are hereditary, with the genes dominant or partly so in the common forms, and the same type of birthmark appearing in the same position in successive generations, at birth or in later years. Where there is danger is in a few kinds of birthmarks which may be forerunners of cancer. These are not the common ones which are hairy, raised or warty, or are merely discolorations in the skin. The dangerous birthmarks are generally the rarer ones which are a *combination of smooth, hairless, pigmented and not raised,* or which change color (turning black suddenly), or which increase in size, become ulcerated, or bleed. While you should not give way to unnecessary fears about birthmarks, wherever there is any doubt, consult your doctor!

Of the cancerous birthmarks, only a very few have been proved to be hereditary. Most serious are malignant freckles *(xeroderma*

INHERITED "ODDITIES" IN HUMANS WHICH ARE COMMON TO OR BRED IN OTHER ANIMALS

IN HUMANS		IN OTHER ANIMALS
Sweat-Gland Deficiency	Necessity to pant when overheated	Dogs, wolves
Extra Breasts and/or Nipples	Two, three or four pairs ranged below one another	All animals which bear litters
Midget-type Dwarfism	Very small size but normal proportions	"Toy" dogs, midget birds, fish, etc.
Achondroplastic Dwarfism	Short, stubby limbs	Dachshunds, bulldogs; occasionally in cattle
Albinism	Lack of pigment in eyes, skin and hair	In almost all animals from mice to elephants
Piebald Spotting	Pattern patches of white skin against darker skin	Cows, dogs, etc.
White Blaze	Patch of white hair over forehead	Horses ("Star" forehead)
Hairlessness	Almost no hair on head or any other part of body	Mexican hairless dog
Extra Fingers	Occurring on one or more hands and feet	Cats, guinea-pigs (in latter up to eleven on one foot)
Color Blindness (Total)	Inability to see colors except only in shades of black and white	Almost all mammals except apes and humans

pigmentosum), dark, freckle-like inflammations (affected by exposure to sunlight) which appear in infancy or childhood, and are produced by recessive genes. They usually bring early death. *Coffee-colored spots,* with nerve-end tumors *(neurofibromatosis)* which appear at birth or in childhood over various parts of the body and spread later, may also give rise to cancer, as well as to blindness, paralysis and various internal effects. The condition is dominant or partly so in inheritance.

Large hereditary birthmarks *(naevi)* are of various types, some due to blood-vessel swellings, some raised, some merely pigmented patches of the skin. The blood type (vascular) when it appears on the cheek is due to a dominant gene. A familiar type of hereditary birthmark is the "Nevus of Unna," on the nape of the neck. Most remarkable of all large birthmarks on record is that of a woman in the Soviet Union (reported in the *Journal of Heredity* in 1945), half of whose body, completely down from head to foot on the left side, was one huge birthmark. In addition, her left eye was brown and the right gray, the left side of her head was bald, and her left armpit was hairless. Such a *"mosaic"* condition, reported previously in birds, guinea pigs and mice, but never before in humans, is not hereditary, however, being produced in the very earliest stage of development by an upset in one half of the fertilized egg just after it has divided. Similar upsets in cells during later stages of embryonic development can produce other non-hereditary birthmarks.

Small, fatty growths or yellow patches on the skin and other areas (*xanthomatosis, lipoid proteinosis,* etc.) may be by-products of inherited metabolic disorders which will be discussed in the next chapter.

Among the serious unusual conditions is *absence of sweat glands.* The men afflicted are sometimes called "dog-men" because, not being able to perspire, they pant like dogs when overheated (although dogs, while deficient in sweat glands, have recently been shown to have them). This condition, which is often accompanied by an incomplete set of teeth, sharp-pointed, and hair and growth defects, may be due to "sex-linked" genes (the latter explaining why most of the victims are men).

Among other rather serious hereditary skin conditions are:

"Scaly" skin, in which the skin is dry and scaly, easily inflames and continually sheds. This appears in infancy and is dominant or sex-linked in inheritance. In *"horny"* skin (recessive) the skin is

hard at birth, and becomes cracked at the joints. (Sometimes it is accompanied by small, deformed ears.) The condition may subsequently correct itself, but if it worsens, is sometimes fatal. *"Elephant"* skin, an extreme form of "horny" skin, causes premature birth, with death following shortly. This, too, is a simple recessive.

Psoriasis, a quite common variant of "scaly" skin, in which there are mottled, scaly patches, decreasing with age, may be inherited only as a *susceptibility* (through an "irregularly" dominant gene), the condition developing under certain adverse environmental influences. This is in line with the belief that there are inherited degrees of skin sensitivity, or predispositions to skin irritations of general or specific kinds.

(For those interested, *"shedding"* skin, *"blistering"* skin, *light sensitivity,* and a number of other of the rarer skin conditions, will be briefly dealt with in the Summary Tables under "Skin.")

Albinism, mentioned in earlier pages, is primarily a skin-pigment defect. The common type, due to recessive genes, occurs among all peoples, light-skinned or dark (as it also occurs in most animals). The highest incidence of albinism is among the San Blas Indians of central Panama (7 in 1,000), but the condition is most striking when found among Negroes. (See photo, p. 195.) *Albinoidism* is a mild form of albinism, in which the skin and hair are nearly unpigmented at birth, but some pigment develops later, and the eyes are not affected as in albinos. This is inherited through a "qualified" dominant gene. *Partial albinism* has several manifestations. In the piebald type (dominant) there are stripes on the individual's back, sometimes with white patches elsewhere. (In *vitiligo,* with somewhat similar "patch" effects, heredity is doubtful.) Mildest and most familiar of the partial albinism conditions is *"white forelock"* (dominant), in which there is a "blaze" or patch of white hair above the center of the forehead, usually present from birth on. (In recent years many women have regarded such an unpigmented lock of hair as attractive, and have imitated it by bleaching where it was not naturally present.)

Hair. The most common hereditary hair defect, *baldness,* already has been discussed. Some other hair conditions (for which essential details are given in the "Black Gene" Tables under "Hair") are complete or partial hairlessness, "beaded" hair, and excessive facial hair. Also hereditary may be *premature* grayness (differing from ordinary graying), in which the head hair begins to turn gray in adolescence, but with no effect on the life span. (Note, too, that "natural" gray hair in maturity has no relationship to health or lack of it.)

NAILS. There are many inherited nail defects and anomalies. The more serious may go with certain hair conditions (already mentioned), or may be inherited independently. Among these are *absence of nails* (partial or complete); excessively *thick* nails (found often in French Canadians), sometimes with thick skin on palms and soles; *hooked* or *incurved* nails; *small, thin, soft* nails; *flat* and *thin* nails; completely *milky-white* nails; and *bluish-white spots* on nails. All of the foregoing conditions, present at birth, are inherited through dominant or partly dominant genes. (But absent nails also can be inherited through recessives.)

CHAPTER 24

FUNCTIONAL DEFECTS

THINK of all the different working mechanisms there are in your body: your circulatory, respiratory, digestive, muscular, nervous, glandular and reproductive systems; your sensory mechanisms—of seeing, hearing, tasting and feeling; and finally, your brain. Then think of all the possible things that can go wrong or be wrong to begin with in any one of these intricate mechanisms. That will give you a clue to the endless number of *functional defects* that can be produced by bungling or shiftless genes. At the same time, as you read about these conditions in the pages that follow, never cease to be impressed with how lucky you are that so very, very few of all these possible defects are present in yourself!

EYES. The human eye, because of its importance and accessibility, has been studied so extensively that hundreds of hereditary eye defects or anomalies (unusual conditions) already have been brought to light. Some of these may cause only minor hindrance to the individual except in special cases (marked color blindness being one example), but other conditions produce seriously defective vision ranging up to total blindness.

The percentage of blindness due to heredity is still uncertain. Recent studies in the United States (1944) have indicated that more than half the cases of blindness among young people had their origin before birth, with venereal and other infections, and various other prenatal influences, being important contributory factors. (Prematurely born babies are especially vulnerable to blindness, possibly because of some dietary deficiency.) About one-eighth of the cases of congenital blindness are hereditary, but the proportion for the general blind population may well be higher, because many hereditary types of blindness do not reveal themselves until puberty or maturity.

Hereditary blindness may be present at birth through the failure of genes to guide the proper construction of the iris, retina or some other vital part of the eye mechanism. In other cases blindness may develop later, as an aftermath of other hereditary eye defects affecting the lens, eye nerves, eyeball, etc., at first producing only impaired vision or partial blindness. Significant also are the important sex differences, previously discussed, males being more vulnerable not only to color blindness but to many other and more serious eye defects.

Cataract, or opacity of the lens, is one of the chief causes of loss of vision (if not operated on). Very mild forms of cataract, which never become serious, occur in a great many people. Some congenital cataracts may be due to prenatal infections or certain diseases in the mother (German measles being one example); and some cataracts appearing in later life may also be due to infection or disease, plus the degenerative effects of old age. But authorities are convinced that *most* of the congenital cataracts, and many of those which develop spontaneously before old age, *are hereditary, usually through a dominant gene.* (In one pedigree, among 100 descendants of a blind woman, one-third were blind through congenital cataracts; in another family, over five generations, 44 out of 123 individuals had the condition.) The form and severity of cataracts, and the time of their onset—birth, childhood, puberty or middle age—are usually similar within a family. Many families have been studied, each with a specific combination of cataract traits which also seem to be determined largely by gene action.*

Glaucoma is a serious and rather common condition, in which there is abnormal pressure of the fluid inside the eye, which can lead to blindness unless treatment is early and effective. If glaucoma occurs in children while the eyes are still growing, enlarged eyes may result; if in adults, the eye is already fully formed and does not enlarge. While in most instances among adults glaucoma is perhaps not hereditary, authorities now feel that heredity is involved in more of the cases than they had formerly estimated.

In the rarer infantile and childhood glaucoma conditions, recessive genes are responsible, and a very rare juvenile type of glaucoma is sex-linked. (Glaucoma in infancy sometimes affects only

* Radiation is among the influences that can produce cataracts, and should atomic bombing be carried out, a great increase in cataracts can be expected. The U.S. Atomic Energy Commission announced in June, 1950, that at Hiroshima, where a bomb was dropped, a recent study of one group of 1,000 survivors who had been in the bombed area revealed forty certain cases of radiation cataract, and an additional forty suspected cases.

one eye, and is accompanied by a large birthmark on the same side of the face.) In the adult type of glaucoma, when heredity is involved, the genes responsible may be dominant or sex-linked.

Among other hereditary causes of blindness are these:

—*Retinitis pigmentosa,* in which there is a gradual degeneration of the rods and cones, accompanied by deposits of pigment in the retina, leading to marked visual defects and possibly to blindness. In the early stages the disease is manifested by night blindness (inability to see in dim light). Retinitis pigmentosa comes in a number of forms, sometimes with deafness, idiocy or other defects, with different ages of onset—from very early in life to late maturity —and through various methods of inheritance—dominant, recessive or sex-linked. (Other night-blindness conditions will be discussed later.)

—*Optic atrophy,* a withering of the optic nerve, is of several types, congenital, childhood, adult, etc., inherited in various ways. (See Tables, p. 314.)

—*Cancer of the retina (glioma retinae* or *retinoblastoma),* a rare condition, appearing at birth or in early childhood, fatal if affected eye or eyes not removed. Usually dominant and arising through mutation. (Children so afflicted are reported in news stories from time to time.)

—*Abnormally undersized or absent eyes, "pin-hole pupil,"* and *absence of the iris* are also noted in the Tables.

In addition to the defects which produce blindness, there are many hereditary conditions which impede vision in various ways and degrees. *Astigmatism* (defective focusing) may possibly be caused by a dominant gene. *Far-sightedness,* if extreme and present from birth, may be caused by a partially dominant gene; but if the condition is serious and attended by other eye defects, recessive genes may be responsible. Extreme *near-sightedness* (high mopia), may be recessive or sex-linked in inheritance, and if associated with eye tremor, may be dominant or sex-linked. But it should be kept in mind that in the foregoing defects adequate vision usually can be obtained by wearing corrective lenses.

Some hereditary eye defects affect only special aspects of vision. *Color blindness,* which we discussed in Chapter 22, is one of these. There also are some *night-blinding* conditions, much less severe than retinitis pigmentosa, in which the defect is restricted chiefly to the inability to see in dim light. One such condition is *choroide-*

INHERITED EYE DEFECTS

SOME OF THE POINTS AT WHICH "EYE" GENES MAY GO WRONG

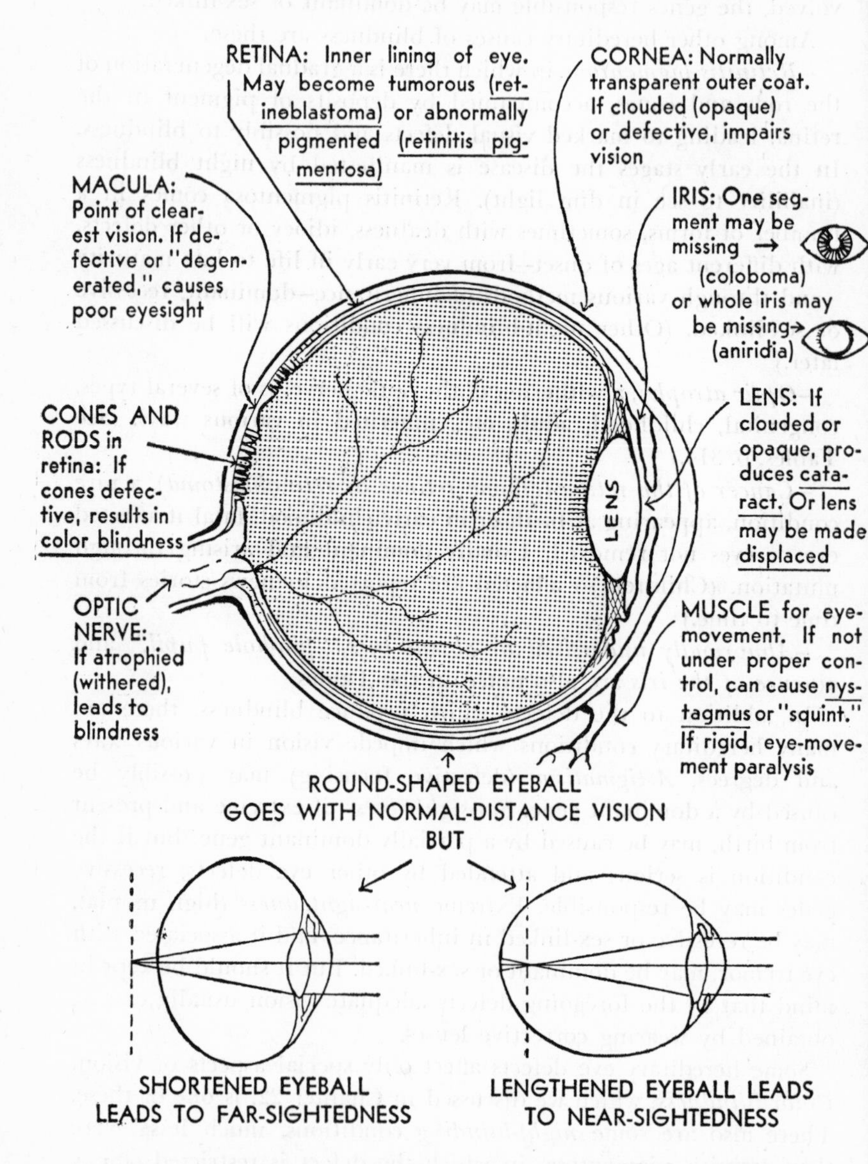
RETINA: Inner lining of eye. May become tumorous (retineoblastoma) or abnormally pigmented (retinitis pigmentosa)
CORNEA: Normally transparent outer coat. If clouded (opaque) or defective, impairs vision
MACULA: Point of clearest vision. If defective or "degenerated," causes poor eyesight
IRIS: One segment may be missing → (coloboma) or whole iris may be missing→ (aniridia)
CONES AND RODS in retina: If cones defective, results in color blindness
LENS: If clouded or opaque, produces cataract. Or lens may be made displaced
LENS
OPTIC NERVE: If atrophied (withered), leads to blindness
MUSCLE for eye-movement. If not under proper control, can cause nystagmus or "squint." If rigid, eye-movement paralysis
ROUND-SHAPED EYEBALL GOES WITH NORMAL-DISTANCE VISION BUT
SHORTENED EYEBALL LEADS TO FAR-SIGHTEDNESS
LENGTHENED EYEBALL LEADS TO NEAR-SIGHTEDNESS

(Also, eyeball may be made abnormally undersized [microphthalmia])

(Chart prepared with aid of Dr. Bernard Kronenberg.)

remia (where the choroid coat of the eye atrophies), whose victims are almost exclusively males. Other types of night blindness are produced by dominant or recessive genes. (While some night-blindness cases have been ascribed to vitamin A or B deficiency, these are clinically different from the hereditary forms.)

A number of common eye defects result from weaknesses or defects in the eye muscles or nerves. *Cross eyes,* most familiar of these, is very often (but certainly not always) hereditary, and if so, may be caused by either recessive or dominant genes. *Eye tremor* (*nystagmoid,* or *oscillating* eyes), if present at birth, is sex-linked in inheritance, but if accompanied by head-twitching, is dominant. *Eye-muscle paralysis* (inability to move the eye at birth, or later), may sometimes be the result of injury or infection, but, if inherited, may be through either dominant or sex-linked genes. *Drooping eyelids (ptosis),* when present from birth, is a dominant condition.

Faulty construction of various parts of the eye itself characterizes many conditions. In the cornea one may find an opaque ring over the iris (dominant); or a cone shape *(keratoconus)* causing extreme astigmatism (recessive). Or there may be an abnormally large eyeball (sex-linked or dominant), which need not affect vision. *Dislocated lens* may be caused by a qualified dominant gene, and if in combination with a displaced pupil, the cause may possibly be recessive genes. In certain families this is associated with long fingers ("spider fingers") and toes, and abnormal length of the long bones (in the *Marfan syndrome),* where it is inherited as a dominant.

There are many other inherited eye defects and anomalies too rare to justify discussion here, but the interested reader or specialist will find them adequately treated in some of the books listed in the Appendix.

EAR DEFECTS. Estimates of the proportion of deafness cases that are wholly or partly due to heredity range anywhere from 10 to 45 per cent. This uncertainty results from the fact that environmental influences are heavily involved in many of the hearing defects, and that in tracing back pedigrees of deafness one can never be too sure about the primary causes. Such conditions in the mother during pregnancy as syphilis, German measles and other infections, or vitamin deficiencies, can produce in her offspring congenital deafness, while in childhood, serious deafness can result from various infectious diseases—meningitis, scarlet fever, mumps, etc. Because these early hazards were much more prevalent in former years, we can assume that proportionately more of the congenital and childhood deafness cases were environmental. In addition, of course, later illnesses and accidents, and degenerative effects of old age, are to be considered, and in recent years psychiatrists have shown that some cases of deafness are *psychosomatic*—resulting because, literally, certain individuals don't want to hear. (A number of these cases were reported among soldiers in World War II.)

While all this complicates the study of "ear genetics" there nonetheless is abundant evidence regarding the inheritance of some types of deafness, and where medical records are clear it often can be determined what part heredity has played in a given case, and what chances there are of transmission to children. Moreover, the fact, as noted, that environmental causes of deafness have been reduced in recent years (particularly in the congenital conditions and those in childhood resulting from infectious diseases) has made it easier to detect the inherited conditions.

Congenital deafness, when hereditary, may have resulted directly from defective gene action in constructing the ear mechanism. But usually, the effects of faulty "ear" genes are gradual, beginning with partial deafness in childhood and reaching a more serious state in maturity. Where a child is deaf at birth, however, the condition is especially serious because speech impairment is a natural consequence, inasmuch as inability to hear before the speaking stage develops makes it extremely difficult to learn to imitate sounds. Formerly, congenital deafness usually meant *mutism* as well (to the point where "congenital deafness" and "deaf mutism" were often used erroneously as synonymous terms). But in recent years new teaching techniques are enabling a large portion of the congenitally-deaf to learn to talk fairly well.

At this writing there are at least 50,000 persons in the United States who were born deaf or who lost their hearing before they acquired speech. (The total number of deaf or partially deaf runs into millions.) *Close to one-third of the congenitally-deaf cases are believed to be hereditary.* There still is doubt as to the genetic mechanism responsible, but evidence points to recessive genes, possibly more than a single pair. The fact that children with normal hearing can be born to parents both of whom are apparently genetically deaf suggests that more than one set of genes is involved in the condition (although there is the possibility that prenatal influences also are contributory factors, and that, in the absence of these, deafness may not result even where the inherited predisposition is present). What is quite certain, however, is that certain types of deaf people have a very much greater than average chance of producing deaf children; and also, that where parents are closely related (as in cousin marriages) there is a much increased possibility of gene combinations for deafness coming together in a child.

In maturity, the most common of the serious ear defects is middle-ear deafness (with estimates of those affected in the United States running as high as several millions). Often it results from injury or infection, but the hereditary form, *otosclerosis,* is caused by the deposit of soft and spongy, and hard (sclerotic), bone in the capsule of the inner ear. This usually develops in the late 'teens or early twenties, becoming more serious in later maturity, especially among women after childbirth. In general, the incidence of otosclerosis in women is twice that in men, leading to the theory (advanced by Dr. Edmund P. Fowler, Sr., in 1949) that the "female" hormone, *estrogen,* may be a stimulus in the development of the condition.

Where, in either sex, heredity is the predisposing factor, most cases of otosclerosis are due to recessive genes (one pair or more), but some cases appear to be dominant. *Inner-ear,* or nerve, deafness, another type, which as a rule begins in middle age, definitely is dominant in inheritance.

(As a hopeful note, new operational techniques have made it possible to improve hearing in some individuals with otosclerosis by creating "windows" in the inner ear to let in sound waves. There is also some possibility that hormonal treatments may be helpful, but this awaits proof. In any event, improved hearing devices now enable the partially deafened person to hear, often quite as well as the normally hearing individual.)

"Word deafness" is more a defect of brain-functioning than of the ear, as the hearing is normal but the individual is unable to understand the meaning of the sounds. It affects many more males than females, appears in infancy, and is inherited through a "qualified" dominant gene.

In the outer ear there are several hereditary abnormalities, among them *complete absence of the ear,* usually on one side; *cup-shaped ear* (ear turned in), and *imperfect double ear* (one or both ears being "doubled"), these conditions all being dominant or partly so in inheritance. In none of these cases need hearing be affected. Also interesting, as a curiosity, are natural "earring" holes in the ear lobe, which make it look as if the ears had been pierced.

SPEECH DEFECTS. Defects and disorders of speech are among the most common of handicaps (in New York City alone, for example, there being in 1948 about 30,000 schoolchildren with such defects ranging all the way from lisping to stuttering). But despite the widespread incidence of these defects, and their repeated occurrence in several members of the same family, the question of their inheritance is extremely uncertain. This is with the exception of those speech disorders which are the direct consequence of other hereditary defects, such as cleft palate, or of some of the nerve and muscle disorders which we'll discuss later.

The most common speech disorder, *stuttering,* or stammering (the terms now being used interchangeably), which afflicts about one person in a hundred, has many puzzling aspects. Most psychologists today incline toward the theory that it is almost entirely the result of emotional and psychic disturbances, dating from early childhood. (In 85 per cent of the cases stuttering begins before the age of eight.) But this leaves unexplained a number of facts. To quote Dr. James S. Greene, medical director of the National Hospital for Speech Disorders, "If stuttering is purely psychogenic, how can we explain that over 50 per cent of our cases give a family history of stuttering, and that the incidence of males to females is at least five to one?"

The fact that so many more boys than girls have speech defects—ranging up to ten times as many boys in some groups studied—certainly is one of the cogent reasons for suspecting an organic basis in at least a certain percentage of the cases. This, as we noted in a previous discussion in our "Poor Male" chapter, would be consistent with findings of greater male defectiveness in many other categories (including reading disabilities). While psychologists maintain that, as a presumable cause, little boys are usually under greater emotional stress than little girls, the evidence is hardly sufficient to explain away the whole sex difference in speech disorders on this basis, nor have the purely psychic factors which could account for all of the cases been identified. What we know only is that many sufferers from speech disorders can be cured or helped greatly by psychological treatment or careful training. Also offering some support to the psychological theory of causation is the fact that under the strain of service in World War II, many men developed speech disorders or had these worsened. But, as always, there is the question (which will come up again when we deal with mental breakdowns), why did only a certain few of the men develop speech defects, when under the very same stresses, the great majority of G.I.s did not?

From another angle, to say to every person who stutters, "It's because you must be 'emotionally' or 'psychically' disturbed," is manifestly unfair, particularly when we do have some reason to believe that organic factors, and possibly hereditary factors, may be involved. Here, however, we are also, for the most part, in the theoretical realm (except where there are defects of the larynx, palate or tongue, or in certain nervous disorders). Some of the best recent evidence comes from the studies of twins with speech defects. As Dr. S. E. Nelson and others have reported, where one of an identical twin pair stutters, the other does so almost invariably, whereas among fraternal twins, stuttering in most cases is confined only to one of the pair. The conclusion was that "personal contact is of slight importance as a factor in the incidence of stuttering. Since it is found that there is a disproportionate tendency for the disorder to occur in the ancestry of those afflicted, it appears that there must be some sort of transmission operating to cause stuttering to 'run' in certain pedigrees."

If there is such "transmission," the gene pattern for it hasn't yet been discovered. Several authorities believe the answer will be found in some inherited organic defect—perhaps delayed development of the speech-controlling areas of the brain—which, under special stress, would lead to stuttering, particularly in a child during the first years of learning to talk. If the theory of a developmental delay is valid, it may help to explain the much higher incidence of speech disorders among boys, inasmuch as their general biological development (as we saw in earlier chapters) lags behind that of girls. Strengthening the "organic" theory is the fact that symptoms of stuttering often show themselves in infancy, and in some cases are believed to be of prenatal origin.

The theory that left-handedness and stuttering have some relationship is now open to doubt, in view of evidence, in one study at least, that the proportion of left-handed persons among stutterers (about 7 per cent) is only slightly higher than that of "lefties" in the general population. (See also discussion, p. 136.)

Also of interest is the report by Dr. Wendell Johnson (1944) that there is no case on record of stuttering among North American Indians, and that their languages apparently haven't even a word for it. This may have some genetic significance, or it may merely mean that Indians under their tribal conditions don't encounter the stresses which might bring on stuttering, for further evidence shows that speech disorders have developed among some of them who have attended mission schools and come in contact with White teachers.

ALLERGIC DISEASES. Almost everybody is allergic to something, and if you've ever had skin tests made, you've probably been surprised at some of the findings. There was the G.I. in World War II who had to be discharged from service because he was found allergic to the khaki uniform. There was a Pittsburgh girl who advertised the sale of her new Angora wool cape because her boy friend was allergic to it. There was the man whose sneezing fits every Sunday were traced to his allergy to the colored inks in the comic section. And there was the California wife who, in 1949, had her marriage annulled on the grounds that she was *allergic to her husband!* (A psychiatrist testified that while she loved her husband, she was in some way so emotionally upset in his presence—even by talking about him—that it produced a serious skin rash all over her body. She had previously suffered from asthma.)

These allergic oddities could be extended endlessly, to substances and influences of every conceivable kind, to a large variety of foods and drugs, to alcohol and tobacco, to cats and dogs, and to almost anything you could think of.

Where allergies become serious is when they are tied up with asthma, violent hay fever, eczema or migraine headache, or when they greatly interfere with a person's eating or living habits. (Such serious allergies occur in about one in every ten persons.) There is also the danger that severe allergies in children may interfere with food utilization sufficiently to retard growth, weaken bones and muscles, cause many intestinal and skin disorders, and also lead to behavior problems.

All allergies involve some malfunctioning of body chemistry and an abnormal sensitivity of membranes or body tissues. What causes them? "Psychosomatic" theories hold that most allergies arise from, or are at least made acute by emotional disturbances, and there is evidence to support this in many cases. For one thing, the incidence of allergy appears to be much higher than average among persons who are neurotic. But it is also possible that persons may become neurotic as the result of being continually afflicted with a severe allergy. In any case, why are so many persons allergic to only *specific* substances, often with no awareness of what causes their trouble? Why do we so frequently find the same type of allergy running in families—for one particular food, such as sauerkraut or mushrooms, or for one drug such as quinine? And why—without "psychosomatic" factors—do we find among lower animals some strains which are considerably more allergic than others? In answer, there is much to indicate that peculiarities in body chemistry and, hence, "predispositions" to develop allergies of various or specific kinds may be inherited, perhaps in about three-fourths of the cases (with purely "acquired" allergies contributing the rest). Some authorities believe that all allergies are related, others that specific allergies go with specific eccentricities in the chemical functioning of different individuals and at different ages. All this complicates the problem of tracing heredity.

As to the possible genes involved, Dr. Alexander Wiener (the blood-chemistry expert whose *Rh* work will be discussed in the "Blood" chapter) believes studies by himself and others show that "allergy inheritance" may come through two kinds of dominant genes, the double combination of which produces marked allergic symptoms before puberty (twice as often in boys as in girls), whereas one of the genes, singly, asserts itself only after puberty, producing milder symptoms or none at all. In a study in 1946, Dr. Karl A. Stiles reported that in one large family group of 232 persons, almost a quarter had respiratory allergies—more than three times the incidence in the general population. He suggested that an "irregular" dominant gene might here be responsible. Other studies also have indicated dominant inheritance for some types of allergy, among them the tendency to asthma.*

While there is still some doubt as to the precise inheritance of allergies, many specialists believe the evidence is sufficient so that in families where the conditions are prevalent, pregnant or nursing mothers should take extra precautions with their diet, should be alert for allergic symptoms in their babies and children, and should see that apparel and surroundings are as free as possible from known

* A special type of allergic reaction, revealed only by a rise in the pulse rate when a particular food is eaten, has been reported by Dr. Arthur F. Coca as running in families. He terms this type of allergy *"idioblapsis,"* and lists among its unusual symptoms tiredness, dizziness, psychic depression, constipation, overweight, etc. How it may be inherited has not yet been established.

irritants. Also to be kept in mind is that, if and where tendencies to allergy are inherited, different members of a family may not be allergic to the same foods, and that foods which may be good for most children (such as cream, orange juice, cereals, chocolate or even raw fruits and vegetables) may be bad for some. If in doubt, ask the doctor!

Migraine ("sick headache," usually on one side) is considered by many authorities as an allergic condition, caused by periodic swelling of blood vessels in the brain through some chemical disturbance (or perhaps by a peculiarity in the blood vessels themselves). Its inheritance has long been suspected, and most theories point to a dominant gene. That migraine is influenced by hormonal factors or the general chemical functioning of individuals is indicated by its two-to-one occurrence in women as compared with men, and by the fact that afflicted women tend to suffer their worst attacks during their menstrual periods, when their body chemistry is least efficient.

One of the most severe of the allergic conditions, fortunately quite rare, is *angioneurotic oedema,* a periodic sudden swelling of the skin or mucous membranes, which may cause death if occurring in the larynx or vital organs. Its onset, when it is most serious, is usually in childhood or at puberty, and about 50 per cent more boys than girls are affected. This condition has been ascribed to a dominant gene.

OTHER CHEMICAL DISORDERS. As is true of chemistry students, there are innumerable ways in which "chemistry" genes can flunk out or fall down in their assigned tasks. Most of the major defects and abnormalities resulting from defective chemical genes have been dealt with in previous chapters and sections. Additional ones, which produce mental defects, sexual abnormalities and some more of the blood conditions, are still to be discussed. Here we will touch on a few which don't fit into other categories.

Gout—that old affliction of Dr. Samuel Johnson and other historical personages—has long been suspected of being hereditary, but only recently (in 1948) has the manner of its inheritance been revealed. Also clarified is the reason for the much higher incidence of gout in men than in women. It appears that an excess of uric acid in the blood *(hyperuricemia),* which leads to gout or a susceptibility to it, may be produced by a *dominant* gene which works differently in the two sexes because the male chemical environment heightens its action. (If you're interested—the male "urate" level is ordinarily already higher, asserting itself at an earlier age, and the "male" hormones are an additional stimulus to the development of gout.)

Urinary disorders or abnormalities of many kinds may be hereditary. Some have little effect on health, others go with serious defects. (See Tables, p. 310.)

A number of inherited *disorders of fat metabolism* may also lead to mild or serious effects. One condition involves the abnormal metabolism of *cholesterol,* a fatty substance. A common effect is *xanthelasma,* in which there are small yellow patches on the eyelids. The metabolic disorder responsible is inherited through a dominant gene. But if a person receives *two* of these genes (as may happen if both parents have xanthelasma) the *double*-gene combination produces the much more serious condition of *xanthoma tuberosum.* The result then may be a marked elevation of blood cholesterol, and the formation of fatty deposits in various areas of the skin, in the internal organs and in the arteries, the latter effects leading to the condition known as *atherosclerosis.* (Discussed in Chapter 21, under "Arteriosclerosis.")

BLOOD DISEASES AND DISORDERS. The most dramatic of the blood diseases, hemophilia, has already been discussed. But far more common are many other hereditary blood diseases and defects, chiefly the *anemias* which involve deficiencies in the quantity or quality of the blood. While most cases of anemia are due to infectious or other diseases, malnutrition, etc., certain types arise from hereditary abnormalities in the construction of the red blood cells. One such condition, *acholuric family jaundice,* characterized by fragile blood cells, with, occasionally, anemia, jaundice and enlarged spleen, has been established as due to a dominant gene.

With respect to some of the other blood-cell conditions, a significant fact is that the most prevalent types are found concentrated largely among persons of certain races or stocks. *Cooley's* ("Mediterranean") *anemia* is found preponderantly among persons of Italian, Greek and Armenian descent. It appears to be transmitted through a dominant gene which singly produces mild blood abnormalities, but in a double dose (if one gene is received from each parent) causes very serious effects, including skeletal abnormalities and Mongoloid features, usually with death in early infancy or childhood. Because the single gene, even though mild in its actions, reveals itself through easily recognized blood-cell peculiarities, this is a case where "carriers" can be detected.

There is another blood condition which follows a similar pattern of inheritance.* *Sicklemia,* a mild disorder, results from one dominant gene; *sickle-cell anemia,* a very serious disorder, from two of the same genes. Sicklemia is so-called because of the curious, twisted "sickle" shape of the red corpuscles. The condition is found chiefly among Negroes (in about 7 per cent of those in the United States and about 15 per cent of those in Africa). This one-gene condition, as we said, has only mild effects. But if a man and woman equally afflicted with sicklemia each pass on their defective gene to a child, the double-gene dose will produce a serious anemia which is often fatal.

(One other form of anemia or jaundice, peculiar to newborn infants, is *erythroblastosis fetalis,* formerly thought to be directly hereditary, but now known to be caused by *"Rh"* or other blood-type incompatibilities, which will be given detailed discussion in Chapter 28.)

Quite different from the anemias are the hereditary *bleeding* diseases. In one group of these there are, in addition to hemophilia, several much milder conditions which result from lack or insufficiency in the blood of the substances required for proper coagulation. In another category are the conditions where bleeding or hemorrhages result from weaknesses in the walls of the small blood vessels, caused by dominant genes. So produced are hereditary nose-bleed (spontaneous and excessive), and a condition where there is bleeding under the skin, producing purple patches. A double dose of the gene for the latter condition may kill the individual in infancy.

Leukemia, a fatal disorder in which there is an excessive production of white blood cells and a deficiency in the red ones, offers some suspicion of an hereditary susceptibility, but the evidence for this is still very slight. (Many authorities believe that it is actually a cancer of the blood-forming organs, involving the presence of malignant white blood cells in the blood stream.) While acute leukemia usually appears in childhood with no identified cause, there is evidence that milder forms, in adults, may be induced by undue exposure to radioactivity. Thus, the toll from leukemia among doctors who have been exposed to radiation is much higher than among laymen, and a very high incidence of leukemia was

* Clarification of the genetic mechanisms involved in *Cooley's anemia,* and also in *sicklemia* and *sickle-cell anemia,* came through findings by Dr. James V. Neel, of the University of Michigan, reported in 1949.

reported among Japanese who were exposed to the atomic bomb. In the United States the number of leukemia deaths appears to be rising, about 6,000 such deaths now being reported annually. Among other mysterious aspects of the disease is the fact that proportionately many more males die from the disease than do females (25 per cent more males in infancy, and almost twice as many males as females at adolescence).

TASTE AND SMELL. Hereditary deficiencies—or differences—in these senses probably exist in many forms and degrees, but so far the only clues have come from tests with certain chemical substances. Most familiar to many students who have taken such tests is "taste blindness" to "PTC" (short for—hold tight!—phenyl-thio-carbamide), a substance which tastes bitter to about seven out of ten persons, but not to the others. This non-tasting has been found to be inherited through simple recessive genes. (Race differences with respect to "PTC" tasting will be discussed in Chapter 42.) Taste reactions to other chemicals also suggest inherited differences, with the likelihood that this may extend to many foods, perfumes, etc. However, there is as yet no evidence of any "taste blindness" that might be considered of serious import.

Hereditary "smell" deficiency, has been established only in *anosmia*—total absence of smell—a very rare condition reported as dominant in some families. Also, with possible inheritance, it has been found that some persons with otherwise normal noses can't detect the odor of a skunk. But who would call that a *"defect"*?

MUSCLES AND NERVES. *Inherited* muscular defects, while not too common, include some of the most serious of the hereditary afflictions. These conditions may result from defective gene action in not properly constructing given muscles or sets of muscles, or in not providing for their adequate nutrition, leading to *atrophy,* or shriveling. Since muscle activity is controlled by nerves, it is often some nerve defect which inhibits the functioning or causes the withering of specific muscles, so it is not always easy to tell in a given case whether the fault lies with "muscle" genes or "nerve" genes. Moreover, the complex nature of many of the muscular disorders makes it difficult to classify or describe them, or to trace pedigrees; and, added to all this, many conditions which appear to be similar to the hereditary ones may be of purely environmental origin, due to birth injuries, accidents, diseases, etc.

Thus, we will limit our discussion here to those muscle and

nerve conditions whose inheritance has been most clearly established, and which are most significant. (Other conditions in this category in which there is any element of heredity will be found listed in the Summary Tables, p. 313.)

The hereditary nerve conditions are of several types, of which *Friedreich's ataxia* is the best known. This comes on in childhood and is symptomized by wobbly gait and speech defects. It is inherited as a recessive. In some families a milder form occurs with onset at about age 21. This form is dominant. One form of childhood paralysis *(spastic paraplegia),* is partially sex-linked in inheritance and is more common in males. *Periodic paralysis,* characterized by intermittent attacks during which the muscles remain soft (flaccid), comes on in youth and is inherited as a dominant.

Inherited *muscular atrophies,* with shriveling or degeneration of the muscles, are also of various types. The best known is *peroneal atrophy,* which comes on in childhood and affects the feet, spreading to the calf muscles, and perhaps later also extending to the hands as well. Other muscular conditions include *Thomsen's disease,* with muscle stiffness and slow movements, which comes on in childhood; and *myotonia atrophica,* affecting adults, in which there is slow relaxation after muscular contraction. (In this latter condition the afflicted persons if they shake hands may find difficulty for a time in letting go.) Finally, there are the serious *progressive muscular dystrophies,* in which there is muscular wasting, leading to weakness and invalidism, nearly always lasting for years.

Missing muscles are not an uncommon phenomenon. To anatomy students who can't find one muscle or another in a human specimen it may be explained that complete, or partial, absence of particular muscles is often due to inheritance (dominant). On the other hand, added muscles may also be present in some individuals through inheritance.

Some of the other conditions that affect muscular action are primarily nerve defects or by-products of other defects, and for special ones of interest, we again refer you to our Summary Tables.

But the most serious of the nervous disorders, such as *Huntington's chorea* and *epilepsy,* will be discussed in the following chapters, where we shall also deal with perhaps the worst of all the inherited functional defects.

CHAPTER 25

SICK MINDS

IN THE seventeenth century three brothers came to the United States from England bringing with them one of the most terrible of all known "black" genes.

Through these three who settled in New England more than a thousand persons in the United States have come to as horrible an end as anyone could imagine—death from *Huntington's chorea.*

A single dominant gene causes this condition.

A man (or woman) to all appearances normal, perhaps even brilliant, goes on into maturity with no sign of any waiting doom. Then, quite suddenly, usually in the thirties, or a few years earlier or later, he begins to disintegrate. His speech becomes thick, his brain and nervous system go to pieces, his body collapses. In a few more years the individual is a helpless wreck, lingering on until he is carried off by merciful death. *And no cure for this condition is yet known.*

But this is not all. A person with a gene for Huntington's chorea may marry and raise a family before the disease strikes. Because the gene is a dominant, all the children of the victim are thus suddenly confronted with the one-in-two possibility that they likewise may be doomed, with *no way of finding out beforehand*—nor, inasmuch as those with the gene may not always develop the disease, of ever being certain that they are not "carriers."*

The drama in this gruesome situation, which confronts scores of persons in the United States today, was recognized by Eugene O'Neill when he used it in his memorable play, *Strange Interlude.*†

* Hope that this will not always be so is held out by recent findings (R. M. Patterson, et al., 1948) that the *brain-wave patterns* of about half the offspring of Huntington's chorea patients (in a group of 26 studied), show certain abnormalities which may be either advance symptoms of the disease, or a clue to those who are "carriers" of the gene for it. But it may take another forty years before the validity of these assumptions can be tested, inasmuch as many of these offspring are still young children.

† Mr. O'Neill wrote to us: ". . . No, I cannot say that I had the hereditary mental defect in *Strange Interlude* identified as Huntington's chorea. On the

Although the case history he based it on was apparently one of the New England pedigree, it should be noted that similar pedigrees of Huntington's chorea also are found in other countries (Germany and Switzerland among them), and that some of the present victims in the United States may be descendants of these stocks.

Akin to Huntington's chorea is an even rarer condition, *Pick's disease* (lobar atrophy), which may also be inherited through a simple dominant gene. In this disease there is a gradual deterioration of the brain in middle life, with the symptoms being an abnormal craving for sweets, untidiness and restlessness, weeping spells, repetition of sentences, constant hand movements, etc. Eventually the victim cramps up in bed, almost in the position of prenatal life, and before long, dies. What adds to the frightfulness of Pick's disease is that, as in Huntington's chorea, by the time the disease comes on, the victim already may have children who face an even chance of a similar doom.

But lest the reader be unduly alarmed, let us emphasize that the two conditions mentioned are extremely rare, that they have little relationship to other forms of insanity, and that *no common type of insanity is known to be inherited so simply and directly through dominant genes.*

However, in terms of numbers of persons affected, there is vastly greater threat and tragedy in the common forms of mental disease, such as *schizophrenia (dementia praecox)* and *manic-depressive insanity,* or in the mental defects, such as feeble-mindedness. It is in these conditions that the question of inheritance has the greatest meaning to individuals and to society.

The statistics on the common mental disorders and deficiencies are appalling. Rough estimates are that *anywhere from one in every twenty to one in every twelve* persons* in the United States is or will be, at one time or another, afflicted by some mental disease requiring hospitalization, while at least one in fifty children *is mentally deficient* (in the moron class or lower). This means that there is hardly a family which does not have some member or some

---

other hand, I knew what I wrote was valid because it was based on an actual history. Evidently, from what you say, this must have been the case of Huntington's chorea, although I never heard it described except by the general term of hereditary insanity. So I think your mention of the disease in *Strange Interlude* is justified by the fact, even though it gives me more credit as a diagnostician than I deserve."

* The increased estimate was offered by Dr. Benjamin Malzberg in 1949 on the basis of his recent studies.

very close relative among the mental victims. Half of all our available hospital beds are occupied at this writing by the 800,000 mental disease patients, and many millions more outside of hospitals are receiving or are in need of mental treatment. In another category, the feeble-minded contribute perhaps two million more to those who cannot make normal adjustments, among them being hundreds of thousands who have to be institutionalized.

Thus, when we also bear in mind how the mental diseases and deficiencies affect their victims, robbing most of them of normalcy during a large part or all of their lives, and of the tragedy to their families and the cost to society, it can be seen that these conditions are far more serious in their total impact than are any of the "killer" conditions, including heart disease and cancer. *And as we are going to learn, the case for heredity in these mental conditions is much stronger.*

But let us first make certain general distinction between the mental diseases ("insanity"), and the mental deficiencies (feeble-mindedness, etc.):

Where a person is insane or partly so, it is because of some disorder or derangement of the brain, which warps his thinking and behavior. His condition need in no way be related to his intellectual capacity (for he may even be of the very highest intelligence), but results from some disruptive change, sudden or gradual, in the orderly workings of his thinking mechanism.

Where a person is mentally deficient, however, it is generally because he *starts out with an inferior* brain—not a brain gone wrong, but one initially slow in its workings, either because of imperfect construction or of some early mishap. The degree to which the brain is limited in its capacity to function determines the type of defect, ranging down from the moron to the imbecile and idiot.

Now we turn to detailed consideration of the various mental conditions and the relative rôles that heredity and environment may play in them.

MENTAL DISEASES.* *Are we going crazier?* The question might well be asked for our total population if we merely compare past and present figures, and find that there are now proportionately

* "Insanity"—the old general term for mental diseases collectively—has fallen into disfavor with psychiatrists, but because of its continued widespread popular usage, we shall employ it here from time to time. Also to be noted is that "insane asylums" now are almost universally called "mental hospitals."

thirty-five times as many persons in our mental institutions as there were a century ago (making full allowance for population growth). But for most of this increase the reasons are obvious: The facilities for identifying and for taking care of the mentally diseased have been vastly expanded, which alone would account for many more people being in such institutions. In addition there are some new factors: The growing proportions of older people who have automatically swelled the numbers of *senile psychotics;* the mental casualties of the two World Wars; and, on a broad scale, the speed-up in living, greater concentration of people in cities, etc., which has made it more difficult for those mentally unstable to adjust to jobs or social relationship.

But just as we can make no accurate comparisons between the relative numbers or types of insane people now and in the past, because no comparable statistics are available, it is also impossible to give any accurate answer to this question:

Are there more or fewer "mental" cases in the United States than in other countries?

All we have to go by are the *recorded* numbers of cases in each country, which may prove very little, for standards of psychiatric diagnoses vary; and especially, there often are enormous differences between one country and another in the relative proportions of mentally diseased and defective persons who are classified as such, and hospitalized or institutionalized. To illustrate, Professor Lionel S. Penrose recently compiled figures for the numbers of inmates of mental institutions in various countries (as of about 1935). For every thousand population, there were in institutions of the United States 3.21 insane and 0.63 mentally defective; in England, 3.75 insane and 0.97 defective; in Sweden, 3.00 insane and 0.85 defective; in Italy, 1.62 insane and 0.01 defective; and in Japan, 0.16 insane and 0.01 defective. In other words, the United States had *twenty times* as many insane persons in institutions as had Japan, and *sixty-three times* as many mental defectives in institutions as had either Japan or Italy.

For the Soviet Union no statistics in this field are known to the author, but such statements (popular in certain circles) that "in the Soviet Union there is far less insanity than in the United States" or that "in World War II far fewer Soviet soldiers developed psychoses" have no validity whatsoever, because psychiatric diagnosis and treatment in the United States has been on an entirely different plane—in all probability more extensive and superior. For the present, therefore, it is futile to attempt to show how any differences in political or economic systems can affect populations mentally. Similarly, one can prove nothing at all about the relative incidence of mental conditions among civilized people as compared with primitives.

But whatever may be the facts with regard to the relative numbers of insane people at different periods or in different places, there is little question that environmental factors have played and do play an important part in bringing on or worsening mental diseases. At the same time, the evidence is increasing that *heredity, too, is a significant factor in most, if not all types of insanity, and the principal cause in many cases.* In fact, many authorities now go so far as to say that no person is likely to become insane unless he has a certain *constitutional vulnerability* to mental disease.

You frequently have heard it said, "She went crazy because . . ." of this or that (like Ophelia in *Hamlet*), or "he was driven to insanity by ——," etc. But how much can psychological stress by itself do to produce mental disease? And why is it that in adverse situations to which a great many persons are exposed, only some become insane? These are questions which have been investigated in many recent studies.

Take the mental casualties among soldiers in World War II. Even in the worst of the war situations, only a small proportion of the men broke down mentally, and some did so under the mildest stresses. Why? Army psychiatrists say it was because most of these men who cracked up were *more vulnerable* than others, or already mentally unstable before they entered service; and that even in ordinary civilian life, many of them eventually would have become mental cases.

Or take the "blitzkrieg" in England: The frightful rain of Nazi bombs might have been expected to cause many mental breakdowns, but surprisingly enough, the number of hospitalized mental casualties during this period dropped even below prewar standards. Or, most terrible of all, consider the Nazi concentration and extermination camps, where the horrors surpassed anything ever forced on human beings. Yet, while many of the victims may have lost their minds, we know that innumerable persons emerged from these excruciating ordeals, broken in health, but with their sanity still intact.

Thus, even under the worst conceivable stresses, there seem to be selective factors at work which single out only certain individuals for mental breakdown, and not others. This is particularly evident if one takes note of the "traumatic experiences," or serious emotional conflicts in early childhood, which often are given as reasons for later insanity. But we find that under any or all of the conditions cited as predisposing to mental instability, only some children are affected, while most others develop normally. Further, many cases of early insanity appear quite spontaneously, with nothing unusual in the child's background to explain them. Or going to the opposite pole of life, in the cases of old-age insanity *(senile dementia),* why do only some of the old people become mentally deranged, whereas so many others live on well into the nineties, with their minds unimpaired? (For instance, George Bernard Shaw, the late Chief Justice Oliver Wendell Holmes, the painter Rubens, etc.) It is possible that the brains of some individuals are genetically "geared" to function efficiently for a longer period than the brains of others.*

Finally, there are the cases of insanity ascribed to alcoholism and syphilis. Taking the first condition, if we ask, "Does alcoholism by itself produce insanity?" there are many authorities who will say, "No." Certainly, there are countless chronic alcoholics who go to their graves without ever becoming insane, which might support the theory that where alcoholism and mental derangement go together, a predisposition to insanity already may have been there, and, in fact, may have contributed to the chronic alcoholism. Even with the syphilitic insane there is the possibility of predisposition, not to syphilis, of course, but to the subsequent mental derangement, there being much evidence that the disease is much more likely to affect the brains of some individuals than others (men, for instance, as compared with women).

Thus, making every allowance for the important influences of environmental factors in bringing on or in worsening mental diseases, the foregoing facts, and many others which follow, have strengthened the belief among psychiatrists that in almost every case of insanity some hereditary factor is involved, either as a direct cause or indirectly through increased weakness under stress. It

* One study on the "inheritance of senile dementia," reported to the Stockholm Genetics' Congress in 1948 by Dr. A. Cresseri, cited evidence that pedigrees of senile dementia patients showed an abnormally high incidence of this condition and other mental diseases among their relatives, leading to the conclusion that "old-age insanity" is "influenced by a specific constitution."

should be clear that such heredity does not necessarily doom a person to insanity (in fact, in a large percentage of cases it does not) or leave him without hope if insanity does develop. Increasing knowledge as to the prevention and cure of mental diseases has made the situation considerably more hopeful. But by this very fact it has become increasingly important to be on the alert for pre-psychotic symptoms at the earliest opportunity, and this is where the knowledge of hereditary predispositions may be so valuable.

Theoretically, it would be very surprising, indeed, if there were not many types and degrees of inherited defect in the human brain, as there are even in the less complex organs, and if these defects did not produce abnormalities of many kinds in the thinking mechanism. However, it has been extremely difficult to trace the direct connection between a given type of mental disease and the organic defect responsible (as, for instance, if your automobile wasn't working right, you could trace the trouble to a faulty spark plug, or a clogged cylinder). Not even when the brain of an insane person is taken out and examined after death, are medical experts yet able to distinguish any differences, in construction, convolutions, etc., from those of a normal brain. The only organic clues provided so far are indications of chemical differences in brain-nerve cells of some insane persons as compared with normal ones, with recent theories suggesting as causes "oxygen starvation," or vitamin deficiencies, or inadequate production of certain hormones or "enzymes" vital to brain workings. There is also the revived theory that certain forms of body build go with some types of mental disease. But whatever the organic factors may be, all of those mentioned *could be due* to faulty gene action as well as to environmental adversities.

One important indication of a possible difference in the *physical* functioning of the brains of insane persons as compared with normal ones comes through the *electro-encephalograms* ("EEG" for short), or brain-wave recordings. Based on the fact that every person's brain continuously sends out rhythmic electrical beats, it is now reported that the brain waves of many persons with mental disease, even in preliminary stages, follow quite different patterns from those of normal persons. Added importance to this finding has been given by evidence that *the brain-wave pattern of any given individual, whether normal or abnormal, is to a great extent hereditary.* Where parents are mentally abnormal, a far higher than average percentage of the children have abnormal EEGs, even though these children themselves have yet not shown (or may never show) symptoms of mental disease; and in reverse, parents of mentally diseased children are also very likely to have abnormal EEGs, even though the parents themselves need not be psychotic. Most interestingly, Dr. William G. Lennox and others have shown that, among identical twins, in only 4 per cent are the brain waves dissimilar, whereas in fraternal twins the brain waves are unlike in 95 per cent of the cases.

But great strides have also been made by psychiatrists in detecting, identifying and classifying the mental diseases.* In earlier years there was constant confusion and inaccuracy in trying to establish heredity patterns for mental diseases because different types often were lumped together, under the general heading of "insanity," or one type was mistaken for another. Today much clearer distinctions are being made, and although there is often an overlapping or mingling of symptoms, the great majority of mental patients can be put into quite definite categories, these being principally the *schizophrenics,* the *manic-depressives,* the *senile* (or "old age") *psychotics,* the *psychopaths* and the *alcoholic* and *syphilitic* insane.

From this point on we shall take up these different types of insanity in detail, and largely in the order of their seriousness and prevalence.

Schizophrenia, also called *dementia praecox,* has these names for two reasons. Schizo-phrenia, Greek for "divided mind," is so applied because a victim of the disease has in many respects a "split" personality, a cleavage in the mental functions between the normal and abnormal. In the second term, the *praecox* (Latin), refers to the precocious aspect of the disease, the fact that it often appears at puberty, or before—much earlier than any of the other common mental diseases. "Schizophrenia," however, is the term now most commonly used.

* The growing knowledge about mental and behavior disorders and defects also has brought with it a clearer classification among the specialists who deal with them. Thus, it may be helpful to the reader to distinguish among these specialists, including the *psychiatrist,* the *neurologist,* the *neuropsychiatrist,* the *psychoanalyst* and the *clinical psychologist.* The psychiatrist is a physician who specializes in mental *diseases,* the neurologist one who deals primarily with nervous disorders, and the neuropsychiatrist one who combines both these practices. On the other hand, the psychoanalyst confines himself largely to *personality disorders,* chiefly the "neuroses," and he himself need not be a medical man. (The great majority of psychoanalysts, however, are psychiatrists, although the majority of psychiatrists have not taken the special training to qualify them as analysts.) Finally there is the clinical psychologist, whose function, if he works in the field of mental abnormality, is chiefly one of classifying the various cases, testing, and doing some corrective work or training of defectives.

The first symptoms of this disease usually are "introversion," or a withdrawal by the individual within himself. It may involve, in its various phases, shyness, timidity, aloofness from others, lack of interest in outside things, and more increasingly, states of ecstasy and hysteria, sometimes with suicidal attempts, or a growing emotional dullness and a withdrawal into the dream world of childhood. There are also subclassifications of schizophrenia: (a) the *paranoid,* quarrelsome and with delusions of persecution (Rudolph Hess, the Nazi leader who parachuted down into Scotland during World War II probably being of this type); (b) the *hebephrenic,* acting as if in a pleasant stupor, withdrawn into himself, smiling quietly (like the central figure in the play, *Harvey*—the genial alcoholic who conversed with an imaginary six-foot rabbit); and (c) the *catatonic,* going into tantrums or becoming rigid, in an "I won't" attitude. Then there are the milder and simpler forms of schizophrenia, the "schizoid" types, in which there are only occasional periods of abnormal or freakish behavior, but with no mental deterioration, often characterizing the extreme cranks and erratic individuals.

Schizophrenia is by far the most serious of the mental diseases, not merely because it is the most prevalent (accounting for more than half the cases in mental institutions), but because it is the most difficult to cure, is the most likely to induce dangerous and criminal behavior, and, because of its early onset, it exacts the greatest toll in years per individual, sometimes almost the entire life span. While it usually first manifests itself between the ages of 18 and 36, there is growing indication that many cases of schizophrenia *(dementia praecocissima)* begin in very early childhood, as early, some reports suggest, as the age of one or two, with the possibility that the child was mentally abnormal even at birth. (Most psychiatrists who have studied these early cases report no convincing evidence of any "environmental crises" as the causes, according to Dr. Lionel S. Penrose [1949].)

The fact that schizophrenia so often appears spontaneously, with no special factor in the environment to explain it, adds strength to the belief that it has some organic basis which in most cases is probably hereditary. For example—to supplement the general organic theories for mental disease previously mentioned—there have come findings from the Worcester Foundation Laboratories, in 1948, that the adrenal glands of schizophrenics do not respond with increased output of needed "stabilizing" chemicals in times of stress, as do those of normal persons. This, if fully established, may help to explain the added vulnerability of *potential* schizophrenics to mental breakdowns. But whatever the outside—or "inside"—influences may be, there is growing belief among authorities that *schizophrenia does not occur unless certain inherent predisposing weaknesses are present.*

Evidence for an hereditary basis for such a predisposition comes from many significant findings. Extensive studies among twins by Dr. Franz Kallmann, Dr. J. Rosanoff and others, have shown that where one of a pair of *identical* twins has schizophrenia, the odds are very great that the other twin also will have the disease. (In Dr. Kallmann's group, the disease occurred in both twins together in 85 per cent of the cases;in Dr. Rosanoff's group, in about 70 per cent.) On the other hand, among *fraternal* twins (whose heredity differs) all studies show that the disease does not appear in both together any more frequently than in any two children in the same family, i.e., in about 15 per cent of the cases. Even though environmental influences are often more alike for identical twins than for "fraternals," this by itself could hardly explain the vastly higher correlation in the appearance of the disease among them, or the many strange cases in which both developed schizophrenia at exactly the same time and with the same outcome. On the other hand, the fact that among many identical twins schizophrenia frequently does not appear in one, though it does in the other, proves that heredity by itself is certainly not always the sole or direct cause of the disease, and that environment, too, must be involved.

Dr. Kallmann and others also have shown that where schizophrenia has appeared in one member of a family, the chances are very much greater than average expectancy that it has appeared or will appear in other close relatives, the chances increasing with the degree of blood relationship. (Where parents have the disease, Dr. Kallmann reports that the chances of a child's being affected are nineteen times higher than that for the average population, and for grandchildren, nephews and nieces five times as great.) He also points out that there is no evidence whatsoever that "insanity is catching"—that mere association with a parent who is insane will make a child psychotic unless there is an hereditary predisposition.

But finding the genes responsible for schizophrenia or the predisposition to the disease, is another matter, because of the complexities of the disease, its various forms and times of onset, and the ever-present factor of environment. An assumption at present is that *inheritance in schizophrenia may come in an irregular way through several interacting genes, possibly a pair of recessives plus one or more secondary genes, all governed in their expression by certain environmental factors as yet not identified.* More simply stated, for a person to inherit schizophrenia, or the tendency, the genes would have to come from *both parents,* and even then, the disease need not appear unless the individual is exposed to certain outside influences—probably some special psychological or physical strain. The severity of the condition, and the time of its onset, may depend upon the outside influences as well as on differences in gene action.

Manic-depressive insanity, usually reported as less prevalent than schizophrenia, differs from it in its symptoms, time of onset, method of inheritance, and susceptibility to treatment.* The disease gets its name from the fact that its victims go from moods of mania to depression in alternating spells. At milder stages or in milder forms (referred to as *cyclothymia),* manic-depressives reveal themselves by their tendency to become over-elated or overdepressed, to overact and to talk too much, and by their difficulty in settling down to ordinary routines and social relationships. When this behavior carries to extremes, and those afflicted no longer are able to keep contact with reality, they give way to serious maniacal outbursts and require institutionalization. However, while unlike the schizophrenics, the manic-depressive insane may often recover after a comparatively short period of treatment (sometimes no more than a few months or a half year), a menacing aspect of the disease is that

* That manic-depressive insanity is actually far higher in incidence than schizophrenia is the contention of Dr. Tage Kemp, of Denmark, according to estimates for his country which he presented at the Cold Spring Harbor (Carnegie Institution) Symposium in June, 1950. Detailed studies in Denmark, Dr. Kemp reported, show that whereas the "expectancy" of schizophrenia is about 900 per 100,000 population, the incidence of manic-depressive insanity is 1,640 per 100,000 population. ("Expectancy" refers here to all persons at a given time who had been, are, or eventually can be expected to be afflicted with the disease in question, for any period or in any degree.) Also, with respect to manic-depressive insanity, Dr. Kemp reports that the 1,640 figure is an average for the two sexes which, if broken down, shows an incidence of the disease among females twice that among males: a manic-depressive "expectancy" of 2,240 females per 100,000 population as compared with 1,020 males. As to the discrepancy between the Danish figures and those previously reported elsewhere for the relative incidences of manic-depressive insanity and schizophrenia, a possible explanation (as given by Dr. Kemp to the author) is that the small and compact Danish population has been more accurately and intensively studied, leading to a more thorough detection of the manic-depressive cases, and a more correct diagnosis of many cases which are often mistakenly classified as schizophrenic.

individuals apparently cured may suddenly crack up again under undue stress and commit dangerous acts.

Manic-depressive insanity usually comes on during maturity, in middle life and occasionally in the older ages or in the late 'teens, but never as early as does schizophrenia. But, as in schizophrenia, while adverse environmental influences are involved in bringing on manic-depressive insanity, *a predisposition toward it is hereditary.* Here, studies of twins again are significant: Where one identical twin is a manic-depressive, so is the other in most cases, whereas in fraternal twins, the simultaneous appearance of the disease occurs no more often than in any two children of the same family. Also, numerous pedigrees tend to establish the inheritance of the disease. However (and again as in schizophrenia), there still is uncertainty as to the genetic mechanism involved, although some outstanding authorities *believe that the predisposition to manic-depressive insanity is inherited through semi-dominant, or irregularly dominant genes,* the irregularity being due perhaps to the required presence of certain other genes, and in addition, to certain adverse factors in the environment.

Comparing schizophrenia and manic-depressive insanity for the chances of inheritance there is another significant difference. We have pointed out that in schizophrenia *matching* genes for the predisposition must come from both parents. There is doubt as to the situation in manic-depressive insanity, but on the basis of the gene-mechanism believed involved, it is possible that two or more *different* genes may combine to cause the predisposition, so that the contribution from each parent need not be precisely the same. In either mental disease, the hidden genes in the population are prevalent enough so that where one parent has the disease there is always a chance that the other parent, though normal, may supply the other gene or genes required to produce the disease-predisposition in a child. However, the chances differ for the two diseases. According to Professor Penrose, in schizophrenia, where only one parent has the disease, the chances of a child's being similarly affected is roughly about *one in ten;* in manic-depressive insanity, where only one parent is afflicted, the chance for a child being similarly afflicted has been reported as high as roughly *one in three.* Another difference is that, where schizophrenia is more likely to crop out and has an earlier onset in males than in females, the reverse is true for manic-depressive insanity. In either case, estimates of the chances of having inherited the predisposition must be qualified by the sex, and by the age of the individual. On the latter point, if a person in whose family schizophrenia has appeared is well on into maturity with no sign of mental abnormality, there is little chance of being afflicted with the disease; in manic-depressive insanity, however, one must wait longer to be sure if there is a threat.

But this is especially important: Whatever the genes involved, *the manic-depressive tendency is very probably inherited separately and independently from that for schizophrenia.* It means for one thing, that where insanity appears or has appeared on both sides of a family *in the two different forms,* the chances of its occurring in any given child are not nearly so great as where the mental disease on both sides is of the same type. On the other hand, it is possible that *both* types of mental disease may run in the same family (in view of the high general incidence of these conditions). So, in tracing pedigrees or drawing conclusions from them, it is hardly enough to say, "There is a history of insanity," but it is important to know precisely what form or forms of insanity one is dealing with. Whether or not a "mixed" heredity, with one type of insanity appearing on one parental side and another type on the other, tends to heighten the hazards of becoming psychotic, has not been established.

The *psychopathic personality* has been identified in recent years as a distinct type of mental aberration, midway between sanity and insanity. This is what makes the condition so dangerous, because the psychopaths, although mentally sick (hence the name), may never be recognized by those about them as anything more than cold, selfish, emotionally immature and "peculiar" individuals, and so may go through life causing innumerable heartaches, if not, as in many cases, actually committing criminal acts. Their exact numbers are not known, but they may reach into hundreds of thousands. (In World War II, tens of thousands of American draftees were screened out as "psychopathic personalities," and many thousands more who saw service, and later entered mental hospitals, were classified as such.)

As identified by psychiatrists, the individuals with psychopathic personality are basically immature, live in the present and for themselves alone, have no firm emotional attachments or loyalties, are resistant to discipline, are chronic liars, and follow the early childhood pattern of getting things by ingratiation and extortion, going into tantrums if they do not get what they want. They may be found in every level of intelligence, and often are extremely shrewd or even brilliant, rising to high eminence through dynamic acts which may take violently antisocial forms. Thus, Adolph Hitler, in the opinion of most authorities, was a psychopath to an intense degree, while Hermann Goering was one of a milder type. Many of the most vicious gangsters and criminals, as well as lesser criminals (particularly swindlers), are psychopathic personalities. Yet it should also be noted that where the peculiar energies of the psychopath are accompanied by great talent and directed into creative activities, very high achievement may result—Richard Wagner and Voltaire being listed as examples.

However, the term "psychopathic personality" can be easily misapplied. In the opinion of Drs. P. M. Lichtenstein and S. M. Small it should be reserved only for individuals who have shown consistent maladjustment of this kind since childhood. As they point out, "The psychopath was just never put together properly, or was defective to begin with."

What causes the psychopathic personality is still a question. Possibly it may be something in the brain and nervous mechanism which inhibits normal emotional reactions.* But that is a guess. The fact that the condition dates back to earliest childhood, that it cannot be explained easily by any unusual circumstances, and that it persists throughout life regardless of any changes in the environment, leads to the inference by many psychiatrists that heredity is involved. However, no genetic studies so far have thrown any definite light on the possible mechanism of inheritance.

Not to be confused with the condition just described are various other forms of "queer" or psychopathic behavior which may result from glandular abnormalities, such as overactivity or underactivity of the thyroid, the pituitary, or the sex glands, or from brain tumors, or from accidents which may produce sudden changes in behavior in individuals previously normal. But it is even more necessary to make distinctions with regard to the *"psychoneuroses"* and other forms of personality disorders, which fall outside the range of insanity. The conditions are of many types and degrees: the "compulsive neuroses," "anxiety neuroses," hysterias, hypochondrias, etc., down to

* Recent research at the University of Iowa offers some evidence that psychopathic personalities might often be due to physical disorders of the brain. Irregular brain-wave patterns were 58 per cent more common in a group of psychopaths than in a control group of normal persons. (*Scientific American,* March, 1950.)

the plain garden variety of neuroses which almost anyone can develop under the properly adverse circumstances. Any good book on psychoanalysis will describe these conditions in detail, and tell what environmental factors may be involved in their causation. That heredity also may play a part in any of these conditions—by making it more likely for some individuals to become neurotic, and more severely so than others, under the same circumstances—is quite probable. Studies of mice, rats, dogs and other animals certainly do indicate that there are inherited degrees of emotionality and of susceptibility to neuroses under certain enforced conditions. But in human behavior there are so many complex influences that it is well nigh impossible in the case of the neurotic patterns to isolate and identify any suspected hereditary factors. We can only say that any two neurotic parents stand a good chance of having neurotic children, but to what extent this will be because of the home environment, or to what extent because of inherited "predisposition," remains at present in the realm of conjecture.

Alcoholism could also be added to the mental diseases or personality disorders, for it is now so regarded by psychiatrists. The same could be said for *drug addiction* and other types of self-destructive or anti-social behavior. But because these are still punishable under our legal codes, or are regarded as acts of wilful wrongdoing under religious and social doctrines, we shall deal with them in a later chapter on "Crime"—keeping in mind, however, that most authorities would now place virtually all crime itself in the category of "Sick Minds."

CHAPTER 26

SLOW MINDS

"YOU'RE an idiot!" or "—an imbecile!" or "—a moron!" are expressions which you may apply at times (lovingly or angrily, but never too seriously) to your husband, wife, sweetheart or best friend. You might imagine that you'd have no difficultv recognizing a *real* idiot, imbecile or moron if you met one. Quite possibly you'd guess right in many cases, but then only in a general way. For you'd have to be an expert to identify accurately the feeble-minded individuals of the different grades and types. And even the experts can make mistakes.

As we noted in the last chapter, "mental deficiency" is a catch-all term for "subnormal" intelligence applied to about 3 per cent of our population (in the United States and probably in most other countries). But what do we mean by "mental deficiency"? A general definition, to quote the American Association for Mental Deficiency, would be "a person with a mind so retarded as to make him incapable of competing on equal terms with his normal fellows, or of managing himself or his affairs with ordinary prudence." There need be no hesitancy about applying this to those in the lowest mental levels, the idiots and imbeciles. Our real difficulty comes as we go up the scale with the *morons,* and try to identify and grade them. Here we are forced to accept rather arbitrary standards based on existing intelligence tests. A person scoring between 90 and 110 on the Stanford-Binet Scale is considered as having a normal "IQ" (intelligence quotient). But a score below 90 is rated in this way according to the scale:

90-80: Dull
80-70: On the borderline between dullness and subnormalcy
*Below 70: Feeble-minded.**

* The term "feeble-minded" was formerly used (and occasionally still is) to designate mental defectives only above the grade of idiots or imbeciles, but the usual practice now is to apply the term collectively to all those below 70 IQ, and to identify the upper defectives by the term "moron," as we shall do here.

69-62: High-grade moron
62-55: Mid-grade moron
55-50: Low-grade moron
50-20: Imbecile
20- 0: Idiot

We can see from these gradings that even if we accept the tests as valid measurements of mental deficiency in different degrees, there is much room for faulty classification. If an individual varies in his responses under different conditions, or if his examiner makes a slight error, a shift of a few points in IQ can classify him as an "imbecile" rather than a "moron," or a "moron" rather than a "dull-normal" person, or as "dull" instead of completely normal. Beyond that, there always is the question of how accurately the tests measure *basic* intelligence (which will be dealt with more fully in the chapter on normal IQs), and what allowances are made for environmental factors. Also, two individuals with the same low IQ may be deficient for quite different reasons or in different phases of the tests, or may vary greatly in their capacity to have their IQs raised by special training or treatment. All of these and other difficulties in the way of diagnosis and classification have greatly complicated the problem of establishing the inheritance of most types of mental deficiency.

Nevertheless, there is much to suggest that *heredity is either directly responsible or plays an important part in the production of the large majority of the mental defectives, with probably no more than 40 per cent due solely to environmental factors.*

Each type of mental defective, however, must be considered separately, for the factors producing one type seldom have any relationship to those producing another. This was largely overlooked in the early studies of pedigrees of mental deficiency, when idiots, imbeciles and morons were lumped together indiscriminately on the wholly erroneous assumption that intelligence was a unit, and that all different degrees of mentality were merely the results of variations in a few "key" genes.

Our first clear distinction, then, must be between the two main groups of mental defectives: the idiots and imbeciles, in the one group, and the morons in the other. The first group is very much rarer in incidence, all the low-grade defectives together comprising no more than about one-fourth of one per cent of the general population. Morons, the second group, may number about 2 per cent, or somewhat more, of the general population. The most important differences between the two groups, however, are in their physical natures and the factors causing them. Almost all of the idiots and imbeciles are *physically as well as mentally defective,* their mental impairment being accompanied by, or resulting from, some usually rare structural, glandular or neurological abnormality which produces a variety of other effects. In this class are the *Mongolian idiots,* the *cretins,* the *microcephalics,* the *amaurotic family idiots,* and a small proportion of the mentally retarded epileptics.

The *morons,* on the other hand, are very largely *"aclinical"* cases —without any physical abnormalities, constitutional defects or symptoms of disease to explain their condition—their mental deficiency, so far as is known, being due directly to some basic slowness in the workings of the brain. Making a comparison with stature differences, Dr. Penrose points out that mental levels ranging from low to high may be as normal and natural, biologically, as stature ranges from very short to very tall. Again—in contrast to the idiots and imbeciles—the factors causing morons are much more common and ordinary, whether hereditary or environmental. However, there also are a minority of the morons whose backwardness may be due to some nutritional deficiency, to various diseases, to reading disabilities, hearing or other special sensory motor defects, to emotional disturbances, or to lack of proper training. The proportions of these probably are decreasing with improvements in living conditions, medical care and education.

Thus, whatever may be the factors that produce idiots and imbeciles, they are *different from and independent* of those responsible for morons. Which is to say, idiots and imbeciles may appear in a family irrespective of the intelligence of the parents, because, as we've noted, they are not primarily products of defective "intelligence" genes but of some over-all abnormality. Morons, on the other hand, being in most cases direct products of such defective "mental" genes, are far more likely to occur in families where low-grade intelligence is common than in families of normal intelligence. Emphasizing further the distinction in the way the two main groups of defectives are produced, we have the paradox that two moron parents, generally, are not much more likely to have an idiot child than are two brilliant parents. This, however, requires some qualification, for among low-level families in depressed communities, where mating between defectives, and adverse environmental factors are combined, the likelihood is increased of mental defectives of all types appearing together.

Supporting the foregoing conclusions are innumerable studies made in the United States, Great Britain and other countries. We shall not bore you with detailed figures and percentages, but taking up the morons first, here are the principal findings:

—More than 75 per cent of the morons come from about 10 per cent of the population, from families with a high incidence of mental defect.

—Where one member of a family is a moron, the chance is about five times the average that another member will be similarly retarded.

—Where both parents are morons, the chances are anywhere from 60 to 75 per cent that any given child also will be mentally subnormal.

—In identical twins, if one is a moron, so is the other in virtually every case, although among fraternal twins this holds true in less than 50 per cent of the cases (some studies putting it at 25 per cent).

But with all these, and many more facts, geneticists still are not certain as to precisely what genes are responsible for producing morons. What can be said is that earlier conclusions that morons were produced by a pair of simple recessive genes are hardly tenable, at least in most cases, for if this were so we would not have many instances of two moron parents producing normal children. At the same time, however, the fact that in such matings, collectively, a majority of moron offspring do result, and that mental defectiveness runs heavily in certain families for successive generations, does indicate that not too many genes are involved. The most acceptable theory, then, is that *feeble-mindedness in the moron grades is usually produced by multiple genes—a pair of recessives PLUS some supplementary dominant gene or genes.*

While we have dealt largely with the rôle of heredity in producing morons, we should not lose sight of the fact, already stressed, that some individuals are mentally retarded, or have been erroneously classified as such, because of learning obstacles, emotional blocks, or other factors unrelated to their inherent mental capacities. Throughout the United States such retarded young people by the thousands, who formerly might have been consigned to the mental and social scrap heaps, now are being salvaged by special treatment.

Yet for the great majority of the *truly* feeble-minded, while IQs may be raised somewhat and better adjustment made possible, hope for great improvement is premature. Any startling claims in that direction must be approached with great caution.*

Of course, anything that could be done to help mentally retarded persons to have a happier and more useful life would be of immense value. But geneticists would still point out that in the case of those whose deficiency is due to hereditary factors, no improvements in their own capacities would in any way lessen the chances of their passing on their defective genes, and producing genetically defective offspring.

Other reported methods of raising the IQs by chemicals or diet also are still in the uncertain category, with no evidence available that any of these methods can do more than temporarily improve *test performance* without actually raising the intelligence level. Preliminary reports of limited successes with the *glutamic acid* treatment have been considerably modified by follow-up studies, but the experiments still are going on. If this, or some other chemical treatment, proves at all effective, it might be so, principally (or only) in the cases of those whose mental backwardness is due to some chemical or metabolic deficiency.

IDIOTS AND IMBECILES. These unfortunates, we already have noted, are in a class entirely different from the morons in every important respect, but among themselves they also differ radically in the nature of their conditions and the ways in which they are produced. Their relative numbers are extremely hard to determine, because many are not entered in the records or are improperly classified, and those of some types die off at earlier ages, and at much higher rates than others. The rough estimate might be made that of the very low-grade mental defectives one encounters, about 20 per cent are Mongolian idiots; another 10 per cent are microcephalics; another 10 per cent embrace the cretins, the amaurotics, the seriously

* Success in raising IQs by an average of 10 points in certain mentally retarded groups has been cited in a number of studies. But in 1946 the unusual claim was made by Dr. Bernadine G. Schmidt, a teacher of special classes in Chicago schools, that the IQs of 254 boys and girls, all previously listed as feeble-minded, with an average IQ of 52, had been raised within eight years *by an average of 40 points*. However, access to the original data on which the findings were based was not given to some psychologists who sought to check on the findings, and the conclusions have been seriously questioned by a number of authorities. Writing in the *Psychological Bulletin* (July, 1948), Professor Samuel A. Kirk raised doubts as to whether the original IQs of Dr. Schmidt's group had not been greatly undervaluated, and also pointed to other possible flaws in the study.

retarded epileptics, the hydrocephalics and certain other types; and the balance includes those whose conditions are the results of prenatal upsets (especially in the prematurely-born), birth injuries, infectious diseases, accidents, etc. (Very few cases of idiocy, however, result from falls on the head or other accidents in infancy and childhood.)

The *Mongolian idiot,* or imbecile, is so called because of the small, slanting eyes with inner skin folds, characteristic of this condition, which give him a "Mongolian" look (to Caucasians), although in no other way does the name apply, nor is there any racial connection.

Seeing this type of idiot smiling, lively and cheerful, as he usually is, you might well wonder what he (or she) has to be so happy about. For the very same mishap in development which retards him mentally also brings with it many other abnormalities, apparent at birth: bridge of nose flat and sunken, forehead generally large and misshapen, ears small and malformed, tongue fissured and often protruding, voice guttural, and hands frequently deformed ("stubbed" or "webbed"), with peculiar palm patterns. Moreover, Mongolian idiots have a hard time surviving, many dying in early childhood, and if they do manage to live up to and beyond puberty, their growth is stunted and in most cases they fail to develop sexually. To date no cure for Mongolian idiocy is known, though in certain cases thyroid treatments result in some improvement if thyroid deficiency is involved.

What can account for this strange assortment of afflictions? The fact that they appear repeatedly in the same cluster (with so much similarity that almost all Mongolians look as if they were brothers and sisters) indicates that there must be some single "key" factor which asserts itself in the very earliest prenatal stages, thus affecting many aspects of the child's development. We have seen in a previous chapter that such "syndromes" may occur through the action of "key" genes or through some early glandular upset. One theory, then, is that Mongolian idiocy is almost entirely environmental in origin, resulting from some glandular (pituitary or ovarian) deficiency in the mother which communicates itself to the child in embryo. A basis for this belief is the fact that greatly disproportionate numbers of Mongolian idiots are born to older mothers, particularly those beyond the late thirties. (The father's age, by the way, has no bearing on the matter.) Specifically, as Dr. Penrose reports, where in mothers up to age 34 the incidence of Mongolian-idiot births is less than 1 per thousand, in mothers aged 35 to 39 it approaches 3 per thousand; in those aged 40 to 44, more than 7 per thousand; and in "old" mothers, aged 44 to 49, it averages 27.5 per thousand, or about once in every thirty-six births. (In the extreme ages for motherhood, Dr. Clemens E. Benda believes the ratio of Mongolian idiots may reach as high as one in ten births.) All this clearly indicates that some unfavorable influence associated with the aging of the mother often gives the child a bad start—perhaps from the moment the fertilized egg is implanted—with respect to this condition. The exact factors involved, however, are not known, nor is there any evidence of any particular type of maternal illness or disability associated with Mongolian pregnancies.

But there is much to suggest there also has to be something defective in the *child's heredity* to cause him to develop specifically as a Mongolian idiot. As evidence, in identical twins, when one is a Mongolian idiot the other also is in every case reported so far, although this is not so with fraternal twins, who, while sharing whatever adverse prenatal conditions there may be, do not have the same heredity. On the other hand, if a mother has had one Mongolian idiot it seldom happens that she has another, although the same prenatal environment may prevail. However, there are cases of two Mongolians being born to the same mother, not twins and not necessarily in succession. Added to this is the fact that where the condition appears it is found with more frequency in relatives than in the general population.

All of this has led most authorities to the conclusion, as stated by Dr. Sidney L. Halperin (1945), that "some genetic factor, as yet unknown, is involved in Mongolian idiocy, possibly due to genes whose expression may be incomplete or a matter of degree," i.e., which won't produce their effects except in a certain unfavorable prenatal environment. Whether or not the "Mongolian-idiocy" genes are simple recessives, as some studies suggest, remains to be proved.

The *cretin,* whose mental age usually ranges from that of the imbecile up into the moron class, is clearly a product of prenatal thyroid deficiency, in many cases being born to mothers who are goitrous. (However, the mother's age is not a factor in cretinism, as it is in Mongolian idiocy.) This thyroid deficiency not only stunts the child's mental growth, but dwarfs the body, so that at the age of 25 a cretin may look and act like a very dull small boy with a large head, pug nose, pot belly, thick lips and protruding tongue. Because cretinism may run in some families more than others under like conditions, it has been suggested that it might have some hereditary basis—that in addition to the defectiveness of the mother there might be some inherited thyroid defect or special susceptibility in the child (perhaps through recessive genes)—but this still is open to some question. What is clear is that very early thyroid treatment of the cretin, as soon as the condition shows itself (usually by the sixth month), may help a great deal to restrain its effects. However, earlier hopes of a complete cure have not been borne out, follow-up studies of treated cases showing that while there is much improvement, only a few cretins attain a near-normal mentality, and all remain physically retarded.

The *microcephalic* is an unfortunate of the "pinhead" type, often exhibited in circus side shows, whose head is much smaller than average, and whose intelligence may range between that of an idiot and an imbecile. The condition results from an early stoppage in the growth of the brain and the skull enclosing it, the individual usually being also dwarfed. It is clear that some of the cases of microcephaly *are inherited through recessive genes,* there being many instances of families with several microcephalic children. But the condition might also be caused by some prenatal upsets, such as a pituitary deficiency, and in rarer cases, by careless radiation of the mother during pregnancy. Quite a number of such "X-ray" microcephalics have been reported in medical studies, and in a notable law suit in New Jersey in 1941, parents of one of these were awarded $50,000 in their suit against a doctor. While increased medical precautions have greatly lessened the chances of similar prenatal mishaps occurring through X-ray treatments, an entirely new threat is held out by the possibilities of atomic warfare, for radiation so set loose might conceivably have the same effects in producing microcephalics.

Amaurotic family idiocy results from a peculiar hereditary defect in the nerve cells of the brain and spinal cord, which causes these cells to swell up, fill with fat, and produce not only idiocy, but blindness and paralysis, and in most cases, death within a few years. This form of idiocy is of several types, differing in time of onset, seriousness, and the genes responsible. Most common, and earliest in onset, is the *infantile* type of amaurotic idiocy, which is due to a pair of simple recessive genes, and occurs most often where parents are closely related.

Gargoylism is a rare affliction in children, discovered only in recent decades, which not only causes severe mental defect, but also produces extreme dwarfism and other external and internal abnormalities, and is usually fatal before adolescence. It is due to a peculiar disorder of fat metabolism which, as in amaurotic idiocy, affects the brain and nerve cells. Whether or not it is inherited (as has been claimed), and if so how, is a question.

Hydrocephalus ("water head") is a condition in which the brain fills with fluid, swelling the head. While this may produce convulsions and mental defect, it often does not (especially if there is early treatment to drain off the fluid), and there are many cases of hydrocephalic children who attain high degrees of intelligence. A few instances of several cases in the same family have been reported, but theories of its heredity are doubtful. (The same condition, however, has been found inherited in many domestic animals—dogs, rabbits, livestock, etc.—in whom it usually proves fatal very quickly.) Where the condition appears after infancy, it is probably due in most cases to brain tumors, which are not hereditary.

An odd, chemically induced type of mental defect is *phenylpyruvic amentia* (or idiocy), named after the acid found in the urine of those affected. The condition, involving some metabolic disorder which retards the brain workings, is produced by simple recessive genes, and accounts for somewhat less than 1 per cent of the mental defectives.

Epiloia (tuberose sclerosis), another curious condition, produces not only idiocy but epilepsy, tumors and other defects, with malformations in the brain resembling potato roots. It appears to be inherited as an irregular dominant.

Many other rare hereditary conditions which produce idiocy or imbecility among their effects could be added to our list, but these are of interest only to specialists and to the very few unhappy families concerned. But to conclude this discussion we might answer one of the most common questions asked of doctors by fearful parents after an idiot child has appeared: "What danger is there of having another?" A former tendency was to reply, "Lightning doesn't strike twice in the same place." This might be so if the child was rendered defective purely through some prenatal accident. But we can see now that too much optimism certainly is unjustified in those cases where an idiot or imbecile is the direct result of heredity, as in the amaurotics, or even where heredity may interoperate with adverse environment, as in producing Mongolians, cretins or microcephalics. While it remains true that two successive idiots or imbeciles are not common in the same family, and are much less likely to be born to the same mother than are two successive morons, Dr. Penrose concludes that "when two parents of normal intelligence have one idiot or imbecile child of unspecified type, the chances of another are roughly one in forty, or ten times the average. If the parents are blood relatives, the chances are considerably higher." However, in the specific cases of amaurotics and those other rarer idiots who are produced by *simple recessive genes,* the chances in any instance of a "repeat" defective are still higher, following the regular Mendelian ratio that if a mother has had one such child, the probability is *one in four* of any succeeding child being similarly defective.

By and large, idiots and imbeciles are of far less concern to either their parents or to society than are the *morons,* because if the lowest-grade defectives survive much beyond puberty, they are generally kept in institutions and do not present the problem of trying to adjust them to schooling, jobs or social relationships. Even more important, most idiots and many imbeciles remain sexually undeveloped or sterile, or otherwise are in no position to reproduce themselves. Thus, the overwhelming proportion of idiots and imbeciles comes from the ranks of normal parents. Morons, on the other hand, not only are far more numerous, but living much longer and in most cases being outside of institutions, are under continuous handicaps in schools, jobs and social relationships, contributing heavily to the "problem" groups. Of greatest concern to society, they are likely to marry and produce a high percentage of offspring who if not all genetically defective, will be improperly reared. What should or can be done about the morons will be left for discussion in our concluding chapters on "Eugenics."

EPILEPSY. The first point to stress about epilepsy is that it belongs with the mental defects only to the extent that a certain proportion of the epileptics are mentally retarded. For the large majority, however, the condition is solely a nervous ailment.

In many respects the "falling sickness" still is a mystery, which might seem strange in view of its having perhaps the longest recorded history of any of the mental or nervous afflictions, with countless millions having been victimized by it through the ages. In the United States alone it is estimated that there are today more than a million persons epileptic in some degree, and many times that number with a "predisposition"—who could develop epilepsy under certain adverse circumstances.

Because it may affect behavior in a peculiar way, and frequently (though not necessarily) impairs the mind, epilepsy in the past was all too often associated with insanity, and in most mental institutions epileptics were indiscriminately herded together with the insane. In some benighted localities this still is being done, but fortunately, the tendency more and more is to regard epileptics as primarily victims of nervous disorders who should be treated as such, and only where there is some accompanying serious impairment of the mind (in a minority of the cases) is the need felt to institutionalize them.

To be understood, first, is that epilepsy is not the name of a disease, but is a general term applied to a symptom, or symptoms, of a variety of convulsive disorders which may be otherwise completely unrelated. In fact, we should more properly speak of the "epilepsies," classifying them according to the manner in which they arise—through organic abnormalities, diseases, injuries, tumors or chemical disturbances affecting the brain and nervous system. What they have in common is only the epileptic symptoms—sudden loss of consciousness, or loss of control over the nervous and muscular system—manifested in dozens of abnormal behavior patterns. The lesser patterns, without seizures, come under the heading of *petit mal,* the more serious, under *grand mal.* In this latter class are the convulsive fits, falling, foaming at the mouth, etc.—an unhappy spectacle which perhaps many readers have seen. Often the epileptic does not fall but becomes pale and stares blankly, being wholly or partly unconscious meanwhile. During such states he may commit strange and irrational acts, and not be aware later of what he has done. (In some instances, among unenlightened peoples in the past —and still true in many primitive tribes—epileptics were regarded as divinely inspired individuals whose strange behavior was dictated by holy spirits.)

On the question of inheritance, we may say at once *there is no conclusive evidence that epilepsy in its common forms is directly inherited, but there is much to suggest that some predisposition may be hereditary.* In only a very few rare diseases in which epilepsy is a concomitant has direct heredity been clearly proved as the cause. One of these is *myoclonus epilepsy,* which comes on in childhood and differs from the ordinary type in that there are intermittent spasms and tremors between seizures, and when seizures occur there is no loss of consciousness. This condition appears due to a single pair of recessive genes.

But keeping in mind always that the epilepsies are merely symptoms of many unrelated conditions, proof of inheritance in rare forms has little meaning with regard to other and more common forms. Again, a clear distinction must be made between epilepsy which results from obvious injuries, or diseases, and that which seems to appear spontaneously with no known outside causes. (In these latter cases epilepsy is called "idiopathic.") Thus, even though epilepsy may occur in several members of the same family, or with frequency in a pedigree, one must be quite sure that a common factor is involved before drawing any conclusions regarding inheritance.

However, there are some significant findings: The incidence of epilepsy is about five times higher among close relatives of epileptics than in the general population, and where one member of a pair of identical twins is epileptic, so is the other in about 70 per cent of the cases (four times the correlation in fraternal twins). But most striking are the brain-wave studies made by Dr. William G. Lennox and Dr. Frederic A. Gibbs of Harvard University which show that the abnormal wave patterns characteristic of most epileptics also occur in some degree in a very high percentage (as much as 60 per cent) of their close relatives, even though the majority of these persons are themselves not epileptic; that where a child is epileptic, one or the other parent is likely to have an "epileptoid" brain-wave pattern; and that in identical twins, if one is epileptic and the other not, the same brain-wave pattern is nevertheless present in the non-afflicted one as in the other.

Thus, most authorities believe that *epilepsy is not inherited as such, but as a tendency or susceptibility* by way of some weakness or defect in the brain or nervous system, and that the condition does not assert itself unless there is a "push" given in the wrong direction by some accident or injury (prenatally, at birth, or later), or by some infectious disease, metabolic disorder, tumor or other adverse influence. As Dr. Penrose suggests, a strong enough stimulus, such as passage of electric currents through the brain, might

HEREDITY IN BRAIN-WAVES ("EEGs")

From recordings by Dr. William G. Lennox and Drs. E. L. and F. A. Gibbs*

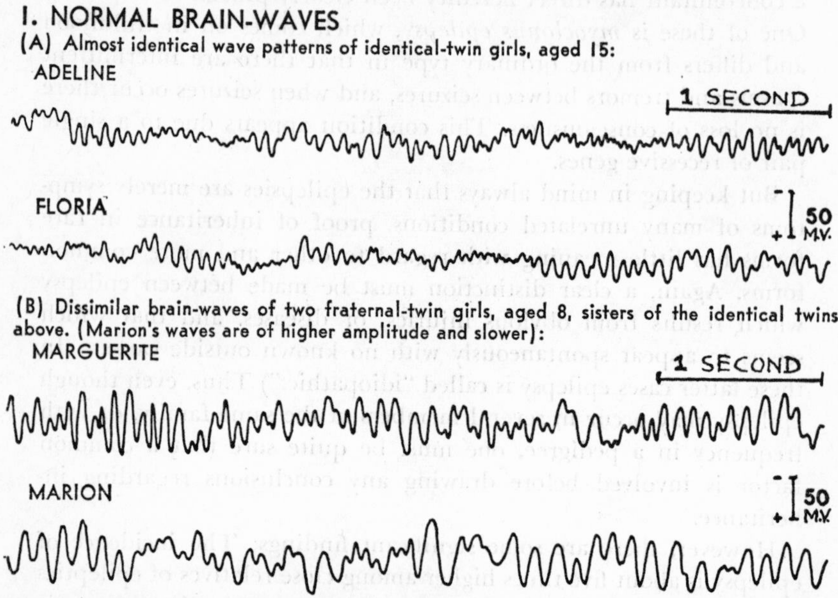

I. NORMAL BRAIN-WAVES

(A) Almost identical wave patterns of identical-twin girls, aged 15:

(B) Dissimilar brain-waves of two fraternal-twin girls, aged 8, sisters of the identical twins above. (Marion's waves are of higher amplitude and slower):

(Short horizontal lines with each graph, at right, shows waves per second; small upright lines represent deflection made by 50 microvolts of current. All records from the left occipital region of brain, except for 2-A, below, right occipital.)

2. "EPILEPTIC" BRAIN-WAVES

(A) Identical "epileptic" patterns of identical-twin sisters, aged 11, both with frequent *petit-mal* seizures. (In each case the initial short section shows patient's normal wave, followed by extreme "spike-wave" pattern coinciding with first few seconds of a period of unconsciousness.)

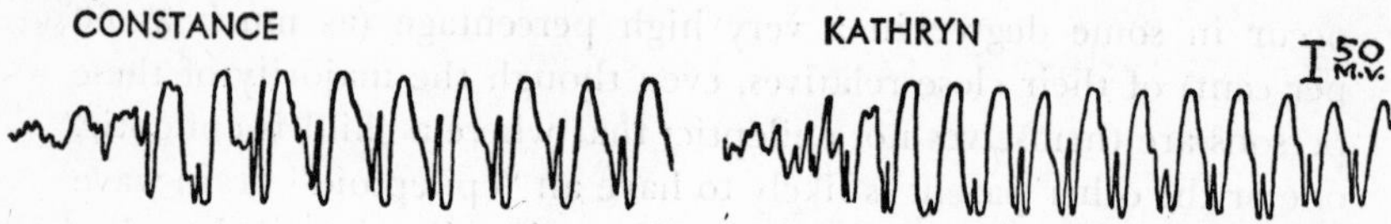

(B) Similar abnormal patterns of another pair of identical-twin sisters, aged 10, but only one of whom has epilepsy (5 to 10 *petit-mal* seizures daily), the other girl being as yet outwardly normal).

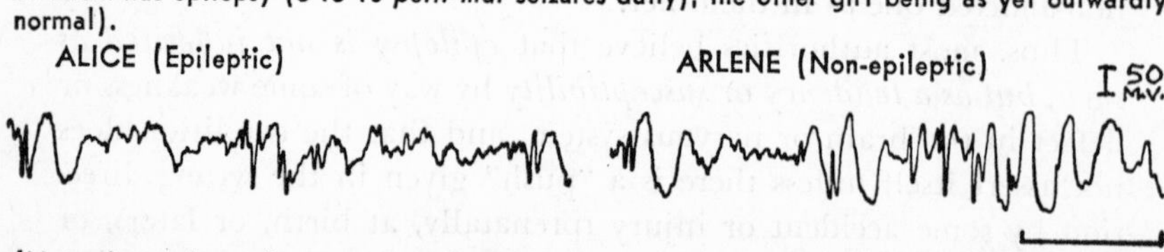

(Note that Arlene, the as yet non-epileptic twin, has brain-waves even more abnormal than her epileptic twin. However, tests show that Arlene, too, has a special predisposition to epilepsy, and might develop it under stress.)

* Tracings and data prepared for author by Dr. Lennox. Recordings No. I appeared originally in article by Drs. Lennox and Gibbs, *Journal of Heredity*, Aug., 1945; recordings No. 2 to appear in article by Dr. Lennox, *Journal* Amer. Medic. Assn., 1950 (in press).

produce convulsions in everyone; but in some individuals there may be genes which, by producing slight structural or chemical changes in the nervous systems, might cause them to have seizures under mild stimuli which would not affect normal persons.* But only guesses have so far been made as to the genes involved in producing the "epileptic tendency." Tentative theories are that these genes are either recessives or two dominants (one dominant producing an abnormal brain-wave pattern, but in a double dose producing epilepsy or the tendency to it).

As to environmental factors, other recent studies indicate that unfavorable prenatal conditions provided by the mother—particularly if she is older—will greatly increase the chance of a child's being epileptic, if the tendency is present. One study (Beall, Stanton, 1947) indicates that the chance is four times greater where the mother is in her late forties than for a mother in her twenties. (This does not mean, however, that the prenatal factors involved in epilepsy are in any way the same as those for idiocy, where the mother's age also is significant. The fact is that Mongolian idiots are rarely epileptic.) Also suggested in some studies is that there is a relationship between *migraine* (the two conditions often going together in many individuals or families) and epilepsy, and if the mother, or the father, are sufferers from migraine, there is an increased chance of the child's being epileptic. (One theory is that a double dose of "migraine" genes will produce epilepsy.) In sum, Dr. Lennox concludes that in the case of an "average" epileptic parent, there is about a 1 in 40 chance that any given child also will be epileptic, but that this chance is lessened if acquired factors contributed to the parent's epilepsy, if his or her seizures began late, if the family is free of epilepsy or migraine, or if the afflicted parent marries someone free of the predisposition.

On the question of epilepsy as related to mental defect, statistics are not too certain. However, rough estimates are that about two-thirds of the epileptics are average or above average in intelligence, about 23 per cent slightly below average, and only 10 per cent sufficiently backward mentally to be institutionalized. It also has been brought out, by Dr. Lennox, that where persons with normal minds develop epilepsy as a result of "predisposing heredity," mental

* Significant here are also many studies with experimental animals, showing that in rats and mice there are certain strains which have definite hereditary degrees of susceptibility to convulsions. (One super-sensitive strain of mice who can be killed by sound, will be discussed in Chapter 27.)

deterioration is much less likely to occur than in people in whom epilepsy is purely acquired as the result of some accident or injury. Thus, the average IQ of epileptics without brain injury is 96, of those with brain injury, 77. But whether or not epilepsy affects intelligence, it can hardly fail to influence the sufferer's personality according to the nature and severity of the symptoms, the age at which the individual becomes afflicted, and the attitude of the family, friends and others.

Finally, a few words about the possibility of "curing" epilepsy. At this writing some promising results have been reported, through treatments with drugs, diet, etc., in reducing, or in some cases almost eliminating the seizures in many epileptics. But experts have warned that this does not constitute a "cure," that in many cases treatment does not help, and that in all cases where one is dealing with "hereditary" epilepsy, the afflicted person, if married or of marriageable age, should give very careful thought to the possibilities of transmitting to a child whatever genes may be involved in producing the condition. At the same time, the reader, if personally concerned, should keep in mind all the other aspects of epilepsy which we have discussed, and should not reach any decisions without consulting a specialist. That, by the way, would be good advice with regard to all other nervous or mental ailments we've discussed.

CHAPTER 27

SEXUAL ABNORMALITIES

THERE is the familiar story of the husband and wife who could not decide whether they wanted a boy or a girl, and so got a child who wasn't either.

We are speaking not of a "male who behaves like a female," or vice versa (to be discussed in a later chapter), but of human beings who are *biologically* "in-betweeners." Such individuals may be produced—not through any thinking by the parents, need we say!—but through some genetic or environmental upset which may also account for various other kinds of abnormalities or defects in sexual construction.

The Bible says, "Male and female created He them. . . ." There is no need to dispute that. But however distinctly the first man and woman might have been differentiated the one from the other, in the billions that are assumed to have sprung from them can be found every gradation of sexuality. In short, sex is a highly variable characteristic, and there is not always a clear-cut distinction between "male" and "female."

Think back to the chapter, "Boy or Girl?" We learned that sex determination depends on which combination of "sex" chromosomes an individual receives at conception. An X and a Y produce a male. Two Xs produce a female.

This is fundamentally correct. But as in all other human characteristics, the best laid plans of the chromosomes "gang aft a-gley." Let's see what can happen.

First: *The X and Y chromosomes are not the sole arbiters of sex or sex characteristics.* While they carry the principal genes which start sex development off in one direction or another, there also are "sex-influencing" genes in other chromosomes received equally by both sexes. At any rate, *all individuals carry in them at the outset the potentialities to develop characteristics of either sex.* This can be seen in the earliest stages of prenatal life when similar sex glands and rudimentary "maleness" and "femaleness" sex organs are found in both sexes. The process of sex determination from there on is merely this:

In the normal XY individual the "maleness" organs and sex characteristics develop step by step to their fullest point, while the "femaleness" organs and characteristics remain in the rudimentary stage.

In the normal XX individual the "femaleness" organs and characteristics develop to their fullest point, while the "maleness" organs and physical traits remain suppressed.

But at any point along the way, from conception onward, something may go wrong with the process. Even when the sex of the individual appears to be "set," the process may go in reverse gear to some extent or other. In fact, *the type of sexuality of any individual can be changed in some degree or varied at every stage of life.*

If we turn to more elementary creatures, we can see rather amazing deviations from what we think of in humans as "sex" normalcy. Many lower organisms, such as the snail, earthworm, flatworm, or oyster (as well as most plants and flowers) are normally *double-sexed* in structure and function, either simultaneously or alternately. How can this happen? Strangely enough, the sex-chromosome mechanism in these lowly creatures is basically the same as in humans. They, too, start out with the potentialities of either sex. But in the snail or earthworm, the "sex" genes, instead of sending the individual off in either the "maleness" or "femaleness" direction, allow potentialities of both sexes to assert themselves, and both types of sex organs to develop. In the oyster, however, the "sex" genes are so regulated that they allow first the male organs to develop, then go into reverse and make way for the female development, the process being capable of repetition from year to year. Or, as we might state it in verse:

The oyster leads a double life,
One year, it's husband, next year, wife.
It's both a father and a mother;
It's both a sister and a brother.
No wonder, if all this is true,
The oyster ends up in a stew!

Another double-sexed type, but strictly in the freak class, is the gynandromorph, or "half-and-half" creature, in which one side of

ODDITIES IN SEX

THE TAPEWORM

s hermaphroditic (double-sexed), each section
omplete with both male and female organs,
nd able to fertilize itself.

THE SNAIL AND THE EARTHWORM

while also double-sexed, have their sex organs so placed that each individual must mate with another of its kind, but playing both male and female roles.

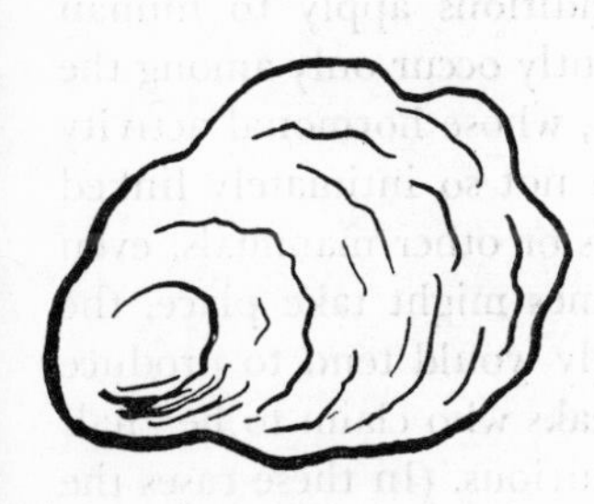

AN OYSTER

lternates from one sex to another. It starts
fe as a male, becomes a female, may turn into
male again, etc.

IN BEES

the same egg, if fertilized, will produce a female; if not fertilized, will develop into a male.

BEFORE

AFTER

IN POULTRY

female may turn outwardly into a "male," or a male into a "female," as a result of some upset in the sex organs or hormonal balance.

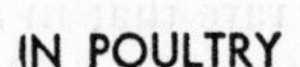

the body may be of one sex, the other side of the opposite sex. Or, sometimes, the gynandromorph may be male in the upper half, female in the lower half, or vice versa. Such freaks (confined entirely to the invertebrates) are fairly common in many species which are normally single-sexed, including butterflies, moths, wasps, bees, flies, ants and spiders. (If you were or are a naturalist, you may have caught one of them.)

One way for a gynandromorph to be produced is by having one of the X chromosomes in a prospective female go awry or get lost during the very first stages of cell division after conception. In all the cells which subsequently develop, those with the original two Xs will produce female characteristics, those with only the single X will produce male characteristics.

Now in what way do such queer conditions apply to human beings? The true gynandromorphs apparently occur only among the more elementary creatures, such as insects, whose hormonal activity is limited and whose different organs are not so intimately linked together as are our own. In human beings or other mammals, even where derangement of the sex chromosomes might take place, the sex hormones circulating through the body would tend to produce a "blending" effect throughout. Circus freaks who claim to be "half man, half woman" may be set down as spurious. (In these cases the freak is generally a male in whom one breast is overdeveloped, giving him a female contour on one side, a male contour on the other.) One instance has been reported of a human with male sex organs on one side and female organs on the other, but while regarded by some as a "true gynandromorph," this individual was more likely of the type we will discuss next.

"Intersexual" conditions, in which an individual has organs of both sexes, or mixed secondary sex traits of both sexes (breast development, body development, face and body hair, etc.), occur among human beings in various gradations. There are males with undeveloped masculine genitalia and various degrees of female genital development, and females with undeveloped or incomplete female organs and with rudimentary—or sometimes fairly well-developed—male organs.

The *"true hermaphrodite"*—the completely "in-between" individual, with *sex-glands* as well as organs and other characteristics of both sexes—is so exceedingly rare that in all medical annals to date only forty cases have been reported. Such individuals may be produced if the rudimentary "maleness" and "femaleness" sex glands and organs, present in embryos of both sexes, go on to develop equally (through some upset which results in a "tie" race), instead of following the normal procedure in which one of the sex mechanisms takes precedence over the other. *But no case is on record of any human being who was able to function reproductively as both male and female.*

Where there is only a partial upset in early sex determination or sexual development, we have the much more common condition, in about 1 in 1,000 persons, known as "pseudo-hermaphroditism" (or, more properly, "intersexuality"). In this the individual has *either* ovaries or testes—*not both*—but may nonetheless have external organs of both sexes, with one type usually predominant. Thus, while genetically either a male or female, the pseudo-hermaphrodite may be mistakenly classified in infancy or childhood as of the wrong sex. Such cases from time to time make newspaper headlines. Many readers may recall that after the 1935 Olympic Games, officials had red faces when they discovered that the Czech "girl" who had won the women's 800 meter run was in reality (though at the time unbeknown to her) a *male pseudo-hermaphrodite.* A subsequent operation which released the male organs embedded in her abdomen turned "her" into a man. Again, in 1936, one of England's leading "women" athletes, holding records for the shot-put and javelin throws, underwent a similar operation which transformed her into a male. (Since then all female entrants in the Olympic Games have been required to undergo a careful physical examination.) In the opposite direction, a Polish army "male" sergeant was reported as having been "changed" into a woman, and of having then given birth to a child. But in the great majority of cases, pseudo-hermaphrodites are females wrongly classified as males.

One recent case inspired a fascinating piece of "chromosome-detective" work—the first known study of the chromosomes of an intersexual human—by Dr. Aura E. Severinghaus of Columbia University. A 39-year-old "woman" hospital patient in New York was found to have secondary sex characteristics and genitalia that apparently were a combination of male and female types. What was this person genetically? Dr. Severinghaus made an examination of the sex-gland cells and found that the cells contained the *XY*—male—chromosome combination. (See our illustration, next page.)

Whether hermaphroditism in humans—true or pseudo—has any

hereditary basis is a question. In goats, there is evidence that the frequent occurrence of hermaphrodites in certain breeds may be influenced by heredity, and recessive genes have been reported as involved. "Hereditary" intersexual conditions also can be produced through breeding in some experimental creatures (particularly the fruit fly). But in humans, apart from some instances where intersexual conditions have occurred in the same families several times,

WAS "IT" A FEMALE OR A MALE?

—When the sex-cells of an "in-be-tween" person were examined, this was revealed:

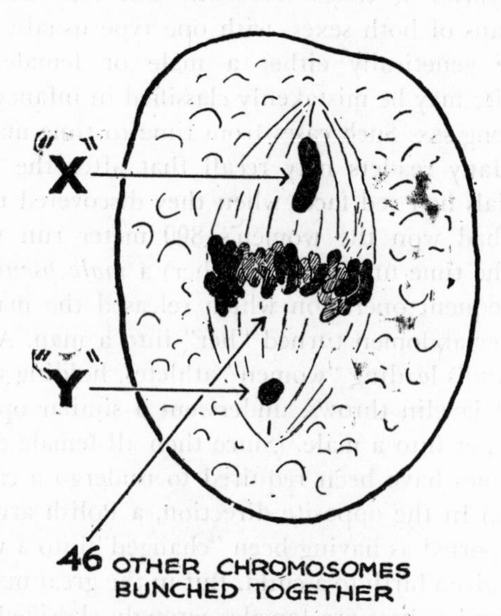

The XY Chromosome combination proved that "it" was genetically a man, and not a woman, as previously thought. (Figure redrawn from study by Dr. Severinghaus.)

there is as yet little to suggest that the "in-betweeners" generally result from anything more than some early accident in the workings of the sex chromosomes, or some glandular upset.

When we dealt with the oyster, we touched on the subject of *"sex reversal."* While nothing like the oyster's *normal* change from one sex into another happens among animals on higher levels, abnormal sex reversals in various degrees may sometimes occur.

The most striking cases are in poultry. In several instances, hens who had been peacefully pursuing their lives as egg-laying biddies, suddenly found themselves developing into roosters, complete with hackles, spurs, tail feathers and lusty crows, and, sometimes, with male organs. In one such case reported in the *Journal of Heredity* (1947), a New Hampshire red hen, which had formerly laid eggs, was claimed to have actually *fathered* chicks after her transformation. All of these, or milder cases of sex reversal in poultry, pheasants, etc., are due to ovarian tumors or other internal upsets which suppress the action of the "female" hormones and shift glandular control to the "male" hormones normally present in the female in subordinate amounts. This makes possible the development of male organs in some degree. In laboratory experiments, various degrees of sex reversal in hens have been induced by removal of the ovaries or by treatment with "male" hormones.

But although many a woman has said, "I wish I were a man," there is no chance of anything like the sex transformations of hens occurring among human females. The mechanism of sex determination for birds differs in certain ways from that for humans and, apparently, there is also a difference in hormonal action which makes it possible for the balance from "femaleness" to "maleness" to be shifted more easily.* What may, and sometimes does occur in a woman, however, is a modified change in the secondary sex characteristics, such as development of hair on the face, deeper voice, enlargement of the features, hands and feet, etc. Most frequently responsible for these changes is the condition known as *adrenal virilism,* which upsets the hormonal balance. But removal of the ovaries, or ovarian tumors in mature women, *rarely produces any noticeable masculinization.* Only in young girls, *before puberty,* does removal of the ovaries or impairment of their workings produce marked effects, such as failure of the sex organs and breasts to develop, or of the mature female bodily proportions to be achieved. Also in the pre-puberty stage, tumors of the adrenal glands in a girl may produce various "masculine" physical characteristics, including a deep voice and excessive facial hair, as well as sex-organ abnormalities. (In boys, the same kind of adrenal tumors may cause other abnormalities, and if occurring in early childhood, may pro-

* For an explanation of how the sex chromosomes in bird species work in reverse from the way they do in humans, with the XX-chromosome combination producing males, the XY-combination females see footnote, Chapter 8, p. 44.

duce the "infant-Hercules" type with premature physical development.)

The results of castration among human males are very often misunderstood. It is only when the testes are removed *before puberty* that the more significant physical characteristics associated with eunuchs are produced. Castration after puberty, when the masculine physical structure already has been set, produces only gradual changes. (Nor is there any sudden turn in the quality of the voice.) But, even without removal of the sex glands, any glandular disorder or upset before puberty which inhibits the proper workings of the "male" hormones may cause a boy to grow up with *"eunuchoid"* characteristics in the female direction—large hips, narrow and sloping shoulders, absence of beard, sparse body hair, high-pitched voice, etc. One quite common condition which can produce modified traits of this type is *cryptorchidism,* failure of the testes to descend into the scrotum, as they do normally, usually in prenatal life. While cryptorchidism has been found to be hereditary (recessive) in breeds of dogs, especially the dwarf types, its inheritance in humans has not been established. (One pair of identical twins both with the condition was reported in 1946.) In any case an early operation, or hormonal treatment, can usually correct the difficulty, although in a large percentage of the cases the individual may remain sterile.

In maturity, also, and especialy in old age, changes in glandular workings may often cause men to develop more highly pitched voices or take a mild trend toward "feminization." But—contrary to a popular fallacy—in neither sex, male nor female, does removal of the sex glands (testes or ovaries) *after puberty,* necessarily interfere with sex functioning. *Eunuchs, if so produced in maturity, may have sex relations like other men.* The "sex impulse" in men and women—in its physical aspects—is engendered, and sex functioning governed, not by the sex glands alone, but also by other hormonal action, and particularly by nervous and psychic stimuli.

Hardest to believe for most people, when they first hear it, is that *sterility* may be inherited. How? Simply, by those recessive genes which, coming together, produce defects in the sex organs or the functioning of the sex glands sufficient to prevent reproduction. Added to the directly sexual conditions causing sterility, there are certain defects and diseases, mentioned in preceding "Black Gene" chapters, which in various ways prevent or inhibit reproduction. Among them are some types of idiocy or imbecility, some forms of dwarfism, and one type of progressive muscular atrophy (this latter causing sterility only in mature life). Mechanical difficulties in sex functioning, because of hereditary defects in the sex organs, also may cause total or partial sterility. In males, *hypospadias,* a misplaced opening of the urethra on the underside of the penis (believed to be produced by a partly dominant gene), may prevent insemination, although an operation or other treatment may remedy the trouble.* Certain abnormalities in sperms which lead to sterility might also, in some cases, be hereditary. In females various rare abnormalities of the sex organs or their functioning (*"agenitalism," "infantilism," "eunuchoidism,"* etc.) which prevent reproduction have been suspected of being inherited in some cases, but the evidence is insufficient to warrant elaboration here.

Among the *secondary sex characteristics* (which are unrelated to sexual functioning), certain peculiarities, such as unusual hairiness in men, or unusual breast shapes in women, appear to be inherited, but they have as yet been given little accurate study. Extremely large or very small breasts, in women, often occur in successive generations of the same family, and may well be hereditary, just as within the normal range different types of breasts characterize women of certain strains and tribes. Also believed hereditary, in both sexes, are *supernumerary nipples* (extra nipples), reported in about one woman in 90 and one man in 60. Usually there are only one or two extra nipples, but some individuals have up to four and five pair, arranged above and below the normal two. Most extra nipples are in retarded states of development, but occasionally one or more in a woman are functional. In some instances complete extra breasts also are present. How these, or extra nipples, are inherited in humans is not clearly known, but it should be kept in mind that the presence of several pairs of nipples is normal in all mammals who bear litters. Indeed, one geneticist, with an eye to the increasing numbers of triplets, quads and quints, has toyed with the thought that extra nipples in human females might well be an evolutionary provision for human "litters," too.

That degrees of *fertility* in humans may be influenced by hereditary factors is another possibility. The more than average production of twins and other multiples, as well as the prolific childbearing in certain human strains as compared with others (when no control

* The incidence of hypospadias is about 3 in 1,000 males, according to the Danish statistics, cited by Dr. Tage Kemp (1950).

over births is employed), is thought to have some hereditary basis, just as the number of offspring in a litter or the frequency of reproduction among various species of other animals is apparently genetically controlled. No "excess fertility" genes, however, have yet been identified.

The "timing" of sex development is also, quite clearly, influenced by genes. It is no accident that puberty, maturity, or the menopause in women, come to most human beings at approximately the same time. So, too, where in certain strains or families there is a frequent deviation from the average "timing," with puberty and menopause arriving markedly earlier or later, and with no known environmental cause, heredity is apparently responsible.

But in making comparisons of the time of onset of puberty in different families and stocks, one must be sure that environments are approximately equal. Favorable environments have been conclusively shown to bring on earlier physical maturity in human beings and other animals (as also in plants), while unfavorable living conditions tend to cause delay in the onset of puberty. Thus, in the United States, puberty has been arriving earlier for girls today (at an average age of about 13½), than for their grandmothers, and earlier in girls of the more favored groups than among those in the underprivileged groups. It is a popular but persistent fallacy that girls mature earlier in the tropics (India, Africa, etc.) than in the temperate zones, or that Negro girls mature earlier than Whites. These assumptions have been exploded by many studies.

However, the extreme cases where puberty comes on in a child as early as the age of 2 or 3 (*pubertas praecox*), are most often due to glandular upsets, resulting from tumors of the pituitary or ovaries. But in some cases there appears to have been only an abnormal speed-up of the "time-clock" mechanism for the onset of puberty. Whatever the cause, one of the most striking cases was that of the Peruvian girl who in 1939 gave birth to a child at the age of 5. Another case, studied by Yale University experts, was that of a New Haven girl who reached puberty at the age of 3½, went through an apparent menopause at 13 and died at 18 following an operation for brain tumor.

When we think back now to all of the abnormalities in sexual development, how very few of the serious ones are hereditary, and how infrequently these occur, what should never cease to impress us is the near-perfection with which the "sex" genes operate in the sexual construction of the overwhelming majority of human beings. Perhaps in no other major aspect of our makeup and functioning do we find fewer serious hereditary defects. What we *do* with our sexual mechanisms, of course, is another matter, to be taken up in a later chapter.

CHAPTER 28

THE BLOOD TYPES

SHE had wanted the baby so much, and yet she had killed it. Innocently, it was true. But if she had any more babies, she might cause their death the same way—*through an hereditary "something" in her blood which was hostile to theirs.*

That is what doctors could have told not just one mother, but many thousands, when medical geneticists in 1940 announced discovery of the "Rh" blood factor. Here was the solution to the mysterious deaths annually, from a certain blood disease, of vast numbers of fetuses and newborn infants. And, fortunately, there quickly came the knowledge and techniques for preventing the great majority of these tragedies.

The "Rh" discovery has been only one of a series of momentous findings by the scientist "blood detectives," all of which involve the fact that hereditary chemical differences of many kinds exist in the blood of human beings. Previously it had been known, through sad experience, that blood transfusions often ended disastrously. It wasn't so hard to understand this when the blood of lower animals was transfused into humans (as was sometimes done in the preceding century), or when bloods of different species of animals were mixed. But why, when the blood of one human being was introduced into that of another, were there also serious consequences in many cases—*even if it was the blood of a mother or father given to their own child,* or the blood of one brother given to another? The answer, we know now, is that it is just as possible for two persons in a family to inherit different kinds of blood as it is for them to inherit differences in eye color or any other physical traits.

Yet this did not begin to become clear until 1900 (by coincidence also the year in which modern genetics was born), when the late Dr. Karl Landsteiner discovered the existence of the *"A," "B," "AB,"* and *"O"* blood types. He showed that some persons carried in their blood one kind of chemical substance *(A)*, others carried a different substance *(B)*, some carried both substances (hence being of the *AB* type), and many individuals carried neither, being designated as of the *O* type. Later it became apparent that these blood types were inherited, but it was a statistician, Dr. Felix Bernstein (neither a geneticist nor a medical man!), who first figured out, in 1925, exactly how the genetic mechanism worked.

The main blood groups result from three variations of one main gene. Two of these, the genes for *A* and *B* blood, are *dominant* over the gene for *O* blood, but are of almost equal strength in relation to each other. So here's what happens:

Gene *A* produces, principally, a substance known as "Antigen A."

Gene *B* produces, principally, "Antigen B."

Gene *O* produces neither antigen.

Every one of us inherits two of any of the above genes—one gene from each parent. We therefore may receive two genes of the same kind—*AA*, or *BB*, or *OO*—or mixed pairs, *AB*, *AO*, or *BO*. The *"O"* gene being recessive, an *AO* combination results in *A* blood, just as does the *AA* combination, while the *BO* combination produces *B* blood, just as does the *BB* combination. And, as the *"A"* and *"B"* genes are of almost equal strength, when these two are linked the blood will be of the *AB* type, carrying antigens of both kinds.

Within the individual himself, it is of little importance which type of blood he has inherited. Trouble comes only if he is given a transfusion with blood that clashes with his own, producing clumping, or disintegration of the blood cells. This is most likely to happen if an *O* group person is given bloods of any of the other types, or if "A" individuals are given blood with *B* substance, or "B" individuals blood with the *A* substance. On the other hand, *O* blood, having neither *A* nor *B* substances, can be used with the least risk in emergency transfusions. In reverse, *AB* blood, while least useful in transfusions—having elements alien to all other three types—can nevertheless *receive* any of the other bloods most easily. (See our illustration.) But while these facts were considered sufficient to go by in former years, what has now become apparent is that clashing substances other than those produced by the main blood types may exist in individuals, and that the safest procedure in transfusions is to give a person blood as much like his own as possible in every respect. This was most strikingly made clear through the "Rh" discovery.

YOUR BLOOD TYPE

Was inherited through a pair of any of these genes—two of the same kind or a mixed pair—one gene coming from each parent:

(Symbols) Ⓐ Ⓑ Ⓞ

Each gene produces different blood substances. Genes "A" and "B" are of equal strength, and when brought together, work independently. But Gene "O" is recessive; and if coupled with "A" or "B," does not function. Accordingly:

IF YOU RECEIVED GENES:	Ⓐ+Ⓐ or Ⓐ+Ⓞ	Ⓑ+Ⓑ or Ⓑ+Ⓞ	Ⓐ+Ⓑ	Ⓞ+Ⓞ
YOUR BLOOD TYPE IS:	**A**	**B**	**AB**	**O**
	Containing "A" substance	Containing "B" substance	Containing "A" and "B" substances	Containing only "O" substance

ALTHOUGH LOOKING ALIKE, THE BLOODS ARE NOT COMPATIBLE, SO IN TRANSFUSIONS IT IS SAFEST TO MIX BLOODS OF THE SAME TYPE. BUT IN EMERGENCIES:

AB BLOOD

—Containing both "A" and "B" substances, most easily receives the others

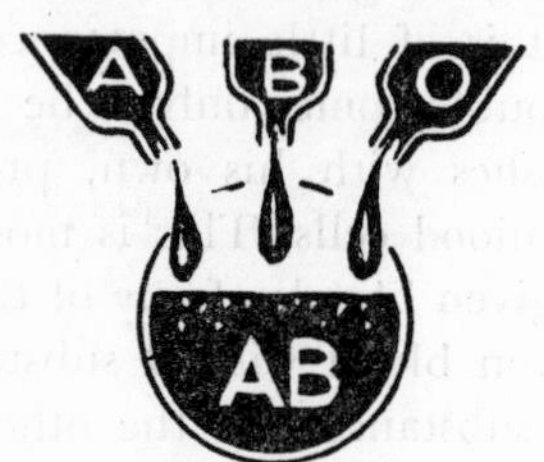

—But, because it also has something foreign to each, clashes most if infused, producing clumping

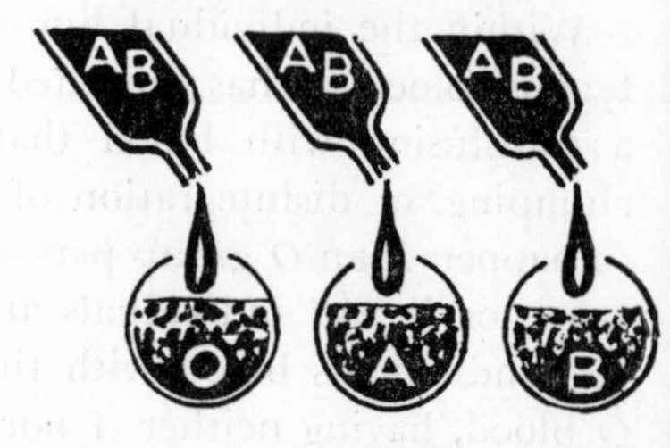

O BLOOD

—Being "weakest," is least able to receive any of the others

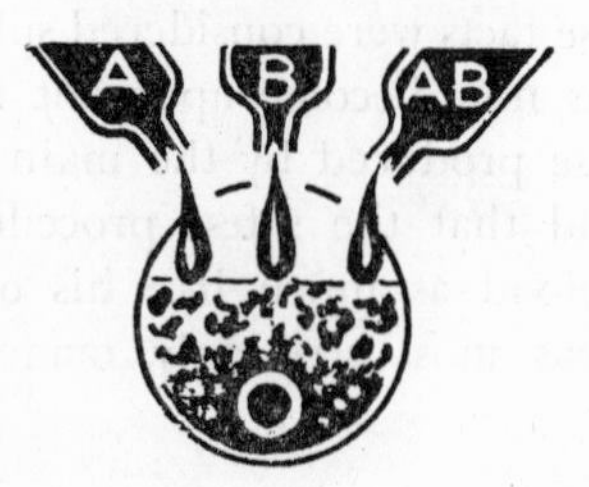

—But can be transfused into the others with the least clotting

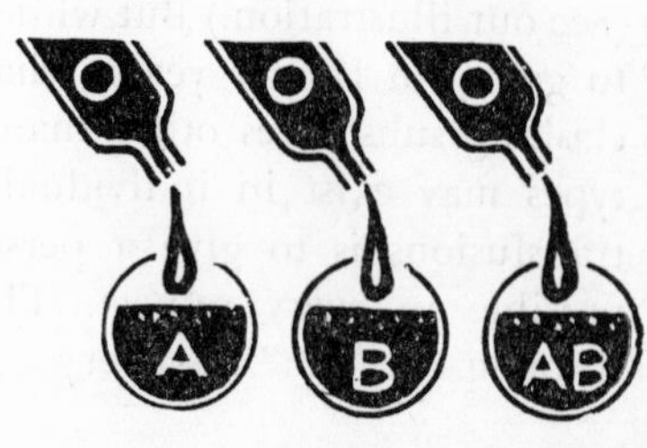

For the story of the "Rh" factor we turn again to Dr. Landsteiner and to two other outstanding medical scientists associated with him, Dr. Alexander Wiener and Dr. Philip Levine.* It was Drs. Landsteiner and Wiener who jointly discovered the "Rh" factor through their experiments with the *Rhesus* monkey (hence the "Rh" name), and then proved how this factor was inherited by human beings and the rôle it played in repeated transfusions. It was Dr. Levine who subsequently proved that the "Rh" factor was responsible for the blood incompatibility between mother and child which produced *erythroblastosis fetalis*—the serious type of anemia or jaundice peculiar to newborn infants which had been causing so many fatalities.

Subsequent findings by Dr. Wiener, and by others (including, in England, Drs. R. R. Race and R. A. Fisher), not only clarified the intricacies of "Rh" inheritance, but also showed how most of the "Rh" hazards could be prevented or overcome. These are the chief facts:

In addition to the main blood-type substances, the "Rh" chemical substance is carried in the blood of about 85 per cent of all White persons, but is absent from the blood of the remaining 15 per cent.† This "Rh" substance is produced through the action of a *dominant* gene. Whether a person inherits one such gene or two, his blood develops the substance, and he therefore is known as of the *"Rh-positive"* type. If, instead, a person inherits two *recessive* "Rh" genes, and therefore does not develop this blood substance, he is known as of the *"Rh-negative"* type.

But it is almost entirely in prenatal life, as we said, that the "Rh" factor has its importance. For if a mother is "Rh-negative," and the

* Earlier, in 1927, Drs. Landsteiner and Levine had discovered the *"M," "N"* and *"P"* blood substances. While these provided new blood-type classifications, they had no medical applications, as the substances caused no clashes in transfusions. However, they advanced blood-type knowledge, and have great value in tracing heredity, as we shall explain later.

† There are marked race differences in the incidence of the "Rh" factor. Among the Mongolian peoples, including Chinese, Japanese and "pure" American Indians, virtually all individuals are Rh-positive, with "Rh-negative" blood almost completely absent. American Negroes are about 92 per cent "Rh-positive," 8 per cent "Rh-negative" (African Negroes having even fewer "Rh-negatives"). The lower incidences of "Rh-negative" types have highly important meanings, for the smaller the proportion of "Rh-negative" mothers in any group, the less frequent are the cases of prenatal "Rh" clashes. Thus, Chinese babies escape this danger almost entirely, and the "Rh" disease is much less common among Negroes than among Whites. Further racial aspects of the "Rh" factor, and of other blood-type differences, will be discussed in the next chapter and in the "Race" chapters.

child she carries is "Rh-positive" (through having received the gene for this blood substance from its father), this is what may *sometimes* happen:

1. As the developing fetus begins to produce the special "Rh" substance in its blood, some of this may filter through the placenta into the mother's blood stream.

2. The mother's blood begins to manufacture an "*anti*-Rh" substance, or "antibodies," to combat the invading foreign chemical.

3. Some of the antibodies from the mother then filter through the placenta and into the child, attacking and destroying its blood cells, or in other ways seriously impairing them.

But only in about one-sixteenth of the cases where the mother is "Rh-negative" and the child "positive" does this occur (or did it occur before any precautionary measures were known). In other words, about one in every twelve pregnancies involves a "negative" mother and a "positive" baby, and yet babies with the "Rh" disease (erythroblastosis) appeared in no more than about one in every 150 to 200 full-term deliveries. Why so few?

Here are some of the answers: The production and interchange of the clashing blood substances between mother and child does not always take place. There are differences in the types of "Rh" substances and antibodies, some being weaker than others (not inciting, or not clashing with their opponents so violently).* *But most important, the amount of antibody attacking the fetus, and the stage in its development when the attack begins, depends largely on what prior experience the mother has had with the hostile "Rh" substance, either through bearing previous "Rh" babies or having had transfusions at one time or another with "Rh-positive" blood.*

If an "Rh-negative" mother is bearing her *first* "Rh-positive" baby, and an interchange of their blood substances does take place, the antibodies she produces are very rarely strong enough to harm the

* For the technically-minded: Up to the present writing there have been discovered three types of "Rh-positive" factors, the original "Rh" factor (the most common and the one responsible for most cases of erythroblastosis), and two weaker ones. In "Rh-negative" bloods, similarly, there are three contrasting "Hr" factors, one or more of which may also occur in "Rh-positive" blood (for example, if the individual carries "mixed" genes, one "positive" and one "negative"). When making blood tests, the various factors mentioned can be found in different types of "Rh" and "Hr" bloods. Alternative names for the "Rh"-"Hr" types have been suggested by Drs. Fisher and Race in England. These involve use of the letters, C, c, D, d, E and e, in place of the corresponding "Rh" and "Hr" terms. (See "Blood Group Nomenclature," Herluf H. Strandkov, *Jour. of Hered.*, April, 1948.)

HOW AN "RH-DISEASE" BABY IS PRODUCED

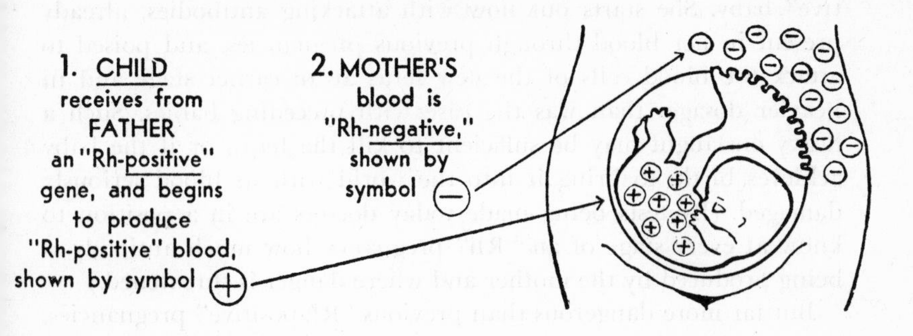
1. CHILD receives from FATHER an "Rh-positive" gene, and begins to produce "Rh-positive" blood, shown by symbol ⊕
2. MOTHER'S blood is "Rh-negative," shown by symbol ⊖

3. Some of the CHILD'S "Rh-positive" blood substance travels through placenta into MOTHER

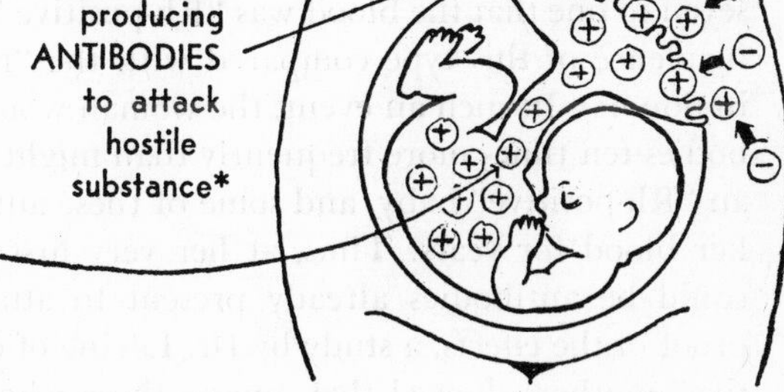
4. MOTHER'S blood begins producing ANTIBODIES to attack hostile substance*

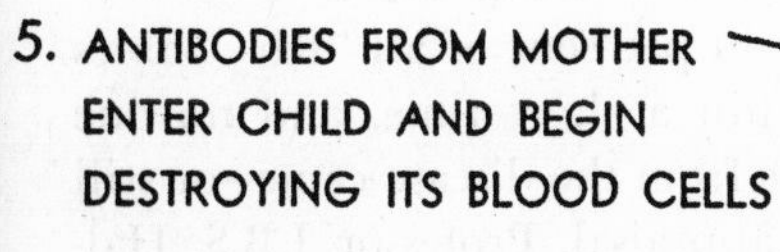
5. ANTIBODIES FROM MOTHER ENTER CHILD AND BEGIN DESTROYING ITS BLOOD CELLS

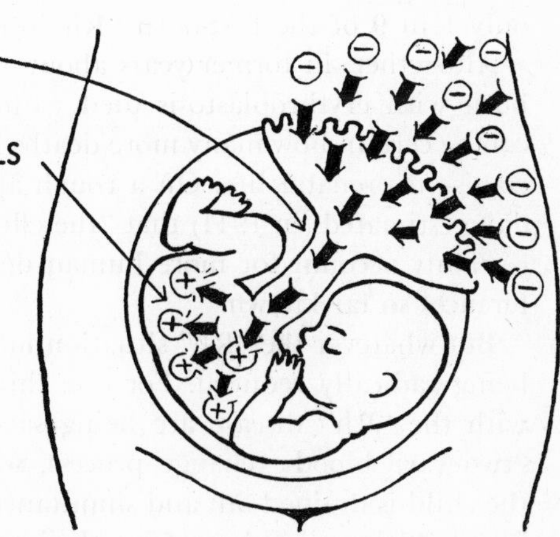

*If "Rh-negative" mother has had previous "Rh-positive" pregnancies, or transfusions with "Rh-positive" blood, antibodies already are present.

(Chart prepared with aid of Dr. Alexander Wiener.)

fetus. But suppose the mother is carrying her second, or a later "positive" baby. She starts out now with attacking antibodies, already present in her blood through previous pregnancies, and poised to attack the blood cells of the new fetus at an earlier stage and in heavier dosages than was the case with preceding babies. Such a heavy onslaught may be sufficient to kill the fetus, or if the baby achieves birth, to bring it into the world with its blood seriously damaged. (By tests being made today doctors are in a position to know at every stage of an "Rh" pregnancy how much antibody is being produced by the mother and where danger is threatened.)

But far more dangerous than previous "Rh-positive" pregnancies, as we said, is the result of an "Rh-negative" mother's having had transfusions with "Rh-positive" blood prior to childbearing. In fact, wherever any "Rh-negative" woman underwent a transfusion in the years before the "Rh" factor was discovered, the chances were almost seven to one that the blood was "Rh-positive" (because of the relative incidence of this type compared with the "negative" type of blood in donors). In such an event, the woman would have developed antibodies ten times more frequently than might come through carrying an "Rh-positive" baby, and some of these antibodies could linger in her blood for years. Thus, at her very first "Rh" pregnancy there could be antibodies already present to attack the child. Offering proof of the effects, a study by Dr. Levine of one group of "Rh-negative" mothers showed that among those who had prior transfusions with "positive" blood, 10 out of 16 lost their first "Rh" babies, whereas among those who had had transfusions with "negative" blood, only 1 in 9 of the first-born "Rh-positive" babies died.

Altogether, in former years about 40 per cent of all "Rh" babies born with erythroblastosis died within a short time, and no one can be certain how many more deaths from the disease came—or still come—in prenatal life. On a rough appraisal, Professor J.B.S. Haldane estimated (in 1944) that "the effects of the *Rh* gene differences certainly account for more human deaths than any other gene differences so far known."

But whatever the "Rh" situation might have been, its dangers are being radically reduced. For one thing, many hundreds of babies with the "Rh" disease are being saved annually by the dramatic "two-way" blood-exchange process, whereby all defective blood of the child is drained out and simultaneously replaced by healthy new blood. The greatest hope for reducing "Rh" casualties, however, lies in these precautionary measures recommended by the leading authorities, which could prevent most of the threats from ever materializing:

No young woman with "Rh-negative" blood should ever be given a transfusion with "positive" blood. (In fact, irrespective of the relation to childbearing, repeated transfusions of "Rh-positive" blood in a "negative" person may eventually produce bad reactions. This applies equally to *men* with "negative" blood.)

All couples before having children should be tested for their "Rh" types. Where the husband is "positive" and the wife "negative," it should be immediately established if the wife has ever had any blood transfusions, and further tests should be made to see if she carries "Rh antibodies." Also, in the husband's case, follow-up "Rh" blood tests of himself, members of his family, and any children he may previously have had, may establish whether he carries *two* "Rh-positive" genes (true of 60 per cent of the "positive" individuals) or only one such gene. In the first instance, *every* child will be "positive" and will face the "Rh" threat with the "negative" mother; in the second instance, the chance is only fifty-fifty that any given child will be so threatened (the odds being even that the child may receive the father's "negative" gene, and have negative blood like the mother's).

If an "Rh-negative" mother already is carrying a "positive" child, tests of her blood at various stages will reveal if and when she develops antibodies. Should these be in amounts dangerous to the child, it is possible that treatments may be developed to neutralize them; or in extreme cases, the birth can be hastened through Caesarean delivery (for it is in the final weeks of prenatal life that the danger is greatest), and prompt employment of the "two-way" blood-exchange process may then save the child.

Mothers of the "Rh" babies *should not nurse them,* because even after an "Rh" baby is safely launched into the world, a threat may still come to it through the *mother's milk,* which may carry antibodies just like those in her blood which attacked the child in prenatal life.

Wherever a "negative" mother already has had several "Rh-positive" babies (one or more of whom may have been lost) and blood tests show that she is heavily sensitized with antibodies, warning may be given of the hazards or futility of further attempts at childbearing. But it should be clear that in ordinary circumstances an "Rh-negative" mother has almost no risk of losing her *first* "positive" baby through erythroblastosis (unless she has had "Rh-positive" transfusions) and no more than one chance in twenty-five of losing a second "positive" baby in this way. Moreover, with all the safeguards that now have been set up, *there no longer is any reason why an "Rh-negative" woman and an "Rh-positive" man should hesitate about marrying and having children.*

We have by no means presented all the intricacies of the "Rh" factor and the "Rh" disease, for most of these go beyond the scope of this book. An additional fact to be noted, however, is that erythroblastosis, or blood diseases very much like it, may in some instances result in ways other than from the "Rh" incompatibility we have dealt with. Mother-child differences in the main blood-group types, *A, B,* and *O* (as, for instance, if the mother was of group *O* and the child of group *A*), sometimes may lead to an interchange of clashing blood substances in prenatal life. More rarely, complicated interactions between the different "Rh" *sub-types* in mother and fetus, may produce the "Rh" disease, even where the mother is primarily "positive" as is the baby.

The belief that the "Rh" factor might be involved in some cases of *feeble-mindedness* arose through preliminary investigations, but follow-up studies have made this less certain. While the possibility still remains, this also awaits further research.

So far we have considered only the *medical* aspects of the blood-type discoveries. But they have had many other important applications, some of which we will discuss in the special chapter following (which hardly belongs with the "Black Gene" chapters, but nevertheless may be most easily placed here in connection with the blood types).

CHAPTER 29

HOW DO YOU KNOW THE BABY'S YOURS?

THERE used to be a jolly old judge in Milwaukee who specialized in doubtful paternity cases, or what the state so bluntly calls "bastardy actions."

By "specialized" we mean that he showed a special aptitude for trying these cases, and accordingly most of them were assigned to him. For one thing, he seemed fully aware of the fact that such actions permitted no strict adherence to legal procedure. The evidence offered—aside from the highly contradictory statements of the plaintiff and defendant—was hearsay and much colored by perjury, and the judge viewed the proceedings as largely a matter of deciding who was lying and who wasn't.

One case in particular (of the many before him which we covered as a "cub" reporter) stands out in our memory. The young woman plaintiff had given rather convincing testimony, and the young man whom she named as the father of her child had taken the stand. Under a barrage of cross-examination he admitted having visited with the young woman on the night in question, but insisted that his deportment had been blameless. No amount of forceful questioning could shake him. At this point His Honor intervened.

"Tell me," the judge asked, "was there by any chance a *moon* shining that night?"

The young man thought a moment and innocently replied. "Why, yes, sir. I think there was."

The judge nodded with mock gravity, then sat back in his big chair and gazed at the ceiling, seemingly in deep thought. "Ah!" he said at last, and bent forward as if to take the entire courtroom into his confidence. "It's all very simple. *Some* man had to be the father of the child. Well, there was a moon shining that night. All we have to decide is whether it was this young fellow or the *man in the moon.*"

Now, any lawyer could tell you that such a remark coming from a judge was legally improper, and that, in fact, the entire procedure in doubtful paternity cases was (and in most places still is) highly questionable. But the justice or injustice of the law in this respect (where the main objective is merely to see that the child doesn't become a public charge) is not an issue here. What we wish to point out is that a fairer, and certainly much more scientific approach to deciding these cases has now been made possible through the blood tests already in use in many of our states, and in other countries.

Primarily, these tests in disputed paternity proceedings are "exclusion" tests. They cannot prove that any given man *is* the father of a child in question, but they can often exclude him as the possible father by proof that *his blood is not of the group or type it would have to be for the child to be his.*

When first legally sanctioned in 1935 (in New York through a measure devised by Dr. Alexander Wiener and in Wisconsin through the sponsorship of Dr. Philip Levine), the paternity tests were based on the main blood groups, *A, B, AB* and *O,* and on the supplementary *M* and *N* types (which we'll discuss in more detail presently). With these tests a one-in-three chance was provided for a man unjustly accused of fathering a given child to clear himself. The discovery of the "Rh" factor and its various subtypes raised the chances for exclusion of an innocent man to 55 per cent.

How the "non-paternity" blood tests are applied can be illustrated through some actual court cases.

A young woman in New York sued a prominent society man for a huge sum, claiming she had borne him a child on his promise to marry her. Tests showed that the child's blood was *A,* the mother's *O*. The child's *A* gene therefore must have come from the father. But the accused man's blood was *O* (like the mother's), proving he could not have contributed the *A* gene, so the charge against him was dismissed.

Other exclusions using merely the main blood-group tests can come if the child is *O* and the man *AB* (or vice versa), or if the baby is *B* and neither the accused man nor the mother have *B* or *AB* blood, etc.

Next, if nothing can be shown through the main blood groups, there are the *M* and *N* tests. These (referred to in a footnote in the previous chapter) involve two supplementary blood substances one or the other of which, or both, are present in all human bloods. Producing these substances are two *dominant* genes. If a person inherits two *M* genes (one from each parent), he has "M" blood; if two *N* genes, "N" blood; if a different gene from each parent, "MN" blood. So again, if a baby has *M* blood an *N* man can't be the father, or if the baby's blood is *N*, an *M* man can't be the father. Similarly, if the baby's blood is *MN* and either of these substances is not in the mother's blood, it would have to be in the father's blood.

Another actual court case to illustrate: A married woman brought a surprising action *to prove that her child was illegitimate*—that not her husband, but a lover, was its father. And it was her husband who was contesting the claim. The first tests, with the main blood groups, left the question open. But the *M* and *N* tests proved, indeed, that the husband could not have been the child's father.

Ironically, in another and widely publicized paternity action against a famous motion picture actor, the *M* and *N* tests, by proving *nothing,* lost the case for the unfortunate man. This occurred in California, in 1945, in a court where blood tests were admissible as evidence, but not binding. On the main blood-group tests, the baby's blood was *B,* the mother's *A* and the actor's *O, which ruled him out as the father.* But the clever lawyer for the woman hammered home the point that the *M-N* tests did *not* eliminate the actor as the possible father, and the jury, apparently under the impression that it was a "fifty-fifty" proposition, brought in a verdict against the man. This hardly would have been possible in states where the blood tests are given more legal weight.

The first court action in which tests for the "Rh" factor determined the outcome was in New York City in 1947. A young man of 20 had reluctantly married a girl of 16, when she was already pregnant, on her claim that he was the father of her expected child. After the baby was born, blood tests were made. The *A-B-O* and *M-N* tests left the question open, but when Dr. Wiener followed up with the "Rh" tests, the evidence was clear that the husband could not be the child's father, and the judge so ruled.

With at least six different "Rh (positive and negative) blood" genes involved, there are available many more blood-type combinations and possibilities for paternity exclusion. The principle is the same as in the tests previously discussed: If there is present in or absent from the baby's blood any "Rh" substance which would require the father's blood to be of a certain type, any man whose "Rh" blood is not of that type must be automatically excluded as a parent. As the simplest example, if a baby is "Rh-positive" and the mother is negative a man also negative couldn't be the father. But even if the man's blood is positive, there still are the three different subtypes to consider with regard to conformity. Likewise, where "Rh-negative" blood is involved, the subtypes play an equally important part.*

Cases of "changelings"—where babies are given to the wrong parents—provide another use for the blood tests. Such mixups occur with extreme rarity now as the result of modern hospital precautions, but when they do turn up, blood-testing of the babies and the two sets of parents concerned can almost always straighten things out.

An unusual "changeling" case which called forth Dr. Wiener's services was one in 1947 involving a pair of 5-year-old twin boys and another boy living in Switzerland. The father of the twins had been puzzled by the great differences between them. Watching a Boy Scout parade one day, he saw in the ranks a lad who looked amazingly like one of his twins. Investigating, the man discovered that this boy had been born in the same hospital and at the same time as his sons. Arrangements were made for blood tests of the three boys and their parents. The *A-B-O* and *M-N* tests proved nothing, so samples of the blood were sent overseas to Dr. Wiener, and "Rh" tests were made. These revealed conclusively that there had indeed been a mixup, and shortly after the Swiss courts ordered that the wrong "twin" be exchanged for the right one. (A study by Swiss geneticists of eye colors and other hereditary traits in the boys added to the evidence, and finally, there was a "cross-grafting" skin experiment, in which skin transplanted from the true twin to his other twin took hold, whereas that from the "false twin" did not.)

One other extraordinary "twin" case deserves mention. A widow who ran a boarding house in Chicago gave birth to fraternal twin boys, and two of her favorite boarders, who also were her suitors, each claimed that he was the father. Blood tests showed, surprisingly, that only one man could have been the father of one of the twins, and that the second man had probably fathered the other. Such

* In special cases, the blood expert may consider a few factors and subtypes other than those we've mentioned. *A* blood may be of two types, "A_1" and "A_2." Similarly in the *M* and *N* tests, the "*N*" factor may be of two types ("N_1" and "N_2"), and an "*S*" factor has also been found associated with *M* and *N*. Then there is the "*P*" factor (positive and negative), discovered by Drs. Landsteiner and Levine, and the new "Kell" and "Celano" factors, discovered by Dr. Levine (in 1949), tests for which, however, are only rarely made because of a number of technical difficulties presented.

"double" conceptions, common among lower animals, have on occasions occurred among humans. (We don't know what happened subsequently with the widow, the boarders and the twins.)

What has been said about the efficacy of the blood tests in establishing paternity or parentage requires certain qualification. For example, take the statement that the tests offer a "55 per cent chance of exclusion" for a man unjustly accused of fathering a child. This estimate is an average for a mixed population with all the varieties of blood groups and blood types represented in certain proportions. The chances for exclusion obviously would be much reduced in a highly inbred community, or among persons of certain racial strains, where an unusually high percentage of the men, women and children all have the same blood types.

To illustrate: Among Whites in the United States, about 42 per cent have *O* blood, 40 per cent have *A* blood, 10 per cent *B*, and 8 per cent *AB*. But in some American Indian tribes almost all the members have exactly the same blood types (one tribe being reported with close to 100 per cent *Os*, and other tribes with up to 95 per cent having *O*, *M* [or *MN*], and "Rh-positive" bloods). Obviously, if a disputed paternity case ever came up involving members of these tribes, and the accused brave attempted to clear himself through blood tests, one could only say, "Lo, the poor Indian!" Likewise, though to a lesser degree, in many groups of Chinese and Japanese, and among Negroes who are highly inbred (especially those of certain African strains), there is a much closer similarity of blood types of one kind or another than there is among Whites. For example, among Chinese and Japanese, "Rh-negative" blood occurs in less than 1 per cent, and among American Negroes its incidence is 8 per cent or less, while other blood types occur with disproportionately higher or lower frequencies as compared with the incidence in Caucasians. In certain European groups, and possibly in some localities in the United States, where the population is relatively more inbred than elsewhere, the blood tests also would have reduced value.

From another angle, blood similarities or distinctive combinations of blood types characterizing different peoples are now proving highly important to anthropologists in tracing origins and relationships of races and ethnic groups. (We'll deal with this again in a later chapter on "Race.") One amazing fact is that it is possible to determine blood types of individuals dead for thousands of years if their bodies are fairly well preserved, as has been shown in blood-typing Egyptian mummies as well as human bones frozen for ages in the Aleutian Islands.

Anticipating a point to be brought out in the "Race" chapter, that all human blood types arose in the course of evolution through mutations (sudden changes) from the same original blood genes, here is a question that will now occur to any alert reader (if it hasn't already occurred): Can the blood tests be 100 per cent reliable in paternity "exclusion" cases *when there is the possibility that a mutation may have taken place in a blood gene* which the man has passed on to the child, producing a type of blood apparently so inconsistent with the man's own that it would legally "exclude" him as the father, although he actually is? Undoubtedly this *could* happen, but in view of the extreme rarity of human mutations—for a specific gene maybe once in fifty thousand times—the chance is so remote in any given case that it virtually could be ignored. Otherwise almost no evidence offered in a court case, and certainly no circumstantial evidence, would have any validity. Moreover, in support of the blood-test evidence, Sidney B. Schatkin, a legal expert on the subject who has brought paternity actions on behalf of several thousand mothers in New York courts, reports that in almost every case after the tests absolve a man, the accusing woman confesses that the charge was "incorrect."

A further use for the blood tests proposed by Dr. Wiener is in identifying criminals, or clearing men accused of a crime, wherever they have left blood behind them. The day is foreseen when blood-typing may be almost as much a routine in police records as finger-printing. Still another use may be in contested will or "missing heir" actions, when an individual claims to be the son (or daughter) of the deceased. If records of the dead person's blood types are available, tests of false heirs would in most cases expose them.

Before leaving the subject, "How do you know the baby's yours?" it is important to point out that the blood types are by no means the only hereditary clues. Any trait or traits produced by genes, normal or abnormal, discussed in previous chapters, would offer evidence wherever the parentage of an individual is in question. It is only because other traits cannot be reduced to such simple formulas as the blood types, and that they are in most cases not so clear-cut in inheritance or as likely to reveal themselves when the child is born, that they have not received much recognition in the courts.

However, away back in 1910 (years before the blood tests were used in court actions), a case of disputed paternity was decided in Norway through the circumstance that the child in question had the hand abnormality, *brachyphalangy* (stub fingers), which had been established as due to a dominant gene. The mother, normal, accused a certain paperhanger in her community of being the child's father. He was brought into court. "Let's see your hands!" ordered the judge (who had been briefed by a geneticist). When the hapless defendant held up his stub fingers (a condition in which he was unique in the entire community), the court promptly adjudged him the father.

Any other inherited surface abnormality in a child caused by a simple *dominant* gene might provide similar evidence if it is not present in the mother, but is found in the man accused of being the father. Preceding chapters have listed a number of such identifying characteristics that would be significant if blood tests were inconclusive, among them being many easily recognizable inherited defects or abnormalities of the hands, feet, teeth, skin, features or body as a whole. As an extreme example, just suppose you were the judge where the child of a normal mother was an *achondroplastic dwarf*—and the man accused of being the father was a similar-type dwarf!

Dominant structural abnormalities, however, are comparatively rare. Much better chances for establishing heredity (where blood tests are inconclusive) might be offered through combinations of normal and common hereditary traits, such as eye color and iris pattern, hair color, skin color, hair form, and some of the distinctive shapes of noses, mouths, ears, etc. While genetic similarity or dissimilarity between any child and man in one or two of these characteristics would have no meaning, concordance in a series of them, or lack of concordance, might be significant evidence. For instance, suppose the child had dark eyes, black and curly hair, and a "Hapsburg" lip, all of which traits are produced by dominant genes. If the traits were not present in the mother but were present in a man accused of parentage, and in no other man who could be suspected, the evidence would carry much weight. Even more definitely, if the man lacked all of these traits (if he had blue eyes, straight blond hair and thin lips) and the child's dominant traits were not present in the mother either, the man could be excluded. But remember that what has been said applies only to *dominant* traits. Where a child's features, coloring, etc., are the result of *recessive* genes, it would be extremely difficult for any man to prove that he does not carry them.

YOU BE THE JUDGE

Study carefully the evidence in each of these *doubtful paternity* cases. Give your decision as to whether the accused man in each case may or may not have been the father of the child in question. (Correct answers at the bottom of the page.)

CASES INVOLVING ONLY BLOOD TESTS:

Case	*Child's Blood*	*Mother's Blood*	*Accused Man's*
1.	A, MN, Rh+	A, N, Rh+	O, M, Rh−
2.	O, N, Rh−	O, N, Rh+	A, M, Rh+
3.	AB, M, Rh+	A, M, Rh−	A, N, Rh−

CASES WHERE BLOOD TESTS ARE NOT CONCLUSIVE, AND OTHER INHERITED TRAITS ARE CONSIDERED:

Case	*Child*	*Mother*	*Accused Man*
4.	Blue eyes	Blue eyes	Brown eyes
	Fair skin	Fair skin	Brownish skin
	Blond, straight hair	Blond, straight hair	Black, curly hair
	Slanty eyes	Straight eyes	Straight eyes
	"Mongolian" spot (base of spine)	No Mongolian traits	No Mongolian traits
5.	Brown eyes	Green eyes	Blue eyes
	Black, curly hair	Red, straight hair	Blond, straight hair
	Dark skin	Fair skin	Fair skin
	Thick lips	Thin lips	Thick lips
6.	Brown eyes	Blue eyes	Brown eyes
	Red, wavy hair	Blond, straight hair	Red, curly hair
	Drooping eyelids	Normal eyes	Drooping eyelids
	"Hapsburg" lip	Normal lip	"Hapsburg" lip

DECISIONS:

1. Man not excluded. (Child could carry hidden "O," and "Rh−" gene.)
2. Man excluded by *MN* tests. (Has pure *M* not carried by child.)
3. Man excluded by all three tests.
4. Man not excluded. All of baby's feature-traits reported are *recessive,* so man could be carrying recessive genes for any or all of the traits, producing them in baby if same genes were present in baby's mother.
5. Man probably not father. Gene for "thick" lips is common, but man lacks all the other feature-traits in child which are *dominant* and do not appear in mother, so should be found in father.
6. Man quite likely father. Unusual combination of drooping eyelids and "Hapsburg" lip, both dominant, in him and child, point to relationship, and other features add to the evidence.

If you turn back to our "Feature Forecast" Tables, you will see how it is possible for many parents to produce children who bear very little resemblance to them.

Whatever the present inadequacies may be in establishing the parentage of any given child, we have every reason to anticipate discovery of so many more hereditary factors—perhaps new blood substances, many new feature and structural genes, etc.—that conceivably in the future there may be few cases where a clear-cut decision can't be given. In fact, in these days when experts can tell that a certain bullet was fired from a specified revolver, that a letter was typed on exactly such and such a machine, or that a brush stroke on a painting was made by a certain old master dead four hundred years, it would be strange if we should continue unable to determine whether any child—unique in so many ways from other children—did or did not stem from such and such a parent.

CHAPTER 30

HOW LONG WILL YOU LIVE?

"YOU'LL go when your number's up!" is a popular saying with soldiers. Many other people share this fatalistic belief—some through their religions—that every person comes into the world with the time of his exit already stamped by Fate.

We can doubt this, certainly, as applied to any exact hour, month or year. But in a very general way there is indeed a "time clock" which governs our stay on earth, and which is set earlier for some individuals than for others. Thus, when you hear, "So-and-so is of long-lived stock," or "So-and-so is of short-lived stock," it may well have meaning with regard to inherited differences in potential longevity. Though not always!

Within certain limits the life span of human beings, as of all other species, seems to be set by inherited factors. The oldest living things are trees. Different varieties are characterized by different limits of longevity, the farthest limits, into thousands of years, being reached by certain cypresses and the American sequoias, with the granddaddy of all now living things believed to be an almost 7,000-year-old bald cypress in Tula, central Mexico.* Soil, climate and other conditions are, of course, vitally important factors, but there is also something in the *nature* of trees that determines their potential age and that makes a tree of one variety live longer than another growing by its side.

Animals, whose biological mechanism is much more complex, and

* In the first edition of this book the oldest living tree was given as a macrozamia of Australia, credited with having reached the age of 15,000 years. The information came from a well-known scientist, but a subsequent checkup showed that it was based on a chain of amusing errors: An Australian botanist had found a macrozamia to which he ascribed the age of 1,000 years; a typographical error in a local newspaper changed this to 10,000 years; and an overzealous wire-service correspondent jumped this again to 15,000 years, which figure, cabled around the world, got into the well-known feature, "Believe It or Not," by Robert Ripley—and also into a book by our scientist friend. Actually, as we now know, the macrozamias are mere striplings compared to other trees, and may not live to be even 1,000 years.

whose lives are far more hazardous, are narrowly limited in their life spans, but these limits likewise vary greatly with different species. Under the best of conditions elephants live to be no more than about 70 years; horses, about 35; dogs and cats, about 20; parrots, about 45; oxen, about 30. Wild animals and birds probably have much shorter life spans than domestic ones. Among fish, of the fresh-water species, carp, pike and catfish may live to be almost 100, but ages of deep-sea fish are unknown. Tortoises appear to be the longest-lived of lower animals, with recorded ages up to 150 (those given as beyond this being questionable).

How long can a man live?

Cold-eyed scientists and insurance actuaries are now dubious about ancient records of human longevity. Figures in the Bible are believed to be based on a different method of computing years—in fact, on two different methods—than was later employed. For instance, the age of Adam is given as 930, of Methuselah as 969, of Cainan as 910, Jared, 962, etc. But all these were pre-Flood personages. After the Flood we find the ages cut to about one-fourth—Abraham, 175, Isaac, 180, Jacob, 147, Moses, 120—leading to the belief that a "year" had a different meaning before and after the Deluge. In fact, Dr. Andrew Efron of Yale reported (in 1940) discovery of a secret ancient "key code" of trees and branches for calculating ages, and concluded that a confusion of the symbols may have led to the miscalculations in the biblical ages. By proper interpretation of the code, Dr. Efron said, Adam's age might be scaled down to 96, while Noah would have been 48 when he built the Ark, not 600.

As we come down to comparatively recent times we find that *only obscure persons,* usually in off-the-track localities, have been credited with phenomenal ages. England's champion oldster is listed as Thomas Parr ("Old Parr"), a Shropshire farmer who died in 1635 at the alleged age of 152. More recently we have heard of a Turk "158 years old," or a Russian "138 years old," or an American ex-slave "125 years old," etc.

To all such figures scientists raise skeptical eyebrows, attributing them to errors, hearsay testimony and the well-known tendency of centenarians to exaggerate their ages—especially when no birth certificates are available. What we can say is that only about three or four persons per 100,000 in the United States are reported in the 100-year age group, and that very few have gone much beyond this.

Our all-time authenticated longevity record to date was that of Mrs. Louise K. Thiers, a Milwaukee woman who died in 1926 at the age of 111 years, 138 days. In Ireland, a spinster, Miss Katherine Plunkett, died in 1932 at the age of 111 years, 329 days. Also apparently authentic, was the report that a Canadian, Pierre Joubert, who died in 1814, had reached the age of 113 years, 124 days.

Let us say, then, that 115 years is now considered about the maximum of human longevity. The present average life expectancy, highest in history, is still far short of this, namely about 68 years. Nevertheless, there are some families whose members, for successive generations, live on an average well beyond this age, and other families for which the average longevity is consistently lower. This has led to the belief that the extent of longevity is in a large degree governed by hereditary factors which, acting on specific organs and tissues, or on the body as a whole, set potential limits to one's life span.

Perhaps, as with automobiles, every human being starts life with a qualified "guarantee" as to how many years he can be kept going. We might call this "conditioned longevity." That word "conditioned" is extremely important, for nowhere does environment play so significant a part as it does in relation to length of life.

Quite true, Mr. So-and-so may boast that he comes of "long-lived stock," and may produce figures to show that his parents and all his ancestors lived to the age of 90. But let Mr. So-and-so, driving home from the club some winter night with one-too-many under his belt, try to round an icy horseshoe curve on high, and all the statistics as to his potential life expectancy may be of no avail.

In the matter of longevity we can think only in terms of broad general averages. You read everywhere that the length of life has been steadily increasing, how in George Washington's time the average was about 35 years, how in 1901 it was about 50 years and how today it is approaching 70. But applied to yourself, this does not mean that because your parents lived to an average age of 75, you will live to be 90 or 100. What has been increased, through greatly improved hygiene, medical treatment and living conditions, is not the *potential longevity* of human beings, but the *chances* of survival.

The very young are the ones who have had their expectation of life most sharply increased through the tremendous reduction in death rates from diseases of infancy and early childhood. (Where a century ago more than *one in every six* babies born died before

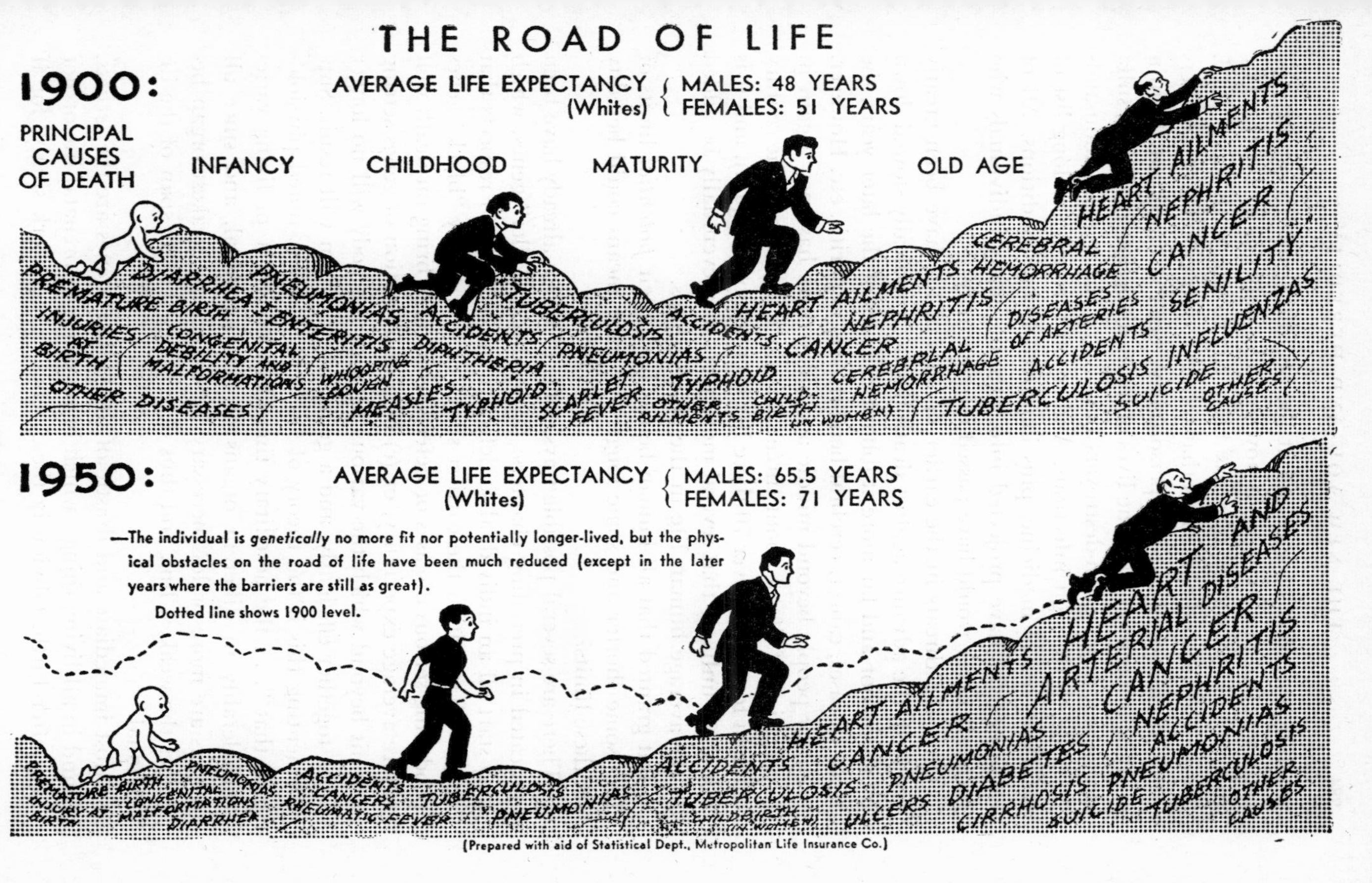

(Prepared with aid of Statistical Dept., Metropolitan Life Insurance Co.)

reaching one year of age, and at the beginning of this century the ratio was still one in eight, it now averages only *one in thirty*.) The tuberculosis mortality rate has been cut to one-sixth since 1900. Many plagues and epidemics that formerly carried off vast numbers of children as well as older persons have been stamped out. Insulin treatment has prolonged the lives of many diabetics. Penicillin, sulfa drugs and other germ-destroyers have saved many more thousands from death through infections. And so on through the long list of achievements of medicine, plus improved living conditions. All of these benefits have projected into later life many individuals who formerly never would have passed into maturity.

Once the threats in the earlier decades of life have been greatly reduced, the advance against death has been radically slowed down by the major and far more stubborn enemies of the later years, the heart diseases, cancer, cerebral hemorrhage, nephritis, etc. However, even for people beyond middle age today there has been a gain in expectation of life of about three years since the turn of the century (though for people over 70 there has been almost no gain); and it is not at all unlikely that several more years may eventually be added to the average human life in the older groups.

But granted that all human beings have their *potential* limits of life—some shorter and some longer—by what means could heredity set these limits?

There are several possible ways, some of which already have been indicated in preceding chapters: (a) by direct "killer" genes, which may start off an individual so defective in certain vital respects that death will result in the earliest stages of life; (b) by "black" genes producing serious diseases or defects which will bring on death well before average expectancy; or (c) by a combination of genes setting a limit beyond which the various parts of the body will no longer work together efficiently, and a general breakdown will result. Supplementing this is the theory of Dr. A. J. Carlson, noted physiologist, that ". . . the hereditary time-clock or power of living varies considerably in different organs of the individual, and since all organs are more or less necessary for living, the weakest organ becomes the weakest link and thus determines the life span of the individual."

Most immediate and drastic of the "killer" genes are the *lethals*, found in all living things, which bring death in prenatal life or not long after birth. Obviously these genes cannot work singly, for if they did, no individual carrying one of them could live to propagate. Lethal genes, therefore, must work at least in *twos,* contributed through both parents. Among the principal ones are those genes which singly produce serious effects and which, if two come together, have their effects so intensified that death results. A great many lethals have been identified in experimental animals and in domestic animals. Examples in humans are believed to be double genes for *brachyphalangy* (stub fingers) and for *telangiectasis* (a blood disease), no case being on record of an individual known to have carried a pair of any of these genes and to have lived.

Four other human genes established as lethal if inherited in pairs are those for *"elephant skin," multiple bone fractures* in the embryo, *fibrosis of the pancreas,* and *familial jaundice* of the newly born. (The latter condition, however, may no longer be considered truly lethal, as it may be cured by an immediate blood transfusion.) But many more human lethals undoubtedly exist. In fact, there is reason to believe that in numerous instances of assumed "false" pregnancy the woman actually was pregnant, but the embryo was killed off by "lethal" genes; and that many cases of miscarriage also can be attributed to lethals.

In addition to the prenatal lethals there are the "killer" genes which bring death in infancy or early childhood. Among them (discussed in previous chapters) are the genes for *amaurotic family idiocy, malignant freckles* and *progressive spinal muscular atrophy* of infants, and also for *glioma retina* (infantile eye tumor), unless the eye is removed.

But to quote Professor Herman J. Muller (1947), "Probably the great majority of persons possess at least one recessive gene or group of genes which, had it been inherited from both parents, would have caused the death of the given person between birth and maturity." And noting that this does not include those genes which produce death only in the prenatal stages, he adds, "That such genes are still not more abundant is only due to the fact that, in the past, individuals getting them from both parents did die."

In another category are a variety of inherited diseases and defects such as hemophilia and several other blood conditions, certain nervous disorders, rare tumors, etc., which hasten death by many years. To a more limited extent, but for larger numbers of persons, the genes for diabetes, some of the heart conditions, etc., also, obviously, are life-shorteners. Indeed, any hereditary differences among families with respect to the major diseases, as we've discussed them in our "Black Gene" chapters, would have a direct bearing on their relative longevity.

Finally, apart from the direct causes of death through specific diseases, there are the "natural" factors which apparently set general time limits for how long anyone can live. Various theories have been advanced as to what these may be: wear and tear on vital organs, aging of the tissues, slowing up of the glands, loss of elasticity in the arteries, deterioration of the blood or brain cells, "vitamin starvation," etc. Wherever the responsibility may lie for the eventual body breakdown, it seems apparent that hereditary influences are involved. In fact, once the early environmental hazards are passed, and persons get into the sixties and seventies where little has been done to lengthen life, individual differences in longevity are increasingly more likely to be conditioned by heredity.

First and foremost of the genetic factors governing your length of life are those which made you a male or a female. Throughout your life your sex has been and will be the most important single influence on your life span, *with the advantage overwhelmingly in your favor if you are a female.* Environment has something to do with this, but, as we saw in our chapter, "The Poor Males," the big advantage of females in longevity derives primarily from the inherited sex differences which produce in the male many more defects and make him an easier prey for most of the major diseases. It is hardly surprising, then, that this contributes to a shorter life expectancy for males at every age.

At the very start, in prenatal life, we've already noted how about 30 per cent more male embryos are killed off than females. In infancy, male deaths continue to average about 30 per cent higher. In childhood and youth the margin of difference decreases to about a 12 per cent higher male mortality, which is sufficient so that by early maturity the numerical advantage with which the males started off (close to 6 per cent more males born than females), has been almost wiped out. Thereafter, as the excess of male mortality rises again to what it was in infancy—30 per cent more males dying than females—the proportion of females surviving becomes steadily greater. By middle life, 15 per cent more women have survived, by the seventies, 20 per cent more, and in the oldest ages, from about 90 on, women begin to outnumber men two to one. In Great Britain, where male casualties of two world wars are in part responsible, the disparity was so great that in 1947, in the age groups of 50 to 54, there were about 27 per cent more females; and in the ages 70 and over, 43 per cent more females. In Germany and France the disparities have been reported as even greater.*

In the accompanying Table you can see for yourself how the fact of your sex bears upon your expectation of life at every age. Undoubtedly, special environmental hazards for males—in occupation, in war casualties, in the far higher accident rate, in greater strain of living, etc.—account for some of the differences in longevity. But when we bear in mind that in the earliest years when there are no such environmental distinctions the male mortality is far higher, and that throughout life where a male and female have the very same disease the threat of death is generally greater for the male, it becomes evident that inherent factors largely determine the sex dif-

THE YEARS REMAINING†

IF ONE'S PRESENT AGE IS:	THE AVERAGE FUTURE LIFE EXPECTANCY IS: *For Males:*	*For Females:*
10	58.4 more years	63.5 more years
15	53.6 " "	58.6 " "
20	49 " "	53.8 " "
25	44.4 " "	49 " "
30	39.8 " "	44.3 " "
35	35.2 " "	39.6 " "
40	30.7 " "	35 " "
45	26.5 " "	30.5 " "
50	22.4 " "	26.2 " "
55	18.8 " "	22 " "
60	15.4 " "	18.1 " "
65	12.4 " "	14.4 " "
70	9.8 " "	11.2 " "
75	7.5 " "	8.3 " "
80	5.4 " "	5.8 " "
85	3.6 " "	3.7 " "

† Figures for Whites, based on 1948 death rates in the United States, as compiled and reported in March, 1950, by the National Office of Vital Statistics, Washington, D. C.

* In the total ratio, for all ages, of males to females in the United States, there has been a significant change in the past forty years. Where in 1910 the ratio was 1,060 males to 1,000 females, by 1950 it was about 990 males to 1,000 females. However, the ratio in former years was much affected by the constant excess of males brought in by immigration.

ferences in longevity. Even among lower animals females outlive males.*

Also significant is that as environment has improved for both sexes, females have profited the most. Thus, between the years 1900 and 1949, while the expectation of life at birth for White males had gone up by 17 years, that for White females had gone up by 20 years. (Figures issued by the National Office of Vital Statistics in 1950, based on 1948 death rates, showed that the average length of life of White women in the United States had reached a new high of 71 years, and for White men of 65.5 years.) One of the greatest special benefits to women has been the tremendous reduction in deaths related to childbearing, which in former periods took so high a toll among them. But apart from this, there is much evidence to show that as environmental hazards of any kind are reduced, the *inherent* biological advantages of women steadily have more opportunity to assert themselves. (By way of contrast, in India, with the worst living standards of any country in 1931, the average length of life was practically the same for both sexes.)

Coming now to people in general, some of the reasons for the sex differences in longevity may be applied to random individuals of either sex. If the initial genetic difference between women and men merely in their sex chromosomes (as their genes otherwise are the same) can so greatly affect their relative life spans, it would follow that among individuals of either sex any important differences in genes governing constitutional makeup and body-functioning also could shorten or lengthen their potential longevity. (This being in addition to any "black" genes for specific diseases or defects.) But what evidence have we to support this theory?

We call, first, upon those favorite subjects of study, the *twins*—"identicals" versus "fraternals." To see how these compare in longevity, Drs. Franz J. Kallmann and Gerhard Sander have undertaken a study in New York State of the histories of more than 2,000 members of twin pairs, all ages 60 or over, and at this writing have the completed histories of 58 pairs both of whom have died. In the case of the "identicals," the interval between deaths averaged three years; of the "fraternals," more than six years. In one pair of identical

* Detailed discussions and tables bearing on all these points will be found in the author's book, *Women and Men,* Chapters 6, 14, 15 and 16, where the social implications of the growing excess of women in the later ages also are discussed. Additional data will be found in *Length of Life,* by Dublin, Lotka and Spiegelman (Revised edition, 1949), Chapter 7.

twins, both died of natural causes the same day, at the age of 86, and another pair died five days apart, at the age of 85. But among the fraternal twins, there was no case of both members dying less than three months apart. Also, among the living "identicals," the physical similarities persist into the oldest ages, with the symptoms of senility (general enfeeblement or lack of it, various defects, etc.) being remarkably alike for both, often even when they have been living apart. In fraternal twins there is no such corresponding similarity.

What can we make of this evidence (assuming that additional case histories will follow the same lines)? Bearing in mind that while identical twins have exactly the same genes, fraternal twins nonetheless also have close family relationships, the much shorter interval between deaths for "identicals" and the correlation in aging symptoms would reinforce previous conclusions about the influence of heredity on life spans. But we also see that this influence works only roughly. For perhaps most significant is the proof that *even with exactly the same genes, two individuals may die years apart.* Considering, further, that living conditions for twins are apt to be much more similar than for any two persons at random, we have here unquestioned evidence of how strongly environment also can affect length of life.

All this has even more meaning when we proceed to the "inheritance" of longevity in different families, or in larger groups of our population. For many years it has been known through numerous studies by insurance companies and independent investigators that there is a significant correlation between the average life spans of grandparents, parents and children. The findings have been such as these:

–Men with the longest-lived parents have unmistakably lower mortality at every age.

–The chance of reaching the four-score mark is considerably greater for those with long-lived parents than for the others.

–Children of one long-lived and one short-lived parent occupy an intermediate position in longevity.

–Among those who live to a very old age (90 or over) about seven out of eight have had one or more long-lived parents, and a large proportion, two or more long-lived grandparents. (Studies by the late Dr. Raymond Pearl.)

Collectively, various studies (as summed up by Metropolitan Life statisticians) indicate that the difference in expectation of life at age

25 between persons with better records of parental longevity and those with the poorer records may be anywhere from 2 to 4 years.

All of the foregoing findings, however, must be weighed in the light of much other evidence that *differences in social and economic levels, and in occupation, help greatly to make some families longer-lived than others.*

One hardly needs figures to show that even with no differences in heredity, families living for successive generations under depressed conditions would not have the same average life spans as those in more favored environments. On the broadest scale, we have only to compare the longevity rates of human beings today with those of the past. But more specifically, we can take families or groups within the present population and apply this simple formula: *The higher the income and social level, the lower the mortality rate, and the longer the average life span; the lower the income and social level, the higher the mortality rate, the shorter the life span.*

Many studies have validated this formula. United States Public Health reports (1949) showed that when 973 cities were classified in four groups, according to average incomes in 1939-1940, the group of cities with the lowest per capita buying income ($595 per person) had an infant mortality rate *almost three times* that of the city group with the highest per capita buying income ($727). For persons of all ages, in the 92 larger cities (with populations of 100,000 or more), there was an average mortality rate about 25 per cent higher in the lower-third income cities as compared with the upper-third.

Another good illustration is the comparison between Negroes and Whites in the United States. There was a time when many believed that the much higher death rate of the Negroes, and their much shorter life expectancy, was due largely to "inferior" heredity. We know now that the explanation has been their much inferior environment, for with every step in the advancement of the Negroes, the margin of difference between them and Whites in longevity has been reduced. In 1900, Negroes at birth had an average life expectancy of only 32.5 years for males, and 35 years for females—*16 years less than the average for Whites.* In 1948, the life-expectancy figures for Negroes had advanced to 58 years for males and 62.5 years for females—*only about 8 years less than for Whites.* With continued economic and social advances for the Negroes, there is little reason to doubt that the differences in life expectancy will be much further reduced if not entirely eliminated.

Among Whites themselves, we must also be cautious regarding reported "hereditary" differences in longevity between persons of different stocks and nationalities. One used to speak of "hardy, long-lived 'old Americans'" as compared with the "weaker immigrants," but as conditions improved for the newer arrivals and their descendants, the differences in longevity have been almost wiped out. Within the ranks of the foreign-born, however, marked differences in death rates and longevity still persist. For instance, one detailed study by Dr. Massimo Calabresi of Yale (1945) showed that among foreign-born stocks in New York state, the Irish had very much the highest death rates and those born in Italy the lowest; further, that the mortality differences between the two groups for specific diseases were in many respects duplicated among those in their homelands. While noting that subtle differences in diet, habits, occupations and activities undoubtedly affect the relative life spans of those of different nationalities, he also suggested that ". . . there is no reason to doubt that there is a statistical difference in the frequency distribution of genes among different groups of the human species," which might apply to hereditary diseases and disease resistance generally, and contribute toward the higher mortality rates among those of some nationalities as compared with others.

Nevertheless, there is much to show that throughout the United States, any marked differences in relative average length of life between people of one group or another, or between those of one community, city state or region and another, are governed far less by their ancestral origins than by the existing conditions under which they live.

On a broader scale, comparing Whites in one country and another, *Length of Life* (Dublin, Lotka and Spiegelman, 1949), reports that the contrasts in the current records for longevity between the backward countries of the world and the more advanced countries are almost as great as those between the ancients and the most advanced modern peoples. Thus, as late as 1931, India had an average length of life less than 27 years (only 5 years more than the average estimated for ancient Rome). In Egypt, up to 1937, the average length of life was about 30 years for males and 31.5 years for females. Contrast this with averages for New Zealand in the same year—65.5 years for males and 68.5 years for females. It would certainly not be hard to show that the disparity is directly correlated with differences in living standards, diet and medical care.

The "formula" given a few paragraphs back can be applied in a number of ways. *How much rent do you pay?* Do you have a telephone? An automobile? An automatic refrigerator? Answers to all such questions, taken together as an index of your economic and social well-being, have a bearing on your expectation of life and on that of other members of your family. This has been graphically shown through intensive studies made by Howard Whipple Green of the Cleveland Health Council. Dividing the city into "economic tenths" from the highest to the lowest (on the basis of 1937 figures) he found that infant mortality increased almost step by step as one moved down the ladder from the "haves" to the "have-nots." But compared with the situation in Cleveland twenty years before, the mortality-rate differences between groups have been much narrowed down as the direst degrees of poverty have been eliminated, and as babies of even the less-favored classes have been getting increasingly better medical care, nutrition and attention.

However, the conditions under which people live may not be entirely unrelated to their hereditary makeup.

As one illustration, *Length of Life* points out that where parents are potentially shorter-lived, there is an increased chance of a broken home and an unfavorable environment resulting for the children while they are still young. To quote, "If it is the mother who dies, the children often receive poor care and improper nourishment; and the premature death of the father usually means an even severer handicap . . . often poverty and destitution. . . . All these factors are hazards to the life and health of this group (comprising those with a poor ancestral history) and it is therefore not surprising that its longevity is lower than that of groups more favorably situated. In these circumstances the influence of inheritance and environment are intertwined."

Where heredity may also enter the picture indirectly is in the matter of one's *occupation,* to the extent that jobs and professions may be influenced by hereditary capacities. For obviously, a person's occupation has much to do with his whole standard and manner of living. Thus, studies in the United States and England show that average length of life grades down, step by step, through different occupational classes. At the top in life expectancy are professional men (clergymen highest, then lawyers and engineers, then doctors). Slightly below are businessmen (proprietors and managers) and white-collar workers. Then, grading down, are skilled workers and unskilled

OCCUPATIONAL DIFFERENCES IN LONGEVITY

COLLEGE GRADUATES have mortality rates well below the average, especially those who enter the professions.

CLERGYMEN live considerably longer than average laymen. (Their general economic status may be lower, but they live more temperately, enjoy good medical attention and have fewer accidents.)

DOCTORS have a mortality rate somewhat higher than most other professional men (especially in heart and arterial diseases), but with death rates below average for cancer, and much lower for infectious diseases, surgical conditions and accidents. Specialists have much better life expectancies than non-specialists.

LAWYERS have among the lowest death rates in the professional group. Engineers and scientists are somewhat behind them in longevity.

WOMEN TEACHERS have among the lowest death rates for women in any occupation. Male educators also have much better than average longevity.

ARTISTS, writers, actors, musicians and poets have average life spans well below those of professional men—poets usually being the shortest-lived of these.

FARMERS are particularly long-lived, either because farm life tends to promote health and strength, or because men have to be healthier and stronger to continue as farmers.

UNSKILLED LABORERS have the highest mortality rate, going with low incomes and unfavorable environments. Sandblasters, stonecutters, pottery workers and miners are among those with the highest death rates:

workers; and with the shortest average life expectancies, miners and granite workers. Farmers are in a special class, right up with the professional men, or perhaps, even a bit higher in length of life. (For other classifications see our accompanying Chart.) Between the most-favored and least-favored occupational groups with respect to longevity, the English records, as reported by Dr. Christopher Tietze (1943), showed a difference in length of life averaging more than 7 years. It is more than likely, however, that with increased safety precautions and improved living standards for bottom-level workers, this great difference in longevity will be much reduced.

But while we can easily trace the connection between better jobs and better living conditions, and longer life expectancies, as compared with the results of inferior jobs, we must not entirely overlook certain other possibilities. Among them is the fact that people who are genetically handicapped, particularly in intelligence, may be destined to have inferior jobs, and thus to create inferior, life-shortening environments for themselves and their children. It also is possible that abnormal behavior tendencies, where and if influenced by heredity (as will be explained in later chapters), may have something to do with directing *some* individuals into more hazardous jobs or patterns of living which may shorten their life spans. On the other hand, persons who are genetically favored in capacity, and who can also govern their lives more intelligently, may be given an extra push in the direction of longevity. In short, every aspect of a person's makeup—his mental as well as his physical heredity—and almost everything that happens to him, have an influence on his longevity.

Here we may pause for some specific questions:

Does your body build have any relation to your longevity?

Yes, but only to the extent that it reflects good health or lack of it, or the efficiency or inefficiency of the body mechanism. Persons who are 25 per cent or more *overweight* have a death rate about 75 per cent higher than those of average weight, largely because marked obesity usually accompanies some disease which of itself would shorten life (for instance, diabetes and degenerative diseases). Young adults who are much underweight suffer a higher than average mortality, chiefly through tuberculosis and other respiratory diseases. But at older ages, some degree of underweight may be conducive to longer life.

The situation with respect to *height* is complicated. In those under

40, tall men are reported as having the highest mortality, short men the lowest mortality, but in ages thereafter the reverse begins to apply, with short men having the highest mortality. As a rule, in the older age groups those of average height and weight generally have the lowest mortality. While hereditary differences in body build may be important, one must also take into account the differences in environment as they affect body development, and in turn, longevity as a whole.

Does "faster living," overwork or strain, shorten life?

Yes. Professor A. C. Ivy, noted University of Chicago physiologist, holds that the rate of living has a direct bearing on aging, and points out, "It has been conclusively demonstrated by experiments on plants and animals . . . that the faster the rate of living, the shorter the length of life." Studies by the late Dr. Raymond Pearl of some 2,000 persons aged 90 or over indicated that, besides heredity, the only outstanding trait shared among them was that "the vast majority were of placid temperament, not given to worry." He also challenged the theory that "hard work never kills a man" by evidence that continued hard physical labor does shorten life if a man has passed 40, and that sustained fatigue is often a cause of premature death. As to the effects of strain, it may be significant that only twelve of the thirty deceased presidents of the United States outlived their expectation of life at their inauguration—the long-lived being concentrated for the most part in the early and less turbulent period of the nation's history—while of the most recent presidents, Harding, Coolidge and Franklin D. Roosevelt died 8 years earlier than their expectancy.

Is your blood pressure or your pulse rate any clue to your length-of-life prospects?

Yes. The Metropolitan Life experts report that "mortality rises steadily and markedly" with increasing high blood pressure, primarily due to the heart-arterial-kidney diseases. *Low* blood pressure, however, unless it is extremely low, on the average may be actually favorable to longevity.

In *pulse rates,* abnormalities are fairly common, and in the majority of cases are not very prejudicial to life expectancies. But an extremely rapid rate—exceeding 100 per minute—may reflect some underlying disease, such as heart disease or hyperthyroidism—and usually forecasts some degree of life curtailment. Intermittent pulse rates (skipped beats) and irregular pulse are both associated with moderately higher-than-average mortality rates. In extreme cases they will mean exclusion for life insurance.

Does marriage increase life spans?

Married men, it appears, do have average longer lives than single men (although some wag has said, "It only seems longer!"). As Mortimer Spiegelman of the Metropolitan Life Insurance Company reports, married men have lower mortality rates at all ages, with a death rate in the ages 25 to 44 only half that of bachelors. By and large, the married man probably receives better care and has a more favorable environment than the single man, but the statistics are loaded by the fact that the men who don't marry include proportionately many more who in the first place are sickly or defective, or mentally unstable or abnormal, or otherwise potentially shorter-lived. Among women, the married have an advantage in longevity over the unmarried only up to the age of 40, the mortality rates thereafter being practically identical for the two groups.

Does drinking alcoholic beverages shorten life?

Authorities are in disagreement. The present majority opinion appears to be that drinking in moderation does not affect longevity (except where there are certain diseases), and in recent years many doctors have maintained that an occasional drink may be beneficial, even recommending it for some persons with heart conditions. *Heavy drinking*, however, is quite another matter. It hardly requires proof that it generally leads to curtailed length of life.

How about smoking?

Except in certain conditions (ulcers, heart, etc.) or where excessive addiction is otherwise harmful, there is no direct evidence that average smoking ordinarily affects longevity, according to the *Journal of the American Medical Association* (October, 1948). Some doctors, however, dispute this, and others consider the question still open. (Significant may be recent studies of the effects of smoking on the production of lung, lip and mouth cancers.)

Do athletes have shorter lives than non-athletes?

Popular belief is that they do, but the facts don't support this. *Length of Life* reports that a study of longevity records of college graduates indicates that up to middle life those who were athletes have somewhat lower mortality rates than college graduates as a whole, though in ages thereafter the former athletes have a slightly higher mortality average. But "mental athletics" pays off better! For the same study shows that honor graduates (high-scholarship students) have an expectation of life almost 2 years more than the general average for college graduates.

One hears various other theories: Brunettes live longer than blondes; "over-sexed" people have shortened lives; premature gray hair means early death; bald-headed men die before those not bald; men with more hair on their chest outlive those with little hair, etc. Not one of these theories has yet been found to have any scientific basis.

In sum, the most we can say about how long you will live is that it depends chiefly on these factors: First, on environment—the way in which you were started off in life and the conditions under which you lived thereafter and now live, work, and take care of yourself. Second, on your inherited vigor or weakness (as applied both to specific diseases and defects and to general resistance factors), with *particular attention to your sex*. And third, on *luck*.

We have placed environment first because, while there are many hereditary conditions which, as you've seen, transcend environment in cutting lives short at early ages, these are the great exceptions. Otherwise, the greatest differences in length of life among human beings—those of the past and present, and those of backward groups and advanced groups today—can be attributed far more to environment than to heredity.

Nevertheless, it also has been made clear that the more the *big environmental disparities* are reduced by giving ever larger numbers of people the benefits of improved living conditions and medical care, the more the *little hereditary differences* with respect to longevity can assert themselves. (We already have seen how this has operated in women as compared with men.) For human beings in general, length of life will be more and more governed by the *potential limits* set for us by our heredity, both as individuals and as members of a species, in the same way that hereditary limits are apparently set for the life spans of all other animals.

But does this imply that nothing can be done to extend the potential limits of human longevity as they exist today? Or that the "conditioned" longevity of humans is forever set?

No, for in the opinion of most authorities, the human life span very likely will be increased. Not by much, however! The feat of the late Dr. Alexis Carrel in showing how a piece of living tissue (chicken heart) could be kept alive indefinitely, may have inspired, in some, wild notions about eventual similar immortality for human beings. But keeping an isolated piece of tissue alive, even forever, is far from the same thing as keeping all the vital parts and organs of a complete human body growing and functioning uniformly, through all the vicissitudes of a lifetime. As Dr. C. Ward Crampton, a specialist in old-age study, has said, "A man does not grow old in one package . . . a man of 65 may have a 40-year-old heart, 50-year-old kidneys, and an 80-year-old liver." Thus, strengthening or prolonging the life of the weakest part of the body mechanism may increase life expectancy, as may happen if we can find cures or preventatives for the major killers of the later years. But most scientists believe that only so much can be done and no more to keep the whole body going efficiently, and that the potential human longevity limits will never be much beyond what they always have been and still are today. Few believe that even the Methuselahs of the future will get farther than 120 years or so (though some scientists believe a maximum of 150 years is not impossible).

What of all the "rejuvenation" and "life-prolongation" theories? High hopes have been raised by one after another of these, but the Ponce de Leons remain as far from their goal as ever. One set of theories has centered on the belief that the Fountain of Youth is aflow with hormones. Injections of mashed-up sex glands (Brown-Sequard), monkey-gland operations (Voronoff), cutting and tying of sex-gland ducts (Steinach), all have had their day—and their setting sun. More recently there has been the "male" hormone *(testosterone)* "rejuvenation" treatment. But the results remain questionable, and an Oxford authority, Dr. V. Korenchevsky, warned of possible danger. He pointed out (1947) that the various causes of old-age breakdown can't be removed by "stimulation" (particularly by testosterone), and that, in fact, "just as a tired old horse may collapse if whipped to do extra work, the administration of hormones, instead of 'rejuvenating' an old body is more likely to hasten its collapse." (However, this is not a reflection on the valuable use of hormones in many forms of medical treatment, and it is still possible that treatment with a balanced combination of a number of hormones may prove effective in some cases of senility.)

The greatest recent to-do has been about the "Bogolometz serum," which was hailed by some enthusiasts in 1946 as "more important than the discovery of the atomic bomb." The theory of Alexander A. Bogolometz, a Russian scientist, was that the principal centers of body degeneration and disease were in the "connective" tissues, and his serum was expected so to strengthen these tissues—as well as healing wounds, dissolving cancer cells, accelerating bone repairs, etc.—that, given proper diet and hygiene, humans could live out what he believed was their "natural" life span of between 125 to 150 years. But, at this writing, hopes for the serum are being much minimized by follow-up researches in the United States. These indicate, according to Professor Henry S. Simms of the Columbia University School of Medicine (as told to the author in 1948), that while the serum may prove of a little benefit, "no far-reaching results are in sight," and that "it would not be surprising if ten years from now little more was heard about the Bogolometz theory." (Incidentally, Bogolometz himself died in 1947, but he hadn't used the serum on himself, not believing he was one of those who could be aided.)

So it goes. There is also the diet school, which includes those who have sought longer life through yogurt, sour milk, pumpernickel bread and garlic. And if you were a mouse or rat, you might be excited by recent experiments showing that nucleic acid in yeast has increased the life span of mice by 9 per cent; that underfed mice have longer life expectancies than the overfed; and that among rats those fed an omnivorous diet live significantly longer than the pure "vegetarians." (George Bernard Shaw notwithstanding.)

Nonetheless, prospects are bright that in the years ahead means will be found to extend the length of life of a great many more older adults by retarding or preventing degenerative diseases of the arteries, heart, kidneys and other organs. As environmental hazards are reduced, it is also likely, as we said, that the inherited longevity potentials of humans will assert themselves more, and we will really have proof of just how long you and others can live. However, keeping more people alive longer—without also devising means of keeping them happy and useful—will greatly add to the social and economic problems which steadily are becoming more acute as the army of the aged continues to grow. It may be that Nature has been wiser than we think in setting the potential longevity of humans at the prevailing limits. More *quality* in the years we live, rather than more *quantity*, might be our goal.

But assuming that you might still want to be around a few centuries hence "to see what's cooking," there is one other interesting possibility: Russian scientists, working in the Arctic, have found that plants which had been frozen into the ice for thousands of years could be revived and made to grow again. Said Professor P. N. Kapterev: "As a result of our experiments, it can be stated that there is really a possibility of resuscitating organisms long after they have been frozen."

Well, who knows? Perhaps, someday, one of us, fresh out of college, will be frozen by the method described in the frozen-food advertisements: "WHAM! A blast of Arctic cold strikes suddenly and seals in all the juices. . . ." We could then be kept in *status quo* indefinitely under perfect refrigeration; and a hundred or two hundred years from now we could be "defrosted" and enabled to begin living and moving again in another world, as characters in drama and fiction already have done.

Anyway, the only immediate method in sight of much prolonging our lives seems to be by spending a stretch of years in a deep freezer.

CHAPTER 31

"BLACK GENE" ROLL-CALL

THIS is not a happy chapter.

It summarizes and brings together all the "black" genes previously discussed and some additional ones of lesser import. Also—which is its most ominous aspect—it forecasts the chances of transmitting any given defect, disease or abnormality to a child.

At first glance the array of "black" genes may appear to be Tables of Doom. But really, there are some brighter sides to the picture. As we've pointed out, the defects and diseases which can be blamed directly on heredity are as nothing compared to the interminable array of ills that are wholly or largely due to environmental causes. Moreover, many of the hereditary conditions are serious to the individual only when he considers them as such.

For instance, most of the eye conditions: Near-sightedness or far-sightedness, in their usual forms, can hardly be thought of as spelling doom—not, certainly, when there is an optician around the corner. In certain jobs, such as that of the aviator, forest ranger or policeman, weak eyes may indeed be a bar or serious handicap. But we prefer to think of one of the most near-sighted of men, Arturo Toscanini, and of how the very fact of his weak eyes tended to develop in him the miraculous musical memory which contributed to his achievements.

If a deviation from the standard for any characteristic is a defect, then we are all, each and every one of us, defective. Looking through the list of "black" genes (and remember, not all the minor ones have been included), it is more than likely that you will find at least one condition which strikes home to you personally, or which is present in your immediate family. Most cases justify no further comment than "My, my—so that's inherited. How interesting!"

But, unfortunately, many conditions cannot be dismissed so lightly. For example, blindness, or conditions that lead to blindness; deafness; diseases such as diabetes, hemophilia and other blood disorders; certain tumors; serious and unpleasant skin conditions; deformities of the features and of the body; grave mental disorders; etc. If any of such conditions are present in you or in your immediate family (bearing in mind always that we are speaking of the *hereditary* types) then they may well give you pause. This is where you should study seriously the "Forecast" Tables.

The practical value of knowing that a condition is inherited, and exactly how it is inherited, already has been suggested in preceding chapters. To summarize the principal points, such knowledge can put doctors on the alert for the appearance of an hereditary ailment or defect; it can help in diagnosis and in taking preventive measures, leading to cures or to forestalling the worst effects; and it may give prospective parents who have serious inherited defects, or whose families have them, a clearer idea of what hereditary dangers may or may not confront their children.

As illustrations of how "black-gene" forecasts may help, there are several interesting cases reported by Professor Laurence H. Snyder, one of the leaders in the field of medical genetics. One case involved the serious type of jaundice, *hemolytic icterus,* caused by a dominant gene, whose worst effects, usually developing in maturity, can be forestalled by removal of the spleen. A man with this condition was saved by the operation, and when it was learned that he had four grown sons (each of whom had had a fifty-fifty chance of having received this "black" gene), arrangements were made for them to be examined. Two of the sons were indeed found to have the symptoms, and the operation for spleen removal was immediately advised for both. One son underwent the operation. The other refused it—and a year later he died of the disease.

Another case reported by Dr. Snyder was of a man who had a peculiar ulcerated corn on one foot, which seemed to defy treatment. It was recalled that the man's two brothers had been treated for certain related conditions resulting from *spina bifida,* inherited through a dominant gene. X-rays of the patient's spine showed that he, too, had this condition, previously unsuspected, and made possible remedial measures.

In still another case a man of 54 was operated on for a stomach cancer of a type believed to be hereditary. A brother, two years younger, was thereupon examined and was found to have a developing cancer of precisely the same kind, in the very same location.

The presence of a number of inherited conditions can be determined by laboratory tests well in advance of the time that their serious effects are manifested. One such condition is *xanthoma tuberosum,* a disorder of the fat metabolism which may lead to heart involvement and premature death. Where this disorder has appeared in one member of a family, clinical tests of other members will reveal whether or not they have the tendency to the disease, and if so, special diets and other appropriate measures may forestall serious consequences.

"Carriers" of "black" genes—persons who themselves are not or will not become victims of a condition, but are in danger of transmitting a gene for it to their children—pose special problems. Those who carry "hidden" single genes for diabetes, amaurotic idiocy, some forms of epilepsy and mental defect, tendencies to schizophrenia, or any other recessive conditions requiring two genes to develop, are in this category. In some instances such carriers can be singled out by a knowledge of the previous appearance of the condition in their family: for instance, where a parent has or had hereditary diabetes, it is fairly certain that every child is a carrier of a "diabetic" gene; should both parents have been diabetic, the likelihood is that every child is not merely a carrier of two "diabetes" genes, but is himself or herself threatened with development of the disease in maturity.

In certain other conditions, such as *amaurotic idiocy,* where the afflicted individuals die early in childhood, carriers of a "hidden" single gene can reveal themselves only if they have a child with the disease. In that case, the knowledge is useful to the parents involved as a warning that there is a one-in-four chance that any succeeding child of theirs will be similarly defective.

But there are several recessive-gene conditions we have dealt with where carriers reveal themselves quite easily because their single gene, while not producing the serious disease itself, may nonetheless manifest itself in some minor effect. Thus, persons who carry a single gene for Mediterranean *(Cooley's)* anemia have a very mild form of anemia which can be detected through a microscopic examination of their blood cells; and carriers of a single gene for *phenylpyruvic amentia* (the chemically induced type of imbecility discussed in our "Slow Minds" chapter) have certain surface peculiarities, such as abnormal skin conditions.

In the case of certain inherited brain and nervous disorders, there are now high hopes that carriers of genes for these may be detected by means of their electro-encephalograms (brain-wave recordings). As we noted in our discussion of epilepsy, there already is some evidence that persons themselves normal, but carrying a hidden gene for the condition, may, in many instances, show abnormalities in their EEGs. In the very rare condition, *Huntington's chorea,* where a single dominant gene can produce the drastic disease, we also have noted the possibility that those carrying the gene, and the tendency to develop the disease, may *in some cases* likewise reveal themselves through abnormalities in their brain waves, long before the disease itself appears. (While this can't help the individuals affected, there being no preventive treatment now known for the condition, it may at least warn them against having children.) But for the common mental diseases, particularly schizophrenia, there is as yet no way of detecting carriers of "hidden" genes by clinical methods, and in these cases one can only make guesses based on family histories.

Another means of detecting "black"-gene carriers which holds considerable promise is through the "gene-linkage" technique, still in its beginning stages with respect to humans, though it has proved highly effective in the case of experimental animals. This method consists in fixing the location of a given "black" gene on a specific chromosome which is known to also carry a gene for some easily discernible surface trait. The latter will then become a marker or "tracer" for the hidden "black" gene (somewhat like the bob on a fishing line telling of the hook dangling beneath). For example, if a gene for some rare disease is proved to be a chromosome-mate of a gene for some dominant surface trait—perhaps a certain eye color, or shape of finger, or quirk in ear formation—we will know in many instances that persons with the surface trait are probably carriers of the "black" gene in question; or, at least, that those who do not have the trait are not carriers.

In fruit flies, a great many of these linked genes have been identified, but as these creatures have only four pairs of chromosomes, it has been relative easy to "map" the location of specific genes on each chromosome (though this required the development of highly ingenious techniques). In humans, who have twenty-four pairs of chromosomes, tracking down linked genes is infinitely more complicated, and so far, linkage has been established chiefly for only a small number of genes on the X and Y chromosomes. But this, as we have seen, has already helped us greatly in distinguishing between males and females as carriers of the various "sex-linked" genes, for color blindness, hemophilia, etc.

Some of the most difficult problems are presented by the "qualified" genes which have different degrees of "expressivity," i.e., where effects are conditioned either by the presence of some other gene or genes, or by some special environmental factors. As an example, an "allergy" gene in the same family may express its effects in different individuals in variable ways, and lead to different conditions "running the gamut of hay fever, asthma, rash, eczema, etc." (as Dr. Snyder points out). Other instances of where the effects are variable or qualified are provided by the genes for certain types of cataract and glaucoma, deafness, muscular and nerve ailments, and various hand and foot abnormalities. In these "qualified" cases the same "black" genes may produce serious effects in one person, moderate effects (or effects of a different type) in another, or no effects at all in still another. Even an expert would be hard put to make accurate forecasts of what such genes could be expected to do in any given case.

Where inheritance comes indirectly, in the form of a "predisposition" or "susceptibility," forecasts must also be highly conditional. But at the same time, foreknowledge of any inherited tendency (for example, to rheumatic heart disease, or to schizophrenia) may be of inestimable value if it is possible to set up environmental safeguards. Should common cancer, or some of its forms, likewise be proved to involve an inherited susceptibility, and should the genes for this be identified, one can hardly overestimate how much this could contribute toward early diagnosis and treatment, and the saving of lives.

As the science of medical genetics progresses—and it has been growing by leaps and bounds as its recognized value has spurred on research—the "black"-gene forecasts are certain to become considerably more accurate and extensive. At the same time, continued discoveries of new cures and treatments are likely to reduce the gravity of many more of the inherited conditions (in the way that the threats of diabetes, some of the blood conditions, various eye defects, etc., have been reduced). Thus, as you look through the Summary Tables and Forecasts, we urge you to think of the hopeful as well as the gloomy aspects of conditions which may concern you personally.

If you already have some serious hereditary condition, or if you are fearful of transmitting it to a child, an optimistic view may be that a cure or treatment for it exists or will presently be available.

Another fact which may hearten the individual is that no *recessive* condition, even if present in one parent, will crop out in a child unless a matching gene is also transmitted by the other parent. (This applies, remember, to diabetes, albinism, most inherited mental defects, and all other conditions where *two* recessive genes are required.) But this does not console society, for actually, as will be more fully explained in a later chapter, it is the recessive hidden genes that constitute our greatest problem.

The *time of onset* of any condition is also of great importance. To the lay mind an inherited condition which is present from birth, or that manifests itself in childhood, with perhaps fatal consequences, is considered more ominous than one which does not appear until late in life. From the standpoint of society rather than the individual, quite the reverse may be true in many respects, because where a condition does not develop until an individual is grown up it may permit him to reproduce and pass on the genes. Thus, if you are still young, and a condition which has its onset in maturity is known to run in your family, there is always the possibility that it may yet appear in you and that you may transmit it.

As we said, we are not here listing every single one of the known "black" genes, down to the rarest and most minor ones (these often being merely variations of others that are listed). To attempt such thoroughness would give this book the character of a medical treatise, which we heartily wish to avoid. However, a conscientious effort has been made to present every condition that could be of interest to any considerable number of readers.

A final word of caution: In reading the brief description of each condition, be careful not to confuse it with something else which might have similar symptoms, or which is *not hereditary*. Also be sure to make allowances for the rôle of environment wherever it is a factor, and for the time of onset. Wherever in doubt—and certainly for every serious condition—don't fail to consult your physician.

So now to the Tables, presenting, first, the classified lists of "black" genes, and following them, the forecasts for each type of inheritance.

SUMMARY TABLES—"BLACK" GENES

Herewith are listed all principal or unusual diseases, defects or "abnormal" conditions in which there is proof of heredity to date, or in which heredity is believed to play some part. (Included are all the conditions discussed in the text and, in addition, a considerable number of other conditions which warrant attention.) With each condition is given its type or types of inheritance as now established. Where there is uncertainty, a question mark follows.* (At the end of the Tables will be found a "Forecast" section, giving the chances of inheritance, of any condition listed, for yourself or your children.)

KEEP IN MIND THESE ABBREVIATIONS AND THEIR MEANINGS:

Dom.—Dominant. Only *one* gene required to produce effect. (A parent with a dominant condition will pass it on to one in two children.)

Rec.—Recessive (simple). *Two* of the same genes required to produce effect. (For a child to have a recessive condition each parent must contribute exactly the same gene.)

Sex-L.—Sex-linked recessive. Gene is carried on X chromosome. Only *one* such gene needed to produce effect in *male,* but *two* required in *female* (as with any other recessive).

Sex-L.Dom.—Sex-linked dominant. Rare type, in which a gene on X chromosome is dominant, producing, singly, same effect in females as in males.

Part. Sex-L.—Partially (or incompletely) sex-linked. Very rare cases where same gene is carried on both Y and X chromosomes. (See "Forecasts," p. 323.)

Rec.+.—Recessive-*plus.* Condition is caused by a pair of the same recessives *plus* some additional different genes (another pair of recessives, or other genes not identified).

Dom.+.—Dominant-*plus.* Condition is caused by a dominant gene *plus* some other gene or genes not identified.

Dom.-Dom.—Double-dominant. Two of the same dominant genes

* *Note to physicians.* Some of the conditions listed as hereditary may be clinically similar to conditions caused by certain acquired diseases or environmental factors: for example, some cases of congenital deafness or blindness, various eye defects and structural abnormalities, etc. In many cases, careful diagnosis and study of the case history will reveal the distinction between the hereditary and non-hereditary types, as in eye-muscle paralysis, where the hereditary type is present from birth while the non-hereditary type is a sequel to injury, meningitis, etc.

required to produce effect. (One gene of this type alone produces milder effect.)

Dom.-q. or *Rec.-q.*—Dominant-qualified, or, Recessive-qualified. Genes which do not always produce their effects, or may produce variable effects, often depending on environment and sometimes on the workings of other genes.

?—Question mark after name or description of condition indicates "heredity doubtful or uncertain." After gene mechanism it means uncertainty as to exact manner of inheritance.

HEART AND BLOOD VESSELS

High blood pressure (hypertension). Predisposition *possibly* inherited. *Dom.*(?)

Arteriosclerosis. Inherited predisposition possible, but not established. (?)

–*Atherosclerosis* (disorder of cholesterol metabolism which may lead to arteriosclerosis). Heredity possible, but method of inheritance not yet known. (?)

Rheumatic fever (childhood rheumatism). *Rec.-q.*

Low blood pressure (hypotension). Rare inherited type. *Dom.*(?)

Varicose veins. Most often due to external causes, but in some families may be hereditary. Where so: *Dom.-q*

CANCER

Common types: Possible predisposition or inherited susceptibility in some degree, but manner of inheritance uncertain. Applying particularly to (a) *breast cancer,* with greater than average susceptibility apparently inherited by women in some families; (b) *cancer of intestines* and *cancer of rectum;* and (c) *cancer of stomach* (although latter may be much influenced by unfavorable diet).

Rare types:

a. *Malignant freckles (xeroderma pigmentosum).* Induced by exposure to sun. Usually fatal (childhood). *Rec. (Part. Sex-L.)*

b. *Epiloia (tuberose scleroses),* "butterfly rash." Tumors of skin and brain, often with mental derangement. Frequently fatal in childhood. May arise by mutation. *Dom.*

   –*Adenoma sebaceum.* Same as above, but no mental derangement. *Dom.*

c. *Polyposis of the colon.* Intestinal growths in early adult life, often leading to cancer. *Dom.*

d. *Glioma retina (retinoblastoma).* Tumor of eye, fatal unless eye removed. Infancy or childhood. *Dom.*

e. *Retinal angioma.* Blood tumor of eye. Sometimes familial, but manner of inheritance uncertain. (?)

f. *Coffee-colored spots (neurofibromatosis).* Numerous dark skin growths, also growths on nerves and brain, sometimes becoming cancerous. May also cause deafness or mental defect, depending on site of growths. *Dom.*

Hodgkin's disease. Lymph-gland disorder; may involve bone marrow, causing severe anemia. Fatal. Heredity in doubt. (?)

Leukemia. Excess white blood cells. Usually fatal. More common in males. Heredity doubtful. (?)

METABOLIC DISORDERS

Diabetes mellitus (common type). "Sugar sickness" due to pancreas defect. *Rec.*

False diabetes. Two separate types, (a) *diabetes insipidus* and (b) *sugar urine* (*renal glycosuria*). Neither harmful. Both: *Dom.*

Glycogen disease. Starch accumulation in organs. *Rec.*

Excess fat deposits (in organs). Several types, differing in nature:

a. *Niemann-Pick disease* (enlargement of liver and spleen). Fatal in early childhood. *Rec.-q.(?)*

b. *Gaucher's disease.* Fatal in children, not adults. *Rec.-q.*(?)

c. *Xanthoma tuberosum.* Fatty deposits in internal organs and arteries, leading to *atherosclerosis.* Double-gene type of *xanthelasma.* (See p. 217.) *Dom.-Dom.*

Urinary disorders.

a. *Alkaptanuria.* Dark urine, sometimes causing arthritis. *Rec.*

b. *Cystinuria.* Occasionally with one type of kidney stones (cystine). *Rec.-q.*(?)

c. *Pentosuria*—fructosuria. Faulty assimilation of these sugars. *Rec.*

d. *Porphyrinuria.* Associated with reddish teeth. (See, Mouth and Teeth, *Defective Tooth Enamel.*)

Gout. Believed inherited as susceptibility; much more common in males. *Dom.*

Protein disorders. Cystine and albumin. *Rec.-q.*

—*Lipoid-proteinosis.* Numerous small fatty growths, face and scalp; and sometimes also in larynx. Serious. *Rec.*

BLEEDING DISEASES

Hemophilia (defective blood-clotting). Males only. *Sex-L.*

Pseudo-hemophilia. Unrelated to above, far less severe. In both sexes. *Dom.-q.*

Nose-bleed (thrombasthenia). Hereditary type only. Spontaneous and excessive bleeding. *Sex-L. Dom.*

Bleeding under skin (telangiectasis). *Dom.*

ANEMIAS

Cooley's (Mediterranean) anemia.

–Mild (single-gene) type. Slight anemia, no serious effects. *Dom.*

–Severe (double-gene) type. Usually fatal (childhood). *Dom.-Dom.*

Sickle Cell.

–Mild (single-gene) type: *Sicklemia* ("sickle"-shaped corpuscles). Usually no serious effects. *Dom.*

–Severe (double-gene) type: *Sickle-cell anemia.* Usually fatal in childhood. *Dom.-Dom.*

BLOOD-CELL ABNORMALITIES. (These two conditions are not harmful.)

Oval-shaped or elongated red corpuscles. *Dom.*

Undeveloped white blood cells *(Pelger's anomaly).* *Dom.*

JAUNDICE

Acholuric. Fragile blood cells, sometimes with anemia. *Dom.-q.*

–*Familial non-hemolytic.* Milder form of above. *Dom.-q.*

Erythroblastosis fetalis. Jaundice in newborn, due to mother-child "Rh" or other blood-factor conflict. (See text, Chapter 28.)

GLANDULAR DISORDERS

Goiter (common). Thyroid deficiency, generally environmental, but "susceptibility" claimed in some cases. (?)

–*Exophthalmic goiter* (Graves' disease). Heredity claimed, but uncertain. (?)

Kidneys, polycystic disease. Multiple cysts, serious in pregnant women. *Dom.-q.*(?)

Lymphedema (abnormal swelling of legs and ankles). More common in women. *Dom.-q.*(?)

Fibrosis of the pancreas. Infancy. Frequently fatal. *Rec.*(?)

ALLERGIES

Heredity in dispute, but some authorities claim the following as predisposition:

–*Common allergies,* causing asthma, hay fever, rashes, upsets, etc. *Dom.*+(?)

–*Allergies to specific substances.* *Dom.*(?)

Angioneurotic oedema. Sudden swelling, critical if in larynx. *Dom.*

Migraine headache (one-sided), considered a form of allergy. *Dom.*(?)

MENTAL DISEASES

Major Conditions. (If and where heredity is a factor in these, it is believed to be as a predisposition.)

–*Schizophrenia (dementia praecox).* "Split personality." *Rec.*+(?)

–*Manic-depressive insanity.* Alternating cycles, excited and depressed states. *Dom.-q.*(?)

–*"Psychopathic personality."* Some inheritance suspected, but uncertain. ?

Huntington's chorea. Progressive mental deterioration, usually middle age. *Dom.*

Pick's lobar atrophy. Another type of mental degeneration in mature years. *Dom.*

Cerebral sclerosis. Gradual failure of intelligence, vision, muscular power. Childhood or youth. *Rec.*

–Other types, varying symptoms and ages. *Dom., Sex-L.*

MENTAL DEFICIENCIES

Feeble-mindedness (moron type). Subnormal mentality, I.Q. from 70 to 50. Often environmental. Where hereditary, may be: *Rec. + (q)* or *Dom. + (q.)*

Mongolian idiocy. Congenital idiocy due to intra-uterine effects plus possible hereditary factors. (?)

Cretinism. Congenital idiocy through mother's thyroid deficiency, hereditary factor uncertain. (?)

Microcephaly. "Pinhead" type idiocy. Heredity in some cases. *Rec.*(?)

Amaurotic family idiocy. Nerve and brain defect with blindness and paralysis. Most serious type in infancy, rapidly fatal. Also juvenile and adult types, less severe. All *Rec.*

Gargoylism. Rare metabolic disorder with mental defect as one of many consequences (extreme dwarfism, etc.). Heredity doubtful. *Rec. or Sex-L.*(?)

Phenylpyruvic idiocy. With a urinary abnormality. *Rec.*

Laurence-Moon syndrome. Mental defect with retinitis pigmentosa, extra fingers and obesity. *Rec.-q.*

Wilson's disease. Retarded intelligence with peculiar jerky hand movements, facial distortions. Childhood. *Rec.*

Hydrocephaly. ("Water head.") Heredity claimed in some cases but dubious. (?)

Epiloia. See under rare Cancers.

EPILEPSY. General name for symptoms of various nervous disorders of different types. Hereditary predisposition claimed for some types (less than 25 per cent of cases), but uncertain. (?)

Myoclonus epilepsy. Rare type, with tremors and spasms between seizures. Childhood. *Rec.*

NERVE AND MUSCLES

Hereditary Ataxias. Varying types, depending on nerve centers affected.

–*Friedreich's Spinal Ataxia.* With wobbly gait, speech defects. Childhood. *Rec.*

–*Marie's Cerebellar Ataxia.* Jerky movements, speech defects. Adults. *Dom.-q.*

–*Hereditary tremor.* Slight involuntary movements. Childhood. *Dom.*

Hereditary Paralysis. (Excluding all environmental types.)

–*Spastic paraplegia.* Rigidity in lower limbs, spreading upward. Childhood. More common in males. *Part. Sex-L.*

–*Family periodic paralysis.* Intermittent brief attacks in adults. *Dom.*

Muscular Atrophies. Shriveling or degeneration of muscles.

–*Peroneal.* Legs, feet and hands. Childhood. *Dom., Rec., or Sex-L.*

–*Spinal.* Infancy. Fatal. *Rec.*

–*Progressive.* Associated with cataract, sterility, etc. Maturity. *Dom.-q.*

Myotonia Atrophica. Slowed relaxation after muscular contraction. Early adult. *Rec.*

Thomsen's Disease (myotonia congenita). Muscle stiffness, slow delayed movements. Childhood. *Dom.*

–Related types with varying ages of onset: *Dystrophia Myotonica* and *Paramyotonia* (rare). Both *Dom.-q.*

Amytonia Congenita. Flabby, immobile muscles at infancy. *Rec.*(?)

Myasthenia Gravis. Muscular weakness, without atrophy. Inheritance doubtful. (?)

Progressive Muscular Dystrophy. Serious muscular wasting, leading to weakness, invalidism. Several types with varying ages of onset, symptoms and heredity.

—Early adult type, onset about age 18. *Dom.*

—Pre-adolescent type, onset about age 11. *Rec.*

—Childhood type, onset about age 5. Males only, often with declining mentality. *Sex-L., Rec.*

EYES

1. Major Conditions

Cataract. Opaque lens, common cause of blindness. Onset and type varying in different families. (Old-age cataracts may not be hereditary.) Where inherited: *Dom.-q.*

Glaucoma. Increase in pressure in eyeball, often leading to blindness. Types varying in onset, nature and importance of heredity: (a) *Adult* type—common forms not usually hereditary, but where so, *Dom.* or *Sex-L.;* (b) *Juvenile* (rare), onset puberty, *Sex-L.;* (c) *Infantile,* most serious, *Rec.*

Optic Atrophy. Withering of optic nerve, leading to blindness.

—*Birth type.* Occasionally associated with deafness. *Dom.*

—*Childhood type.* *Rec.*(?)

—*Adult type (Leber's disease).* Blindness only in center of eye. *Sex-L.-q.*

—Associated with *ataxia.* *Dom.*(?)

Retinitis Pigmentosa. Degeneration of retina due to deposit of pigment on sensitive regions. May result in *night blindness* only, or more serious vision-loss, depending on severity. Various types and ages of onset. *Dom., Rec., Sex-L.*

Night Blindness. Vision failing in dim light and other visual defects. Birth.

—With no other eye defect: *Dom.* (Japanese type, *Oguchi's disease: Part. Sex-L., Rec.*)

—With near-sightedness. 99% of cases males. *Sex-L.*

—With extreme near-sightedness. *Rec.*

Day Blindness. Inability to see in bright daylight, with total color blindness. *Rec. (Part. Sex-L.)*

Glioma Retinae. Tumor of eye. (See under Cancer, Rare types.)

2. Eye-Structure Defects

Defective Cornea. (Defects in transparent covering of front of eye-ball, iris and pupil.)

–*Cloudiness within lens,* impairing vision. Onset variable. *Dom.-q.*

–*Opaque ring within cornea.* Childhood. *Dom.*

–*Cone-shaped cornea (keratoconus),* causing extreme astigmatism. Childhood, progressing. *Rec.*

–*Enlarged cornea. (Megalocornea.)* Vision usually normal. *Sex-L.* or *Dom.*

Defective Iris.

–*Segment of iris missing.* Birth. *Dom.-q.;* also *Rec.* or *Sex-L.*

–*Complete absence of iris (aniridia).* Birth. *Dom.*

–*"Pin-hole" pupil (persistent pupillary membrane.)* Iris almost closed; may cause blindness. Birth. *Dom.*

Displaced Lens.

–Due to atrophied suspensory ligament. Sometimes at birth, sometimes adult. *Dom.-q.*

–Same as above, with displaced pupil. *Rec.*(?)

Small Eyes (microphthalmia). Entire eye undersized, frequently with other eye defects. *Dom., Rec.* or *Sex-L.*

–Same as above, with teeth defects also. *Rec.*

–Extreme form *(anophthalmos),* eyes completely absent, thus blindness from birth. *Rec.*+(?)

Pink Eye Color. Eyes unpigmented, but with no other albino effects. Birth. Confined to males. *Sex-L.*

3. Eye-Movement Defects

Cross-Eyes (strabismus). Eyes not focusing together. Childhood, may disappear later. *Not always hereditary.* *Rec.* or *Dom.*

Quivering Eyeball (nystagmus). Eye tremor, usually weak vision. Birth.

–Common type, occurring by itself. *Sex-L.*

–With head twitching. *Dom.*

Eye-muscle paralysis. Inability to move eyes. Birth or later, increasing in severity. (May result from injury, meningitis, etc.) *Dom.* or *Sex-L.*

Drooping Eyelids (ptosis). *Dom.*

4. Optical Defects

Astigmatism. Asymmetrical focusing of light rays. Birth. Heredity uncertain. *Dom.-q.*(?)

Near-Sightedness (Extreme).

–Distant vision blurred. Birth, increasing with age. *Rec.* (or *Sex-L*).

–Associated with *nystagmus* and poor vision. *Dom.* or *Sex-L.*

Far-Sightedness (Extreme). Inability to see clearly at far or near distance. Birth, may decrease with age.

–Not pathological. *Dom.-q.*

–Serious with other eye effects. *Rec.*

Color Blindness (Common). Confusion of red and green. Birth. Several types. *Sex-L.*

–*Total Color Blindness.* See Day Blindness, p. 314.

Mirror-reading (and *Writing*). Seeing in reverse and upside-down. Sometimes with stuttering. Birth. *Dom.-q.*

EAR CONDITIONS

Deafness. (Excluding all environmental cases.)

–Deafness at birth, resulting in defective speech. *Rec.*+

–Middle-ear deafness *(otosclerosis).* More frequent in women. *Rec.*+ or *Dom.-q.*

–Inner-ear (or nerve) deafness. In middle-age. *Dom.*

Word Deafness. Hearing normal but inability to interpret sounds. More common in males. *Dom.-q.*

Outer-ear Deformities. All the following present at birth:

–Absence of ear, usually one side only. *Dom.*

–Cup-shaped ear (ear turned over at top). *Dom.-q.*

–Imperfect *double* ear (one or both). *Dom.*(?)

Ear Fistula. Gill-like opening near ear passage, external or internal, sometimes with discharge. *Dom.-q.*

Dense hair-growth on ear. No effect on hearing.) Direct father-to-son dominant inheritance (Y chromosome).

BODY STRUCTURE

Dwarfism.

–Midget type (*ateleotic,* or "Lilliputian"). Heredity believed through multiple genes. *Rec.*+ or *Dom.*+*(q).*

—*Achondroplastic* (stunted arms and legs). Where hereditary, *Dom.-q.*

—*Gargoylism.* Extreme drawfism as one effect of rare fat-metabolism disorder. (See under Mental Deficiencies.)

Hand and Foot Abnormalities. Many different types, single genes producing variable effect within same family. Most common: *Stub-fingers* (brachyphalangy), middle finger joints missing; *extra fingers and toes* (polydactyly); *stiff fingers,* joints fused; *webbed fingers or toes; split foot or hand.* (See illustration p. 198.) All *Dom.* or *Dom.-q.*

(A special type of *webbed toes* [slight webbing between second and third toes] is transmitted from father to sons through the Y chromosome.)

"Spider" Fingers (Arachnodactyly). Abnormally long, thin fingers. Often with eye or other defects. *Dom.-q.*

Clubfoot. Possible heredity in some cases. (Uncertain.) *Rec.*(?)

Brittle Bones (blue sclerotic). Fragile bones, with bad teeth, deafness, bluish eye-whites. Birth. *Dom.-q.*

Deformed Spine (Spina Bifida). With various other effects. *Dom.-q.*

"Cobbler's (or "Funnel") Chest." Abnormally hollow chest. *Dom.-q.*

"Tower Skull" (Oxycephaly, Acrocephaly). High-pointed skull, several types, sometimes with eye, bone, or mild mental defects. *Dom.-q.*

Cranial Soft-Spot (cleidocranial dysostosis). Infant "soft spot" in skull persisting to maturity, with other bone defects. *Dom.-q.*

Crouzon's disease (craniofacial dysostosis). Skull and jaw abnormalities. *Dom.-q.*

MOUTH AND TEETH

Cleft Palate and Harelip. Failure of palate to fuse, sometimes with teeth defects. Birth. Sometimes environmental. Where hereditary: *Rec., Sex-L. Dom.-q.*

Missing Teeth.

—Upper lateral incisors absent or small. *Dom., Rec.* or *Sex-L.*

—Molars or other teeth missing. *Dom.*(?)

—*"Fang Mouth."* All teeth missing except canines. Associated with inability to sweat. (See under Sweat-Gland Defects.)

Defective Tooth Enamel. (Referring only to conditions not environmental.)
- —Discolorations, inherited:
  - (A) Brownish ("honeycomb" teeth). *Dom.* or *Sex-L. Dom.*
  - (B) Reddish enamel (*porphyrinuria*). *Rec.*
- —Transparent (opalescent dentin). *Dom.*
- —Pitted Teeth. (Sometimes with cataract.) *Dom.*

Extra Teeth. Frequently associated with cleft palate. *Dom.*(?)

Teeth at Birth. Incisors present at birth. *Dom.-q.*

Overgrowing Gums (gingival hyperplasia). Gums covering nearly all of teeth. *Usually environmental* (infection, etc.) but in rare cases hereditary. *Dom.*

HAIR AND NAILS

Baldness (alopecia). Where not due to environmental factors:
- —Pattern (common type) baldness. In maturity, almost exclusively in males. *Sex-Limited Dom.*
- —Patch baldness. Small bald area on scalp; may spread. Birth or puberty. *Dom.-q.*
- —Congenital *(hypotrichosis).* Hair defective or never developing. Various types, associated with teeth, nail or scalp defects. *Rec., Dom.,* or *Sex-L.*

Defective Hair.
- —Infantile down remaining through life. *Dom.*
- —Beaded hair *(monilethrix).* May lead to baldness. Infancy. *Dom.-q.*
- —Excessive long, soft hair on face and elsewhere. ("Dog-face.") Other effects. Childhood. *Dom.-q.*
- —Defective hair with abnormal nails. (Mostly among French Canadians.) Puberty. *Dom.*

Premature Grayness. Head hair only, beginning in adolescence. No relation to aging. *Dom.*

White Forelock (or "Blaze"). (See under Skin—*Albinism.*)

Defective Nails.
- —Nails absent, partially or wholly. *Rec.* or *Dom.*
- —Thick nails, protruding at angle. *Dom.*
- —Thickened nails, also skin on palms and soles. *Dom.*+
- —Spotted nails, bluish white. *Dom.*

—Thin nails, several types, small and soft, or flat. *Dom.* or *Dom.-q.*

—Milky-white nails. *Dom.-q.*

SKIN

Birthmarks (naevi). Common types—hairy, raised, warty; discolorations or pigmented spots of variable size. Also (one type) slight depression over eyebrows, extending to temple. *None of these harmful.* Some hereditary. Where so: *Dom.*

—*Malignant types* (rare, pre-cancerous). (See under Cancer, p. 309 and text pp. 200, 202, 207.)

Mongolian Spot. Bluish patch near base of spine, at birth, disappearing. *Rec.*+ or *Dom.*

Fatty Skin Growths.

—On eyelids, or elsewhere (*xanthalesma*). *Dom.*

(See also *xanthoma tuberosum,* double-gene type of *xanthalesma,* under Metabolic Disorders—excess fat deposits.)

Scaly or Horny Skin (Ichthyosis).

—Common type, with shedding. Infancy. *Dom.* (or *Sex-L.*)

—Cracked skin, ears often defective. Birth, may disappear later. *Sometimes fatal.* *Rec.*

—*"Elephant Skin,"* extreme form of above. Causes premature birth, *death.* *Rec.*

—*Psoriasis.* Mottled scaly patches. If hereditary, only as tendency. *Dom.-q.*

—*Bark-like skin (ichthyosis hystrix gravior).* Direct father-to-son dominant inheritance (Y chromosome).

Thick, or Shedding Skin (Keratosis).

—Skin flaking over entire body. Birth. *Rec.*

—Same as above, but skin thicker. Several types, one with casts of palms and soles shedding. Birth or puberty. *Dom.*

—Thick or discolored skin on limbs, but not shedding. Childhood, more among males. *Dom.-q.*

Blistering (Epidermolysis).

—Blisters easily raised. Childhood. *Dom.-q.*

—Severe type, from birth, leaving scars with other defects. *Rec.-q.*

—Rare extreme form, with bleeding. *Death in infancy.* *Rec. (Part. Sex-L.)*

–*Darier's disease.* Follicle defects, causing hair loss, goose-flesh; often leads to mental deficiency and small stature. Several types. Birth or childhood. *Dom.-q.* (or *Sex-L.*)

Sunlight Blistering.

–With scarring *(porphyrinuria congenita).* Especially in males. *Rec.*(?)

–More severe form of above, occasionally fatal. *Rec.*

Albinism. Lack of pigment in skin, hair.

–Complete, skin and hair "dead white," also with pink eyes. *Rec.*

–Mild form *(albinoidism),* with some pigment. *Dom.-q.*

–Partial, white stripes or patches on body. *Dom.* or *Dom.-q.*

–White forelock or "blaze." Unpigmented patch of skin on scalp, growing white hair. *Dom.*

Sweat-Gland Defects.

–Complete inability to sweat, with missing teeth and other defects. *(Anidrotic ectodermal dysplasia.)* Mostly males. *Sex-L.*

–Milder type of above. *Dom.-q.*

–Excessive sweating *(hyperhidrosis).* *Dom.*

"Rubber" Skin (cutis laxa). Highly elastic tissue, capable of freak stretching. *Dom.-q.*

MISCELLANEOUS

Sense of Smell Deficiency (Anosmia). Total absence of sense of smell. *Dom.*

Sex-Trait Abnormalities.

–In males: *Hypospadias.* Abnormal opening in urethra. Birth. *Dom.-q.*

–In both sexes: Extra nipples or breasts. (?)

Transposed Internal Organs (Situs inversus viscerum). Heart, liver, stomach, etc., on reverse side from normal location. *Rec.*(?)

Double (Multiple) Eyelashes. Double row of lashes on each lid. *Dom.*(?)

THE FOLLOWING "FORECAST" TABLES SHOULD INTEREST YOU IF–

–You are still young, and there is some condition known in your family, generally appearing in later life, which you are worried may also appear in *you.*

–You are planning to marry, and are worried that some condition in either you or your prospective mate, or one that appears in your families, may be passed on to your children.

–You are married and already have children, and are worried that some condition may crop out in them later.

When Using These "Forecast" Tables, Be as Certain as Possible That–

1. The condition you have in mind is the *one listed* in our tables.
2. That, where there are various methods of inheritance, you know which gene mechanism applies in your case.
3. That, where *environment* is a factor in the expression of a condition, you have ruled out the possibility that it has not been covered up, or that, even if the genes are transmitted, the condition might not be prevented from developing in a child. In *rheumatic fever,* or *diabetes* (or some of the mental diseases) as examples, the fact that parents or their families are affected does not positively indicate whether, or to what extent, their children might develop the condition if the environment is favorable. Conversely, the fact that parents themselves do not show the condition, when it has appeared in others in their families, is not conclusive proof that they are free of the genes involved. (This applies especially to all "qualified" conditions in the tables–where a "q." follows the genetic mechanisms given.)
4. That, where a condition can also be caused by environment, the one you have in mind is of the *hereditary type.*
5. That you have paid full attention to the question of *"onset."* (For instance, where a condition appears late, you cannot be sure that the genes are, or are not, present, until the person reaches the required age.)

In No Case Consider Your "Forecast" Conclusive, or Take Any Action on the Basis of It, Without Consulting Competent Medical Authority. In All Cases It Is Best to Consult Your Family Doctor!

I. RECESSIVE GENE FORECASTS

(The most common form of "black" gene inheritance. Because of the vast number of persons carrying "hidden" recessive genes for various conditions, *complete* assurance never can be given that any common recessive condition may not crop out in some child. But the risk diminishes with the infrequency that the condition appears in the parents' families. The more prevalent the condition in the general population, however, the more likely it is to turn up unexpectedly—especially if the parents are closely related. Also keep in mind points made on the preceding page [in No. 3] regarding environmental factors in the expression or suppression of certain conditions.)

WHERE THE CONDITION IS RECESSIVE	*CHANCES CHILD WILL INHERIT IT:*
1. IF BOTH PARENTS ARE AFFECTED:	Almost certainly
2. IF ONE PARENT IS AFFECTED, THE OTHER NOT, BUT IF IN THE FAMILY OF THE "FREE" PARENT—	
a. His or her father or mother is affected, or a child with the defect already has appeared:	Even chance
b. A brother, sister or grandparent is affected:	Less than even chance
c. Some more remote relative is affected:	Possible, but not probable
d. No one, near or far, has been known to have the condition:	Very unlikely but still possible
3. IF NEITHER PARENT IS AFFECTED, BUT—	
a. The condition occurs *on both sides* in one of their parents, or in a brother or sister, or already has appeared in a child:	One-in-four
b. The condition occurs or has occurred in more distant relatives of the families of both:	Extremely unlikely, but yet possible
c. The condition is wholly unknown in the family of either:	Virtually nil

I-A. "QUALIFIED" RECESSIVE FORECASTS: Where conditions are "Rec.-q." the chances of inheriting the *genes* are exactly the same as shown in Table I, but the chances of the *condition* actually appearing in a child may be altered by various circumstances. In general, however, the odds are somewhat lower than in simple recessives for each type of mating.

I-B. "RECESSIVE-PLUS" FORECASTS: Where listed as "Rec.+" the situations are about the same as in Table I, but with the *probability lessened* in most cases.

II. SEX-LINKED (RECESSIVE) FORECASTS

(Where the "black" gene is carried in the X chromosome, and therefore acts as a dominant in the case of males, as a recessive in the case of females. Examples: Color blindness, hemophilia, nystagmus, enlarged cornea.)

	CHANCES CHILD WILL INHERIT:
1. IF BOTH PARENTS ARE AFFECTED:	Almost certainly in all their children
2. IF MOTHER IS AFFECTED, BUT FATHER IS FREE OF IT:	Certain for every son, but no daughter
3. IF FATHER IS AFFECTED, AND MOTHER IS FREE OF IT, BUT—	
a. Her father, mother or a sister has or had the condition:	Even chance in any child
b. One of her brothers is affected:	One-in-four for any child
c. One of her more remote relatives is affected:	Extremely unlikely, but yet possible
d. No known case in her family:	Virtually nil
4. IF NEITHER PARENT IS AFFECTED, BUT IT OCCURS IN THE MOTHER'S FAMILY (in the same situations as noted above):	No chance for any daughter, but for sons same odds as in *3-a.b.c.d.* above

II-A. PARTIALLY SEX-LINKED RECESSIVE FORECASTS

In those few conditions (*spastic paraplegia, Oguchi's* disease, etc.) where the same gene is carried on both the Y and X chromosomes, sons are chiefly affected in the first case and daughters in the second. Except for this, the forecasts are the same as for ordinary *simple recessive genes,* as given in Table I. (For sex-linked *dominants,* see under next section, Table III-B.)

III. DOMINANT GENE FORECASTS

(For all conditions which can be produced in either sex by one gene acting singly, as in acholuric jaundice, drooping eyelids, various hand defects, etc.)

	CHANCES CHILD WILL INHERIT THE CONDITION:
1. *IF BOTH PARENTS ARE AFFECTED:	Very probable
2. *IF ONE PARENT IS AFFECTED, THE OTHER "FREE":	Even chance
3. WHERE NEITHER PARENT IS AFFECTED, BUT IT APPEARS IN THE FAMILY OF ONE OR THE OTHER:	
a. If the condition is always known to show itself when the gene is present:	Nil
b. *If the gene action is sometimes known to be suppressed by environment:	Some likelihood, but not great

*Note: In cases where the gene action is irregular, or influenced by environment, we have the situations which follow:

"QUALIFIED" DOMINANT FORECASTS: In all conditions given in the tables as "Dom.-q." (achondroplastic dwarfism, mirror-reading, hereditary cataract, etc.) the probabilities are modified downward from those shown in the preceding table, the forecasts depending upon the degree to which the gene expresses itself or is suppressed by environment.

"DOMINANT-PLUS" FORECASTS: ("Dom.+," very rare, as in thickened nails, etc.) Relative probabilities are about as shown in Table III above, but greatly reduced in most cases.

III-A. DOUBLE (DUPLICATE) DOMINANT GENE FORECASTS

In the few conditions where two of the same dominant genes produce a *severe* effect, but a single gene produces only *mild* symptoms (as in *Cooley's anemia, sickle-cell anemia, xanthoma*), the risks in the children for the severe or the mild conditions are as follows:

1. Both parents with severe type: All children will probably have severe type.

2. One parent severe, other mild condition: Chances fifty-fifty a child will have either the severe or mild type.
3. One parent severe, other parent normal: All children will probably have the mild-type of condition.
4. Both parents with mild condition: One-in-four chance children will have the severe condition; one-in-two chance the mild condition; one-in-four chance child will be completely normal.
5. One parent with mild condition, other parent normal: Chances fifty-fifty a child will either have the mild condition or else be completely normal.

III-B. SEX-LINKED DOMINANT FORECASTS

Where the dominant gene is on the X chromosome (as in the *thrombasthenia*-type nosebleed): If the mother has the condition, the expected forecasts for *all* offspring, male and female, will be the same as for the regular dominants, Table III, 1 and 2. Where the father has the condition, *every* daughter, but only the daughters, will get it.

Partially sex-linked dominants: In the few cases where the gene may be in the Y chromosome as well as in the X, the forecast is the same as for an ordinary dominant if it is the mother who is affected. However, if the father has the condition, the risk will be greater for his sons if inheritance had been through *his* father (i.e., via the Y chromosome), but greater for the daughters if the father's mother had had the condition.

CHAPTER 32

YOU AS A SOCIAL ANIMAL

WITH this chapter, we enter a new phase in our book.

So far we have been considering human beings chiefly as biological mechanisms. Now we begin to think of you, and all the rest of us, as *social animals*—in the way that each lives and works in relation to others of his species. That is where we differ most among ourselves and are most unique among all other animals.

In purely physical construction and functioning there is nothing so special about us. From mice to elephants, all mammals have skeletal frameworks, sensory and internal organs, glands, etc., which are essentially much like ours (except, perhaps, for our brains). Most important, heredity works almost as directly and conclusively with us as with lower animals in constructing our bodies according to the blueprints for our species and in determining much of the physical variation among us. Environment, whether natural or man-made, is greatly limited in what it can do to or with our physical makeup, its strongest influence being in a negative direction, through its powers to thwart our development with disease, defect or death. But in the positive direction, despite all the changes in human environment over thousands of years, men today are organically almost the same as they were (even in their mental equipment); and in all the different existing environments, from the heart of Africa to New York's Park Avenue, men continue to be amazingly alike biologically, what physical differences there are being due chiefly to heredity.

But the story changes completely when we consider man as a social animal. While other animals, too, have their social relationships, as one individual to another or in group organizations of herds, flocks, colonies, etc., it is hardly necessary to say that in no other species is there anything remotely like the range of social differences that we find among human individuals, in behavior, intelligence, learning and achievement. True, among lower animals, one individual may be smarter than another in getting food and mates, or in evading enemies, and one may boss another. But taking the most advanced of them below the level of man, our distant cousins, the apes, there is no ape who amasses a billion coconuts while another has nary a one; there is no ape with prodigious learning while another is illiterate; there is no lady ape who sports a fancy wardrobe while another dresses in rags; and there is no ape who can give his offspring vastly more in worldly goods, education and opportunities than can another ape. What any lower animal is or can do in relation to his fellows is influenced to some extent by his environment, but in the main, both as an individual and as a member of his species, his behavior and achievements are rigidly limited by his inheritance.

With humans, not only is the range of behavior-development permitted by their genes infinitely greater, but the opportunities offered by their environments for creating differences among individuals is also infinitely greater. Making this possible above all else are the distinctive capacities humans have for the use of speech and symbols to communicate with one another and to learn from one another; to alter their environments through inventions; and to pass along from one to another all the accumulated fruits of their experience. With the limitless degrees of these advantages being offered in human environments, it becomes apparent that no human being can be judged *individually* as a social animal unless we know how he has profited by or been influenced by his contacts with others. So the difficult job we approach now, in tracking down to their sources the many variations of human behavior or achievement, is that of disentangling all the complex hereditary factors from all the complex environmental ones.

In our surface details—coloring, features and body form—and in our internal construction and many aspects of our physical functioning, we have seen that heredity is either the direct cause or a dominant influence in creating many individual differences among us. To what extent the surface differences may affect our social relationships depends largely on how they are regarded by others (as will be set forth in a later chapter). More important with respect to behavior are any of the serious hereditary defects or diseases, and particularly those affecting the mind, as should be obvious. But in these cases behavior differences result only indirectly, through inherited defects in the body mechanisms. What concerns us most is whether, in normal individuals and under normal conditions, there may not also be hereditary factors that can *directly* produce many gradations of behavior and mental performance and help to account, in one way or another, for the enormous social differences that we find among humans everywhere.

Why do some individuals in any group scale the heights of success, while others sink into the mire of failure? Why, in the very same family, is one person brilliant, the other a mediocrity; one a musician or artist, the other an insensitive dolt; one member kindly and happily adjusted, the other hateful and unable to get along with others? What has made *you yourself* so different in your job, thinking, personality and behavior from so many others with whom you grew up? Is it all a matter of pure chance, or environment? Or are there indeed different gene combinations for social qualities, as there are for physical traits, which *predestine* one person to be this kind of a social animal, another person that kind?

It really boils down to something you may have thought of many times: *Suppose, with the very same genes, you had been reared in an entirely different home, city or country, with different associates, education, opportunities and "breaks"—how much would you still be socially like the person you are now?*

In the pages ahead we hope to throw much light on this question, and on many related questions. But as you will soon see, answers regarding the inheritance of social traits in human beings can be given with no such surety as were those regarding their surface characteristics and organic makeup. It is not only because the social traits are so much more complicated. It is also and perhaps chiefly because the *measurements* of these traits are as yet in a rudimentary stage, and until the measurements are better perfected, geneticists must continue to be greatly restricted in their study of human behavior and performance.

Thus, we may say at once that in many respects we are now venturing into uncertain territory. Previously we confined ourselves to the presentation, almost exclusively, of scientific facts. From this point on, as we begin to analyze the rôle of heredity in such variable and intangible human characteristics as mentality, personality, temperament, criminality, sexual behavior, race differences, etc., we will find our facts becoming more and more diluted with theory. Our genetic evidence, like a stream of clear, fresh water flowing into an arm of the sea, now begins to intermingle with theories of psychology, anthropology, sociology and even politics. And it will be increasingly harder to filter out the facts from the theories—theories which, even in the case of leading authorities, are often tempered by unconscious prejudices or emotional reactions.

The social phases of human heredity are viewed through varied lenses, some rose-tinted, some dark; some which focus on the hereditary factors, some on the environmental influences; some which offer a long view, some a short view. The very directions which researches into human genetics may take, and the findings arrived at, may differ in the degree that the investigators themselves differ in personality, background and emotional makeup. The descendants of *Mayflower* stock and the offspring of recent immigrants, the hidebound reactionaries and the unrestrained progressives, the Russian, English, German and American social scientists as groups often react differently toward the same evidence. Even in American colleges—in one faculty as compared with another—there are different schools of thought with regard to many of the vital points we are going to discuss.

Thus, you also will find yourself taking sides in the ensuing chapters. If you are socially and financially secure and come from a notable family, your reactions and conclusions will be different from those of the man at the bottom or of undistinguished stock. You may say of this, "That sounds unreasonable," or of that, "I don't believe it." And there may be no denying you the right to say it, for often the evidence may be open to various interpretations.

Nevertheless, in among all the "ifs" and "buts" regarding the inheritance of human behavior traits there are a great many highly important facts that have been clearly established. If nothing else, genetics, in combination with its sister sciences, has in a few decades swept away a vast amount of rubbish regarding the nature and causes of social differences among human beings. Freed from the accumulated litter of past prejudices and misconceptions, the facts as we can see them now about ourselves and other people should do much to make every one of us a better social animal.

And now to our first major social question.

CHAPTER 33

THE BATTLE OF THE "IQs"

HERE are two orphaned infants, available for adoption at a placement bureau: They look the same and are "guaranteed" to be equally sound and fit. You are eager to adopt one, and as there is apparently no choice, you are about to toss a coin to decide.

BABY "A"

Then the matron tells you that Baby "A" is the offspring of a charwoman and an illiterate day laborer.

Baby "B" is the offspring of a young woman writer and a young physician.

Would you still feel there was no choice? Or would you pick Baby "B" on the chance that *it had inherited a higher degree of intelligence*?

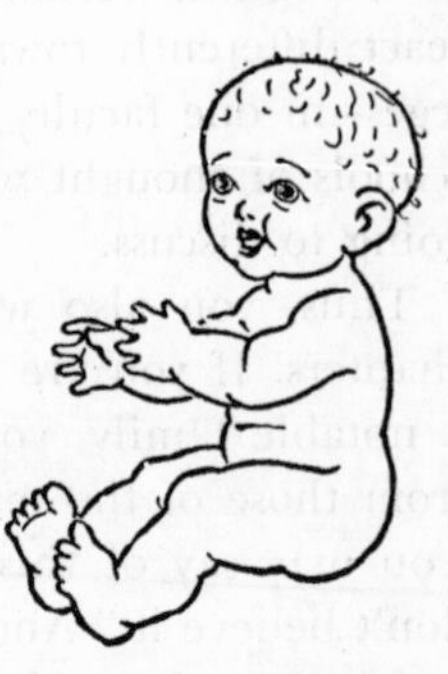

BABY "B"

Around this question, or others closely related, centers one of the greatest controversies in the study of human heredity. There are some authorities who say that no evidence exists which would justify a choice in favor of Baby "B." There are many others who disagree with them.

What is the basis for the arguments pro and con? Let us start at the beginning.

We have seen that some types and degrees of *abnormal* intelligence—idiocy, insanity, etc.—can be inherited, but this tells us as little about the normal mental process as the throwing of a monkey wrench into any complex machine would tell us about its normal workings.

In lower animals, true enough, we know that a normal mouse inherits a certain type of brain, a cat another type, a dog still another, etc. Also, that within each species itself there seem to be different degrees or qualities of brain activity. In dogs, breeds vary in alertness and capacity for certain kinds of performance. As one of many illustrations, during World War II dogs of five specific breeds (and only these or their crosses) were accepted for military use: German shepherd, Belgian sheep, Doberman pinscher, collie and schnauzer. In mice, geneticists have bred strains, one dull, one bright. Similarly, among many other animals, experimental, domestic and wild, what appear to be variations in capacity for mental functioning have been noted.

So if degrees of "normal" intelligence are inherited among other animals, why not among human beings? All logic, and all scientific generalizations, lead to the assumption that there must or should be inherited differences in the construction and functioning of human brains just as there are inherited differences in all other aspects of construction and functioning. But the big question: Is there a direct relationship between the kind of brain mechanism a person has and *what he is doing with it*? Stated differently, is a person's mental *performance* at any given time, fair evidence of the kind of *basic intelligence* he has?

There's the rub! For should we prove that the varieties and gradations of mentality revealed in the workaday, scholastic and social worlds are limited to any great extent by heredity, then we'd be faced with the possibility that dullness, mediocrity and superiority are *inherent* in individuals, and that failure and success may be largely *predestined.*

No wonder that beneath the placid surface of scientific research on this subject a struggle has been going on for years between the "hereditarians" and the "environmentalists." The "hereditarians" are out to prove that certain individuals come to the top, like cream in a milk bottle, because of "inherent superiority" and that, graded according to their "mental richness," they tend to form classes at various intellectual levels. The "environmentalists" challenge this analogy. They are set on proving that while there may be some individual differences, the mental grades are in equal proportions in all groups, and that if we *shake the bottle and equalize the environment,* the levels of mentality in which classes of people now seem to be stratified would disappear.

How are we to settle this?

Our great difficulty is that intelligence can be measured today only by arbitrary procedures, such as those set up by the current intelligence tests. We saw in the chapter on "Slow Minds" how the tests are used to determine degrees of mental deficiency: idiots scoring IQs under 25; imbeciles, 25 to 50; morons, 50 to 70; and the borderline cases, from 70 to 80. Above that we come to non-defective mentality, those with IQs of 80 to 90 being graded as merely "dull" and those scoring 90 to 110 as "normal." Beyond this, there is a classification of scores from 110 to 120 as "superior," 120 to 140 as "very superior," and 140 or over as "genius" (the latter term being used only in a technical sense, not implying that individuals with scores of 140 or more—of whom there are many—are actual "geniuses").

To be noted, also, is that the intelligence tests used for children, up to and including the age of 16, are not the same as those for adults. These tests for children seek to establish how well a child is doing mentally in relation to the "norm" for his age.* But after the age of 16 it is assumed that intelligence doesn't increase measurably, so tests for the subsequent years are aimed not at giving a score for mental performance in terms of age, but in relation to the intelligence of other adults as a class. Thus, the "adult" intelligence tests are the same for late 'teen-agers and for those of all ages beyond, the theory being that any advantages of the younger people, in speed of response or more closeness to schooling, for instance, are balanced by the advantages of older persons with respect to acquired knowledge and experience. While the "adult" tests (Bellevue-Wechsler, Otis, Army, etc.) differ in many respects from those for children, the scores made on them by individuals generally add up to the same relative scores as those made on the earlier tests.†

But how accurate are any of the tests in measuring a person's basic intelligence? As between a person with an IQ of 90, and one

* The IQ (intelligence quotient) is obtained by dividing "mental" age by chronological age: if a child aged 8 has a mental performance up to the average for children of 10 years, the 10 is divided by 8, giving 1.25, or an IQ of 125; if a child aged 8 has the mental "norm" for age 7, the 7 is divided by 8, giving .875 or an IQ of 87.5.

† Dr. Robert L. Thorndike has made such a study (1947) of the relationship between tests of intelligence taken early in childhood with subsequent scores in high school and college. In general there is a substantial relationship among all test scores, but this relationship becomes more and more marked the higher up the educational ladder one goes.

with an IQ of 130, there can be little doubt that the tests do reveal a marked difference in mental capacity or performance. But with regard to the lesser gradations, there is disagreement as to the significance of IQ scores. The same individual may score 108 one day when he isn't feeling well, and 113 the next day; or he may be given one score by one examiner and a somewhat lower or higher score by a different examiner. It also has been claimed that the tests are not equally fair to all (especially as applied to those of different social groups or races, or to rural as compared with city children); that they are not entirely consistent at the different ages; that they measure "classroom" intelligence much more than general intelligence, etc. (We'll deal with this further along.)

Despite the foregoing and other criticisms, the standard intelligence tests are considered sufficiently reliable to be widely used in many important ways. If you have a child, and live in New York (as one of many cities) that child will be placed in a class with average pupils, or backward pupils, or superior pupils, on the basis of its IQ. If you are seeking admission to universities, particularly to professional schools, your performance on intelligence tests might decide your acceptance or rejection. If you were or are in the army, you know of course, the part the tests play in assignments for special jobs or training. And in various corporations and institutions your test scores may be a factor in obtaining a position.

For all practical purposes, then, the intelligence tests must be seriously considered. But how significant they are in studying and establishing the *inheritance* of intelligence is another matter. For only if the IQs are proved to reveal inborn capacities, little affected by environment, can they have meaning to the geneticist. As it is, so long as all the studies made to date bearing on the inheritance of intelligence are based on IQ scores, the interpretation of these studies or any conclusions regarding them must depend on the importance attached to the tests and to their actual or implied weaknesses.

Here is where the authorities fall out. You will not be surprised to learn, therefore, that the findings of various studies made on the same questions may differ markedly. All we can do is to summarize what we consider the valid studies, theories and opinions, on all sides. With respect to the two babies with which we started off, this will constitute the evidence. And you must be the judge and the jury.

Let us now follow the procedure of the investigators. First they ask themselves questions. Then they set out to find the answers. We'll start with this:

1. *Do people of different "classes" or occupational groups show different degrees of intelligence?*

As measured by intelligence tests, "Yes." Extensive studies reveal that the higher up the social and economic scale one goes, the higher is the average IQ. That is to say, unskilled laborers and farmhands as a group have lower IQs than skilled laborers and farmers; above these rank skilled factory workers, white-collar workers and small businessmen; above these, semi-professional people, bigger businessmen and managers; and at the top of the IQ structure are the professional men. Obviously, however, there is much overlapping among the groups, some unskilled workers having higher IQs than workers in levels above, and some professional men having lower IQs than persons in "lower" occupations.

Bearing in mind that we are speaking always in *general terms* and allowing for individual exceptions, it would seem that lower intelligence goes with so-called lower work. But does this mean that the unskilled laborer has a very low IQ because conditions have thwarted his mental development, or does it mean that he is an unskilled laborer because he has a low IQ? Which came first, the low condition or the low IQ?

We ask another question:

2. *Are the intelligence levels of children related to those of their parents?*

Yes. Children of a group of parents of high intelligence—on the average—are reported as having greater mental capacity than children of parents of low intelligence.

Rarely, at best, where both parents are of inferior mentality, does a superior child result. Conversely, parents of superior mentality seldom have a child of very low intelligence, and if they do, it is usually because of some special defect—idiocy or some organic condition or prenatal accident (as was brought out in our "Slow Minds" chapter).

Comparing offspring of parents at various social and economic levels, one finds that children of unskilled laborers have the lowest IQs, children of professional men the highest, with those of the groups in between being similarly correlated (as shown in our accompanying Chart). Studies in other countries give much the same

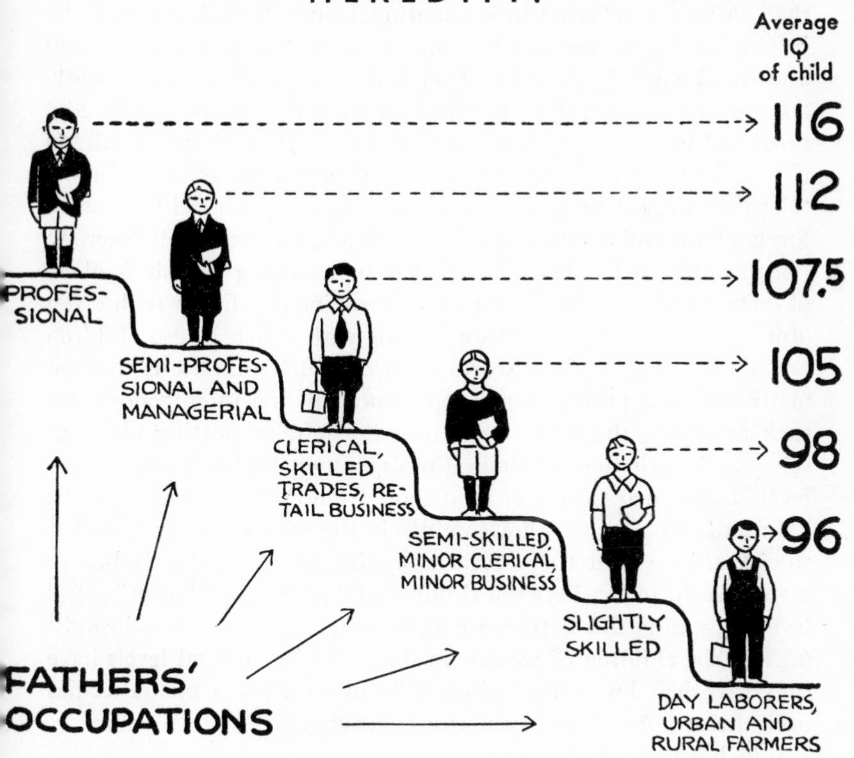

(Based on studies by Terman and Merrill, reported in "Measuring Intelligence")

result. Most surprisingly, even in the Soviet Union there was a study showing this relationship between children's IQs and parental status. (M. Sirkin, Labor Institute, Charkow, 1929.)

We may note on the Diagram that the differences in IQ between adjacent groups of children, as with their fathers, are not radically great, although the total difference, from the top level to the lowest, is about 20 points. If we turn to a recent British study, we find the British Royal Commission on Population reporting (1947) that in its own country "children from the poorest social classes have an 'intelligence' two years below that of children from the better social classes."

One criticism regarding the above data is that the comparisons made are not between the mental *capacities* of children and fathers, but between the *IQs* of children and the *assumed* mental levels of their fathers as reflected by occupational rank. If, as is claimed, the intelligence tests are weighed in favor of "book learning" and acquired knowledge, children from homes of poorly educated workers would be retarded in comparison with those from better educated and intellectually more favored circles. An additional criticism is that in the United States the intelligence tests are presumably "slanted" toward those of native stock as compared with those of foreign-born stock, and toward Whites as compared with Negroes. For example, it has been found that by changing the phraseology of certain questions on the IQ tests (involving familiarity with given objects or experiences) or using words with which Negro children are more at home, their scores go up. Also significant is that on many practical problems not represented in the intelligence tests, such as telling the right shoe from the left, or putting on overshoes, or identifying and finding tools, young children from "lower-level" homes may do better than those from the more favored ones.

But allowing for the shortcomings in the tests, most psychologists would still say that they reveal a significant average difference in mental performance between children of "upper" and "lower" social level. Assuming this is true, we again might draw two conclusions: (a) that the children of parents in the lower intellectual levels have *inherited* their lower mentality; or (b) that the lower mentality has been thrust upon them by inferior environment.

Which is right? We go on:

3. *When children are taken away from their parents in infancy and reared elsewhere, do their IQs still show the influence of their heredity?*

According to some studies, "Yes"; to others, "No."

On the "yes" side, tests have been made in various places of large numbers of illegitimate children placed in institutions, soon after birth. Most had never seen their fathers, who were of all mental or occupational levels. Yet, despite a similar environment for all the children in the institutions, their IQs differed markedly, and were reported as conforming almost as closely, on the average, to the expected mental levels of their fathers as did the IQs of children on the outside. So, too, some studies of children adopted and reared in private homes have reported that the IQs of the children bear a much closer relationship to the levels of their true parents than to those of their foster parents.

But—exactly opposite are the reports from psychologists of the University of Iowa (Drs. Beth Wellman, Marie Skodak and Harold M. Skeels among them). Their findings regarding those children they have studied (mostly of inferior parentage) who were placed in adoptive homes at early ages, are that the IQs followed not the low levels of the true parents, but the higher levels of the foster parents and of others in the homes and social groups in which the children were reared.

Which sets of findings are correct? Getting behind the professional scenes, one can hear either the Iowa studies or the conflicting ones violently criticized or ardently supported, depending on the different schools of thought and procedure. The discrepancies might be explained on various grounds; differences in the "samples" of children studied, as to age, parentage, how selected for adoption, where and by whom adopted, how reared, etc., and by such possibilities as that the true parentage or at least, paternity of illegitimate children, is often very much in doubt.

We'll leave this question open and go on:

4. *How far can training mold intelligence?*

Many studies show that education can increase the *scores* on intelligence tests, but whether or not this means that *intelligence itself* has been improved is another question.

Once more, we have findings of the University of Iowa psychologists that IQs of very young children can be increased materially if they are subjected in early life to stimulating training, as in nursery schools. But some dissenting psychologists claim that there are technical weaknesses in these studies, chiefly the fact that "before and after" intelligence tests made of nursery-age children are apt to be unreliable. A possible clue for some of the marked changes, up or down, which occur in IQs in earlier years is offered by Dr. Nancy Bayley (University of California), who reports that very young children do not develop mentally at uniform rates of speed, even though they might have similar intellectual powers. This may mean that at one stage, in some cases, a child may be below average in IQ, and at another stage, above average.

(Parents should be warned that the *reported* IQ for a child 6 or 7 years old, or under, on the basis of a given test, is often very unreliable. What the child may score on a particular test may often be much influenced by the child's psychological and emotional state at the time, his response to the person giving the test, his home situation, etc.)

At later ages, in primary schools, the IQs of children remain fairly constant from year to year, with some studies having indicated that training seldom causes any marked improvement. However, a study by Professor Irving Lorge (Teachers' College, Columbia University, 1945) indicates that scores made on intelligence tests in adult years may be progressively higher in relation to the amount of added schooling: when a large group of New York boys who had the same IQs in the eighth grade were tested, as men, twenty years later, it was found that those who had gone through high school scored higher on tests than those who had stopped with grammar school, those who had gone through college scored still higher, and the Ph.D.s highest of all—an average of 20 points more than those who hadn't gone beyond eighth grade.

But while many seized on this as proof that intelligence could be progressively increased by training, Dr. Lorge himself did not. He interpreted the evidence as showing only that performance on intelligence tests could be improved. Even then there were questions. Were the marked differences in the later test scores really or solely because of differences in amount of education? Why did one boy stop with the eighth grade and another go on to become a Ph.D.? Might it not have been that even with the same IQs by the eighth-grade tests, the two boys differed in their capacities for further mental development (just as, with the same height, there might be differences in their capacities for further physical growth). From another angle, there are such factors to be considered as home and social environments, "drive," interest in learning, personality, practice with the testing procedures as well as subtle differences between the earlier and later tests—all of which could influence the scores of the more educated as compared with the less educated. Again, we see the difficulty in drawing conclusions from intelligence-test performances of persons of different types or groups.

All this bears on the findings that American soldiers in World War II had considerably higher average scores on intelligence tests than did those of World War I. An important reason, as Dr. Read D. Tuddenham pointed out (1948), was "more and better education for more people." (World War I soldiers averaged only six grades of school; World War II soldiers, ten grades—two of high school.)

In a further analysis of these data, Professor Irving Lorge reported that while half of the gain in IQ was attributable to differences in education, the other half may have been due to much greater familiarity with testing procedures on the part of the new generation of soldiers.

In reverse, there is some evidence that lack of training can depress IQ scores. For instance, studies in Holland after World War II (A. D. de Groot, 1948) showed that in centers where for long periods schooling was seriously interfered with during the Nazi onslaught and occupation, the IQs of children averaged about 4 points less than those of the prewar years.

But evidence that training or other environmental factors, can raise or lower IQ *scores,* still does not answer our question about *inherent* mental capacity, for we know that in the same environments, with the same training, and often in the same homes, children may have marked differences in IQ. So, continuing, we ask:

5. *How far can heredity fix the boundaries of a person's intelligence?*

We turn once more to our human laboratory subjects, twins. If heredity alone determined one's intelligence, then identical twins, with exactly the same genes, should always have exactly the same IQs. But they don't. IQs of identical twins do often differ, although on an average *they are much more alike than those of fraternal twins,* and decidedly more alike than those of ordinary brothers and sisters in the same family. Most interesting are the comparisons reported of identical twins who were separated in early life and reared in different environments. In one case, where one of two identical twin girls had had only two years of grade-school education, and the other had gone through college, there was a difference of 24 IQ points in favor of the latter.

In general, however, the IQs of identical twins even when reared apart are found to be as much alike as, or slightly more alike than, those of fraternal twins reared together. If the much larger number of "identicals" reared together are included, it will be found (as reported by Dr. James D. Page, 1940) that nearly 50 per cent of the identical twin pairs will differ by less than 5 points IQ, whereas among ordinary brothers and sisters only 23 per cent will so closely resemble each other. Further, more than 80 per cent of identical twin pairs will score within 10 points of each other, and no more than 5 per cent may be expected to show differences greater than

AVERAGE DIFFERENCES IN IQ

BETWEEN

IDENTICAL TWINS REARED TOGETHER:

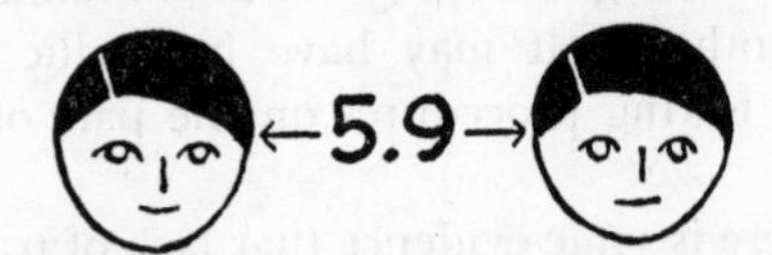

IDENTICAL TWINS REARED APART:

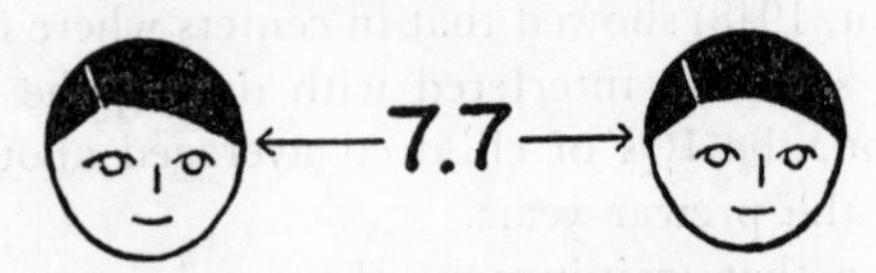

FRATERNAL TWINS REARED TOGETHER:

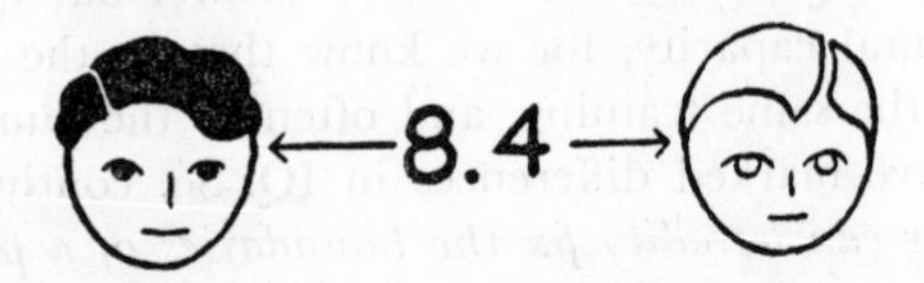

ORDINARY BROTHERS AND SISTERS

(a) Reared together:

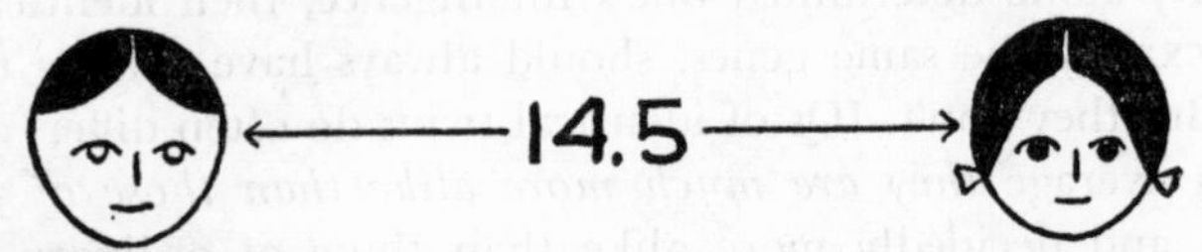

(b) Reared apart:

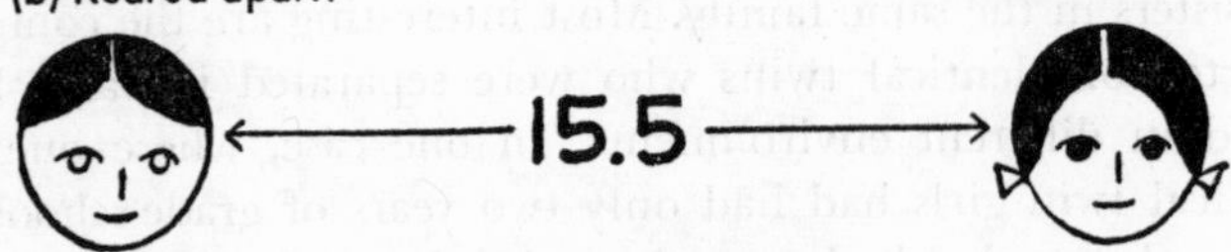

UNRELATED ORPHAN PAIRS

(a) Reared together:

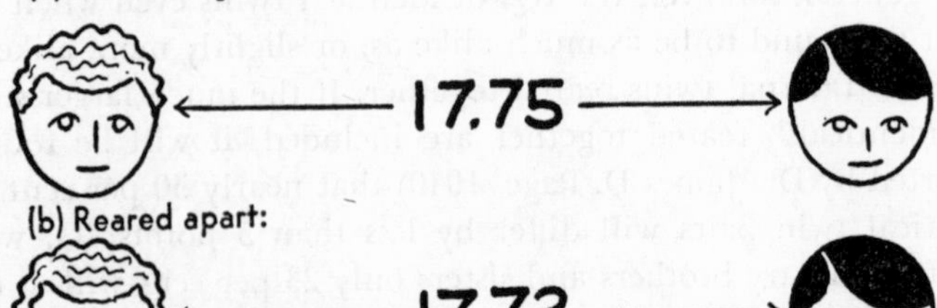

(b) Reared apart:

17.72

(Based on tables from "Heredity and Environment," by Gladys C. Schwesinger)

15 points. All this would indicate that *heredity does not unalterably "fix"* intelligence, but that it does play a great part in determining the *potentialities* for mental development.

Now we try to find out what influences can hamper this development.

6. *Does a poor body produce a poor mind?*

Or, conversely, does a healthy body make a good mind? To the surprise of most of us, there is little proof on this point. A first look at the evidence might prompt a "Yes" answer, for many studies have shown that, in broad averages, children with high IQs tend to be healthier, and bigger for their age, than children with low IQs. But analyzing further, children who are in better physical shape generally come from homes which offer them not merely healthier living conditions, but also more educational and cultural advantages. What we must answer is whether the better physical environment of itself produces higher intelligence, or whether the better cultural environment that goes with it might not also in part be the result of higher intelligence of the parents which they could transmit to their children?

Taking any large population as a whole (and excluding groups against whom there is special discrimination), there is now reason to question how great is the direct relationship between physical condition and intelligence. For one thing, the health and bodily development of children in the United States today (and of those in England and many other countries), is by all counts far superior to what it was in previous generations. *Has there been any over-all increase in intelligence?* Few educators would say yes. From another angle, we have had the experience of two devastating wars and their aftermaths, which have resulted in the undernourishment and health impairment of millions of children in many European countries. And again there is no evidence of any difference in average mental performance because of it, or, at least, of any permanent effects. Studies in Germany after World War I showed that even where children had been literally starved for two or three years, their basic intelligence rarely appeared to have been affected. What, if any, effects on intelligence the ravages of World War II and its aftermath have had with respect to the children of the worst war-torn countries remains to be reported, but there is every indication that the physical deprivation will not prove to have been of as much consequence as the cultural deprivation.

Malnutrition, which differs from starvation in that it refers not to a lack in quantity of food, but to the food elements required by given individuals, has been given some special study with relation to intelligence. The general findings seem to be that even where there is a lack of certain elements in the diet, whatever the physical effects on the child may be, intelligence does not seem to be much affected. Regarding the claimed effects on intelligence of certain chemicals (thiamin, glutamic acid) or vitamins, corroborative evidence is still necessary, as we reported in our "Slow Minds" chapter.

To throw further light on the "poor body-poor mind" theory, we may ask:

7. *Does disease retard mental development?*

If we eliminate, obviously, mental diseases and deficiencies, the answer appears to be mostly "No," but sometimes, "Yes."

Consider *adenoids* or *bad tonsils.* Popular belief used to be that when dull-witted Johnny Jones, who had trouble with his adenoids, got them removed, he would brighten up immediately. But follow-up studies of children after adenoid or tonsil operations have shown no mental improvement.

Hookworm, formerly widespread in depressed areas of the South, also was thought to be responsible for lowered intelligence, but indications are that the real causes were other factors in the bad environments which produced both the disease and the low IQs. Similarly, in the case of *syphilis,* it has not been shown that the disease itself lowers intelligence (unless or until the brain is directly impaired), for the fact that children and adults with the disease tend to have lower than average IQs may mean only that syphilis is most likely to be acquired in depressed environments or in families where IQs are generally low.

However, certain diseases which attack the brain and central nervous system are known to diminish intelligence (sometimes but not always), these including spinal meningitis, hardening of the arteries, brain fever (epidemic encephalitis) and some types of epilepsy. Brain injury in prenatal life or early childhood may of course also impair mental functioning (as was noted in the discussion of idiocy). But there is interesting evidence that in the later years, after the brain has become fairly well "set," injuries to the brain, or even removal of part of it through operation, seldom have much effect on the general intelligence, although there may be interference with certain of the thinking functions.

Where physical defects may adversely affect mental development are in interference with learning tasks and processes, as in cases where children have hearing, seeing or speech disabilities.* In recent years remedial programs for children with such handicaps have helped greatly to insure for them IQs in keeping with their real capacities.

Also worth noting is that history is starred with individuals who rose to the greatest heights despite almost every sort of disease or physical handicap, often dating from birth (as we'll enlarge upon in a later discussion of "genius"). And taking any individual in relation to himself, it can hardly be said that a man in middle life, afflicted with various ills and with a body on the downgrade, is less intelligent than he was in his mid-twenties, at the peak of his physical condition.

On the whole, then, there is little to prove that brawn and brain go together, or that mental capacity is dependent on physical well-being.

Leaving the question of health, we also find it difficult to establish any relationship in normal individuals between outward, or structural physical characteristics, and basic mentality. For instance:

8. *Does head size have any bearing on intelligence?*

Not that we can discover. Disregarding idiots or imbeciles with deformed skulls, exhaustive studies fail to prove that bigger heads or loftier brows mean higher IQs. Eskimos have larger heads than Whites, and the skulls of some prehistoric men had a bigger cranial capacity than the record head of modern times, that of Ivan Turgenev, the Russian novelist (2,030 cubic centimeters). As to the brain itself, the Wistar Institute of the University of Pennsylvania has a collection of two hundred brains of scholars, average persons and low-grade morons, but no scientist who has studied them has yet been able to determine how the brain of a wizard differs from that of a moron, in size or structure.

What has been said can also be used to refute the old theory that because women usually have smaller heads than men, they must also have "smaller" minds. Which brings us to this: If, reverting to our initial problem of choosing between two babies, your decision rested solely on which would be the most intelligent, would you be

* That one type of reading disability may be hereditary, going in many cases with left-handedness or ambidexterity, was suggested in a study (1947) by Dr. R. S. Austis of Harvard, who found a high incidence of these conditions in a group of twenty-one families.

influenced by the fact that one was a girl, the other a boy? In other words:

9. *Is the intelligence of human females inferior, superior or equal to that of males?*

A lot of people may believe this is now a dated question, on the assumption that the intelligence tests have "proved" there is no difference in mental capacity between the sexes. For don't boys and girls have almost the same IQs? Yes—but what few people—even many teachers—do not realize is that *the standard intelligence tests have been deliberately designed to make the scores for the two sexes come out equal.*

The fact is that from the time the tests began to be devised, early in the century, important differences have been found between the sexes in the *way* that they think and in their mental performance on different problems. Girls are consistently better in those phases of the tests involving use of language, rote memory, esthetic responses (such as matching colors and shapes) and social questions (such as guessing ages or noting details regarding people). Boys as a group are consistently superior in tests involving abstract reasoning, mathematics, mechanical ability or structural skills. So in an effort to make tests fit both sexes impartially, "girl-plus" items have been arranged to balance "boy-plus" items, *with certain questions on which those of one or the other sex were too far superior being eliminated altogether.*

How account for this difference in *kind of thinking* between the sexes? Is it all environmental—due to upbringing or social conditioning? Before you can say "Yes," unequivocably, you may have to explain why little boy and girl babies, with apparent spontaneity, may show differences in interests and reactions, or why sex differences in certain kinds of performance may be found in lower animals.

But suppose we seek a constitutional basis for sex differences in human intelligence. It can't be through direct heredity, for there are no differences in the "mental" genes which males and females receive. Indirectly, however, it is possible that the same genetic mechanism (XX versus XY) which produces the general sex differences in physical makeup, glandular and biochemical functioning, etc., might also produce a thinking apparatus in females somewhat different from that in males, either in actual construction or in functioning under different internal stimuli. Which is to say, the same thinking apparatus housed in a female might work differently from the way it would if housed in a male. (That there may be actual chemical differences in female brains as compared with male also has been suggested in several studies.)

The foregoing, too, remember, is still only theory. All we know is that, whether through conditioning or inherent direction (or a combination of both), the more that boys and girls become physically differentiated at puberty, the more pronounced become their differences in aptitude and intelligence tests as well as in their ways of thinking with respect to problems in their everyday lives. Grown up, a man generally can outsmart a woman in some ways, but a woman can outsmart him in other respects (as you need hardly be told). Any attempt to reach a decision as to which has more *total* intelligence will get nowhere.

In short, so long as boys and girls and men and women are destined to be different physically and psychologically in innumerable ways, to be trained differently, to undergo different experiences, to live different lives, to have different incentives and objectives, we can reach only this conclusion:

*No intelligence test exists which can accurately measure the relative mental capacities of the two sexes. No such tests probably ever will be devised. And that being so, no one can say now, or will ever be able to say, whether the sexes are equal or unequal in intelligence, or whether either is superior to the other.**

The difficulty in measuring the comparative mentalities of dissimilar masses of people is further emphasized in our next question:

10. *Do different races and nationalities have different degrees of intelligence?*

In *ways* of thinking, "Yes." In *amounts* of intelligence—nobody can say with scientific accuracy. (Note that these preliminary answers are remarkably similar to what they were for the sex differences.) So long as there are no tests which can fairly measure the relative IQs of people living, learning and thinking under radically different conditions, any conclusions as to the relative *inherent* mental "superiority" or "inferiority" of those of one race or nationality as compared with another must remain highly questionable. As it is, we must bear in mind that the standard intelligence tests, which were devised by White Europeans and Americans to

* Abstracted from a detailed discussion of the subject in the author's *Women and Men,* pp. 84-91 and 301-13.

measure their own mental capacities, are apt to go badly askew and to be unfairly biased when applied to persons of other cultures.

Even within the same country, such as the United States, we must be cautious about interpreting the intelligence test scores made by individuals of different racial and national stocks, or in different regions, *if their home environments, cultural backgrounds and ways of thinking are not the same*—which is apt to be the case. This applies most emphatically to the much-discussed question of Negro versus White intelligence. True, in any given section of the country, the IQ averages of Negroes are considerably lower than of Whites. But also, in any given section, the environments of Negroes are relatively inferior. However, where the conditions for Negroes are better, their IQs are higher (by at least seven points for those living in New York as compared with their relatives in the South). And where conditions for Negroes are good, *their IQs may average even higher than those of Whites living where conditions are bad* (as in certain benighted mountain regions of the South, where IQs of White children may be 10 to 20 points below average). In fact, during World War II, the army rejection rate for sub-standard intelligence was much higher for southern Whites—about 10 per cent in North Carolina, Texas and Arkansas—than for northern Negroes—for whom it was only about 2.5 per cent in Massachusetts, Illinois and New York. (But within any given state the rejection rate for Negroes greatly exceeded that for Whites.)

What is also clear is that as the educational opportunities for Negroes have increased, ever larger numbers of them have been recorded in the upper IQ brackets, approximately 25 per cent of them now doing better than average Whites on intelligence tests. Many Negro children are now being recorded in the very high score brackets (140 to 150 IQ or over), and it is significant that these gifted Negro children, while relatively fewer than gifted White ones, are found to come from much the same types of homes, in terms of economic and cultural status.

In short, while there are some who still believe that the continued lower average IQs of Negroes may be at least partly the result of heredity, the large majority of psychologists feel that this is without proof, and that not unless and until environments for Negroes are completely in line with those for Whites can any convincing comparisons be made.

By now you have seen that while the "intelligence" studies have thrown doubt on many points previously taken for granted, few decisive answers have been given to the main question. So you may ask:

11. *Why cannot science tell us something more definite about the inheritance of intelligence?*

Chiefly, because we haven't quite determined what intelligence is, and haven't as yet any accurate means of measuring it.

The intelligence tests, as has been pointed out, were devised by educators principally for their own domain, the classroom. But academic intelligence and the practical intelligence required in the larger world outside are not necessarily the same. Often the tasks and problems of everyday life demand mental attributes that the standard intelligence tests do not reveal—personality, character, will power, courage, enterprise, "drive," curiosity, intuition, poise and above all, the ability to understand people and to get along with them. Thus, two persons with the same IQ may differ widely in their capacity for achievement and success in life, or a person with a high IQ may prove less successful—actually because he is less intelligent in some important ways—than a person with an IQ considerably lower than his.

(We might note here that Mendel, father of genetics, twice failed in an important examination in botany at the University of Vienna, largely because he had been self-taught and his academic knowledge was deficient.)*

Not until we can define, weigh, and measure intelligence accurately *and fairly with respect to individuals in all environments,* can we have the basic material needed by geneticists to determine its degree and manner of transmission. The first steps may well be to go back to Mendel's procedure of studying one measurable trait—or in this case one measurable aspect of intelligence—at a time, for a serious error previously was in trying to study the inheritance of intelligence as a *unit,* when the evidence now shows that intelligence is compounded of many different elements or capacities, not necessarily related to one another. And if this is indeed so, each of these elements or capacities may be inherited independently, and we may have to track each down separately.

* Mendel also failed in an oral examination in physics and the natural sciences. An 1850 report on this (the original of which has been preserved) says, ". . . Though he has studied diligently, he lacks insight, and his knowledge is without the requisite clarity, so that his examiners find it necessary for the time being to declare him unqualified to teach physics in the lower classical school."

A possibility for achieving this objective may lie in the "factor analysis" technique of breaking up intelligence into its various "primary functions." As outlined by Professor L. L. Thurstone of the University of Chicago, these would include, "verbal comprehension, word fluency, number facility, memory, visualizing or space thinking, perceptual speed, induction, speed of judgment, etc." By measuring each of these "functions" separately, and in relation to one another, Professor Thurstone believes that we can come much nearer to determining a person's mental endowment than through the IQ scores or any other single index of intelligence.

(Many psychologists maintain that one type of mental ability—such as vocabulary development—is generally pretty closely correlated with most other types, but there are sufficient exceptions to support the theory that different elements in mental capacity may be inherited independently. Proficiency in language often is unrelated to proficiency in mathematics, for example. As any student knows, one study may be more difficult for an individual than another, and even though uniformly high grades may be achieved, it may not be because of equal capacity for all subjects, but because of extra application to the weak spots. This application may involve the "personality" element which many investigators believe is at least as important in academic achievement as is basic intelligence.)

Going further with the assumption that there are different elements in mental capacity, scientists may look for a constitutional basis—a physical explanation—for them. Here we have the suggestion of Professor Edward L. Thorndike of Columbia University that different mental abilities may be governed not by different parts of the brain (as was once thought), but by different operations or "hookups" between the brain-nerve cells, sensory organs and other parts of the nervous system. For each kind of thinking, there may be a different hookup, and in some individuals one kind of hookup may be more efficient than another, or all the hookups as a whole may be more efficient than those of other individuals.*

Wherever the explanations or facts may lie, only when we have definitely identified the different elements of intelligence and have studied their manifestation in individuals and their families, under all environmental conditions, can we have any truly scientific con-

* It has been suggested by Dr. Norbert Wiener, in his *Cybernetics* theories, that the human brain works somewhat like the marvelous new electronic calculating machines. But one must also note that even a feeble-minded child is capable of greater thought than any of these machines.

clusions as to the inheritance of intelligence in specific ways or as a whole. As it is, while most geneticists feel certain that there are inherited differences in the mental capacities of human beings, no one would yet venture to make predictions, like those that can be made with other hereditary traits, of the precise ratios and degrees of intelligence that can be expected in the children of parents with such and such IQ scores or levels of mental performance.

Which brings us back to the beginning of this chapter, and the question on which you have been deliberating, as judge and jury:

12. *What, then, is one to decide regarding a choice on the basis of intelligence between Baby "A," the offspring of a charwoman and a day-laborer, and Baby "B," the offspring of a young woman writer and a physician?*

Since we cannot find the complete answer in established fact, we might look for guidance to the opinions of leading authorities (geneticists, anthropologists, psychiatrists and psychologists) who have given detailed attention to all the evidence we have summarized. To the best of our knowledge, these opinions would take two main and divergent directions:

A. *There are those who would say that no choice is justified,* because:

—"We have no *proof* of the extent to which intellectual attainments are due to heredity or to environment. Even with the use of the present 'intelligence' tests, faulty as they are, it is clear that what we call 'intelligence' is greatly influenced by education and conditioning. We have no right, therefore, to compare by the same tests people whose environments are radically different and to consider that their relative scores have any bearing on their relative inherited mental *capacities.*

—"Assuming that there are genes which produce degrees of intelligence, in view of the complexity of the mental processes there would obviously have to be a great many of such genes; which makes it difficult to conceive how, with the constant intermingling that has taken place among people of all levels, 'superior' and 'inferior' 'intelligence' genes could have become noticeably segregated in different proportions within our different occupational groups, especially in so short a time. Therefore,

—"We have no basis for assuming that parents in the unskilled laboring group carry, or will transmit to their offspring, genes for intelligence inferior to those of parents in the professional class.

"Accordingly, we are justified in concluding with regard to the intelligence of the two hypothetical infants that there should be no choice between Baby 'A,' born of a charwoman and a day laborer, and Baby 'B,' born of an authoress and a physician."

B. *On the other hand, we know of authorities who would answer:*

"The view that, lacking clear scientific evidence of how intelligence is inherited, we are not justified in making deductions regarding it, is short-sighted and unwarranted. All the general findings of genetics point to the inheritance of degrees of intellectual capacity in the same way that other characteristics and capacities are inherited. Therefore,

—"Without knowing what the 'intelligence' genes are, we may still rightfully assume that there are some which make for greater intellectual capacity and others for lesser capacity.

—"Allowing for all possible powers of environment to depress or to raise intelligence, we know that many bright individuals born into lower social levels rise to higher levels, and many dull individuals born into upper levels sink to lower levels. With this process having gone on throughout civilization we may reason that in two large social groups differing radically in intellectual attainment, there would be more of the 'superior' genes in the superior group.

—"The average IQ difference of 20 points between offspring of the unskilled laboring classes and those of the professional classes cannot be dismissed as without significance unless it is ascribed *entirely* to differences in environment. There is no proof that this is so. Knowing that in the same environment, even in members of the same family, great differences in intelligence exist, the burden of proving that environment alone is responsible for all these differences rests on those who make the assertion.

—"At the very best, in the situation cited, one can only say that Baby 'A' might be expected to be as inherently intelligent as Baby 'B.' No one would venture to say, and not a single study has indicated, that children of unskilled laborers as a group would be expected to have a better intellectual heritage than those of professional people. On the other hand, many studies do indicate that there is a possibility, if not a probability, that the average child of professional people will turn out to be more intelligent than the average child of those in the lowest occupational groups.

—"The question thus becomes one of odds. Baby 'A' might indeed turn out to be more intelligent than Baby 'B.' But the odds are surely greater—although we cannot say how much greater—that Baby 'B,' offspring of the authoress and the physician, would have inherited the better mental equipment. Therefore,

—"Everything else being equal, on the basis of intelligence there should be a choice in favor of Baby 'B.' "

So here are two clearly conflicting interpretations of the same set of facts. How are you, the layman, to decide? For remember, the two theoretical babies are before you, and you can take only one of them.

You might beg the question by saying, "We are dealing, after all, not with objects but with human beings, helpless infants. So long as there is uncertainty, the humane thing to do, and the democratic thing to do, would be not to condemn Baby 'A' as mentally inferior purely on theoretical grounds, but to give it the benefit of the doubt and consider it as equal." There is merit in this viewpoint, but our problem here is not a humanitarian one but essentially a scientific one. You are called on to decide, solely on the basis of the evidence, whether the offspring of the one set of parents would be likely to turn out more intelligent than the offspring of the other set of parents.

If you conclude that the facts presented are not conclusive enough to warrant a choice, and that you should leave the selection entirely to a toss of the coin, we can assure you that there are high-ranking authorities who will approve your stand.

But if you prefer to be guided by the weight of opinion, at least in a numerical sense, we may say this:

It is our belief that the *majority* of qualified experts of all kinds would subscribe to the second viewpoint previously stated, and would unequivocably advise you to keep your coin in your pocket and to choose Baby "B," child of the authoress and the physician.

CHAPTER 34

THE GIFTED ONES: PART I

MUSICAL TALENTS

A LITTLE boy, hugging a violin, walks out onto the stage at New York's Carnegie Hall. There is a flutter of applause from the thousands of persons filling the auditorium. The little boy tucks his violin under his chin and begins to play. The audience, skeptical, watches, listens. A tiny hand sweeps the bow back and forth, tiny fingers fly over the strings, streams of melody, now shrill, now full-throated, cascade forth. Already, in those first minutes, many mature musicians out front know that in all their years of study and work they have not been able to achieve such mastery. Soon they, and the others, quite forget that this is a little boy who is playing. As if drawn by invisible bonds, they are carried out of the hall, into the night, higher and higher. Then suddenly there is a burst of notes like a rocket's shower of golden stars . . . the music stops . . . and they are all back again in Carnegie Hall, incredulously storming with their bravos a little boy—a little boy who in a few hours may be crying because he isn't allowed to stay up and play with his toys.

The scene has been enacted a number of times in each generation, but not too many times, for little boys like this do not appear often. It may have been elsewhere than Carnegie Hall—in Paris, London, Vienna—possibly in your own town. And sometimes it was not a violin that the child played, but a piano. So Chopin, Mozart, Mendelssohn, Liszt, Schumann, César Franck, and of contemporary musicians, Heifetz, Hofmann, Kreisler, Menuhin, and Claudio Arrau, among many others, revealed their genius to the world as children.

In no other field of human achievement do the young so strikingly scale the heights and so easily outdistance great numbers of competing adults. One might concede that musical *performance*—the rendering of a musical composition on some instrument—is a special type of achievement which does not demand either full physical or full intellectual development (though both are essential for true virtuosity), and hence need not be beyond the reach of a child just because he is a child. But in musical *composition,* one of the highest forms of human creative expression, we also find amazing precocity: Mozart, at 14, with a score of symphonies and short operas already to his credit, offering his newest opera in Milan, and personally directing the orchestra, the largest in Europe . . . Handel, by the time he was 11, composing a church service every week . . . Mendelssohn, at 17—with years of composing behind him—producing one of his greatest works, the overture to *A Midsummer Night's Dream* . . . Franz Schubert, another veteran composer in his 'teens, writing, at 18, in a single day, one of his most notable songs, "The Erl-King."

To music devotees, precociousness among the great musical figures, not only of the past but of the present, is so familiar as to be taken almost for granted. But how explain this? Is it the flowering of some remarkable hereditary endowment? Or is it merely the prosaic result of some unusual type of early environment and intensive training? Any one of these theories has had its advocates.

The subject isn't just one for the musician or the scientist. Music is now important in all our lives. Apart from performance for pleasure or profit, the question of whether you are or aren't responsive to music, and in what way or degree, may greatly affect your leisure activities, social relationships and personality, from childhood on. You may know all too well the difference it makes between thrilling to music or being tone deaf, between coming alive with rhythm on a dance floor or stumbling mechanically, between harmonizing joyfully with others around a piano or hanging uncomfortably on the fringes, trying to croak out a few off-key words. And if you're a parent, you can hardly escape the question of whether your child is or isn't musical, and why or why not, and what to do about it in either case. Thus, many of the points to be taken up in this chapter, on the nature of musical talent and the extent to which it is or isn't hereditary, will have a personal meaning for you.

To begin with, we may note that musical talent, as revealed through performance, is unique among other human talents in the way that the achievements of different individuals can be measured against one another. Exactly the same piece can be rendered by any number of musicians of all ages, backgrounds and nationalities (even the dead as compared with the living through recordings), and one does not have to be an expert to distinguish the superlative performances from the mediocre or inferior ones. No such easy method of comparison is possible in any field where *creativeness* is the determinant—as in writing, or painting, or in musical composition—for creativeness cannot be measured by any known yardstick, and relative judgments of it by contemporary critics are all too often wrong. Accordingly, so long as we confine ourselves to measurable talent for musical *performance* and the degree to which it manifests itself in different individuals and different families, we are in a much better position than in any of the other arts to distinguish the part played by heredity.

In former times, many believed that the inheritance of musical talent could be proved merely by pointing to such pedigrees as those of the Bachs, in whom great musical talent flowed in an unbroken line through five generations, or of the Mozarts, Webers and others. But these days, with a heightened awareness of the influence of environment, the skeptical might ask whether "music-making" did not run in certain families for the same reasons that watchmaking, pottery-making or winemaking "ran" in others, because individuals of successive generations were trained to carry on in the same way. The argument would have validity if it could be shown that any or every child could be trained to be a musician, and that only special environmental influences, and no special *inherent* qualities, were required for great musical achievement.

In the belief that many uncertainties could be cleared up by analyzing the musical histories and backgrounds of outstanding living musicians—not just a few, but a great many, fully representative of the whole number—a detailed study was made for the first edition of this book. Here we will present the principal findings, involving these three groups, two of world-famous musicians and singers, the third group, for comparison, of gifted students:

1. Thirty-seven of the outstanding pianists, violinists and conductors of the world (comprising, in the view of critics, a large majority of the greatest living virtuosi).

2. Thirty-six of the outstanding singers, representing the principals of the Metropolitan Opera Company (season 1937-38).

3. Fifty students of the Juilliard Graduate School of Music, comprising a highly selected group of younger musicians and singers, still to make their marks.

In all three groups, information came directly from each individual (except in the few instances where it was supplied by some close relative), regarding the age at which his or her talent had appeared, how it had shown itself, the age when the professional debut was made (for members of the first two groups), and the incidence of musical talent in parents, brothers and sisters, and other near relatives.

One of the first points brought out was that, in almost every case, *musical talent expressed itself at an extremely early age.* Among the instrumentalists it appeared at an average age of 4¾ years for the virtuosi, and in the Juilliard group, at about 5½. (The singers will be dealt with later.) This expression of talent was often in unusual ways. Artur Rubinstein, born into a very poor home in Warsaw where no musical instrument was to be heard, spontaneously began to sing little songs of his own making to express what he wanted or to designate various members of the family. Eugene Ormandy at the same age of 1½ knew all of the records of his father's hurdy-gurdy. Toscha Seidel, at three, would have tantrums when his uncle, a not-too-talented fiddler, hit a "sour" note. In other cases, talent was revealed by evidence of an acute musical ear (or the possession of "absolute pitch"), but in most cases it was simply through actual performance on the piano or violin. Random checks on histories of virtuosi not represented in our study showed similar precocity in almost every instance.

SUMMARY – ALL THREE GROUPS

	Virtuosi Artists (36)	*Metropolitan Singers (36)*	*Juilliard Students (50)*	*Totals for All Groups (122)*
AVERAGE AGE TALENT EXPRESSED	4¾ yrs.	9¾ yrs.	5¾ yrs.	6⅔ yrs.
MOTHERS TALENTED or Musical in Some Degree	17 (47%)	24 (67%)	37 (74%)	78 (64%)
FATHERS TALENTED or Musical in Some Degree	29 (81%)	25 (69%)	29 (58%)	83 (68%)
BROTHERS AND SISTERS, Total	110	103	72	285
Talented or Musical in Some Degree	55 (50%)	43 (42%)	51 (71%)	148 (52%)
NUMBER REPORTING Talent in Additional near kin	13 (36%)	16 (44%)	37 (74%)	66 (54%)

THE INSTRUMENTAL AND VOCAL ARTISTS WHO CONTRIBUTED DATA TO OUR STUDY OF INHERITANCE OF MUSICAL TALENT*

THE INSTRUMENTAL ARTISTS

(Abbreviations used: "Comp."—composer. "Cond."—conductor. "Pian." —pianist. "Vio."—violinist.)

John Barbirolli (Cond.-cellist)
Harold Bauer (Pian.)
Artur Bodanzky (Cond.)
Alexander Brailowsky (Pian.)
Adolf Busch (Vio.)
Guila Bustabo (Vio.)
Walter Damrosch (Cond.-pian.)
Mischa Elman (Vio.)
Georges Enesco (Vio., Comp.)
Walter Gieseking (Pian.)
Eugene Goossens (Cond.-vio.-comp.)
Percy Grainger (Pian.-comp.)
Jascha Heifetz (Vio.)
Myra Hess (Pian.)
Ernest Hutcheson (Pian.)
José Iturbi (Pian.-cond.)
Fritz Kreisler (Vio.-comp.)
Josef Lhevinne (Pian.)
Yehudi Menuhin (Vio.)
Nathan Milstein (Vio.)
Erica Morini (Vio.)
Guiomar Novaes (Pian.)
Eugene Ormandy (Cond.)
Gregor Piatigorsky (Cellist)
Serge Prokofieff (Pian.-comp.)
Sergei Rachmaninoff (Pian.-comp.)
Artur Rodzinski (Cond.)
Moritz Rosenthal (Pian.)
Artur Rubinstein (Pian.)
Artur Schnabel (Pian.)
Toscha Seidel (Vio.)
Rudolf Serkin (Pian.)
Ruth Slenczynski (Pian.)
Jan Smeterlin (Pian.)
Joseph Szigeti (Vio.)
Arturo Toscanini (Cond.)
Alfred Wallenstein (Cellist-cond.)
Efrem Zimbalist (Vio.)

THE METROPOLITAN OPERA SINGERS

WOMEN: Rose Bampton, Lucrezia Bori, Karin Branzell, Hilda Burke, Gina Cigna, Susanne Fisher, Kirsten Flagstad, Dusolina Giannini, Helen Jepson, Marjorie Lawrence, Lotte Lehmann, Queena Mario, Grace Moore, Eide Norena, Rose Pauly, Lily Pons, Rosa Ponselle, Elisabeth Rethberg, Bidu Sayao, Gladys Swarthout.

MEN: Paul Althouse, Richard Bonelli, Mario Chamlee, Richard Crooks, Charles Hackett, Frederick Jagel, Jan Kiepura, Charles Kullman, Emanuel List, G. Martinelli, Lauritz Melchior, Ezio Pinza, Friedrich Schorr, John Chas. Thomas, Lawrence Tibbett.

* Names of Juilliard Graduate Students taking part in the study, and complete tables and details for all instrumentalists and vocalists, will be found in the first edition of *You and Heredity* (1939), pp. 234-78.

Any remaining suspicion that the virtuosi exaggerated the early onset of their talents could be dissipated by the proof that their professional debuts—not merely first public performances but the actual launching of their professional careers—came at an average age of 13. Altogether, evidence from the past and present shows clearly that *great achievement in music is almost invariably correlated with an extremely early start.* Whether or not such an early start is a prerequisite for great musical achievement, the question is still, *What accounts for the early start?* Is it an unusual musical environment? Is it an unusual musical heredity? Or is it a combination of both?

We may look for some answers in what the virtuosi instrumentalists (as well as those of the other two groups) reported regarding the incidence of talent in their families.

Among the virtuosi instrumentalists, the majority had talented parents—one or both. Yet quite a number reported *no talent in either parent,* among these being Toscanini, Schnabel, Seidel, Smeterlin, Rubinstein and Rosenthal (the latter two, however, reporting "musical appreciation" in their fathers). Nor did the differences in the family backgrounds, or in there being both parents, one parent, or neither parent talented, seem to have anything to do with the caliber or quality of musicianship by the individual. Some of the greatest virtuosi came from the humblest and least musical homes, where neither parent had talent; some of the lesser ones came from highly musical backgrounds, with both parents professional musicians. Corresponding situations were found in our vocalist and Juilliard groups, and were consistent with the stories of many other musicians outside our study.

Such a lack of direct and consistent correlation between musical achievement and background would suggest strongly that musical talent does not arise from any unusual *home environment, per se.* Going further, the fact that a highly musical environment also (or alone) cannot produce talent was shown by data on the children of the virtuosi in our study, for about one-fourth of the children were sadly reported by their fathers as being "without talent," and most showed no unusual talent, despite all the opportunity that had been given them to develop it. For example, of Arturo Toscanini's three children, only one, Wanda (wife of Vladimir Horowitz), was reported as having talent, but only in critical ability, and it was the child of this daughter alone, Sonya, then about 4 years old, who out of three Toscanini grandchildren at the time, was reported as showing talent. (A story the maestro told delightedly some years later was of the day when he was at the piano, playing four hands with her, and she turned to him testily and said, *"Grandpa, you're not so hot as a pianist."* At this writing, in 1950, Sonya Horowitz, now 16, is regarded as a "talented pianist," but is not considering music as a career, preferring painting.)

But if environment is not the determining factor in musical talent, can we show that *heredity* is? To do this, we must first offer evidence that talent "runs" in some unusual way in the families or near-relatives of virtuosi. This is what our data did show. Talent or musicality in some degree was reported, by the virtuosi instrumentalists, in almost half the mothers, three-fourths of the fathers, and half the brothers and sisters; by the Metropolitan Opera singers, in two-thirds of the parents and in about 40 per cent of the brothers and sisters; and in the Juilliard group, in 74 per cent of the mothers, 58 per cent of the fathers and 70 per cent of the brothers and sisters.

Thus, in the three unrelated groups of performers, differing in a great many ways but having the common denominator of marked musical talent, there was very much the same extraordinarily high incidence of talent in their families. Added to other facts brought out previously, the case for the inheritance of musical talent might seem a strong one. But much more is needed to satisfy scientific demands. If musical talent is indeed inherited, there must be a *biological* basis for it; there must be certain special *constitutional* traits or capacities which make possible such talent, and which conceivably could be produced by specific genes. A prime requirement, then, would be to identify these "musical talent" ingredients.

That is what the late Professor Carl E. Seashore of the University of Iowa began his attempt to do many years ago (about 1915). He broke down musical "aptitude" (which is not quite the same as "talent," as we shall see) into what he considered its components—the senses of pitch, time, intensity (loudness and softness), harmony, rhythm and tonal memory. For each of these "senses" he devised tests to discover to what extent they might be inherited in persons, and to what extent they could be cultivated. Through the use of these and other musical-aptitude tests (Drake, Whistler-Thorpe, etc.) on many thousands of individuals in the United States and other countries, certain conclusions have been reached:

—The primary senses required for musical aptitude do have a constitutional basis.

—Each "sense" may be present independently of the others. (A person may have a keen sense of pitch, and little sense of harmony; another may be blessed with a combination of all the senses.)*

—Training can develop any of these senses only to the degree that the capacity is *inherent* in the individual.

—By the time a child is 10, his or her future musical performance can be clearly determined, and at 16 an individual is musically "set."

—The musical aptitudes may be unrelated to intelligence: A highly intelligent person may be almost devoid of musicality, whereas a nitwit may be highly musical (there being many cases of morons who are quite good musicians). However, for the maximum development of musical capacity, and success in studying and pursuing music as a career, more than ordinary intelligence may be required.

One of the senses given most study is that of "pitch," and especially of its highest form, "absolute" pitch, which might be described as a "mental tuning-fork." It enables the fortunate musician or singer so endowed to "hit" any note accurately, or to judge the accuracy of any note, without the aid of any instrumental cue. Often, among prodigies, it is one of the first musical aptitudes revealed, but it is not essential to great musical achievement. While many of the virtuosi in our study reported having this gift, the large majority did not. Various studies have indicated that absolute pitch is inherited (see the Kirsten Flagstad pedigree, for instance), and while there has been controversy on this point recently, the strongest evidence that this sense, if not inherent, cannot be acquired merely through training is given by the fact that the large majority of outstanding musicians and singers fail to develop it, despite years of practice, whereas many individuals who have never had training may nevertheless have absolute pitch, often revealed in childhood.

At any rate, the findings for the various senses would tend to prove that there is or isn't something *in* each person, from his earli-

* An interesting finding by Drs. Harvey S. Whistler and Louis P. Thorpe, after applying their new ("California") tests to more than 4,000 persons, is that the sense of rhythm is apparently not highly correlated with success in vocal music, although the senses of pitch and melody appear necessary to a greater degree for vocalists than for instrumental musicians. Nevertheless, for both vocalists and instrumentalists, superiority in any or all of these senses is an important asset.

est years onward, which governs the limits of his musical aptitude. But *aptitude* does not necessarily imply true talent in the sense that musicians understand it. A person may have well-developed senses of pitch, rhythm, time, tonal memory, etc., and yet be as mechanical as an old nickel-in-the-slot player piano. Aptitude is primary and essential equipment for the musician, but while, with it, he can develop technique, something more is needed for real talent and virtuosity. The lack of it may explain why many prodigies fail to pan out in their later years, or why many musicians who can put on a dazzling display of technique leave their audiences unmoved.

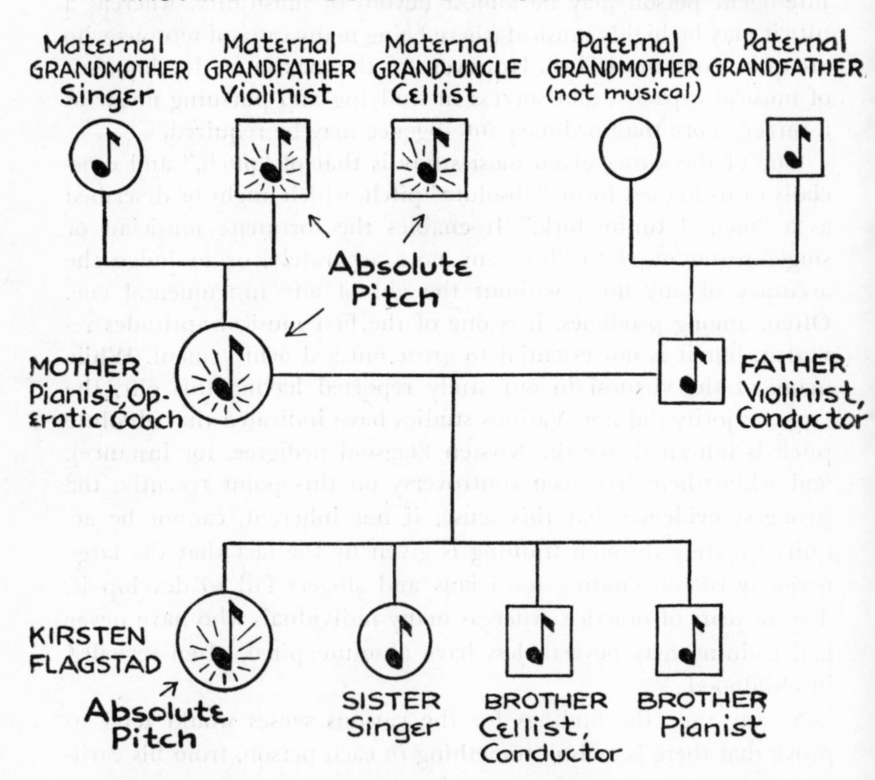

The extra "something" required for talent is a lot harder to define or measure than is musical aptitude. Professor Seashore believed it may lie in the ability of the person to create and express subtle variations permitted within the limits of any musical composition. His nephew, Professor Harold G. Seashore, another leading musicologist, describes this special requirement, which is the antithesis of mechanical playing, as the "artistic deviation from the pure, the true, the exact, the perfect, the rigid, the even and the precise." He has shown, with unusual graph-recordings, that each virtuoso "deviates" in a characteristic way, and that such deviation must be dictated by extreme sensitivity, great emotion, and high intelligence.* These qualities, we may assume, are probably some of the components of great musical talent. But in addition, there must be special traits or equipment for each kind of performer—for the pianist and violinist, unusual powers of muscular coordination and nervous stamina; for the singer, the right vocal apparatus, *plus* appearance and personality; for the conductor, prodigious musical memory, imagination, executive ability, etc.

Quite clearly, there can be no simple formula for all types and degrees of musical talent. But it does appear that just as there are certain basic components required for aptitude, there are certain additional basic traits required to give any musician that extra lift toward talent. As with the aptitudes, these "talent" traits may very well have a *constitutional* basis, and be products of heredity. But establishing a gene mechanism is another matter.

Before any talent can develop, there must be the foundation of musical aptitude, and so an initial assumption would be that there are specific genes for each of the senses that go to compose aptitude. To inherit the required combination of such genes (of the average type) would not be unusual, for they are apparently in pretty wide circulation. Almost anyone who can carry a tune or learn to play a musical instrument must have them in some degree. Conversely, the less frequently encountered individuals who are tone deaf (or "tune deaf") or lacking a sense of rhythm, harmony, etc., may be considered as having defective genes for the senses involved, just as color-blind persons have defective genes for color perception. The first genetic evidence on this point was offered by Dr. H. Kalmus at the Genetics Congress in Stockholm, in 1948. He reported a study showing that individuals unable to recognize melodies, sing or play in tune (although in no way defective in hearing) are found much more often than is generally assumed, and *repeatedly in some fam-*

* Elaborating on this, Dr. Seashore says (in a note to the author), "This artistic variability is observed in the vocal and instrumental vibrato, in deviation from rigid rhythm and time, in subtle 'error' in pitch, in nuances of timbre and loudness. In short, in 'deviations from the regular,' from mechanical reproduction of the musical score."

ilies in ratios indicating that "tune deafness" might possibly be caused by a *dominant* gene. Were such a gene present, regardless of other genetic qualifications it obviously could throw a monkey wrench into a person's whole musical machinery.

Anyway, we may assume that all the required "aptitude" genes are present in good working order in any person predisposed to talent. But apparently he must have in addition certain rarer, "special" genes which act either to intensify the effects of the more ordinary "aptitude" genes or to produce some unusual supplementary effects. What clues have we as to the presence of such genes?

Turning again to our study of the three groups of musicians and singers, an analysis of the incidence of talent in their families showed:

Where both parents had musical talent, more than 70 per cent of the brothers and sisters (in addition to the individual reporting) also had talent.

Where only one parent was talented, there was talent in 60 per cent of the brothers and sisters.

Where neither parent was talented, only 15 per cent of the brothers and sisters had talent.

In each of the groups the talent incidence followed this similar pattern: There were about 12 to 15 per cent more talented offspring resulting from "double talent" matings than from the "one-parent talented" matings, and a strikingly small proportion of talented children, other than the one studied—produced where neither parent was talented.

What type of "special" genes—added to the "aptitude" genes—could produce these ratios? We can offer only a theory. It is clear that no single dominant gene, or no two recessive genes, could account for the ratios. A multiple-gene mechanism would have to be involved, and the simplest one which might fit the requirements would be, at the very least, two different dominant genes. A pair of such genes could be passed on by only a single parent to a given child, or each parent could give the child one of the required genes. If this hypothesis (or some other one corresponding to it) is correct, it could explain many puzzling facts.

Consider Arturo Toscanini, one of the greatest conductors and musicians of all time. Looking at our Chart, you will see that no talent was reported in his father or mother, or in his brother or sisters (or, so far as is known, in other near relatives). If musical

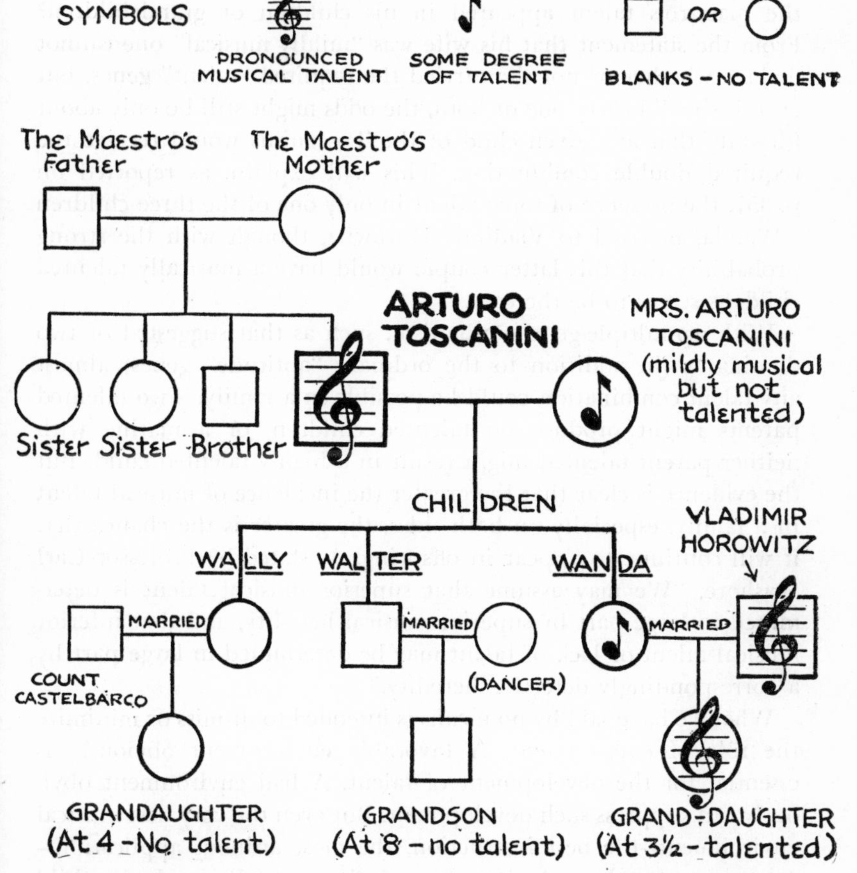

talent is inherited, how explain such an exceptional one as Toscanini's arising in so otherwise untalented a family? On the basis of our theory, it could easily have been possible that on the maestro's paternal side only one of the required special "talent" genes had been handed along, while on the maternal side the other had been carried—neither effective by itself. It may have taken many generations for both genes to be brought together through the mating of the maestro's parents. Then the chance of the combination appearing in one of their offspring was one in four or less, and as it apparently happened, Arturo was so favored. (This refers only to the talent *essentials,* for many additional endowments must also have been his.)

Looking further into the Toscanini pedigree, why has so little of the maestro's talent appeared in his children or grandchildren? From the statement that his wife was "mildly musical" one cannot deduce whether or not she carried the required "talent" genes, but even if she did carry one or both, the odds might still be only about fifty-fifty that any given child of the Toscaninis would receive the required double combination. This will explain, as reported on p. 357, the presence of some talent in only one of the three children —Wanda, married to Vladimir Horowitz, though with the strong probability that this latter couple would have a musically talented child, as seems to be the case.

With a multiple-gene mechanism, such as that suggested of two dominants (in addition to the ordinary "aptitude" genes) almost any talent combination could be possible in a family. Two talented parents might produce no talented children, or a mating with neither parent talented might result in a highly talented child. But the evidence is clear that the greater the incidence of musical talent in a family, especially on both sides, the greater is the chance that it will continue to appear in offspring. As stated by Professor Carl Seashore, "We may assume that superior musical talent is determined in large part by superior musical heredity, and that inferior musical talent or lack of talent may be determined in large part by a correspondingly defective heredity."

What we have said by no means is intended to dismiss or minimize the rôle of *environment.* A favorable environment obviously is essential for the development of talent. A bad environment obviously can suppress such development. But even the very best musical environment—the best instruction, the most arduous application—cannot *create* talent. At least, no one has ever shown that a child without evidence of inherent talent can be turned into a prodigy by training. A lot of parents have tried it with their young hopefuls, and have been disillusioned.

The "veto" power of environment, however, can be demonstrated in many ways, most strikingly in the case of women. For example, take the very small percentage of women found among the great virtuosi. (Even more surprising is the almost total absence of women from the topmost ranks of the composers.) This certainly cannot be because women inherit any less talent potentiality than do men.

We know that whatever genes for talent there are must be carried at least equally by women (for if there are any such genes on the X chromosome, women would have even a greater chance of getting them). One explanation undoubtedly is that women never had, and still do not have, the same opportunity to develop their talents as men are accorded. Many repressive social and psychological factors could be cited. But there also may be something *in the physical makeup* of women, as a group, or in their internal environment (including glandular and sensory functioning) which may act in an inhibitory way.

Asked for her opinion as to why there were so few other women virtuosi, Erica Morini, the violinist, told us, "In my opinion it is because only a few women have the great power of concentration, the strength and the energy required for such achievement. A complete absorption is necessary, and a readiness to give up the pleasures which most women seek." But even where all the qualifications are there, Miss Morini believes that "prejudice" against women musicians may have added greatly to the reasons why, in the past two and a half centuries, records show only seventy-three concertizing female violinists as compared with thousands of males.

In the vocal field, where women are represented equally with men, there is no such sex discrimination, although for talented singers of both sexes the veto effects of environment are much greater than for the instrumentalists. First is the question of voice, the *instrument* on which the vocal musician plays. At the outset, regardless of what talent may be displayed in childhood, singers are dependent on what happens to their voices during puberty. This explains, for one thing, the report by the Metropolitan Opera stars that their formal training did not begin until the average age of 15½ for the women, and 16½ for the men (although in both cases musical talent was reported as showing itself about seven years earlier). Regardless of talent, the singer is continually at the mercy of his or her vocal cords. It is not like the violinist who, if his instrument breaks, can get a new one. Also, without doubt, face, figure, personality—and just plain luck—are more important to the vocalists than to the instrumentalists, and may account for the public success of many mediocre singers and the failure of others with truly great talent.

The fact that the voice is used as the instrument on which the vocal musician performs, suggests the possibility that, again unlike other musicians, the singer may inherit both his instrument and the talent to perform on it. However, while there is good reason to believe that vocal mechanisms of all types and capacities may be inherited, genetic studies of voice have so far not been very extensive. With respect to timbre, one theory is that bass voices in men and soprano in women are determined by a pair of one kind of "voice" genes; that a gene pair of another kind produces tenor voices in men and alto in women; and that a mixed pair of these genes—one of the first kind, coupled with one of the second, produces baritone in men and mezzo-soprano in women. Our own study, based on voice-type data for families of the Metropolitan stars and another group, the Schola Cantorum of New York, showed that where both parents had high voices, most of the children were in the high range (the twenty-six tenor fathers listed producing no bass sons), while fathers with lower voices (baritone or bass) had a marked majority of low-voiced sons.*

Reference to the physical equipment required for singers brings to mind the popular notion that inheritance of a particular shape of hand (a "piano" hand, or a "violin" hand) predisposes one to be a musician. Actually, the basic shape of the hand or fingers has little to do with virtuosity, for every type of hand will be found among musicians—any characteristics in common being developed through training. Where one hand may be better than another, however, is structurally, in perfecting technique. One of the greatest of pianists, Josef Hofmann, said, "My hand is a bad one for the piano—too small, my fingers not long enough for everything—and my technique is limited. I have pupils who have far bigger technique than I."

And need we add there's nothing to the notion that a certain type of face, or a certain kind of hair, goes with musical capacity? If musicians have more "sensitive" faces, credit their way of living; for the appearance of their hair (if they have any), credit their barbers.

One of the hardest questions to answer is, *"Don't people of certain races or nationalities inherit more musical talent than others?"*

The surface evidence might seem convincing: the Italians with

* If human singers can be compared in any way with canaries, some meaning may be found in evidence that the urge to sing, and to sing in a *particular* way, is inherited by canaries of different species. Professor Milton Metfessel (1940) showed that canaries hatched and reared in isolation, with no chance ever to hear other birds, nevertheless broke out into the songs characteristic of their species.

their unusually large number of great composers, singers and musicians, and their enormous popular interest in opera . . . the Jewish people, with their remarkably high representation among the virtuosi pianists and violinists (*Time* magazine having noted in 1943 that, with two exceptions, all of the contemporary first-rank violinists were Jewish) . . . the Negroes, with their many wonderful "spiritual" and "blues" singers, their jazz virtuosity and their "rhythm" . . . and, in contrast, the failure of some peoples, such as the Chinese and Japanese, to produce any distinguished music or musicians—by *our* standards.

But all this need prove nothing with respect to inheritance, for, as most musicologists would point out, various environmental factors could account for marked differences among groups of humans in musical expression. The Italians, with their enthusiasm for opera, would be expected to produce opera composers and singers prolifically, just as Americans produce jazz musicians. Among Jews, it is argued, various cultural influences inspire an urge toward musical expression, and a drive toward achievement, much greater than is true for other peoples, and presumably *might* explain their unusual production of prodigies and virtuosi. So, too, special factors in the cultural environments of any other large groups of people, at given times, might explain to a large extent not only the amount of their musical expression, but its characteristic forms, types and moods—as for instance the music of the Russians, Austrians, Germans, French, Spanish, Americans, etc.

Yet genetic factors might also have to be considered. Theoretically, if genes for superior musical aptitude and talent are unusually prevalent in some families, it would be entirely possible, on a broader scale, for these genes to be more heavily concentrated in some races, ethnic stocks or nationalities than others (just as genes for certain blood types, or for certain diseases and abnormalities, are disproportionately present in some racial groups). As we said, however, this is only theory, for we can never be sure to what extent "talent" genes are or are not present in different populations so long as they vary radically in the opportunities provided for musical expression.*

* One aspect of the question—that with respect to musical *aptitude*—may have been answered negatively. According to Professor Carl Seashore, numerous racial studies in which the musical aptitude tests have been administered revealed no significant differences in the basic sensory capacities (pitch, loudness, time, etc.) of members of one race or ethnic group as compared with another. But whether

For the present, there is general agreement that the relative amount of musical *achievement* in any human group—racial, national, social or however classified—is nowhere near what it could be if all those with talent were able to develop it properly. We could quote here what the father of Yehudi Menuhin, Moishe Menuhin, said to us, "I am sure that there are many other young men now nobodies who might have become as great artists as my son if their talents had been immediately recognized by their parents and they had been given equal opportunities for training and development."

But, also, there always has been the awareness in the inner sanctums of music that only those individuals can be trained to virtuosity who start out with unusual equipment. Pianist Jan Smeterlin expressed the consensus of the musicians and singers in our study when he said, "Heredity without training would not go far, but training without heredity would not go anywhere."

In sum, while all the finer shades of the question can be argued to infinity, it seems conclusive that musical talent, as a human trait, follows much the same pattern of development as do many other traits with an hereditary basis which we have discussed:

What is inherited is a "talent-susceptibility," dependent for its expression on the interoperation of many factors—some from within the individual (sensory, mental, emotional, physical), and some from without (home, social and cultural environments, opportunities for training and recognition, etc.). In some individuals, the "susceptibility" to musical achievement is so strong (talent plus "drive") that even in a minimum or adverse environment it will assert itself. In other individuals, the "susceptibility" is so weak that only in the best environment can it assert itself. And also, just as there are some few individuals with inherited musical capacities which can be developed to an astounding degree, there are others so limited or imperfect in genetic capacities that no amount of training can make them musical.

How does this apply to you? If you don't happen to be a musical virtuoso (assuming you would have wanted to be one) you may by now be clearer as to why you aren't, and can more definitely place the blame on your genes, or your efforts, or your environment. It may be too late to do anything about yourself. But if you're a parent, it

---

the *rare, special capacities* (or genes) for the highest types of musical virtuosity also are equally distributed among all peoples is a question which can't yet be answered.

may be important to consider the musical prospects of your child. From the evidence, you can see that even if you haven't any musical talent, and your mate hasn't either, you may still have a child who is talented, so keep an eye open for that possibility, and allow for its development. On the other hand, if you and your mate are highly musical, don't consider it "unnatural" for a child of yours to show no talent, and don't try to force musical training upon it or show disapproval. (Where there is doubt, a musical aptitude test is advised; and if no talent is revealed, try developing in the child some other interests, instead.)

With awareness of the basis for musical talent there should be a wiser understanding of which children to train intensively and which ones to teach music to only for pleasure or cultural development. While many a musical genius may have been lost to the world through failure to receive training, there also has been many a tragedy because parents have tried to turn a Jimmy into a Jascha.

All of which brings to mind a charming visit the author had with the late Professor Leopold Auer, one of the greatest of music teachers, who developed the genius of many of the contemporary violin virtuosi. Chatting with him a few years before his death, when he was past 80, we brought up the "coincidence" that various of his famous pupils had first names ending in "cha"—Jascha Heifetz, Toscha Seidel, Mischa Elman, etc. These, Professor Auer explained, were his affectionate Russian diminutives for their real names, Jacob, Thomas, Michael, etc., which he had applied to them in special recognition of their talents, and which they later adopted professionally.

"Ah," we sighed, "now we know why we could not become a great violinist. Our name should have been 'Amscha.'" The little man's eyes twinkled. "Perhaps," he answered laughingly. *"But don't forget that these others had the talent before they got the name."*

CHAPTER 35

THE GIFTED ONES: PART II

SPECIAL TALENTS

"YOU, too, can paint!" "You, too, can compose songs!" "You, too, can write stories!"

So you are told by the "Anyone-can-do" advertisements and the "How-to" books. They are correct—up to a certain point. Anyone can indeed learn to draw and paint, compose, write. But can anyone become a *great* painter? A *great* composer? A *great* writer? And if not, why not?

"You're born with it, or you aren't born with it," if it can be said of great musical talent, might presumably be said also of capacities for great achievement in other arts and specialized fields. Proving this is another matter.

In our music talent studies we confined ourselves, remember, to *performing and interpretive* ability, whereby innumerable individuals of all kinds and backgrounds could be compared by exactly the same standards—having them play the same compositions or singing the same songs, and then judging their relative capacities accordingly. But of all the arts, only in music—and only in musical performance and interpretation—is this possible. Had we ventured into musical *composition* we would have been beset with many difficulties. For composing, as we pointed out, is *creative* art, and as in any other creative art—painting, sculpture, writing, etc.—the most important elements are individuality, imagination, inventiveness, emotion, aesthetic judgment and other such intangibles.

What, then, can we say about the inheritance of creative talents? As genetics can deal only with *measurable* traits, there must first be positive criteria for creative achievement, and definite tests for measuring its potentials, before any clear conclusions can be drawn as to the inherited factors. Nevertheless, many popular misconceptions can already be refuted, and much can be said which should

Photograph for this book by M. Lasser, at the Warschauer Haym Solomon Home, New York, September, 1950

A MUSICAL PATRIARCH

The 102-year-old flute player, Isaac Fishberg, shown above with five of his musician sons, is the progenitor of the largest musical pedigree in the United States, if not now in the world: Of twelve living children, six (five sons and a daughter), professional musicians, the others competent amateur musicians; of 37 grandchildren, 15 professional and 4 amateur musicians; and of 60 great-grand- and great-great-grandchildren to date (mostly still very young), several already professional musicians and many more on their way to be. (Many marriages with other musicians through the family line have intensified the "musical inheritance.")

The elder Fishberg (himself son of a violinist), and his children, were born in the Ukraine, Russia. He came to the United States in 1920, most of the others having preceded him, and played professionally until he was 90. (His wife, long dead, was "presumed" to have been musical.)

The sons in the photograph are, left to right, Yascha, Mischa (Mischakoff), Tobias, William and Fishel. Not shown, Nathan ("Arnold Arriga"). Except for William (a non-professional), all are well-known in orchestral and/or concert fields (Mischa being concertmaster for the N.B.C. orchestra under Toscanini).

1920: Samuel Reshevsky, eight-year-old chess prodigy, engaging thirty players simultaneously in a mass exhibition game at Milwaukee (at which the author was present).

(Photo from Bay City Times, courtesy the Chess Review)

1950: Reshevsky, now a top-ranking United States chess master, in a mass-exhibition game at Bay City, Michigan. (See text, p. 380) help you to better understand the presence or absence of various types of talent in yourself or your children.

Governed by such standards as we have, evidence of heredity in creative achievement rests principally on case histories of noted composers, painters, sculptors, writers and other creative artists which show in almost all of them patterns very much like those in the musical performers: the early appearance of talent; its cropping out in all sorts of backgrounds, often spontaneously, with nothing special in the environment to explain it; and its high incidence in certain families and strains. On the first point, it should be noted that while creative talents are usually revealed in childhood (though often unrecognized), it may take many more years for them to ripen than was true of talent for musical performance. Quite definitely, biological and mental maturity is required to a greater degree for creative achievements, and more training and experience also are needed. *A significant fact is that in all history there is no record of a single important piece of creative work done by a pre-adolescent child.*

However, there is enough precocity to impress us in the fact that many composers have turned out notable works when they were still adolescents (as was brought out in the last chapter), that Michelangelo at 18 was already close to being the greatest sculptor of his time, that Shelley, Byron and Keats were publishing brilliant poetry in their late 'teens, and that many great books and paintings have come from individuals in their beginning twenties. With these in mind one might indeed be led to conclude that the seeds for exceptional creative achievement are initially implanted by heredity.

Of the creative talents, that for musical composition gives the most direct evidence of hereditary influence, because of its earlier and more spontaneous onset, and the specific aptitudes involved in it that seem pretty definitely to have a constitutional and familial basis. In painting the evidence is less precise. There are innumerable instances, to be sure, of father-and-son, or brother painters, such as the Bellinis, Fra Filippo Lippi and his son Filippino, the Van Eycks, the Holbeins, the Brueghels, etc., or among contemporaries, the Wyeths, father and son, the Soyer brothers, Isaac, Raphael and Moses (the latter two being twins), and the Albrights, Ivan Le Lorraine and Malvin (also twins). But such histories tell us little, for close contacts and similar training might account in large measure for clusters of painters within given families (though instances are exceedingly rare of where two artists in the same family attained notable distinction).

Nevertheless, there is some evidence that certain capacities making for the "predisposition" toward artistic achievement run in given families in more than ordinary degree. For example, Professor Norman C. Meier of the University of Iowa, studying the backgrounds of hundreds of artists and art students, found in their families, going back for several generations, a much higher than average incidence of individuals with artistic or craftsman ability of one kind or another (woodcarving, toymaking, instrument-making, textile design, jewelry design, etc.). What is implied here is that a certain general type of hereditary endowment (composed of potentialities for various skills, traits and capacities) might run in families, thus providing a *predisposition* toward artistic achievement; that the development of this endowment would depend in part on environmental influences and in part on personal "drives" and inclinations; and that with the same endowment, while some individuals might go into the arts, others might enter entirely different fields (science, business, teaching, etc.) where the creative capacities might yet be put to good use.

But much more research, with dependable tests for specific elements in artistic aptitude, is needed before we can reach positive conclusions regarding the relative rôles played by heredity and environment in producing artists. For the present we might make these theoretical observations regarding the requirements for important achievement in any of the creative arts:

First, a person must have sensitivity, keen perception, imagination, emotion, etc. (We might note that all great creative works, whether in music, literature, drama, painting, sculpture, architecture or terpsichore, embody the same basic principles of composition, form, rhythm, nuances of expression, etc.) These capacities might be considered as resulting from some general kind of hereditary endowment.

Second, one must have the special sensory equipment required for pursuit of a particular art. We already have dealt with the primary musical senses, and have touched on some of the "art-craftsman" capacities. To extend this a bit, the painter must have keen senses of color. But a color-blind person, gifted with the general art capacities, could still become an etcher, a black-and-white artist or a sculptor (although each of these fields might demand certain additional specialized capacities). So, too, we could identify the most important elements in the sensory equipment required for creative writing or any of the other arts. These elements might then in turn be related to special kinds or combinations of genes.

Third, governing a person's achievement in any art will be not only the amount and kind of his artistic equipment, but his "drive," intelligence, personality, temperament and many other aspects of his social makeup and behavior. It is essential to keep in mind that the purely technical equipments, or aptitudes (inherent and acquired), are not the determining factors for the creative arts. Many mediocre composers, painters, writers, etc., have much better "technique" than is possessed by some of the great figures in their fields. (What constitutes "superior technique," however, may be governed by arbitrary and changing standards. On the basis of their "technique" such painters as Van Gogh and Gauguin were classed as hopelessly inferior by their contemporaries, and many modernists of today are equally so scorned by the classicists.) But trying to relate to specific genes such intangibles as do make the great creative artists—"personality," "temperament," etc.—poses our greatest genetic problems (as we shall see in later chapters when we deal in detail with these traits).

And, fourth, there is our old friend, *environment,* with all that it can do to develop, suppress or divert creative capacities. A talent may be all dressed up with no place to go, if it crops out in an environment where no one wants it. Again, under modern conditions, with insistence on specialization, a person with various talents is forced to decide early which talent to cultivate. The wrong choice may lead him to failure where the cultivation of an alternative talent might have brought great success. Few question that environment has stifled many more talents than have ever come to fruition.

Taking all the foregoing points together, we might see, first, that certain combinations of genes, *plus* the required environment running in given families for a time, might produce many talented members; and, second, that if special "artistry" genes of different kinds were present or absent in given individuals of these families, their talents might be expressed in different forms and careers. One member might show special talent for painting, another for writing, another for architecture, or acting, and so on (as can be illustrated by many artistic families, some of whom you yourself may know). But also, and always to be considered, are the personality factors and environmental influences which may cause a talented individual to take to one form of art or another, or to cause him to turn away completely from any of the arts.

The close relationship among the various arts, and the existence of some general basis for aptitude in them, is further indicated by the fact that so many persons—perhaps most—who are talented in one field are usually also talented in other fields. We could fill pages with notable examples, grading down from the most versatile genius of all, Leonardo da Vinci (of whom we shall say more in the next chapter), to the countless multiple-gifted individuals of our own time. To mention just a few, there is Deems Taylor, composer, novelist, and skilled cabinetmaker; Christopher La Farge, playwright, poet, architect, watercolorist; Noel Coward, playwright, song composer, and actor; James Thurber, writer-cartoonist, and Xavier Cugat, dance-orchestra leader and cartoonist (recalling, also, the great singer Caruso who, too, was a talented cartoonist). Author Sinclair Lewis is one of our most gifted mimes. Billy Rose, first a shorthand-writing champion and popular-song writer, then an outstanding theatrical producer, is now also a highly successful popular writer. And Walter Winchell, first a "hoofer" and vaudeville actor, ended up as America's top newspaper columnist. So we could extend the list endlessly, and carry it on to a relationship between the arts and other achievements: Benjamin Franklin, writer, statesman, scientist, inventor; Thomas Jefferson, who was not only all of these, but an architect and a talented violinist as well; or, in our own time, Winston Churchill, statesman and military genius, and also a great writer and a talented painter.

When we turn to such arts as *writing, acting, dancing,* etc., genetic evidence definitely becomes fuzzy. No doubt some special inborn equipment is required for great achievement in each of these fields, but whatever hereditary factors there are appear to be much less specific than those for music or painting. Writers, for instance, might be said to be "born" to a lesser extent than they are made by their environments or themselves.* One can, of course, point to many

* Psychoanalysts have their own theories as to what makes writers, actors, etc. They see the answers not so much in specific talents as in specific *urges*. Dr. Ruth Morris suggests that many creative writers may work from an emotional need, their novels providing a means for "self-analysis," and that Melville, Hawthorne, Charlotte Bronte, Kafka, etc., may have "cured" themselves in this way. In the case of actors, Dr. Otto Fenichel has held that they are motivated by the "basic partial instinct of exhibitionism," with applause giving them "narcissistic satisfaction."

brilliant writing families—such American literary dynasties, for example, as the Jameses, Adamses, and Lowells, or among late-comers, the La Farges, Terhunes and Benets. But assuming that pools of hypothetical "writing" genes may have collected in these families, the strong influences of similar training, education and precedent can hardly be overlooked.

So, too, when in the theater reference is frequently made to a "born actor," something might be made of the fact that there have been whole families of brilliant performers, such as the Booths, the Barrymores (Lionel, Ethel, John, their parents and their uncle, John Drew), and many others. If there are indeed any "acting" genes, the intensive inbreeding in the theatrical profession, more than in any other, would lead to their concentration in given families. But there is also an equally great tendency in this profession for children to be trained or induced to follow in the parents' footsteps. Many chance elements in the theater also confuse the issue with regard to native endowments. The initial requirement of passing a test for "looks" must rule out a great many of those with the greatest ability for acting, while permitting many with mediocre talents to attain success (most noticeably so in the movies).* Here is one of the best examples of how environment may play havoc with hereditary capacities. What would happen to our painting and literature if those who wanted to be artists and writers first had to pass beauty tests?

But all other aspects of achievement in the arts, particularly with regard to the interplay of inherent factors and environment, are dwarfed by comparisons between the sexes. This is a most complicated subject to discuss, and a ticklish one.†

Considering the sexes as two separate groups, the surface facts tell us that one group has been consistently far superior to the other in creative achievement. In the literary arts (novels, drama, poetry),

* Actress Helen Hayes stirred up a controversy when she thus advocated a "weeding-out" process for theatrical aspirants: "There are those whom nature has unfitted for their dreams—girls too broad of beam, men too short or tall . . . those with piano legs . . . and caricatured physiognomies. What on earth makes such youngsters want to be actors?" *(New York Times,* July 3, 1947) In the storm of dissent which followed, Fannie Brice, brilliant comedienne, was reported as commenting that "she won her first dramatic prize in her home town because her 'beam' was the only one among the contestants broad enough to take the entire name of 'Hackensack.'" Others noted that the "weeding" process recommended by Miss Hayes would insure a future of histrionic mediocrity.

† The author has dealt with this subject in great detail in his *Women and Men,* and it is with the background of evidence offered in that book that we here summarize the principal findings.

the critics will tell you that while many women have reached near-greatness, none can as yet be ranked with the greatest of the men. In painting, with large numbers of women now represented, the critics will again say, "There are many fine women artists. There has never yet been a single truly great one." Most puzzling of all, in music, one field in which countless women have been trained for generations, their *creative* efforts have been so negligible (as any musician will testify) that there has never as yet been a single notable symphony, opera, concerto or other truly great piece of music produced by a woman.

How account for this? Making all allowances for the environmental repression of women's capacities (through conditioning, diversion of energies into motherhood and homemaking, lessened opportunity, prejudices, etc.), we cannot ignore the possibility that inherent biological factors might also influence the degree of their creative achievements. Starting with only the difference in their sex chromosomes, we have seen that with respect to a great many traits the same genes work differently in the two sexes: in diseases and defects, physical growth and development, sex organs, biochemical workings and body functioning—the female organism being in many respects superior to that of the male. Might it, therefore, not also be possible for "achievement" genes, if carried by a woman, to work differently and to produce different results than if carried by a man?

A significant point, brought out in the famous Terman studies of gifted children (to which we shall refer again presently), is that where girls and boys start out with the same mental-performance scores, when puberty is reached the girls begin to fall behind in relative achievement, while almost three times as many of the boys continue on to high levels. "Boys not *only* become increasingly more likely than girls to have a high IQ as they advance in age, but they are more likely than girls to retain a high IQ earlier evidenced," Professor Terman tells us. For much of this—even more, for the failure of so many girls and women to convert their capacities into achievement—we can clearly blame environment. Yet the possibility (referred to previously) has been raised by a number of authorities that biological sex differences—including the earlier physical "setting" of girls, and differences in internal functioning—might also have some effect on the *directions* taken by mental development.

If we consider the sex differences in *types* of mental performance at the very earliest ages (brought out in our "IQ" chapter, and revealed even more emphatically in aptitude tests at all later ages), we will see how they have an important bearing on creative achievement. Girls, you recall, show superiority in verbal and language tests and memory, in perception of detail, in "social" tests, and in intuitive responses to and understanding of *people*. Might not this explain why, of all the arts, it is in literature that women achieve their highest excellence? Boys, on the other hand, show marked superiority—more and more as they mature—in mechanical, mathematical and structural tests, and in *abstract* reasoning. *All of these aptitudes play an important part in the planning and execution of complex musical compositions, paintings, sculptured and architectural works, dramas and novels.* Might not this, coupled with the fact that men, biologically, have greater physical drive, do much to explain the male pre-eminence in these fields?

These are questions which can be posed only as theories. Whatever may be the biological evidence offered, we can never ignore the fact that environments for women always and everywhere have been different from those for men, and more likely to repress achievement. Thus, our conclusions must be much as they were with respect to intelligence:

No standards or tests exist by which we can accurately and fairly measure the *inherent capacities* for creative achievement of women in comparison with men; and with little possibility that we can ever fully equalize their environments to permit of such standards or tests, *we may never be able to make any scientific judgments as to whether women as a group are equal to, inferior to, or superior to men in their capacity for high achievement in the arts or any other professions.*

When we move to fields outside the arts—science, medicine, law, business, trades, etc.—and try to analyze the elements for achievement, we find ourselves thinking increasingly in terms of environment rather than of heredity. For while we cannot doubt that there are great differences in inherent capacity which govern the *degree* of achievement within any of the fields mentioned, what sends a given person in the first place into one or another of these professions or occupations is more likely to be a matter of family background, social level or training. For example, the fact that there are families where most of the men have been doctors, lawyers, clergymen or businessmen for several generations might have no more genetic significance than that there are families of house-painters, railroadmen, miners, plumbers or farmers—or where all the women have been housewives.

One must be especially careful, when looking at the upper and lower occupational levels in which a population is stratified, not to conclude that these must represent contrasting groups of "superior" and "inferior" capacity. Some achievement studies in Great Britain have sought to do this very thing, by showing that the small upper-class and professional groups had been supplying the great majority of distinguished men, whereas less than 25 per cent of these had come from the business, laboring and farming classes. But in the United States, it has been shown that 42.6 per cent of the distinguished men have come from these latter classes, and there is every evidence that the percentage will increase. As one indication, a recent study (by William Wance and Richard Butler, 1948) of occupational "inheritance" in four Pennsylvania mining communities shows that with each successive generation more and more of the sons and grandsons of miners have been moving up into higher occupational levels and professions. In the Soviet Union, of course, the overwhelming proportion of present professional men have come from the former "lower" levels.

Even more caution must be used in thinking of people of different races or nationalities as "inheriting" specialized occupational tendencies. One hears it said that Germans have "technical" minds, Jews have "business" minds, Frenchmen "artistic" minds. This is no more valid than saying, from what we see in the United States, that the Chinese have "laundering" or "chop-suey restaurant" minds, the Armenians "rug-peddling" minds, the Norwegians "farming" minds, the Irish "police" minds, etc.

Genetics emphasizes constantly the danger of generalizing about whole peoples or groups, and this is most important with respect to occupations or achievements. What we must confine ourselves to are the individual differences displayed in any group and within any given field, and, as in the arts, we must look for the basic capacities that might go with these differences.

Beginnings in the direction of identifying qualifications for success in many professional fields have been made through a variety of aptitude tests which, together with "intelligence" and "personality" tests are now in use for screening by colleges, industries and the armed services (as vast numbers of young Americans know only too well). But these tests are still too heavily slanted toward acquired knowledge, experience and other conditioned factors to be of much use in getting at the roots of individual capacities, or drawing conclusions regarding anyone's inherited "predisposition" to be outstanding in a given profession.

Mathematical ability, however, is one type of aptitude which does give evidence of being inherited fairly directly, and perhaps simply. For one thing, college records show a high correlation in the mathematics scores of fathers and sons, and of brothers. More significantly, we find phenomenal mathematical ability appearing quite spontaneously in young children (as followers of the "Quiz Kid" programs know), in the same way that musical talent appears. (In fact, certain basic components of mathematical talent and musical talent are closely related.)* Many of the great mathematicians were prodigies, one of the greatest of all, Evariste Galois, having made all his important contributions before he was quite 21, when he was killed in a duel (in 1832). The great Gottfried Liebnitz was another mathematics prodigy, also writing on logic and philosophy when he was 14. Among contemporaries, one of our greatest mathematicians, Dr. Norbert Wiener, was graduated from Tufts at 14, and the ranks of physics (closely allied to higher mathematics) abounds in notables who showed precocity, Dr. J. Robert Oppenheimer, the atomic scientist, and Professor Julian Schwinger of Harvard, being examples.

But while great mathematical ability may lead to high scientific achievement, it can do so only when coupled with creative and other capacities. For a further point is that, again like musical aptitude, mathematical ability may be present independently of other mental powers. Thus, many phenomenal lightning calculators are of mediocre intelligence, their powers arising chiefly from remarkable memories (as was the case with the famed Salo Finkelstein). At the extreme are the *"idiot savants"*—individuals who are feebleminded and can yet perform astounding feats of mental calculation. One such case reported by psychologists in 1945 was of an 11-year-old boy with an IQ of 50, who also had unusual capacities for memorizing and playing musical compositions and for memorizing and spelling words (without knowing their meaning). All this would

* Among the many scientists who also are musicians are Einstein, and the three famed Comptons—Karl, Arthur and Wilson—all college presidents and considered "the three brainiest brothers" in the United States.

suggest that mathematical or arithmetical ability (in a mechanical sense), or some unusual power of memory which makes it possible, is a unitary trait which may be inherited apart from other capacities. Some authorities believe this may be through "qualified" dominant genes, inasmuch as pedigrees are on record of unusual mathematical talent running through as many as five generations.

Chess prodigies offer further examples of a specialized form of mathematical ability and memory which appears to have an hereditary basis. Many of the greatest chess players revealed phenomenal capacities at early ages, among them José Capablanca, Paul Morphy, Rudolph Spielmann, and most recently, Samuel Reshevsky (long national champion and still top-ranking chess player of the United States). Again, as in music, early training is important, for almost every chess master (with the one exception of Akiba Rubinstein) learned to play chess before the age of 10.

The case of Reshevsky has a personal interest for the author, who was starting his career as a "cub" reporter in Milwaukee in 1918 when Reshevsky, then 8 years old and newly arrived from Poland, came to the city on a nationwide exhibition-match tour. The author was sent to interview the prodigy at a private home where he was being lodged. Loud outcries came from the rear yard. Investigation revealed a frail, undersized youngster shouting at some neighbor lads in a language unintelligible to them that he was "*The* great chess player." His adversaries, totally unimpressed, were about to commit *lèse-majesté* when a timely rescue intervened. In other words, *the prodigy appeared to be no different from any other small boy.* Yet, that night, we saw him suavely and single-handedly playing a simultaneous match with thirty adult and expert chess players, moving with bewildering swiftness from board to board, and in short order defeating all but two, who were declared tied because little Sammy was getting sleepy. (In subsequent years Reshevsky tried to fulfill his real ambition of becoming a rabbi, but after some training toward that end, he dropped out, and later became an accountant. At this writing his principal achievement continues to be chess virtuosity.)

The story is not untypical, for very few of the great chess masters have been reported as otherwise distinguished. Apart from the fact that chess virtuosity requires constant application and specialization toward this end, it appears to involve capacities unrelated to other forms of achievement. Thus, Edward D. Lasker, himself a chess virtuoso, reported (1949) that psychological studies of a dozen leading chess masters revealed unusual memory only for chess positions, and no ability to think faster than average persons in other respects. The only distinctive capacities identified were those for objective and abstract thinking, highly disciplined wills and powers of concentration, good nerves, self-control and self-confidence.

As in chess, unusual and special powers of memory may also be the principal explanation for the phenomenal scholarship of some children. Thus, another prodigy of the author's acquaintance, a young miss whose IQ at 12 went so high "it practically burst the thermometer," had not only a remarkable memory, but the ability to "see in chunks" (as she put it)—to read not by word or phrase but by whole paragraphs at a time. The two gifts in combination enabled her to take her studies, and her passage through grade school, high school and college, in kangaroo leaps, but that's about all. Once through with her education she became a cashier, and today is a bright, but not outstanding wife, mother and homemaker.

The foregoing cases indicate that in many prodigies only *part* of the mentality may be prematurely developed. A serious mistake, therefore, is to assume that the child has the adult intelligence that can come only with full biological and social maturity. By overlooking this, and trying to force a prodigy into levels to which he is not adjusted, great harm can be done.

One of the saddest examples was William James Sidis, son of a famed Harvard psychologist. At the age of 3 young William could read and write; in six months he completed a seven-year public school course; at 6 he produced a treatise on anatomy; at 8, a new table of logarithms; at 14, he lectured at Harvard on the "fourth dimension." And then, at 20, he took the road to obscurity, and in 1944, an unemployed clerk, died at the age of 46, of a brain hemorrhage. Almost his last recorded words, in explaining his failure, were, "You know, I was born on April Fool's day."

The case of Sidis may have been pathological, and an exception, for, as we've seen, many prodigies have gone on to great success and happiness. Nonetheless, the fact that forced development of an exceptional child may lead to tragedy is being increasingly impressed on parents and educators. Recognizing that while prodigy children may have certain unusual capacities, they may yet be only average in other respects, the tendency now is not to train them as superhuman freaks, but to keep them at grade levels with children of their own age (in special "high IQ" classes, if possible), while providing them with extra outlets for their mental energies. How well this policy has worked out in recent decades is shown by the famous Terman studies of a large group of gifted children and their subsequent careers.

Starting in 1921 with close to 1,500 California boys and girls whose IQs averaged 150 (going up in some cases to 200), Professor Lewis M. Terman and his associates kept constant check on them, and twenty-five years later were able to report what had happened to the group. An unusually high percentage had gone through college and received Ph.D.s, (five times the college average for men, eight times for women); almost half had gotten into professional fields, many others were embarked on successful business careers, and some had already achieved national distinction. But emphasizing that something more than a high IQ is needed for success a considerable number of the originally gifted children were poor in later scholarship or had been flunked out in college, and some even ended up as only semi-skilled laborers. Thus, the study concluded that "intellect and achievement are far from perfectly correlated."

Are prodigies usually sickly, scrawny, squint-eyed, neurotic little kids with bulging foreheads but no bulging muscles? That was another long-popular notion blasted by the Terman studies. When originally examined, those in the gifted group were found to be superior in health and physique to average children, and taller and heavier for their age. (This has since been shown to be generally true of higher IQ children, and is considered as reflecting the fact, brought out in our "IQ" chapter, that they come, as a rule from more favored homes.) Twenty-five years later, as adults, the Terman "gifted" group were found to have retained their initial superiority in physical well-being, and what is more, they were fully as well-adjusted emotionally, psychologically, maritally and socially as average persons, with the incidence of alcoholism or serious personality disorders among them being considerably less than for the general population. Still another interesting point, not unexpected, was that the offspring of the gifted group were more than ordinarily bright—their 384 children up to that time having an average IQ of 127.7. While this was well below the original average of the *one* set of parents, it followed the established principle (Galton's law of "filial regression") that children of superior parents tend to move backward toward the norm, in part because of mixed matings, and in part because if any combinations of "superior" genes were involved, there would be a lessened likelihood of their coming together again in a child.

We have gone lightly on the matter of heredity, but it is well to note that Professor Terman and others who have worked with gifted children and prodigies are convinced that superior mental traits must be grounded, primarily, in superior hereditary endowment. To paraphrase Professor Terman's words, prodigies do not have any uncanny powers that average persons lack, but merely have a better share of the powers, just as morons have a smaller share. (Specifically, he believes the greatest advantages of prodigies are their capacities for concentration and thoroughness, quickness of mind [in getting points and memorizing], curiosity and inventiveness, self-criticism, initiative and persistence.) Or, to quote Professor Irving Lorge of Columbia University, "Superior intellectual ability is not a miracle. It is as natural as superiority in height or weight. Basically it is genetically constituted, but what the superior individual will do with his intellect will certainly be conditioned to a large degree by his environment and education."

When we sum up our principal points about gifted children and prodigies, we may see that much confusion has resulted from thinking of them as of one type, whereas, actually, they are of a variety of distinct types:

(1) The *"false"* prodigy, who has no extraordinary mental equipment, but because of intensive early training by overzealous parents becomes a "mental athlete" who peters out later.

(2) The *"premature"* prodigy, whose over-all mental equipment, while not basically superior, is merely speeded up in development (perhaps *biologically*), somewhat in the way that some children achieve early puberty, so that he is superior mentally to other children only for a time, until his development stops and he levels off as merely an average individual.

(3) The *"limited"* prodigy, who is endowed with only one or two special inherited capacities, such as a remarkable memory or mathematical ability, which may enable him to become a lightning calculator, an extraordinary chess player or a phenomenal student, but not much else.

(4) The *"true"* prodigy, born with a brain exceptional in many ways, which, from childhood on, gives him superiority over other individuals and, in combination with the right environment, train-

ing, personality, etc., predisposes him to great achievement. In this latter class are all the many prodigies who "made good" brilliantly in innumerable ways. Pages could be filled with their names: Michelangelo, Benjamin Franklin, Sir William Osler, Charles Darwin, Disraeli; the Mozarts, Handels, Beethovens and all the other musical prodigies we dealt with; or in recent times, in addition to those previously mentioned, the late Nicholas Murray Butler, Pablo Picasso, the late Rabbi Joshua Liebman (author of *Peace of Mind*), and many, many others.

So if you have a prodigy in your home, or think you have, it is well to be clear as to just what kind of prodigy you are dealing with. It is also important to know that a child does not have to be a prodigy to be destined for greatness. This we shall see as we go on, now, to more detailed consideration of those individuals—some prodigies, some not—who reached the very topmost rungs of human achievement.

CHAPTER 36

GENIUS

THE most remarkable letter of application for a job ever written came to an Italian duke late in the fifteen century. It was from a young man who claimed that he not only was a wizard at devising and making every conceivable instrument of war—mortars, field-pieces, siege apparatus, portable bridges and numerous contraptions hitherto unknown—but also:

". . . In time of peace, I could equal any other as regards works in architecture . . . sculpture . . . and painting."

Conceit? No. The job applicant was grossly understating his talents. He also was *a musician, poet, mathematician, and scientist* who in the years ahead would prove himself to be far in advance of his times as an *anatomist, botanist, geometrician, geologist, sanitary engineer and one of the most prodigious inventors the world has ever known;* and to cap it all, he would paint "The Last Supper" and the "Mona Lisa," among many other masterpieces.

This was Leonardo da Vinci, ". . . the most resplendent figure in the human race . . . the genius of geniuses . . . a legend in his own lifetime . . . a living miracle."

In Leonardo's life and career we could sum up almost everything brought out in preceding discussions on the rôle of heredity in human achievement. Whatever might be said of the influence of other factors, here was a man who beyond all question was *born* with the seeds of greatness in him.

The illegitimate son of a peasant girl and an unimportant Florentine notary, Leonardo began as a child to display dazzling genius in art, music and mathematics. At 13 he was apprenticed to an artist, but most of his special talents he developed by himself, for in many of the fields in which he worked there was no one to teach him: He was the *first.* Look in your encyclopedia, or go to your library and read Leonardo's fantastic history. You will be hard put to explain him in terms of environment.

Or dip into the story of his contemporary, Michelangelo, who flashed out of a petty and decadent family which, baffled by his prodigy-talents, tried to turn him into *anything but* an artist and sculptor—then regarded as "low" occupations. Here, too, was a man with the seeds of greatness so potent within him that by the time he had barely reached manhood he was already a towering figure in the world of art.

Then there was Shakespeare, who came into the world the very year that Michelangelo was leaving it. What parental influences, what "early conditioning," what schooling can claim credit for his incredible achievements? And so with many geniuses in other fields —Plato, Sophocles, Spinoza, Newton, Lincoln, Edison and the few score more of similar caliber—who rose seemingly out of nowhere to the highest points in the human firmament.

But we no longer need to look upon these individuals as supernatural or inexplicable phenomena. We can find a reasonably simple explanation in the facts already brought out: that geniuses in all probability are "merely" persons endowed with rare and unusual combinations of "superior" genes. If, as was indicated, certain genes can produce various degrees and types of mental capacity, talent and aptitude, then the highest forms of these genes, in multiple combinations, should produce increasingly greater and more complex capacities. What geniuses have, to use a popular American phrase, is "the mostest of the bestest." The card player, thinking of genes as cards, might call the "genius hand" a "grand slam" in bridge, or a "royal flush" in poker. Or in another popular sense, one might say that the genius has "hit the genetic jackpot." But in neither cards nor in any other game of chance is there such an infinite variety of combinations possible as with human genes—nor is there anything to correspond to all the environmental influences that can bear upon the "playing" of a "genius hand" once it is drawn by an individual.

However, the analogy with cards can prove useful in further clearing up the mystery of why genius appears so suddenly and then fails to reappear again in the same family. It may be chiefly a matter of shuffling and reshuffling of genes, which follows the same principle as in other inherited traits. In Leonardo's case, we might assume that in each of the packs of genes carried by his two undistinguished parents there were parts of the "genius" combinations, ineffectual by themselves; the shuffle in the flash of Leonardo's conception brought together all the required genes; and in subsequent reshufflings never did this happen again. Leonardo did not marry (he had little interest in women and spurned the very thought of fatherhood), but even if he had had children, he could have given to any one only half of his genes, and his own combination could not have been duplicated. As it was, the other da Vincis, who had come from obscurity, went back to obscurity. Early in this century a genealogist discovered in the Florentine hills a direct descendant of one of Leonardo's half-brothers. He was a peasant, undistinguished by aught save his name: Leonardo da Vinci.

So with Shakespeare or any other great genius, we can understand now why history gives us no record of any two similarly exalted individuals following each other in the same family. Yes, we have had successions of highly gifted relatives, in many fields, particularly music, as we've seen, but these seem clearly to involve capacities which require simpler gene combinations. But the one-in-many-million (or billion) combination of special genes—*and other special circumstances*—needed to make a Shakespeare or Leonardo are far too complex to be so easily repeated.

In including "special circumstances" we have taken it for granted that wherever we speak of the rôle of heredity in genius we always have in mind the many influences of environment. Indeed, the more complex the genetic mechanism, the more likely it is to be governed in its expression by environmental factors. Thus, we need hardly point out that the presence of the requisite combination of "superior" genes would not insure the flowering of a genius. We have no way of knowing how many *potentially* great geniuses were suppressed in the world's history, or how many are being suppressed today, by adverse circumstances. But we can easily guess that they've been vastly more numerous than those who have managed to fulfill themselves.

One type of genius which is certainly dependent on special circumstances, perhaps more than any other, is that called "genius for leadership." In fact, from what was brought out in our discussion of leadership in the last chapter, and the difficulty of associating it with any direct genetic influences, there is doubt whether we should place men whose claim to fame lay only in their being powerful leaders, in the same category with creative geniuses. The talents of a Leonardo, a Beethoven, a Shakespeare could have asserted themselves in any time or place. But what made it possible for most great military or political leaders—including Caesar, Alexander or Napoleon—to rise to tremendous heights could have been only very special historical environments.

Even when we confine ourselves to "true" geniuses, it should be emphasized that what is commonly meant by a "favorable" or "unfavorable" environment may not be applicable to them. At least, the popular theory has long been that geniuses *have* to be a little "queer," and therefore flower best under influences that are not entirely "normal" or "healthy."

Going far back, Plato believed there were two kinds of "delirium," "ordinary insanity," and "the God-given spiritual exhalation which produces poets, inventors and prophets." About 50 A.D. Seneca said, "There is no great genius without a tincture of madness." And in the seventeenth century, John Dryden wrote the famous lines,

"Great wits are sure to madness near allied,
And thin partitions do their bounds divide."

Such generalizations by philosophers and poets of pre-scientific days might be passed over lightly were it not that during the past half-century many psychologists have claimed that genius and abnormality really do go together as a rule, or at least, that a perfectly "normal" environment is not the best one for a genius. In an extensive review of many studies in support of this theory (which they themselves are inclined to question), Drs. Anne Anastasi and John P. Foley, Jr., present long lists compiled by various authorities of geniuses or near-geniuses reported as "queer" in one way or another. We'll give just a few from the clinical roll-call:

Reputedly suffering from some form of insanity or emotional instability were Socrates, Sappho, Marlowe, Ben Jonson, Bunyan, Swift, Kant, Molière, Baudelaire, Pope, Nietzsche, Schopenhauer, Goethe, Goldsmith, Cowper, Byron, Scott, Coldridge, De Quincey, Southey, Shelley, Emerson, Poe, Victor Hugo, Tolstoy and Bismarck; Wagner and Smetana among many other musicians; and among artists, Leonardo, Tintoretto, Botticelli, Cellini, Blake, Landseer, Turner, Paul Veronese, Raphael, Dürer, Vandyck, Watteau, Van Gogh, Rousseau, Modigliani—on to numerous contemporary notables (whose names we'd better not mention). Reported as epileptics—Mohammed, Paul of Tarsus, Julius Caesar, Francis of Assisi, Alfred the Great, Peter the Great, Napoleon I, Dostoevsky. And so into other classifications, with all those who were physically deformed, diseased, degenerate, sexually abnormal and what not.

But impressive as such lists might seem at first glance, one must not forget that long lists also could be made of great men and geniuses who were *not* "abnormal" mentally or physically: Washington, Franklin, Jefferson and Lincoln, Disraeli, Gladstone and Winston Churchill; Justices Marshall, Oliver Wendell Holmes, Brandeis and Cardozo; Darwin and Einstein; George Bernard Shaw, Sigmund Freud, Thomas Mann, Picasso, Toscanini—a "normal" list which could be extended to many pages. Nor need we omit from this list President Franklin D. Roosevelt, for despite the emphasis placed on his physical handicap by some of his bitter opponents, he was already well on the way to political eminence, and at the same time was an unusually healthy and athletic individual before infantile paralysis struck him at the age of 39. There is certainly no evidence that such genius as he manifested thereafter was in any measure to be credited to his physical disability.

Because the lives of outstanding men have always been subjected to much closer scrutiny than those of ordinary persons, there naturally would be a tendency to exaggerate their peculiarities. Also, there undoubtedly has always been what we may term the "sour grapes" attitude of less gifted humans—the wish to explain achievement far beyond them as due to something morbid and undesirable. Thus, many early scientists were looked upon as sorcerers, and many geniuses were hounded or even executed because their apparently "supernatural" deeds were attributed to evil and sinister sources. Today the tendency is to regard anyone who does something startlingly new—for instance, the extreme modernists in art, literature or music—as merely "crazy." But as Dr. B. Freedman stated it: "The insanity of one age has often proved to be the genius of its successor."

For many other reasons the estimates or opinions regarding abnormality among geniuses—most of whom lived long before there was any accurate knowledge in this field—are scientifically open to question. Suppose, for instance, that such and such numbers of geniuses *were* epileptic, crippled, tuberculous, syphilitic, etc.: What meaning could this have without knowledge of what percentages of average persons at their time were similarly afflicted? In the case of the mental and nervous conditions, particularly, when we consider that accurate diagnoses were hardly made before half a century ago, "psychiatric" judgments with respect to geniuses of the past must be heavily discounted. So even if a certain proportion of them were unbalanced, it would not be surprising in view of what we now know of the high incidence of insanity and nervous disorders in the population at large.

Nevertheless, various authorities have clung to the belief that abnormality among geniuses was and is out of all proportion to the general averages, and have offered theories as to why this should be. From the standpoint of genetics, we cannot avoid going into this at some length because the possibility is raised that "genius" genes in many individuals may be dependent for their full expression either on certain additional genes for "abnormality" or, as we said before, on certain abnormal influences in the environment (internal or external).

The German authority, Lange-Eichbaum (who estimated that only 10 per cent of the world's geniuses could have been considered normal and "healthy"), wrote, "Almost everywhere, and especially in the subjective fields of imaginative writing, religion and music, gifted 'insanity' gains the victory over simple, healthy talent. . . . The psycho-pathological is an excellent pacemaker for talent. . . . This does not signify that genius is itself 'insane,' but that the mentally disordered person is more likely than the sane person to become famous and to be elevated to the ranks of genius."

We could quote from many other treatises; "Men who are considered 'balanced' cannot produce great works" . . . "Insanity tends to stimulate 'creative talent'" . . . "The schizoid disposition is a necessary condition for artistic genius" . . . "Psychosis releases latent creative powers, frees one of inhibition," etc. Even the conservative late Dr. Abraham Myerson, one of the greatest psychiatrists, seemed to have inclined toward these beliefs. Following a study (1941) of twenty brilliant families of New England which produced United States presidents, Supreme Court justices, governors, philosophers, writers, and many other notables, he said they "teemed with manic-depressive psychoses," which he believed were largely inherited and intensified by a high degree of intermarriage. His theory was that the disease, in which the individual swings from elation to despair, may have helped to stimulate energy and drive.

Another noted psychiatrist, Dr. Nolan D. C. Lewis, has held that while insanity need not be a concomitant of genius, some kind of neuroses may be. He was quoted as saying (1940) that "all great works in the world are the doings of neurotics," and, "if a psychiatrist wants to do his bit for civilization, he should help men of talent to stay neurotic." It was on this ground that Dr. Lewis refused to treat a well-known woman novelist, bearing in mind some previous experiences. In one case, he reported, "a famous pianist came to me and asked to be treated for his trouble. I warned him, but he begged me to go ahead. Well, I have cured him, but he no longer is an artist of the piano. He is a fine mathematician." Similarly, Dr. Lewis said he cured a painter who subsequently became a photographer.

On the other side of the argument, many psychoanalysts, among them the late Dr. A. A. Brill, have maintained that creative persons who have been "cured," through analysis, of extreme neuroses or conflicts, have gone on to even greater achievement. We might also refer to the Terman studies dealt with in the last chapter, with their conclusions that the 1,500 highly gifted individuals who were studied were fully as well-balanced as average persons, in addition to being superior in health. But we must note that while the members of this large group were very high in their IQs, and superior in general achievement, there was none among them as yet identified as a true "genius."

(Here is a good place to emphasize again the important distinction between the term "genius" as technically applied in intelligence-test parlance to an individual with a very high IQ, and *"genius"* as referring to the extraordinarily rare individuals we have been discussing. One in a hundred persons may have an IQ of 140 or over, and one in a thousand an IQ of 180. But the true "genius," in whom high intelligence is only one of the components, appears only once among millions.)

Another theory, that geniuses tend to be short-lived, has been pretty well refuted. Undue attention has been given to the geniuses who died young, while ignoring the many long-lived ones, such as Michelangelo, Titian, Rubens, Goethe, Newton, Sibelius, Shaw, etc. A recent investigation (1948) by Dr. R. E. G. Armattoe, British biologist, into the lives of 12,000 geniuses or near-geniuses, produced convincing evidence that the old assumption was quite false.

On the whole, however, it is not inconsistent with accepted psychological theory that certain kinds of defectiveness, abnormality or "inner conflict" may act as special stimuli to persons with genius capacity. We know that the person who cannot easily "belong"—who during the formative years is sickly or physically handicapped and unable to compete on equal terms with others, or who is socially "rejected," or who in any way is "peculiar" or is so considered—may, if gifted, understandably develop a more intense drive to make a place for himself through distinctive work. This is what psychologists call "compensation." Lack of usual or "normal" outlets for the emotions or sexual impulses may further cause an individual to act, think and work differently from others, especially in creative directions. In turn, the greater and more unusual his achievements, the more the individual would be set apart from others, the greater would be the social and psychological pressures upon him, and the more likely he would be to develop eccentricities or even to crack up. Thus, it would hardly be surprising if a high proportion of geniuses did indeed turn out to be "queer'" by average standards, even if they didn't start out that way, and despite there being no evidence that "queerness" genes go with "genius" genes.

If you've said, "I wouldn't want *my* child to be a genius," it may have had more meaning with respect to the past than it has today. For that geniuses don't *have* to be queer, and need in no sense be regarded as "freaks," is being proved more and more by many great personages of our own time who stand the best chance of being considered geniuses by posterity—such men in the "normal" category as we've previously mentioned, or as you yourself could easily think of. Further, as the world becomes more understanding of men of genius caliber, and it becomes easier for them to lead comparatively normal lives, there undoubtedly will be increasingly less association between genius and "abnormality." Perhaps we may not see again such highly versatile or spectacular geniuses as those of the Leonardo type, for this is an age of specialization, and it is much harder for a man to achieve mastery in many fields at once than it was in earlier centuries. But what we can expect is that in every field, with increasing education and opportunities, there will be more and more of those with genius capacity who will have a chance to fulfill themselves and to make their contributions. One thing of which there is no doubt is that genius need not be as unique as it has been, for all authorities are convinced that the seeds, or "genes" for genius, are in abundance among all classes and all peoples, and that if we properly cultivate the soil for them—

not an "unhealthy" soil, but a healthy social environment—a bumper crop of geniuses will result.

If we pause now to summarize our evidence regarding intelligence, aptitudes and talents, we will find that with all the complexities there is nonetheless a pattern for achievement essentially like that for other human traits we've dealt with: Degrees of "susceptibility" or "resistance" to achievement of various kinds undoubtedly are inherited by different individuals, everything else being equal. At the lowest extreme are those persons completely resistant to any outstanding achievement in any environment, because of inferior mental equipment. At the highest extreme are those started off with combinations of special and superior endowments which make them susceptible to very high forms of varied achievement, given any reasonable break by environment. Between these extremes, in gradations up and down, are the great mass of people with moderate degrees of capacity for or "susceptibility" to many forms of achievement, dependent on their environments, yet limited by various genetic lacks with respect to high achievement in special fields. Finally, while in all three groups the interplay with environment is of vital importance, its relative influence is not always the same, and, as we've seen, what constitutes a "favorable" or "unfavorable" environment may vary greatly for different individuals.

Most of us can never hope to be geniuses in any environment, and many of us may not want to be. But there is plenty of work of all kinds to be done in the world, and no one can say, in the long run, which individuals are *genetically* the most important. You may be an obscure woman, or an obscure man, and yet you may be carrying genes which, in combination with those of your mate, may result in a child destined for greatness. So it was with the parents of Shakespeare, Lincoln, Franklin and most other geniuses. What the final score on your genetic contribution to the world's advancement may be can be told only through your children, and theirs, and theirs.

CHAPTER 37

BEHAVIOR

You say, "I did that instinctively," or "I took an *instinctive* dislike to that person," or "My *instincts* told me–," etc.

Are you right? Are there really inborn "behavior wheels" in you and other people, geared by heredity to produce instinctive actions and reactions?

The question has been hotly debated by psychologists. Some (under the influence of the old "behaviorist" school which began to flourish in the twenties) have condemned the very word "instinct," refusing even to concede that lower animals have instincts. "Conditioned reflexes," "stimuli," "drives," "impulses"–yes, these are approved and respectable terms to account for lower animal behavior. As for "instinctive" human behavior–well! Psychology students who so much as mentioned "human instincts" to certain professors would be almost kissing goodbye to their chances for a Ph.D.

But there's been a change in the psychological atmosphere. A mass of evidence from numerous experiments and studies has shown that there really are specific patterns of behavior in each series which arise spontaneously, independent of training, and which can be explained in no other way except as instinctive. To make it official, a group of the nation's top experimental psychologists,* meeting at Princeton in 1947, turned their backs on the die-hard "behaviorists" and formally restored the word "instinct" to good standing. Further, they agreed that if there are instincts in other animals, it is inconceivable that human beings would not also have some. (One authority went so far as to suggest that "human nature is nine-tenths inborn and one-tenth acquired"–a guess which can't ever be proved scientifically one way or another.)

* The authorities included Drs. Leonard Carmichael of Tufts, Karl S. Lashley of Harvard, Frank A. Beach of Yale, Clifford T. Morgan of Johns Hopkins, W. S. Hunter of Brown and Calvin P. Stone of Stanford.

Whatever may be the instinct at work in human beings, one clear fact is that their acts and impulses are greatly influenced by countless environmental factors and the accumulated results of thousands of years of human experience. Each generation derives something from the behavior of the preceding one, each individual from the behavior of those who train and surround him. So what you often think of as an "instinctive" act or feeling may be merely the subconscious clicking together of a series of *acquired* responses.

The facts are quite different for lower animals. Birds, mammals, fish and insects of each species today display the same instinctive behavior patterns—the same ways of building nests or shelters, feeding, fighting, mating, taking care of their young—as did their ancestors ages and ages ago. Experience or training isn't essential (although in some of the higher mammals, such as apes, the instinctive behavior patterns for mating, caring for young, etc., may improve with the individual's practice). But for the most part all the important equipment for the lower animal's existence is inborn. Without ever seeing other examples or blueprints, beavers construct dams, birds build their nests, bees their combs, spiders their webs, with almost perfect results at the first try, and each species spontaneously displays many other complex patterns of behavior. Nor does the lower animal know what it's doing, or why. A tame squirrel, reared in a house by humans, will put nuts behind the legs of a sofa and go through all the motions of burying them. A dog, before lying down on a carpet, may turn around several times as if feeling the ground for rough spots, or flattening the grass to make a good bed. A young starling will go through the motions of fly catching and killing although he has never seen a fly before.

How are such patterns of behavior produced? In general, one might say by a series of "stimuli" and "reflexes," giving rise to a sequence of acts with the end result in similar situations much the same for members of a given species. What might be considered *inborn* is not a whole pattern of behavior as such, but the *tendencies* to respond in specific ways to specific stimuli.

Were the foregoing true of human beings, we could take the case of a fireman in a firehouse, awakened in the middle of a night by a gong and jumping out of bed, pulling on his clothing and boots, sliding down a brass pole, etc. The gong is the initial stimulus which arouses him to action. The presence and sight of his clothing and boots are further stimuli, leading to the "reflexes" of putting them on. The sight of the pole is still another stimulus, causing him to run to it and slide down. Were the tendencies to such a pattern of behavior inherited *rather than trained,* one would expect that the son of a fireman, who had never known his father nor anything about a fireman's routine, would nonetheless react to the whole situation in the same way: If placed in a firehouse and awakened by a gong, he would automatically go through exactly the same sequence of acts; or, even if he were not in a firehouse, he would go through motions representing these acts.

In a not too dissimilar way, then, this may describe the workings of instincts in lower animals, with the "gong" and the other firehouse influences replaced by a variety of stimuli, external and internal, for different reflexes and reactions. Outside stimuli may be conveyed through the senses—a kitten seeing a dog for the first time, a rooster meeting another rooster, birds hearing a loud noise, wolf smelling sheep, bears feeling the approach of cold weather, etc. Internal stimuli may come through hormonal action, various chemical states of the body, hunger, thirst, fatigue, etc. In the case of behavior patterns which follow cycles, such as mating, reproduction, nest-building, caring for young, etc., the stimuli and their subsequent reflexes may be governed by the production of certain hormones at given times, and may also be influenced by climate and various other external influences.

Technically, it is more accurate to speak of instincts as *potentialities* for the development and expression of various forms of behavior, rather than as inevitable determinants of such behavior. This conclusion follows from innumerable laboratory experiments showing how behavior tendencies of lower animals can be much modified, repressed or distorted by training or individual experiences, and how a variety of "reflexes" can be conditioned almost any which way. And, of course in our domestic animals—cats, dogs, horses, etc.—and in circus animals, we have constant proof of what training can do to shape behavior away from "natural" tendencies. (See what happens to "natural instincts" when a cat learns to snuggle up against a dog, or a lion refrains from snapping off its trainer's head when put between its jaws!) Nevertheless, the fact that under natural, or normal conditions, animals of each species, widely separated and in different environments, act consistently in much the same way, would indicate that their basic behavior patterns are governed by heredity.

So we ask: *Are there in human beings, too, genetically controlled stimuli and reflexes which lead to instinctive behavior patterns?* That there certainly are—at least in the first months and years—has been established in the brilliant observations by Dr. Arnold Gesell and his associates at the Yale Clinic. Starting with a large group of infants whose development was followed from birth onward, they have shown that human behavior evolves in detailed and specific patterns as definitely as does the behavior-development of fledglings, kittens, puppies or the young of any other species. Further, observations of the very youngest prematurely born human infants (supplementing studies of behavior in fetuses of lower animals) leave no doubt that months before birth the child is already equipped with behavior patterns to fit many situations.

Proceeding with later stages, the Gesell studies show that just as there is an hereditary "time-clock" mechanism which sets the approximate normal time at which a child cuts his first teeth (and each tooth in turn), and at which various bones harden successively, there is also a genetic "time clock" which initiates the onset of different kinds of behavior, physical and psychological: The time at which the child begins to turn over, sit up, grab things, talk, walk, etc. At approximately 16 weeks, a baby bubbles, coos, chuckles; at 28 weeks, he crows; at 40 weeks, he understands, "No! No!" Given blocks at 4 weeks the infant looks at a block; at 24 weeks he picks one up; at 29 weeks he bangs blocks together; at 18 months he builds a small tower, etc. So with walking, talking and many other complicated forms of behavior.

These behavior "norms" and the sequence in which they occur have been found to hold true for babies in the most diverse homes and of all races. Of course, no two babies behave in exactly the same way, as no mother need be told. There obviously must be inherited factors at work to account for some of the individual differences. (Dr. Gesell found in infant identical twins an almost uncanny degree of identity in the details of postural attitude, hand movements and mechanism of grasp.) It is equally certain that environmental factors also account for differences. But while the child's behavior can be trained in various directions, Dr. Gesell emphasizes that "all educability is dependent upon innate capacities." To quote him further:

"Every child has a unique pattern of growth which is the basis of his individuality and of his ability to profit by experience. Growth can be guided, but it cannot be imparted by environment or education. The child's growth potentials are part of his constitution, and he is fortunate if he is born with a favorable equipment of genes, because he must do his own growing."

It is when a child's behavior development departs markedly from the pattern for each stage that the "norms" have their real importance, providing clues to abnormality, if the behavior is greatly retarded, or to exceptional capacity, if the child is unusually advanced. According to Dr. Gesell, "It may be possible to diagnose as early as the first year nearly all cases of mental defect, brain injury, sensory and muscular defects and various serious personality deviations; whether the developmental outlook for the child is favorable, highly favorable or unfavorable. Further, examinations in infancy, and observations during the preschool years, may reveal various forms of giftedness, temperamental qualities, individual modes of growth and learning, and liabilities and assets in emotional makeup."

The foregoing facts and opinions strike hard at the theory of the extreme "behaviorists," that human behavior collectively and individually is almost entirely a matter of "conditioning," and that any child could be caused to develop almost any which way, at will, through training. It is partly in support of this idea that so much credence was given at various times to stories of babies or children "reared by wild animals," and as a result, acting like these lower animals. Almost every one of these stories has been exploded by subsequent investigation.

There was the "Baboon Boy," allegedly found in 1903 in South Africa, "living with a troup of baboons, exhibiting baboon mannerisms." Eventually it came out that he had been merely a mental case. Then, some years ago there was all the to-do about the two little "Wolf Girls" of India, "Kamala" and "Amala," reported as having been reared by a she-wolf after their mother had abandoned them, and when found, "running on all fours, unable to stand upright, seeing in the dark, drinking by lapping with long tongues, howling at night, eating live raw chickens," etc. Well, as skeptical Dr. Wayne Dennis told a meeting of psychologists in 1941, the symptoms described for the girls were completely consistent with the behavior of some idiots, and there was thus much to suggest that the story of "Kamala" and "Amala" was in the same dubious category as a dozen other reported cases of "wolf children" which have come out of India (where the myth of children reared by lower animals is very widespread).

Most recently, in 1946, came the "Gazelle Boy," a "wild Arab lad grazing and living with a herd of gazelles in the Syrian desert, who fled from hunters at the phenomenal speed of 50 miles an hour." (? ? ! !) Before long, truth caught up with the "human gazelle." Once more, the explanation was "a mental defective" who had briefly strayed from his parents, and who may or may not have been chasing gazelles. As for the "phenomenal speed," a magazine writer, Michael Stern, who subsequently visited the boy's village, said he ran a foot race with "the human gazelle" and left him far behind!

Most questionable, of course, is whether any baby could survive for long under the care and conditions of a wild animal—let alone whether any lower animal would extend this loving care for the years required before a child could shift for itself.* (A more likely guess would be that the only love a wolf would have for a tender young human would be in the form of steaks and chops.) The more serious point of these observations is that immature human beings require a much longer period of dependency from birth to maturity, and more special care, than do the young of any other animals. (Closest to us in this respect are the higher apes, who do not mature until they are almost 9 years old.) This prolonged dependency of young human beings provides, in turn, a greater opportunity for the shaping of their lives by their elders and their environments. Thus, whatever may be the inherited behavior tendencies with which any child starts off, it becomes increasingly difficult with each later stage of development to disentangle the "natural" or "instinctive" elements of his behavior from those which have been acquired.

We should note here, however, that if the behavior of human beings is much more malleable than that of other animals, this, too, is not unrelated to their hereditary equipment. For another very important point is that heredity in large measure governs the capacity for *modification* of behavior traits in each species. As an example, what makes it easier to train dogs than cats, or most other animals, is the possession by dogs of a greater variety and flexibility of inborn tendencies which can be directed, through training, into various specific patterns of reaction. This modifiability, or plasticity,

* Wolves normally nurse their young for about seven weeks, whereas under primitive conditions children have to be nursed two to three years to survive.

of behavior development, increases in going up the evolutionary scale from the lowest to the highest animals—to apes, and finally to humans. (For an analogy in musical terms, where insects might have a behavior-potential range of one octave, human beings would have that of a symphony orchestra.) Thus, if the behavior of human beings can be so greatly shaped by environment, it is primarily because their genetic makeup offers so wide a range for development.

Hardest to analyze in terms of basic factors is the *social behavior* of human beings—the behavior of individuals toward others. Here we must begin again with lower animals and the fact that each species is equipped with a large variety of social drives or instincts. These dictate, among other things, sexual behavior, parental behavior, collective behavior (formation into flocks, herds, colonies, tribes, etc.) and the relationships of individuals within their groups. All of these types of behavior in lower animals can be linked quite easily with biological factors, for the most part genetically controlled. It has been shown repeatedly in experiments, for instance, that the sexual behavior of lower animals can be much modified by a mere shift in the balance and amounts of their "male" and "female" hormones; that a virgin mouse, indifferent to young mice, can be made to develop a strong maternal feeling through injections of a certain pituitary hormone; or that the behavior and relationships of an animal toward others in a group can be completely changed through hormonal treatments.

But how far can we draw parallels with human social behavior?

Two roosters, stags, stallions, male dogs or cats will fight furiously over a female during their "romantic" periods. Two gangsters will shoot it out over a dyed-blond moll; two college boys will come to blows over a coed.

All males of lower animals are normally chivalrous toward their females, never fighting with them, except under rare and unusual conditions. (It would be perilous for the weaker females, and for their species if they did.) Men as a rule are equally reluctant to fight with women—the more primitive the men, the more rigid their restraint—the exceptions being mostly among *civilized* men.

Male birds strut and display their plumage in the presence of females. Adolescent boys and men go to extreme lengths to "show off" in front of their girl friends.

A mother bird will court death to protect her young. A human mother will do the same, without a moment's thought, to save her baby.

Sheep form into flocks, wolves into packs, elephants into herds, etc. Men, too, everywhere, have the "joining-up" impulse, forming tribes, clubs, lodges, fraternities.

In the lower animals each of the behavior patterns noted is unquestionably *instinctive. Is the corresponding pattern of* behavior for human beings also in any degree instinctive?

We can only make guesses. Away back in the earliest stages of human evolution we might almost take it for granted that social instincts were at work in human beings as strongly as in lower animals. With no precepts, books or lectures to guide them, and minds only dimly aware of responsibility or of what was right or sensible, how else except through such instincts could human beings have begun to live together socially, to pair off as male and female, mate, rear their young, form families? If there ever were such human social instincts, the genes for them can hardly have been bred out of us. We must still have them, and in not too different forms from what they originally were, unless they spontaneously underwent some changes. For, as we've previously stressed with respect to heredity in general, no *acquired* changes in human social behavior—or the results of learning and experience through ages back—could of themselves have produced any changes in our genes.

But while we may assume that most of our original "social-behavior" genes are still at work, it is a far harder job to prove what they do and how they do it than it is to show how social behavior is influenced by training, psychological influences and the society in which people live. Think only of the behavior differences between educated people and uneducated, civilized people and savages, or those in one country and another, despite the fact that their biological mechanisms—their glands, organs, nerves and senses—are unquestionably very much the same.

Yet in individual cases it is apparent that the physical or chemical states of the body have important effects on behavior. (You know this in your own case, by the way you act when you're in good health and when you're sick, when you're feeling fresh and when you're exhausted.) The biological changes at puberty are accompanied by a whole host of behavior changes, and another set of behavior changes develops with aging. Different diseases, and glandular disorders of many kinds, also have characteristic effects on behavior, as do chemical reactions of the body to drugs, alcohol, or improper diet. Insofar, then, as normal individual differences with respect to bodily functioning and well-being are influenced by heredity, behavior patterns, too, would be so influenced. As Dr. Roger J. Williams, the biochemist, has expressed it, every individual inherits a distinct "metabolic personality" which governs not only his chemical workings in many ways, but also affects almost every aspect of his behavior and social relationships. (He believes the study of human behavior has been left too much to psychiatrists and psychologists, with not enough participation by the biochemist and physiologist.)*

Where biological factors might be seen most clearly at work are in the sex differences in behavior (of males as individuals compared with females) and in sexual behavior (involving the sexual impulses and relationships). These behavior patterns in both lower animals and human beings have been studied perhaps more intensively than any other form of activity, and there is much to report on the rôle of genetic influences—so much as to demand treatment in a separate later chapter.

Parental behavior in lower animals also has been given much study, and has been found to be so strongly governed by instincts, in detailed and specific ways for each species, as to make us suspect the presence of some similar instincts in human beings. Of course, we think of "mother love" and "parental devotion" as spiritual qualities, and to a considerable extent they may be. But the qualities also exist in lower animals, where the biologist regards them as merely the end results of a series of physical stimuli and reflexes. In fact, the parental impulses of lower animals need not at all be identified with their own offspring. You've seen pictures of mother cats nursing puppies, baby squirrels, baby monkeys or other creatures. Much though we'd like to read something beautiful and

* For the technical reader: Professor Benson E. Ginsburg of the University of Chicago suggests, on the basis of recent findings and theories, that the manner in which genes influence behavior may be, in part, through the enzyme control of metabolic and energy-yielding processes in the nervous tissues, with variable effects on the nerve impulses and motor reactions. This might apply principally to the production, conversion and supply of various forms of proteins, carbohydrates, glucose, etc., to the nerve tissues, with specific variations in metabolic activity, as governed by different genes and/or gene combinations, leading to some of the differences in nervous reactions and behavior patterns characterizing different species and individuals. (*Genetics and Social Behavior,* Jackson Memorial Laboratory Lectures in honor of Dr. C. C. Little, 1949.)

altruistic in these situations, the mother cats are being completely selfish. Once the cat has given birth to her young, a whole biological pattern of urges is set going within her. Her full breasts *require* draining, and she needs and likes the feel of warm little bodies snuggling against her. Possibly the first human mothers (to go back again to the dim stages of our beginnings) were also moved by the same purely physical impulses and reflexes. But today so many psychological and social factors condition women toward or away from motherhood that their degrees of maternal behavior can hardly be attributed to simple instincts.

Nevertheless, we say of this woman, "She's the *motherly type,*" or "She's a *natural-born* mother," and of some other woman, that she isn't. Does science offer any support for this? Dr. David M. Levy, who has intensively studied maternal behavior, is one who says "Yes." He reports finding that degrees of "maternal impulse" may be correlated with various physical characteristics, such as breast type, hip form, menstrual functioning, etc. Further, he believes that certain behavior characteristics in young girls may often reveal those who will tend to be "highly maternal" as women, in contrast with the future "non-maternal" types. Studies of lower animals have also shown that the "maternal drive" is much stronger in some females than in others, while in some species the "maternal instinct" is almost entirely lacking—as in cuckoos and cowbirds, who leave their eggs to be hatched and their young to be brought up by other birds.

Among other individual differences in social behavior established as biologically influenced in lower animals are those involving *"dominance"* and *"submissiveness."* This is most strikingly illustrated by the "peck order" in any group of poultry or birds, as revealed in the studies by Dr. W. C. Allee and others. Put any two females of a bird species together, and it won't take long to determine "who's boss"—one bird doing the pecking, the other submitting and backing away. With a larger number of birds, such as a flock of hens, each bird soon finds its place in the "peck order," dominating those below it in the scale and being dominated by those above. Thus, a "peck hierarchy" results grading from the one hapless bird, at the very bottom, pecked by all the others, up to the one bird at the top who rules the roost. A corresponding situation has been found in various other species, including mice and apes.

What has also been shown, experimentally, is that adding certain hormones (through injection), or subtracting them (through castration), can bring a rise or fall in the "dominance" standing of hens or roosters, and of apes as well. In one experiment, reported by Dr. Alphaeus M. Guhl of Kansas State College, the lowliest hen in a group of eight, when injected with "male" hormones, rose rapidly in the "peck order," dominating one hen after another until finally she subdued the former queen hen and became the new ruler.

All this is far from saying that the degrees of "dominance" or "submissiveness" observed in human beings can be related equally to hormonal influences or other biological factors. Some authorities claim that persons with greater hormonal activity—or at least, with more intense "sex drives"—are more likely to be of the "dominant" type. But there is every evidence that who-dominates-whom in human groups is much more often governed by social, intellectual and psychological factors.

Are degrees of *sociability, aggressiveness, timidity, fear, passivity,* etc., inherited? Studies of lower animals do show hereditary differences in such traits, and may or may not offer clues as to similar differences among human beings. Here are summaries of recent findings at many laboratories, including the Jackson Memorial Laboratory in Maine, where behavior reactions of dogs and other animals are being extensively studied:

Sociability. Different species of animals, and individuals within each species, show varying degrees of "sociability"—the capacity to fraternize or get along with members of their own kind or with those of other species. The extent to which sociability can be bred in animals is best illustrated among dogs. Also, in mice, Dr. J. P. Scott has found that some breeds are much more "sociable" and peaceful with their fellows than others. And rabbits have been bred, some of which are excessively friendly and docile, others so vicious that they will bare their teeth and snap at humans.

Fear. Instinctive fears among lower animals, of specific natural enemies or of specific situations, characterize each species, and as a rule are necessary for the animal's survival. One interesting discovery by Dr. O. H. Hebb of the Yerkes Laboratory is that apes have a natural fear of inert, mutilated or dismembered bodies—even of papier-mâché models of torsos or chimpanzee heads. Elephants, it has been found, have inherent fear of very small animals. In dogs, Dr. J. L. Fuller of the Jackson Laboratory has shown there are individual differences in response to fear-producing situations.

Dr. F. C. Thorne has also reported that degrees of shyness and unfriendliness in dogs, which may be "fear" responses, are influenced by heredity.

Activity. Dogs, again, offer the best examples of inherited degrees of activity. Terriers, originally bred to kill rats and other vermin, are among the most nervous and active of breeds, with wire-haired terriers being somewhat more so than Scotch terriers. On the other hand, English pug dogs, bred originally as boudoir pets, are among the most passive and phlegmatic of canines, as are also Pekingese. (In mice, also, active and inactive strains have been bred.) The different capacities of dogs of different breeds for specific activities are already well known. Familiar examples are "retrievers," "pointers," "sheep-herders," and "carriage dogs" (the spotted Dalmatians, whose special love for movement has adapted them for training to run beneath or alongside horses or vehicles and has long made them popular as firemen's pets).* In all of these cases training has merely served to bring out *inherited* capacities, which are believed related to special characteristics in the glandular, sensory and muscular mechanisms of each breed.†

Again we ask, can we apply any of the foregoing findings to human beings? Not easily. Everyday observation may tell us that among the people we meet there also are marked differences in degrees of sociability, shyness, fear, aggressiveness, activity, etc. Perhaps, as in lower animals, these traits might in some ways be linked with genetic differences in brains, nerves, muscles, glands, senses, etc. But no studies have as yet been made which would confirm this. On the other hand, psychologists have offered abundant

* Another example: Have you noticed how some dogs love to carry packages in their mouths, while others seem reluctant to do so? A Russian investigator reported (in 1944, before genetics became unpopular in the Soviet Union) that the activity of carrying objects appears in some strains of dogs spontaneously, with very little training, while in other strains the behavior is acquired only with difficulty.

† Dr. Scott reports to the author: "We have so far found in dogs no good evidence for the inheritance of complex behavior traits as such. Rather, dogs of each specialized breed seem to possess a *combination* of several simple traits which make them easily trainable for complex behavior. For example, to be a good retriever a dog must show these tendencies: To follow a moving object, then to pick it up and carry it, then to come to the trainer when called, and then docilely to give up the object. All dogs show these traits to some extent, but some are more easily trainable than others. Why, we still do not know, but we may guess that 'natural' retrievers are probably dogs with an exaggerated tendency to pick up things and carry them around, although they usually have had lots of practice before formal training in retrieving begins."

evidence of how each of these traits can be conditioned through experiences and training.

Take *fear,* which is found in a vastly greater variety of forms among humans than among any other animals. Are you afraid of physical danger, deep water, enclosed places, standing on heights? Are you beset with social fears—of not having enough money, of losing status, of being disgraced, of speaking in public, etc.? Are you afraid of sex? While some of the physical fears may be directly linked with "protective" instincts, as in lower animals, and while degrees of individual fear might be hereditary, perhaps most fears in humans—at least the specific forms taken by fear—arise through the endless fancies and impressions of which the human mind is capable. To discover how these fears evolve may be much less the task of the geneticist than of the psychologist—or the psychiatrist.

Even the fear of mice, in women, often regarded as instinctive, may be largely conditioned. That it can be quickly "deconditioned" is shown by the ease with which college girls, working in laboratories, learn to handle mice. (And only the other day this writer saw two little girls walking along a street in New York, each happily leading a pet mouse by a string!) The fear of death, too, going with the instinct of "self-preservation"—presumably the strongest of inherited instincts—may be equally conditioned one way or another. This is shown time and again during warfare, as by the Japanese Kamikazi "suicide" pilots during World War II.

Inherited *sensory* differences among individuals—in capacities for tasting, smelling, feeling, seeing, hearing, etc.—have also been studied. (If you ask, "What has this to do with behavior?" just stop and think how an acute sense of taste may affect one's reactions at the dinner table; how an acute sense of smell might cause a person to avoid certain places, jobs or people; or how differences in sensitivity to sound or touch, or in color perception, may also affect behavior in innumerable ways.) Training, of course, has much to do with human sensory responses. This is best illustrated in the tastes for foods. Do you abhor the thought of eating snails, fried caterpillars, dog-meat, or raw whale-blubber? That's almost entirely conditioned, for to many people in the world these foods are delicacies. But if you can't stand the taste or smell of specific foods which are enjoyed by other people in your family or group, there may well be an inherent basis for it. At any rate, there is little doubt but that marked differences in taste-acuity exist. United States Army studies (1946), for instance, show that one in five soldiers has taste perceptions so accurate he can tell the difference between canned bread stored at mild or warm temperatures, while others can't distinguish between a glass of clear water and one heavily saturated with quinine.

So far the only important findings of inherited human taste differences are those involving reactions to a few chemicals. Back in 1932 Drs. A. F. Blakeslee and A. L. Fox discovered that the chemical *phenylthiocarbamide* ("PTC" for short) tasted very bitter to most people and mildly bitter to some, while others didn't taste it at all. Further study (by Dr. L. H. Snyder and others) showed that ability to taste this chemical was inherited through a dominant gene, present in about 70 per cent of Americans and Europeans, whereas "non-tasting" was inherited as a recessive trait in the other 30 per cent. (All the Dionne quintuplets are "tasters," as is their mother.) In some individuals the inherited reaction to "PTC" is so acute, Dr. F. B. Hutt has reported, that extreme nausea follows several hours after tasting it. Race and ethnic differences in "PTC" taste-perception also have been reported, American Indians and Chinese being said to have the highest percentages (94 per cent) of "tasters," Eskimos the lowest percentages.

While the foregoing data refer to the "PTC" tests, several additional chemical compounds have been found which are tasteless to some persons, bitter to others, etc., and which eventually may be correlated with hereditary factors. (Idiosyncrasies to a wide variety of drugs also are believed inherited, and the possibility that there may be inherited antagonisms to penicillin, sulfa drugs, etc., demands special study.)

What the "taste" findings suggest then, is that many of the aversions shown by children or adults to certain foods may be due to something more than mere "crankiness," acquired quirks or phobias, and may in fact be an instinctive rejection of what isn't good for the particular individual. All lower animals, as everyone knows, have a wide range of inherited preferences or aversions for different foods, and this is essential for their existence. Rats, for instance, when given access to certain foods will as a rule select those which are best for them. Chicks, dairy cattle, and other animals also show ability to select their menus wisely. The same may be true to some extent for humans (though often we have our doubts!). As for human babies, if you think they'll eat anything when left to their own devices, you're wrong. Dr. Clara M. Davis of Chicago reported (1947) an experiment in which young children were allowed to select their own foods for extended periods. Results showed that in their selective appetites they met known nutritional requirements, suggesting that "food appetite is another of the many self-regulatory activities of the organism." Nevertheless, it is possible that if you don't like spinach, lamb or *paté de fois gras,* it may be your genes warning you to abstain.

Sensitivity to smells in various degrees and in various forms may also in time be shown to have a hereditary basis (even though, in many instances, aversion to particular smells may be psychologically conditioned). So far, preliminary study has been given only to extreme cases of "smell blindness" (which we discussed in Chapter 24).

Sensitivity to sound is also beginning to be studied by geneticists. Are you one of those whose teeth get on edge when someone scratches on glass with a diamond, or who say you're "driven crazy" by certain noises that don't bother others at all? That, too, may some day be blamed on your genes. In mice, at any rate, it has been found that some strains are so sensitive to sound that they will be thrown into convulsions by certain loud or high-pitched noises (the "audiogenic seizures"). In fact, some mice may even be killed by sound. One of the most fascinating laboratory demonstrations this author has seen was at the Jackson Memorial Laboratory, in 1947, when these super-sensitive mice were first exhibited. There was a metal washtub with an electric doorbell attached. Mice of ordinary strains, placed in the tub, would merely run to the center and huddle there when the bell was set off. Mice of the special strain, placed in the same situation, would dash madly around, go into convulsions, pop up into the air and drop dead—all in half a minute. As yet no parallel to this has been found in human beings. But who knows?—some of us who are super-sensitive to noise may be genetic kin to these mice.

There are various other sensitivities and senses in humans about which we can only speculate. There is *sensitivity* to pain, or to heat and cold, which in different degrees often has a constitutional basis. There is the *sense of direction,* possessed in acute forms by birds and some other lower animals, and to a lesser extent by some humans, while others of us get lost easily. (Dr. Edwin G. Boring thinks this is merely because some persons are better "mental mapmakers" than others.) There is the *sense of time*—some people being almost living clocks. And there are the often reported phenomena (which may or may not involve mere coincidences) of persons having "sensed" when some distant loved one has died, or who have had a "sense" or "premonition" of impending danger, etc.

The hidden source-springs of some of these and other strange senses allegedly present in human beings remain to be explored. Less mysterious, however, are certain broader aspects of human behavior which we shall deal with in the next several chapters.

CHAPTER 38

LOOKS AND PERSONALITY

IF HUMAN beings in real life were like characters in the movies and comic strips, we could make these definite assertions:

All fat people are jolly, frank and easily moved to laughter or tears.

All blond women are dumb and frivolous—or else are cold, calculating and morally loose.

All black-haired men with swarthy skins and sharp noses are villains.

All redheads are hot tempered and passionate; all men with high foreheads are intellectual; those with receding chins are timid wishy-washies; those with big flopping ears are fools.

The list could be extended endlessly to include the various features and looks that are supposed to indicate jealousy, meanness, trickiness, criminality, aristocracy, amorousness—in fact, the whole gamut of human personality traits.

But are there actually such correlations? If there were, then knowing that heredity has much to do with shaping one's appearance, we might go further and ask whether heredity does not also make a person *act the way he looks?*

The answers given today by many authorities are less clear cut than they used to be. It still can be said that physical features and personality are for the most part not related, and that people can't be glibly classified into personality types by their looks. Yet there are many ways in which facial and bodily details can offer clues to personality. In the "Black Gene" chapters we saw how various inherited abnormalities—mental, neurological, muscular—can have specific effects on behavior and temperament. And in our last chapter it was indicated how, even in normal individuals, differences in glandular workings and other body processes may also influence behavior. (You may recall the statement by Dr. Williams that every individual inherits a distinct "metabolic personality.") To the extent, then, that specific genes or gene combinations may affect both outward construction and mental and emotional functioning, surface traits might sometimes be linked with personality traits. This isn't to say, however, that the popular notions regarding looks and personality are correct. Let's see where the fallacies lie.

A girl is blond, blue-eyed, beautiful. Does a certain kind of temperament, character, personality, go directly together with that combination? Or rather, does not beauty in a girl evoke responses from others which tend to mold her personality in special ways? "Oh, isn't she darling!" "Oh, isn't she lovely!" she hears others say of her from childhood on (regardless of what a brat she may be!). Maturing, she is ever conscious of the effect she has on admiring males, employers, even other women. She has to continually *act* the rôle of being beautiful, and may be elevated into positions which go beyond her capacities. A whole cluster of special personality traits may result. So to the extent that the experiences and effects are alike for all beautiful girls of a given type, they would tend to develop many of the same traits. The mistake would lie in assuming that the *genes* which produce their looks also produce their personalities.

Consider the *very tall girl.* If her growth comes early, she must begin dressing as a woman before her classmates do. The discrepancies in looking like a grown-up when she's psychologically still a young and inexperienced girl can produce a sense of maladjustment. Then the man problem comes along. The tall girl encounters difficulty in finding dancing partners, boy friends or mates. She tends to become more retiring and reserved. And being tall, she's expected to act with dignity and restraint, even if she doesn't feel like it.

Very small girls, on the other hand, tend to develop quite different traits. In buying clothes they must patronize the junior-misses' or even children's departments. Men good-naturedly toss the little girls about, bigger girls baby them, people constantly jest about their "pint size." They're expected to act "cute." These and other factors may make the small girl hypersensitive, high-spirited, high strung.

The *very fat girl,* always a target for pleasantries, may build up a defense by being the first to laugh at herself. You may have observed how at costume parties the big, fat girls so often dress in "kiddy" costumes, exposing fully the plumpness of their arms and legs, just as do the "fat ladies" in side shows. Never feeling quite at ease, it isn't surprising that fat girls as a class develop a number of special personality traits. At the same time, there may be traits originally present which are in part responsible for their obesity. Thus, Dr. Hilde Bruch of Columbia University, who has been studying them, says, "The reason so many fat girls and women stay fat is that they started as timid persons and come to depend upon their bulk as a defense against men, sex, and assuming the responsibilities of grown-up womanhood." Overeating, Dr. Bruch believes, may be a substitute for love, security, and other satisfactions.

The effects of *extreme homeliness* (or what is so regarded) in a girl should be obvious. The indifference of men, the condescending attitude of other women, the greater difficulty in finding various jobs and making a place for herself in society, may well account for the development of certain personality traits. Yet most people confuse the resentfulness, the "touchiness," the anti-social attitude often displayed by homely girls with something basic in their makeup.

Psychologists can easily extend this type of "character diagnosis" to women of many other physical types, and, of course, to men. Very short men, like very small girls, tend also to be oversensitive and eager to dominate (the "Napoleon complex"). Very handsome men, to whom many things come too easy—especially the attention of women—may often be ne'er-do-wells. Again, great physical prowess in a man, or, on the other hand, sickliness or physical inadequacy, may each be correlated with a type of personality.

All of these cases (which may conjure up pictures of some of your friends, or perhaps of yourself) show how looks can influence personality. Accordingly, if outward physical details are due to certain genes, we might think that a child who inherited genes which cause him to *look* like his father would automatically grow up to *act* like his father. In other words, that people who look the same would act the same. But this is hardly true, for two reasons: one (harking back to old Mendel and his peas) is that genes of all kinds may be inherited independently. In the very same family, two individuals who received many of the same "feature" genes may yet have entirely different gene combinations for intelligence and behavior. The second reason, touched on before, is that the effects of looks on personality are largely governed by how the looks are regarded by the individual and those around him.

Consider our girl types again. If our very tall girl found herself in a society of uniformly tall people, she would no longer be maladjusted. Already, in our own country, with the marked increase in stature in the past several generations, tall girls or men who formerly would have been gaped at are now commonplace. Equally, some of those now viewed as "shorties" wouldn't have been thought so a half-century ago. So, too, the way fat girls are regarded depends on where they live. In many parts of the world—in some countries of the Orient and in certain African tribes (where adolescent girls are put in "fattening pens" and are milk-fed like prize porkers)—the plumpest women are considered the most glamorous, and move with the same sense of queenly importance as do the beauties of our own world. In these other places it would be the slim American fashion model who would develop an inferiority complex, and who might tend to have many of the same personality traits which we here associate with our very fat women.

Why specific types of looks are favored, and others are scorned in given groups, involves complex social and psychological factors which we can touch on only lightly. One point is that many of the interpretations given to looks have no more than an allegorical basis. Take *redheads*. Some time ago Mrs. Eleanor Roosevelt wrote in her newspaper column that she'd just seen an old portrait of George Washington showing him with red hair. She observed, "I understand better now why he held out at Valley Forge." Possibly Mrs. R. was jesting; but most people would accept this as further proof that red hair is linked with fighting qualities. Why? Most likely because red suggests "fire": hence, red hair, "fiery nature." Similarly, pale blond hair is thought of as indicating "coldness," fluffy hair, "light-headedness." Why have our traditional stage and story "villains" been depicted as dark-haired men with swarthy skins and heavy black eyebrows? Again, perhaps, because black connotes mystery, death, sinister influences; or also (in the United States) because the type was that of the foreigner who differed radically from the prevailing native stock. It is human to view strangers with suspicion, and we dare say that among many black-haired, swarthy people the villains would be depicted as blond and light-skinned.

It would not be hard to find the allegorical roots for other feature connotations: close-together eyes as supposedly indicating "closeness," "cupidity"; wide-apart eyes, "openness," "frankness"; small eyes, "rattiness," "slyness"; a sharp, thin nose, "sharpness," "meanness"; a protruding chin, "forwardness," "bravery"; a receding chin, "timidity," (as with "Caspar Milquetoast" in the comic strip). So, too, with the meanings attached to the shapes of limbs, ankles, hands or feet: that thick ankles or wrists mean a person is "thick" or "common," or slim ones indicate inherent "gentility." An even worse fallacy is to attribute such differences to either "peasant" ancestry or "aristocratic" ancestry. It is true that persons working at heavy tasks develop heavier bone structures. But the idea that these *acquired characteristics* can be passed along by heredity from generation to generation has, as we know, been exploded. Highly bred race horses and greyhounds may indeed have slim graceful legs (though how about equally aristocratic bulldogs and dachshunds?). No human beings, however, have ever been bred like lower animals to combine both physical features and behavior traits in the same strains.

Unfortunately, though, what people *think* certain features are supposed to indicate has enormous effects on their social relationships and their own personalities. One of the nation's leading businessmen, who has a chin which recedes so far it might almost be mistaken for his Adam's apple, told a gathering of sales executives how he had to battle constantly to overcome prejudices against his looks, and to "sell" not only others but himself on the idea that he wasn't a weakling.

Among young people, psychologists report serious personality disorders in sensitive boys and girls resulting from marked facial peculiarities which cause them to be nicknamed "baboon face," "eagle beak," "fish mouth," etc. Acting on the theory that many criminals may have become anti-social through facial deformities, Dr. John F. Pick and several other plastic surgeons have been performing facial operations on convicts prior to release, and have reported that a much higher than average number of these men have subsequently gone straight. Also, studies of soldiers disfigured in World War II showed personality changes in many of them, and great improvement following plastic operations. However, in ordinary cases it has been pointed out that where an individual is overly concerned with some facial peculiarity which doesn't bother most people, and thinks this is the cause of his failure, it may be a sign of an underlying personality difficulty which no plastic operation can correct. (Many disappointments following such operations are reported.)

A logical inference, then, would be that, where facial and physical abnormalities are *inherited,* certain personality traits might easily develop with them, though only environmentally. Nonetheless, the linkage so often found between a given abnormality and a type of personality (especially where the two run together in a family) may easily lead to the erroneous assumption that both are inherited simultaneously.

So much for certain kinds of *looks* that alter behavior. But there is also a reverse process. Various kinds of behavior, including habits of occupation and living, have specific effects on looks, ranging from the shaping and posture of the body as a whole, down to characteristic movements, facial expressions and mannerisms. Many of these effects come through what scientists call "muscle toning," the manner in which different sets of muscles become conditioned in their workings through repeated usage in similar ways. Every face, for instance, has beneath its surface an intricate network of muscles and fibers, acting variously to produce the expressions of smiling, laughing, weeping, frowning, affection, hate, chagrin, horror, etc. Through use and habit starting from infancy, the facial muscles thus become "toned" by specific patterns of action, giving the face as a whole a characteristic expression, even in repose, which may well provide clues to the individual's personality. So you're often very right in judging from a face that a person is "kind," "cold," "mean," "honest," "alert," or otherwise. But don't trust these surface clues too far! From time to time magazines have published sets of photographs of criminals mixed up with those of highly respectable people, and readers have found it hard to judge which were which.

Likewise, mannerisms of walking, moving the hands, posture, etc., develop largely through the "toning" of the muscles involved, and often do (but sometimes don't) provide an insight into one's personality. But we must not confuse individual characteristics in bodily or facial movements with those developed in whole groups of people as a result of similarities in their working and living habits. Farmers, policemen, sailors, actresses, prizefighters, are examples. Even more emphatically, persons in any given country or locality tend to develop many of the same distinctive traits—of using their hands, walking, registering various emotions, etc.—which can be mistakenly regarded as hereditary.

Thus, too, where you see members of a family walking, using their hands, moving their mouths, etc., in the same way, the likelihood is that they are doing this through imitation and conditioning. But in some cases heredity may also be playing a part. This can as yet be only deduced from the findings of hereditary differences in muscular construction and functioning (also from the peculiarities in hand mannerisms going with certain hereditary diseases and nervous disorders), and from the fact that in lower animals of any species those of different breeds have characteristic patterns of movement.

However, both in lower animals and humans, psychologists have shown that unusual physical mannerisms are often the result of psychological disturbances. Most frequently observed are the "tics"—involuntary movements of the hand or head, twitching of the eyes or mouth, etc. In extreme cases they go with a nervous or mental disorder. Milder examples may be merely a means of relieving tension, or as a reaction to physical restraint. Dr. David M. Levy observes that prayer movements—head-shaking, rocking, weaving-motions, etc.—of monks, Moslems, Orthodox Jews, etc., arise in this way. These movements may carry over into the everyday mannerisms of whole groups of people, and some "tics" may be "catching"—by children from their parents—again illustrating how the results of conditioning may be confused with inheritance.

(Several muscular oddities, in voluntarily controlling movements of the tongue and ears, have been found hereditary. Among them is the ability to roll up the side edges of the tongue, credited to a dominant gene; the ability, in some Chinese, to curl back the tip of the tongue on itself, apparently a recessive trait; and ability to move the ears, with or without the aid of the adjacent scalp, which is believed to be genetically controlled, though in what way has not yet been established.)

Hands, as related to personality, warrant an additional note, beyond the points made previously with regard to hand shapes. Obviously there are "expressive" hands, "sensitive" hands, "nervous" hands, "coarse" hands, etc., resulting largely from the way they have been conditioned through usage, and to that extent telling something of the individual's character and activities.* Dr. Francesco Ronchese, in his book, *Occupational Marks and Other Physical Signs,* lists a great variety of hand characteristics identifying persons in different occupations. But *"palmistry"* is another matter. While palm-line patterns are in large measure determined by heredity (all the Dionne quints, for example, having much the same palms), they have not been found to have any relationship to *inherent* personality traits. It is true that some clues to personality are offered by the way certain palm lines have become etched or their patterns

* *Handwriting* has not yet been found to be much influenced by heredity, nor to provide more than rough clues to personality. A significant fact is that even top "graphologists" may go wrong in about 20 per cent of the cases in telling whether a handwriting sample is that of a man or a woman.

extended through the use of the hands, just as some deductions can be made from the wrinkles on the face. But as to "reading" "love" lines, "success" lines, "life" lines, or "how-many-children-you-will-have" lines—science has one word for that, "Bosh!" (And just in case you're interested, the same now goes for "phrenology"—"reading" the bumps on your head.)

But having so far stressed, largely, how environment can produce links between looks and personality, we must now take up some qualifying evidence as related to the possible influences of heredity as well. First, there are the studies indicating a general relationship between body forms and personality traits. Theories that such a relationship exists go far back into history. Hippocrates, father of medicine, and then Galen, another Greek physician, speculated on this point. Centuries later, Shakespeare had Caesar say,

> *"Let me have men about me that are fat;*
> *Sleek-headed men and such as sleep o'nights;*
> *Yond' Cassius has a lean and hungry look;*
> *He thinks too much: such men are dangerous."*

Oddly enough, when a few decades ago attempts began to be made to correlate body build and temperament on a scientific basis, old Shakespeare was given support. The fat men were roughly identified as of the "placid, sociable" type; the lean men as of the "mental, hesitant" type. Best known of the earlier classifications were those of E. Kretschmer (referred to in Chapter 15): the "pyknic" (fat), "asthenic" (lean), and "athletic" body types, each regarded as linked with different personality tendencies. In recent years the system of body-temperament classification has been much amplified by Dr. W. H. Sheldon. He, too, has roughly classified people into three main types, but has also allowed for various subtypes. Here are the main Sheldon classifications, and "traits" which he and others have reported as going with them:

The *Endomorph:* soft and round physique, with tendency to obesity, general muscular relaxation. Inclined to be home-loving (and food-loving), placid, sociable.

The *Mesomorph:* athletic, muscular, heavy-boned. Associated with fighters, heroes, leaders, lovers of power and action, thrills, exploits.

The *Ectomorph:* the "string-bean" type, flat chested, linear-physiques with stringy muscles. Persons of this type are said to tend toward the "mental," to be keenly aware of their environment, to be introverted, less aggressive, hesitant, not at ease with people, blushing easily.

Granting that people don't fall neatly into one type or another, Dr. Sheldon has devised a system of scoring individuals on components of each type, in different combinations ("4-2-4," "1-7-1," "2-2-3," etc.), the results being determined by the balances and ratios among these components. Thus, he reports a marked contrast between "the long-legged, round-shouldered, completely soft and effeminate boy," and "the ruddy, powerful, barrel-bodied boy who is usually full of bounding energy."

How close the Kretschmer or Sheldon classifications come to establishing a direct relationship between body build and temperament is still debatable. Some authorities regard them as highly valid (Professor Earnest Hooton maintaining that "your carcass is the clue to your character"). Others say these classifications offer only very loose and undependable criteria. In a rough way, however, when combined with other evidence, the classifications have been found useful by psychiatrists in diagnosing certain mental diseases and personality disorders. But with normal persons, even if *average* correlations do exist between body builds and temperament, one must be extremely cautious about applying them to individuals without taking note of all the exceptions and of all the other factors that contribute to personality development. We might thus question the assertion by a writer in a popular men's magazine that the "pyknic" girl (not to be confused with "picnic") "is the one to pick for a loving wife—easy-going, warm, loyal, adaptable, and usually the 'dumber and dumpier one.'"

Equally disputed is the proposed system of classifying people into "endocrine" (or "glandular") types—the "thyroid," the "adrenal," the "pituitary," the "gonadic," etc., on the theory that degrees of activity of the various glands account for specific kinds of personality and capacity. (Dr. L. Berman, a proponent of this theory, predicted, in 1928, that "an adrenal type will probably be the first woman president of the United States." We'll wait and see!)

Also being explored is the possibility that *coloring* of eyes, hair and complexion may have some relationship to temperament (allowing for the qualifications previously noted in discussing these traits). Dr. Clyde E. Keeler and others have reported that in many lower animals differences in coat color do often seem to go with differences in behavior. (A *theoretical* assumption is that the chemical action of the genes which account for color differences might also affect sensory mechanisms.) Horse breeders say that the palomino ("golden horse"), very lightly pigmented, is "gentle and tractable," and that this also is true, more or less, of mountain-bred, dappled gray horses. In contrast, wild bays, duns and sorrels are said to be "spirited and difficult to break in." With regard to mules, Dr. Keeler quotes a Georgia preacher as saying, "A gray mule is de lastin'es mule dey is . . . he jes' takes it easy. But a *brown* Texas mule, he jes' weahs hisself out rushin' aroun'!" (Whether this is anecdote or science remains to be proved.)

Various other correlations between coloring and temperament are reported in dogs, cats, rats, cattle and other animals. But no specific evidence of any such correlations has yet been found in human beings, other than where deficiencies or abnormalities are involved, as in albinos, or in sufferers from certain diseases. No one has proved, for instance, that blond women are like blond horses in being "more gentle" and "easier to tame" than brunettes.

One important reason why the "color" findings regarding lower animals cannot be too closely applied to our own species is that in all the cases noted the animals have been bred intensively to the point where most of their genes are the same, and where the difference of a gene or two for coloring may also change the workings of the behavior genes. Human beings, on the other hand, are all mongrels as compared with most domestic animals (a point repeatedly emphasized in this book), and differ among themselves in a much larger number of genes. Adding the fact that human personality is far more complex than is the behavior of lower animals, and is vastly more influenced by training and environment, it becomes highly doubtful whether, within the normal range, any one or two genes for coloring could produce any great personality differences.

Come to think of it, we haven't yet given a *definition* of "personality," and this is essential for the next phase of our discussion. Do you believe it's easy to define "personality"? Well, you ought to hear the top psychologists argue about it! The big question is whether any human being comes into the world with a "personality," or whether a "personality" can develop *only through inter-relationships with other human beings.* Many authorities hold to the latter conclusion. They maintain that while a newborn infant is a human being, and was one from the moment of conception, it is not a *"person"*—not yet having had social contact with other persons—and is therefore lacking in "personality." From this viewpoint no one could inherit a "personality," or any specific "personality" trait, but at best could possess only the potentialities for developing various traits given a certain kind of human social environment. Further, a "personality" could exist only in a human being. (A dog might have a "dogality"; a cat, a "catality.")

But there is another school of psychological thought. This holds that when a child comes into the world it is not a neutral mass devoid of personality, but already has many personality tendencies which begin to manifest themselves without awaiting social interaction. Thus Professor John E. Anderson of the University of Minnesota believes that the effects of early conditioning on personality have been overemphasized. He says, "If the personality of the infant is so delicate, it should be modified easily and show great changes from year to year. But many scientific studies show that individual personality patterns which emerge in infancy continue to show themselves—traits such as aggressiveness, alertness, tendencies toward smiling, laughing, crying, perseveration, social responses, etc."

In corroboration, Dr. Patricia Neilon published in 1948 a follow-up study of the famed "Shirley babies," originally a group whose personalities in infancy and babyhood had been intensively analyzed and reported on by Dr. M. M. Shirley fifteen years before. After the lapse of time, when the group had reached an average age of 18, Dr. Neilon, studying the same individuals, found that their basic personality patterns, established in infancy, had persisted in a marked degree in most cases, though in some individuals more of the original cluster of traits was retained than in others. Even in chimpanzees, Dr. Elaine Kinder has found that individual "personality" traits appearing in infancy remain relatively constant for years thereafter. (The foregoing merely confirms what most mothers have taken for granted—that each baby, from birth on, is a distinct "personage.")

The important effects of early experiences in shaping, modifying or warping personality are of course to be kept constantly in mind. Psychoanalysts have brought forward a mass of evidence on these points, and have shown how an individual's whole personality structure may be changed through early misfortunes and shocks, or adverse conditioning by their parents. The effects of having a domineering or emotionally frustrated mother or a cruel father, or of being an only child, all have been correlated with specific personality traits. (Freud himself revealed in his personality the effects of having had a father old enough to be his grandfather, and a young, doting and over-indulgent mother.)

Psychological factors, however, aren't the only adverse influences to be considered here. Apart from the obvious effects of mental derangements or nervous disorders, many illnesses and defects may radically affect personality. Sufferers from migraine headaches, for example, have been reported (by Drs. W. D. Ross and F. L. McNaughton) as showing "intolerance, perfectionism, difficulty in sexual adjustment, persistent drive for success, etc." Brain injuries are followed frequently by marked alterations in personality of various kinds—tendencies to become more emotional, or more childlike, to show unjustified optimism or "euphoria" (feeling of well-being), or to have previous personality traits exaggerated. Likewise, after certain brain operations persons may become less truthful and less scrupulous, although their intelligence may be unimpaired. Glandular disorders, allergies and vitamin deficiencies and other biochemical upsets have also been correlated with specific personality changes. All this would indicate that where disturbances in the body functioning are influenced by heredity, these inherent biological mishaps, at early or later stages, may often be as important as psychological factors in modifying personality.

It should be apparent by now that there is an important distinction between "behavior" and "personality" (which will explain our devoting separate chapters to each). Behavior traits, as we brought out, can be inherited directly, and whole behavior patterns can manifest themselves in human infants (as well as in lower animals) spontaneously and irrespective of their social environment. Thus, Dr. Gesell's studies have constantly stressed the inherent "individuality" of each child. But personality is far more complex, and far more indirect in its development. It is "behavior-*plus*"—involving not merely all the individual's behavior tendencies, but all the effects of his varying physical state, changing age, intelligence, senses, talents, capacities, experiences and everything he has been and is in relation to other human beings.

How, then, with all this mixture of influences, are we to get any specific proof about the inheritance of personality? Once more we have to turn to our old reliables, the twins. A good many sets of "identicals" and "fraternals," including quadruplets and also the

Dionnes, have been studied from the standpoint of personality. What conclusions can we draw from them?

In general, the personalities of identical twins tend to be very much alike. But before we can ascribe all this to their identical heredity, we must allow for the fact that the environments of these twins also are usually very much alike. So we must look for special situations. One is in the case of identical twins whose environments *have not been* the same. Another is in comparisons between identical twins and fraternal twins (differing in heredity) who have shared similar environments.

Among the studies of identical twins reared apart have been those of "Millan" and "George" (as reported in the *Journal of Heredity,* in 1943, by Drs. F. E. Stephens and R. B. Thompson). Adopted almost immediately after birth by different families, and brought up in different cities under quite different conditions, they did not see each other until they were 19 years old. Physically they were found to be remarkably alike, and so were they in temperament, intelligence and in general mental characteristics. Both had artistic leanings—one toward music, the other drawing, and both had won amateur boxing championships!

Another case, reported by Professor H. H. Newman, was that of the identical twins Edwin Iske and Fred Nestor, also brought up from infancy by different foster parents in different cities and completely unaware of each other's existence. When they were in their twenties there was a remarkable coincidence. Both had become interested in electricity and were working as expert telephone repair men for the same company, though a thousand miles apart. Traveling representatives of the company noted their striking physical resemblance, which led to the twins discovering one another. Later, Professor Newman found them to be also strikingly similar in mental ability and personality, and noted, further, that "they had been married the same year, to young women of about the same age and type, each had a baby son and—believe it or not!—each owned a fox terrier dog named "Trixie"!

One of the most detailed studies of personality in a pair of twins was that by Drs. Arnold Gesell and Helen Thompson, of the personality development of two identical twin sisters from infancy on through the age of 14. Although strong efforts were made to train the twins in different ways they continued to be remarkably alike in personality. Such personality differences as there were, said Drs.

Gesell and Thompson, were for the most part the same as those observed in their babyhood, and "proved to be so slight that they would be set down as similarities if they were encountered in a study of unselected children or even of ordinary siblings."

Perhaps even more significant have been the findings with regard to *quadruplets*. These "four-somes," available in a number of combinations of "identicals" and "fraternals," have been given special attention by Dr. Iva C. Gardner and Professor Newman. They studied five sets (the Morloks, Badgetts, Keys, Schenses and Perricones, previously discussed in our Chapter 19) who ranged from all four "identicals" (a "one-egg" set), to all four "fraternals" (a "four-egg" set), with "mixed" sets (part identical, part fraternal) in between. In the all-identical set, the four Morlok girls, studied at age 10, differences in personality were found for each, with the girl of largest size being consistently the leader, while the one who had been smallest and frailest from babyhood was the quietest and least self-assertive of the group. But the differences were of a much greater degree in the Schenses, the all-fraternal mixed set (two boys, two girls). Tested at age 9, they were found to be about as much different in mental ability and personality as any average four children born separately in a family. The Perricone quads, another "four-egg" set (though all boys) were found to have temperamental differences even greater than their physical differences. In the Badgett girls (three "identicals," one "fraternal"), studied as babies, the "fraternal" and genetically unrelated sister was found to be distinctly much brighter than the other three and quite different in personality.

Most interesting, however, were the famous Keys girls of Oklahoma—*the first quadruplet set to go through college* (Baylor University, Texas, 1937). A "three-egg" set, consisting of two "identicals" (from one egg) and two "fraternals" (from two other eggs), they were studied and tested at age 22. Despite their all having been continuously in the same environment and in the closest personal association, there were marked differences in IQ and personality between the "identical" pair, who were very much alike, and their "fraternal" sisters, who, in turn, differed very much from each other.

Finally, there were the personality studies of the Dionne quintuplets, made in their first few years by Drs. W. E. Blatz and D. A. Millichamp. Here we find again that even identical heredity coupled with close similarity in environment does not result in identical personality. For each of the Dionnes has in some degree or another a personality differing from that of the others. Among other factors, it appeared likely that their early physical differences (reported in Chapter 19), contributed to the development of these personality differences.

Yvonne, sturdiest of the Dionnes at birth, was reported as the leader of the group, showing such solicitousness for her sisters that she was dubbed by the psychologists "The Matriarch." Annette was considered the most aggressive; Emilie, most happy-go-lucky and most self-sufficient; Cecile as the most variable and unpredictable; and Marie—the "baby" of the group from birth onward—as the least skilled in play, least assertive and least enterprising. Although thereafter no further psychological studies of the Dionnes were permitted, some additional insight into their personalities was provided in 1944 (when they were aged 10½), by Keith Munro, the Dionne business manager until that year. Said he: "They are absolute individualists. Yvonne is boss of the five; Cecile has a greater love of clothes than the others; Emilie is the 'comedienne'; Annette the student and musician; and Marie, the wistful, affectionate 'little sister.' "*

Let's stop a minute. We have almost forgotten that we are dealing with *genetically identical* quintuplets, all five of whom carry exactly the same types of whatever genes there are for personality traits. And yet here are all these personality distinctions among them!

We see, therefore, how the most minor effects of environment (beginning with the Dionnes before they were born) can swerve inherited potentialities for personality in one direction or another. But we must also keep in mind that in the Dionnes a special effort has been made to *look* for differences. This is so even in the case of ordinary identical twins, where, in seeking clues for distinguishing between them, parents and others tend to take note of and to overemphasize the smallest differences in their behavior, as in their features. Twins themselves, too, may enhance their differences by striving to develop "individualities." Thus, while the Dionnes may show more or less varied personalities, there is little doubt but that their similarities in behavior, temperament and mental processes far overshadow their differences, in comparison with any group of girls taken at random. The same principle has been established for identical twins in general.

* A story credited to the late Alexander Woollcott (by Leonard Lyons) is that when he visited the Dionnes, the children lined up before him, and he asked, "Which of you is the smartest?" One of the quints answered, "Marie." "And what's *your* name, my dear?" asked Woollcott. "Marie," was the answer.

The general conclusions we can draw from the twin studies is that heredity is certainly a potent factor in shaping personality (environmental influences, of course, also being taken for granted). Nevertheless, the resemblance in personality between any two identical twins—whether reared together or apart—has been found much less than their similarity in physical characteristics. Thus, there is every reason to say (as Professor Newman has summed it up) that *physical characteristics are affected least by environment; intelligence more; education and achievement still more; and personality and temperament the most.*

More specifically, with respect to the various factors involved in producing personality, the general belief among psychologists is that hereditary influences may be graded in this way:

Most likely to be influenced by heredity: Basic abilities, such as intelligence, speed of reaction, motor skills, sensory discrimination, etc.

Less likely to be influenced by heredity: Temperamental traits, such as emotionality, alternation or evenness of mood, activity or lethargy.

Least likely to be influenced by heredity (if at all): Attitudes, stylistic traits, beliefs, values and other such characteristics in which training or conditioning are clearly major factors.

What we will have to have before we can report with more certainty on the inheritance of personality are better tests for measuring it than are now available. This is not to minimize the value of such tests as the Rohrschach (seeing things in ink-blots), the Minnesota "personal inventory," and various "projective" tests (having people do things). All have been found highly useful for revealing abnormal character traits or special capacities, picking persons for jobs, etc. But they do not reach deep enough below the surface to identify *basic* personality traits which can be directly correlated with genetic factors.*

So for the present we can only *assume* that there are genes for normal personality traits just as there are genes for other aspects of human makeup and functioning. Where, in members of the same

* That seven measurable major factors account for basic differences in personalities was the conclusion reported by Dr. L. L. Thurstone, University of Chicago psychologist (1950). These seven factors, as found in Dr. Thurstone's analysis, are: a pressure for activity, "masculinity" (inclination toward so-called "masculine" activities), impulsiveness, dominance, emotional stability, sociability, and reflectiveness.

family, in a similar environment, we can see great differences in personality, we may ascribe these in part at least to differences in gene combinations. We can also guess that some of the family similarities in personality are genetically influenced. But we're still a long way from identifying specific "personality" genes, gauging their effects or hazarding predictions as to what the personality of a given child will be on the basis of what we know about its parents. In short, heredity can never be considered as charting a fixed and definite course for anyone's personality. At the best, what anyone inherits are the potentialities for a wide range of personalities, the precise form into which a personality will "jell" being determined by circumstances.

Nor do we know of any other initial influence which can chart a fixed course for personality. We emphasize this chiefly with *"astrology"* in mind. We are sadly aware, of course, that millions of people take their "astrological horoscopes" very seriously and attach even more importance to the influence of the stars and planets on their personalities and destinies than they do to their heredity or their immediate environment. We can only say, then, that astrology (not to be confused in any way with *astronomy*) is about the most discredited of the *pseudo*-sciences—despite all its intricate mumbo-jumbo of "zodiacal" symbols and their supposed meanings which have been repeatedly torn to bits by true scientists.

Here are just a few simple questions: (1) Granted that identical twins, born at the same time and "under the same stars," have much the same personalities, why then do *fraternal* twins, also born at the same time, *have radically different personalities and destinies?* (2) If persons "born under Libra" (September 24 to October 23) "should have musical ability"—according to the astrologers—how explain the findings by Dr. Paul R. Farnsworth that out of 1,500 musicians taken at random, fewer were born in this period or the period next to it ("Scorpius") than in any other period of the year? And (3) What happens with the "horoscope" of a baby born *prematurely,* through sudden accident or a Caesarean, two or three months before its scheduled time? Does its personality change instantly? And by what physical means do the stars and planets accomplish this?

A committee of the nation's astronomers, headed by Harvard Astronomy Professor Bart J. Bok, pointed out (1941) that no "astrologers" have ever answered these questions, and summed up the conclusions that *"astrology is a magical practice which has no shred of justification in fact."*

Worthy of more serious attention are the theories regarding the influence of *climate* on personality. You know, of course, how changes in weather and temperature may affect you. Writing in *Science* (September 16, 1949), Professor Clarence A. Mills pointed out that extremes of climate and temperature may affect the body processes, and in turn, the behavior and efficiency of whole groups of people living in different parts of the world, those in very hot, moist climates being more retarded than others. But this refers to whole groups of people, rather than to individuals. In any case it offers no support whatsoever to astrology, for the "constellations" are the same for people in all climates (except those at the North and South Poles, whom we needn't worry about).

Abnormal personality, so far as heredity may help to produce it, has been discussed in some of its more marked forms in our "Black Gene" chapters, and to a limited extent in this chapter. Further aspects will now be taken up as we proceed to a detailed treatment of two of the most important phases of personality, "criminal behavior" and "sexual behavior."

CHAPTER 39

ENTER THE VILLAIN

IF YOU'RE a reasonably law-abiding citizen, and you read about a particularly vicious crime, you may say, "*I* could never do a thing like that. I'm just not built that way!" Seeing a picture of the criminal, you may imagine that he even *looks* like a different sort of creature from what you are.

Whether you are or aren't right can be decided only by answering the question, "What makes the 'criminal'?"

Is it Heredity, with a special set of "black" genes for criminality? Is it Environment, with the products of "bad early conditioning" and warped moral judgments? Or does Heredity load the gun, leaving it to Environment to pull the trigger?

Here is a case where, perhaps more than in any other phase of this book, you must be the judge and the jury.

The charge that criminal acts can be blamed on "bad heredity" in individuals or on "taints" running in certain families is as old as the hills. But the evidence is almost entirely circumstantial. Much of what has been offered in the past is, as lawyers would say, "incompetent, irrelevant and immaterial." What can be offered today is still far short of anything conclusive.

To prove any inheritance of criminality there must be the assumption, first, that it is a distinctive and clearly defined type of abnormal behavior (which, as we shall see, is open to some question); and second, that this behavior has a *biological* basis—that it results from some specific physical or mental peculiarity in certain individuals which *predisposes* them more than other persons to become criminals.

Among lower animals we refer to tigers and wolves as "killers," jackals and buzzards as "ghouls," magpies and cuckoos as "thieves," leeches as "parasites," and so on. If these and hosts of other animals were judged by human standards, we would say they were all of them congenitally "criminal" or "anti-social."

But we do not hold the lower creatures strictly to account for what they do (although we may condemn them to death, nonetheless, when they menace us), because we do not credit them with the same sort of intelligence that we have, or with any will or conscience. We ascribe their acts to "instincts," to "uncontrollable impulses"; we say they were "born that way." On the other hand, what the human animal does we like to think of as dictated by intelligence and reasoning powers. On this assumption, that what *we* do is done wilfully, are based all our existing codes of law and morality, with punishment for "bad" behavior and reward for "good" behavior.

Are we entirely right? Is it possible that many human criminals, though entirely sane, are yet no more responsible for their acts than are lower animals? That some humans, too, are impelled by uncontrollable impulses and anti-social "instincts"? That they are *born that way?*

The theory that the criminal is a "throw-back" to lower forms of humans, an individual in whom the "primitive urges" or "baser animal passions" break loose through civilized restraints—has popped up at various times. Toward the end of the nineteenth century the Italian criminologist, Cesare Lombroso, startled the world with his purported "scientific proof" that criminals, by and large, differed from normal human beings in various physical characteristics indicative of "degeneracy." Lombroso's theory was soon deflated by an onslaught of contradictory evidence. Years later, in 1939, Professor Earnest Hooton again attempted to prove, on the basis of his studies, that criminals as a group tended to have in more than ordinary degree such characteristics as low foreheads, compressed faces, narrow jaws, very small ears, extremes of broad or thin noses, etc.—all of which he regarded as evidence of "organic inferiority" and "primitivism." He also sought to show that specific types of crimes tend to go with specific physiques, and even more, with specific races or ethnic groups because of their *biological* differences. We cite this only for the record, because Dr. Hooton's contentions have stood up little better under professional attack than Lombroso's.

In refutation, one of the greatest of anthropologists, the late Dr. Alex Hrdlicka, brought forth (in 1940) his own detailed measurements of 1,000 juvenile delinquents as proof that there were no physical criteria for distinguishing the "potential" criminal or the "criminal type." He and others also pointed out that while persons in prisons or reformatories tend to be more physically defective or abnormal than average persons—for a variety of social and psychological reasons—there is no evidence whatsoever that any specific abnormality or defect goes with any kind of criminal tendency. Similarly, recent studies have shown that brain-wave recordings of criminals, or fingerprint and palm-print patterns, are essentially no different from those of average persons.*

Most closely approaching factual evidence—and even here there is room for doubt—have been studies of criminality in twins. Professor J. Lange, who studied twins in German prisons (prior to World War II), reported that in almost every instance where one member of a pair of identical twins had taken to crime, the other also had become a criminal. Further, the types of crime committed by the twins were the same, or closely related. Among fraternal twins (who share some, but not all, of the same hereditary factors) he did not find this similarity. A later study of crime in twins was made in the United States by Dr. A. A. Rosanoff and others, who also reported (1941) a much closer correlation in criminal behavior in identical twins than in "fraternals." Of 137 sets of identical twins, where one member was delinquent or "disordered," so was the other in all but 18 cases, whereas among 272 sets of fraternal twins (like and unlike sex included), there were 170 cases where only one of the pair was "bad."

These twin studies are open to several interpretations. From one angle, it might be argued that the much greater likelihood of two identical twins taking a criminal path together is evidence of their

* More recently, Dr. William H. Sheldon and several others have suggested that there is a general correlation between juvenile delinquency and body build (the "somatotype"). Dr. Carl C. Seltzer reported (1950) on a study of the physical characteristics of 500 delinquent boys, aged 9 to 17 years, each compared with a non-delinquent boy matched for similar age, background, IQ and ethnic stock. The findings were that the delinquents as a group not only were *not* physically inferior, but, on the contrary, tended to be "superior" in physique by ordinary standards, i.e., more "masculine" and "mesomorphic," with superior development of the arms, shoulders, chest, waist and neck, narrower hips and smaller lower extremities. While not implying that there is any fixed "criminal" type or that criminal tendencies are inborn, Dr. Seltzer did conclude that "personality traits which under certain circumstances predispose to criminality or criminal behavior are correlated with certain somatic characteristics found in greater proportion in the delinquent than in the non-delinquent population." (The report was given at the Cold Spring Harbor Symposium, Carnegie Institution, June, 1950. A number of geneticists present questioned its implications with regard to inherited factors.)

having the same inherited tendency to do so. From another angle, one can concentrate on the exceptions as proof that even with the same heredity, but with slight differences in environment, one person can become a criminal and the other not. Or, if we compare identical and fraternal twins, it might be argued that while the identical pairs are much more apt to proceed together on a criminal path, it may be not only or because they have the same heredity, but because they also, as a rule, are much more likely than fraternal twins to have had the same social and psychological environments.

Another approach in the search for a biological basis for criminal behavior has been by way of mental factors. In former years it was accepted as fact that crime and mental defect or disease were directly correlated, and, therefore, that persons who inherited defective or abnormal mentality were more or less predisposed toward criminality. (Some "authorities" were sure that if we could prevent the breeding of mentally defective or insane persons, we could reduce crime to a fraction.) Recent studies have thrown much cold water on this concept. Intelligence tests reveal not only that the majority of criminals are of average and normal mentality, but that a considerable proportion (especially those convicted of forgery, larceny, embezzlement, etc.) are of superior intelligence. True, the over-all IQ in prisons and reformatories may be considerably below average, but contributing to this in at least some degree is the fact that persons of low intelligence are more likely to get caught doing wrongful acts, and to be sentenced to institutions, than are cleverer persons who commit the same crimes.

Less important than the IQ in crime may be the degree of "emotional maturity" or emotional stability of the individual. Here there is evidence that many, if not most habitual criminals are persons who have failed to "grow up" emotionally and psychologically, and who, despite their having a sense of right and wrong, are averse to discipline, resent authority, are selfish, and are unable to adjust properly and happily to others. In only some of these cases can the underlying factors be linked with personality disorders, such as a "psychopathic personality," which may have an hereditary basis.

To generalize, it might be inferred that the more conscious, rational and deliberate a crime is, the less likely it is to involve any constitutional predisposition. Or, the other way around, the closest to the "biological" criminal would be the one who is closest in behavior to the lower animal; that is, one whose acts arise through lack of moral feeling, social responsibility or an inherently warped or disordered mind.

The principal difficulty in trying to track down hereditary factors in crime is that we are not dealing with a clearly measurable trait, and certainly not with a single type of act. In fact, most authorities would agree today that crime is not an act in itself but the *nature* of a given act, which can be judged only by the intent behind it and the circumstances under which it is committed. The act of killing a man, for instance, is by no means always murder. There are killings in the line of duty—by police officials or soldiers; accidental killings; killings in irresponsible fits of insanity, etc. And where sanity begins and ends in killings is not always easy to establish, as is often shown by the completely conflicting opinions presented in the same court case by psychiatrists.

Even where killings are unquestionably rational and deliberate murders, the motives and reasoning behind them may be so varied as to make it difficult to classify the murderers as of any one type, and hence, to link their acts to any one kind of heredity. Can one consider the slaying by a jealous husband of his wife's lover, or the killing by a distracted father of his idiot son, as acts similar in nature to cold-blooded machine-gun murders by paid gangsters? Not even an "urge to kill" can be considered as a trait peculiar to murderers, for if we are to accept the belief of psychoanalysts, the impulse to kill somebody at one time or another is latent in almost all human beings. What sets murderers apart from others is that *they carry through this impulse*. The question, then, is whether or not in some individuals the "killing point" is reached more quickly because of something in their heredity.

The same thing could be said about almost any other crime—theft, burglary, embezzlement, assault, rape, prostitution, etc.: That it is not merely the impulse to commit a flagrant offense, but the carrying out of the act, which principally distinguishes the criminal from the non-criminal. Equally important, it is not any isolated act or acts, but a whole and consistent pattern of behavior which characterizes criminal conduct.

Thus, there may be a tendency to overemphasize the point that almost every one of us at one time or another has been guilty of some offense, which, judged solely by itself, might have been technically punishable by a reformatory or prison sentence. Dr. Austin L. Porterfield found this to be true of nearly all the students in a

Texas *divinity* college..Another study, by the Randen Foundation, of a cross section of almost 2,000 men and women in New York state, revealed that 99 per cent had committed some act technically punishable by six months or more imprisonment, ranging from malicious mischief to thefts (stealing towels, spoons, stamps), robbery, gambling, fraud, assault, etc.

Nevertheless, as we said before, it would be mere quibbling not to distinguish between the majority of persons who are only occasional transgressors in minor respects, and those who go to extremes in vicious and flagrant wrongdoing, and who consistently act in a way which by any civilized standards would be considered criminal. There is no reason why we cannot draw a line here, as well as we can between persons who are occasionally and mildly sick and those who suffer from serious chronic diseases and disabilities, or between those who crack up temporarily and only under severe stress, and those who with little or no stress become insane. As with extremes in other traits, then, the possibility remains open that *degrees of susceptibility or resistance to criminal behavior may be inherited.* But for the time being this is purely speculation.*

Whatever may be the possibility that "Heredity loads the gun" in crime, there is little question of the way in which "Environment pulls the trigger."

Throughout the United States enormous differences in the rates for murders and other crimes are found in various sections, states and cities, which have little relationship to the ancestral origins or biological makeup of their populations. Almost uniformly the murder rates for *Whites* in southern cities are far greater than in most northern cities, including Chicago and New York. Within the North itself, the murder rate in Chicago averages annually at least ten times that in Milwaukee, ninety miles away. Yet no one would claim that Whites of the South have a much more "murderous" heredity than those of the North, or that the people of Chicago are inherently ten times as murderous as those of Milwaukee. So with any

* Professor Sheldon Glueck of Harvard writes, in his book, *Crime and Justice:* "A tendency to law-abidingness is not something we are born with. To be able to guide one's conduct in accordance with ethical and legal standards requires hard and ceaseless effort. All about us are the pressures and pulls and temptations of life. . . . Some persons are relatively impervious to deleterious influences, while others are easily affected by them. . . . In criminal conduct, therefore, as in most other forms of human expression, every person has his own breaking-point. Thus, the criminal act occurring at any given time is the outcome of constitutional and acquired and social forces."

communities or regions, in this country or abroad, which present radical contrasts in crime rates, we can find the explanation very easily in environmental differences. Wherever living conditions are worse, poverty and ignorance proportionately more widespread, police more inefficient or corrupt, courts more lax, *and people more tolerant of wrongdoing,* there the murder and crime rates will be higher.

Perhaps you remember this story:

In a "hell-roaring" mining town of Wild West days, there was a commotion one evening. An old Forty-niner stuck his head out of a barroom and saw his son being led to jail by the sheriff.

"Hey!" he called out. "What's my Willy done?"

The sheriff yelled back, "He got mad and killed one of them eastern dudes!"

"Shucks," said the old-timer, going back to his tippling, "I thought mebbe Willy'd stole a horse."

This is not so far-fetched. Horse-stealing was a hanging offense in the frontier days, when a murder was often looked upon as an indiscretion. A not-too-dissimilar easy attitude toward murder on the part of juries today, coupled with lack of restriction against "totin' a gun," has a lot to do with high murder rates, not only in individual sections of the country but in the United States as a whole compared with European countries. Or, at least, the latter *used* to be true.

In the years preceding World War II the murder rate in the United States was far above that of almost any European country. For homicides (including manslaughter), the rate in large American cities was almost *twenty times* that in England, and about three to four times that in Germany or Italy, with the rates of other counries somewhere in between. Knowing that the hereditary factors of the people in the United States could be no different, collectively, from those of their European progenitors, the conclusion was obvious that there was something in the environment of this country which tended to produce more murders. But think how quickly the situation could change!

In the space of a few years, Germany (some of whose authorities had previously pointed to the much higher murder rate in the United States as evidence of "barbarism" and "biological inferiority") shocked the world with an avalanche of crimes more horrible in their cruelty and viciousness than the world had ever known.

One need hardly elaborate on the grim facts: how millions of helpless civilians were tortured and murdered; how persons of the highest cultural levels—many doctors and scientists among them—participated in the most fiendish acts; and how, even disregarding the Nazi state policy, in innumerable instances revolting crimes were committed by individuals with the basest personal motives.

Psychologists some day may offer a full explanation of the Nazi reign of terror. Whatever their findings, it will stand forever as proof of how human beings—*almost any group of human beings*—can react in a degraded environment. For, just as we said before that there can be nothing inherently more criminal in Americans than in Europeans, scientists would still say, without question, that *there was and is nothing inherently more criminal in the Germans* as a whole people than in those of any other country. (If anything more were needed to prove this, it could be shown in the splendid record for law observance made by persons of German ancestry in the United States—who, incidentally, comprise almost half the population of Milwaukee, one of the most law-abiding cities of the country!)

The foregoing can be just as well applied to people of other stocks, racial, ethnic or national. Unfortunately, there has been a persistent belief in the United States that differences in crime rates among persons of different foreign stocks or races were in large measure hereditary. This belief was one of the important reasons for checking immigration and fixing quotas. For instance, it was felt that immigrants from southern and eastern Europe would have many more among them *inherently* predisposed to criminality than those from England, Germany or the Scandinavian countries.

How true was the theory that Italians were more "hot-blooded," and therefore more easily moved to murder, or crime in general, than other people? Statistics did show that in certain large cities there was a higher percentage of murders by Italians than by *native* Whites of some other stocks. But further investigation revealed that the comparison was unfair, because the mass of Italians in these cities lived under conditions more than ordinarily unfavorable. Moreover, many of the murders by Italians which received most attention were committed by transplanted members or affiliates of the old Mafia or Black Hand, who had no more in common with other Italians than some of our native gangsters had with other Americans. Finally, in recent years studies have shown that the crime rate among second-generation Italians is hardly greater than among other native Whites.

The whole question of crime in relation to our foreign-born was thoroughly investigated some years ago by the National Commission on Law Observance and Enforcement. Studying the "high delinquency" areas, or slums in American cities, the commission found that while these areas were inhabited largely by the foreign-born, it was not the nationalities of the people, but the conditions surrounding them, that produced the high crime rates. Although the nationalities of the people in these areas changed almost completely over a period of twenty years, the rate of delinquency in these areas remained about the same. Furthermore, when the older national groups moved to more favorable sections, the delinquency among their children consistently declined.

In the matter of presumed race differences, there is the popular impression that Negroes are also *by nature* more "hot-blooded" and inherently more criminal than other people. But it is becoming increasingly apparent that if bad conditions can explain high crime rates among Whites, the immeasurably worse conditions under which most Negroes live could quite easily account for their still higher crime rates, without blaming their heredity. Also to be borne in mind is that the *recorded* crime rate of American Negroes is vastly magnified by the fact that for any given offense they usually are much more likely to be arrested, convicted and sentenced heavily than are Whites (most obviously true in the southern states).

In making comparisons previously between crime rates in the South and North, we referred, as you may have noted, to the rates for *Whites only*. For another wrong assumption is that the very high crime rates in southern cities can be blamed chiefly on their large Negro populations. While the higher percentages of Negroes—and accordingly, of the most underprivileged groups—do help to swell southern crime rates, their presence is by no means the sole or determining factor. This was proved in the 1948 studies by Professor Austin L. Porterfield of Texas Christian University who devised a "crime index" by which the relative numbers of serious crimes for each state (murder, assault, robbery, burglary, etc.) were measured against the national crime averages for 1946. With this index, Dr. Porterfield showed, among other things, that there was no direct relationship between the size of the Negro population and the overall rate of crime. Mississippi, with the largest percentage of Negroes

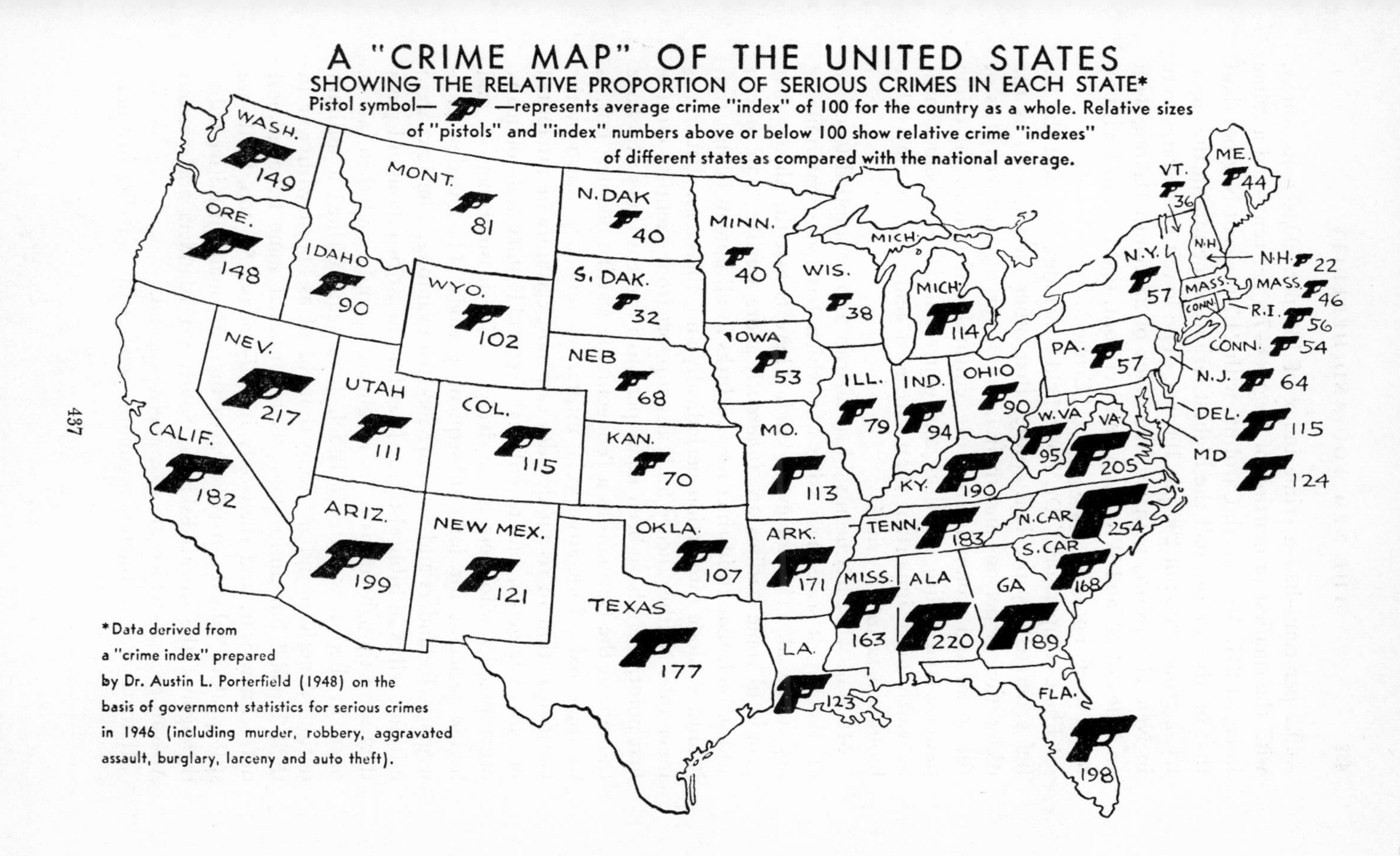
A "CRIME MAP" OF THE UNITED STATES
SHOWING THE RELATIVE PROPORTION OF SERIOUS CRIMES IN EACH STATE*
Pistol symbol— —represents average crime "index" of 100 for the country as a whole. Relative sizes of "pistols" and "index" numbers above or below 100 show relative crime "indexes" of different states as compared with the national average.
WASH. 149
ORE. 148
CALIF. 182
NEV. 217
IDAHO 90
MONT. 81
WYO. 102
UTAH 111
ARIZ. 199
COL. 115
NEW MEX. 121
N. DAK 40
S. DAK. 32
NEB 68
KAN. 70
OKLA. 107
TEXAS 177
MINN. 40
IOWA 53
MO. 113
ARK. 171
LA. 123
WIS. 38
ILL. 79
MICH.
MICH. 114
IND. 94
OHIO 90
KY. 190
TENN. 183
MISS. 163
ALA 220
GA 189
FLA. 198
S. CAR 168
N. CAR 254
W. VA 95
VA. 205
PA. 57
N.Y. 57
VT. 36
ME. 44
N.H
N.H. 22
MASS.
MASS. 46
CONN.
R.I. 56
CONN. 54
N.J. 64
DEL. 115
MD 124
*Data derived from a "crime index" prepared by Dr. Austin L. Porterfield (1948) on the basis of government statistics for serious crimes in 1946 (including murder, robbery, aggravated assault, burglary, larceny and auto theft).

—49.2 per cent—had a crime index of 136 per 100,000. Kentucky, with the smallest proportion of Negroes—7.5 per cent—had a crime index of 237. And North Carolina, with 24.7 per cent Negroes (half that of Mississippi), had the highest serious-crime rate in the country, a crime index of 296 per 100,000. (The lowest crime rates were in New Hampshire, with a crime index of 22, South Dakota, with an index of 32, and Wisconsin and Vermont, tied for third with an index of 26. For other rates see our "Crime Map.")

"These comparisons," Dr. Porterfield concludes, "support the belief generated by previous studies that other factors, such as the dislocation of persons and their families, varying characteristics of the social and economic structure, cultural variation in the crime patterns and police practices, and general social well-being, must be vastly more important than race as a genic fact, or any other biological factor in crime."

Much of what has been said so far can also be applied to crime on the largest scale—aggressive war which lets loose mass murder and wholesale crime of every kind. There is first the theory that people of some nations are *inherently* more warlike than others; and second, that an instinct for war lurks in all human beings, that it must explode into action periodically and, therefore, that war is inevitable. Neither theory finds any support from scientists. On the first point, there have been many persons in recent times who have thought of the Germans as a "congenitally warlike people," but, as we indicated before, any special militaristic tendency shown by the German nation in recent decades can most certainly be attributed not to their genes, but to cultural factors. History tells of many other peoples who were aggressively warlike in some periods and highly peaceful for long subsequent periods. The Swedes, Norwegians, Icelanders and Swiss are modern examples. The Jews were militant tribes in biblical times; later for almost two thousand years they were thought of as a "non-fighting" people, and then, all at once, in their new state of Israel, Jews again formed a militant nation. American Indians were thought of as "born with war in their blood," but anthropologists tell us that some tribes almost never knew war, and then only in self-defense. So, too, while we still speak of "blood-thirsty" savages, there are many primitive tribes throughout the world—Eskimos, South Sea Islanders and various African groups—which are extremely peaceful.

If there are no differences among peoples in "warring instinct" there is still the assumption that the "instinct" is equally present among all peoples. And here the principal fallacy is thinking of war as a "return to the animal state." Quite the opposite is true. While bloody clashes may occur between *individuals* in the lower animal kingdom (usually between males in the mating seasons), battles between two large groups of mammals of the same species are unknown. Among man's nearest animal relatives, the anthropoid apes, there are no wars. (Dr. Edward L. Thorndike cited the fact that among howler monkeys, when a clash between an invading "nation" and a defending "nation" occurs it takes the form of a "howling" contest, in which the group that out-howls the other is victorious. But not a drop of blood is spilled, nor anything destroyed.) Furthermore, if war had an "instinctive" basis, wars would occur most readily between peoples who differed most in their biological makeup. Yet many of the bloodiest wars in history have taken place between the most closely related stocks (the wars among the Indians and among African tribes, the civil wars in the United States, in Spain and China, various European wars, etc.). And in World Wars I and II the lineup of sides had nothing whatsoever to do with their ethnic or racial affiliations.

There is, therefore, much to prove that murderous wars between large groups of humans are not prompted by any *biological* urges. If official verdicts are needed, there is the statement drawn up by 2,000 American psychologists in 1945 with the conclusion, "no race, nation or social group is inevitably warlike"; and the declaration by an international group of scientists, convened in 1948 by the United Nations (UNESCO): "There is no evidence that wars are necessary and inevitable consequences of 'human nature' as such."

The discussion of war brings up another important fact: That active waging of war has always been almost entirely confined to males, for obvious reasons related principally to the biological differences between the sexes which govern their rôles and functions. (Stories of "Amazons" of the past have proved to be largely myths; nor do any minor new trends with respect to female participation in war alter the main implications.) This leads us to the point that in all behavior associated with killing, violence or other crimes, there also are marked distinctions between women and men. Are these differences, too, like the rôles of the sexes in war, *biologically conditioned?*

Consider the statistics: About *twenty-five times as many males as females* are in prisons and reformatories in the United States. In *convictions* for different offenses the yearly average runs to about ten times as many men as women for murder and manslaughter, about seventy-five times as many men for robbery, 120 times as many for burglary, more than twenty times as many for larceny, twenty-five times as many for forgery, etc. Making full allowances for the fact that men usually are more severely dealt with by law, there is no question but that anywhere in the world women commit vastly fewer criminal acts. The evidence is also clear that wherever restraints against women are relaxed, or social conditions become disorganized, their relative crime rates shoot up. This has been happening in the United States, especially in murders. Where once murder was thought of as the typically "masculine" crime, the figures just given show that the ratio of killings by women, as compared with those by men, is now relatively much higher than for other major crimes. (The knowledge that chivalrous juries usually acquit fair murderesses after they have dutifully recited, "He struck me . . . then everything went black . . ." must be considered as having been a spur to many women with an urge to dispose permanently of some annoying male.)

Nonetheless, "conditioning" may not be the whole answer for sex differences in crime. In any offense involving aggression, we must note that among lower animals, too, the males are more likely to indulge in acts of violence than are females. All the way from male mice, dogs and cats, through roosters and rams to bulls, bull moose and bull elephants, the male is more rambunctious and harder to keep in check than the female. Nor do human mothers have to depend on psychological studies to convince them that from babyhood on, boys show more tendency toward unruliness, aggressiveness and destructiveness than do girls. Thus, while as with other complex traits, there can be no genes for criminal behavior carried by males and not by females, the possibility remains that over-all sex differences in biological makeup and functioning might in some measure contribute to a greater degree of criminality by the males in any given environment.

There is, however, one type of wrongdoing—*prostitution*—which, for biological reasons, is almost exclusively female. (The exception is only with respect to prostitution among homosexual males.) Here is one of the clearest examples of where the wrongdoing lies not in the act itself but in the psychological circumstances under which it it is carried out, and the way in which it is regarded by others. For, basically, aside from the moral factors, prostitution is not "abnormal," nor is it everywhere considered as wrongdoing. In his notable studies of chimpanzees, Professor Robert M. Yerkes revealed that many ape females take advantage of the fact that their sexual capacities are much greater than those of males to wheedle food in exchange for sexual accommodation. He concluded, ". . . Prostitution is a natural development among the primates."

The principle involved in prostitution—of promiscuously exchanging sex favors merely for money or some other practical return—is capable of so many applications and interpretations that it would be impossible to draw clear-cut distinctions among large numbers of women on this basis. What we can do only is to limit the term to those who engage in acts of prostitution professionally and wilfully, with full knowledge that the acts are morally or legally wrong. As with other wrongdoing (although prostitution is peculiar to itself), the question is then whether there is in some women a special inherent quirk which impels them toward this behavior.

The one fact of which there is no doubt is that prostitution is fostered by bad social environments—poverty, improper upbringing, the chaotic conditions of war and its aftermath, etc. Yet, even in the worst environments, only a limited number of women become prostitutes; and in the best of environments, where good jobs or opportunities for marriage are plentiful, many women take to the profession out of preference. Moreover, while studies of prostitutes tend to show that a higher than average proportion of them are mentally defective or psychopathic, many will be found who are of superior intelligence, and many also who come from good homes. Another common assumption is that prostitutes start off as women carried away by abnormal sexual desires. But studies by Dr. Tage Kemp of Copenhagen, and by others, show that few prostitutes are oversexed or perverted. In fact, many authorities incline to the belief that prostitutes are more often *undersexed,* and that their comparative lack of emotion and their indifference to sex relations facilitate their taking up and carrying on their pursuit.

From all these observations it may be concluded that by whatever devious ways women may be led into prostitution, no inherent constitutional basis for the "oldest of the professions" has yet been established.

In a special category are those acts which do not necessarily involve offenses against others—though they can often lead to such—but are primarily offenses against the individual himself. Included among these are *alcoholism, drug addiction* and *suicide*. While these acts are regarded as violations of laws, morals or religious codes (but not universally), the modern scientific view holds them to be mainly expressions of personality disorders or diseases. Whether they should be treated at all under the heading of "crime" is another question.

The theory that *alcoholism* has an hereditary basis starts off with the clear evidence that it "runs" in certain families far more than in others. One would easily argue that it is because of precept and association, in the way that other bad habits can be passed along. But there are authorities who doubt that this is the complete answer. (From practical experience we know that some individuals enjoy the taste of whisky almost at once, and others can't abide it; that some people require a great deal of alcohol to make them drunk, and others get "high"—or sick—on one or two drinks; that some persons can't seem to stop drinking, and others can "take it or leave it" at will.) Thus, while there is general agreement that environmental influences may largely determine whether and how alcoholism develops, there is also the belief that differences in *predisposition* to alcoholism, as to many other conditions, may be governed by heredity. One possibility, long held forth, is that this "predisposition" may work through mental or emotional factors (as in the case of severe neuroses or psychoses). More recently there have been theories that inherited peculiarities in the metabolic or chemical workings of individuals may be involved.*

Dr. Roger J. Williams and his associates of the University of Texas caused a stir among scientists in 1949 by reporting that various strains of rats and mice showed marked hereditary differences in their "alcohol appetites" which were bound up with dietary factors (the setting up of "blockages" with respect to the proper utilization of needed foods). Assuming that these findings regarding potential "rodent drunkards" can be applied to humans, Dr.

* The theory that alcoholism may often result from a disturbance in the functioning of the pituitary gland, and that treatment with pituitary and adrenal hormones may be effective for chronic alcoholism, was advanced in 1950 by Dr. James J. Smith, of the New York University-Bellevue Medical Center. Another recent treatment being experimented with is the Jacobsen-Hald treatment, originating in Denmark, and involving the administration of a certain drug (*"antabus"*) which produces a violent revulsion to alcohol.

Williams advanced the theory that "alcoholic craving which develops in compulsive drinkers constitutes a perverted appetite as a result of one or more dietary deficiencies." Further, he suggested that if means could be found to correct these deficiencies, heavy drinking in individuals could be greatly reduced.

Another study, reported in 1944 by a group of doctors of the Shadel Sanitarium for Alcoholics, of Seattle, Washington (Dr. F. Lemere and associates), stressed the theory that alcoholism may be tied up with a form of allergy. After finding that a family history of inebriety occurred in about two-thirds of the 500 alcoholics studied (four times the incidence in normal drinkers) and that there were indications of "a specific inheritance of the disease in many cases," the Seattle researches concluded: "The usual explanation that alcoholism is simply an expression of an underlying neurosis or inadequacy is insufficient. . . . Rather, alcoholics seem to have an innate susceptibility to alcohol which we believe is akin to an allergy to a food or an idiosyncrasy to a drug. . . . The inheritance is that of an abnormal reaction to alcohol in that the effects of the drug are more attractive and less obnoxious than in the normal drinker."

These theories, of course, are yet to be proved. In the meantime, the unquestioned fact is that whether or not there are inherited degrees of "predisposition," alcoholism can be greatly increased or decreased in any group by the training of the individuals concerned. We see this in the enormous differences in the rates of alcoholism among persons of different nationalities and religious groups, without regard to their heredity; in the radical increase in drinking in certain groups where it was hitherto unknown; and particularly, in the great increase in alcoholism among women. Essentially then, whatever inherited factors may be involved in alcoholism, it is, like crime, primarily a social and psychological problem.

Drug addiction, though given much less study than alcoholism, may be considered as involving approximately the same basic factors. (In one group of drug addicts it was shown that a third had started off as alcoholics.) However, there are certain differences in the psychological and emotional factors associated with the two habits. Principally, the much stronger legal and social pressures against drug addiction (in most civilized countries) and the greater difficulty, expense and furtiveness involved in pursuing the habit, make it likely, as a rule, that drug addicts will start off as initially more unstable, with more personality disorders and with a greater disregard for convention, than is the case with alcoholics. At any rate, strong government action in fighting drug addiction and the sale of drugs has resulted in the fact that, while the incidence of alcoholism has been increasing, the number of drug addicts has been cut to less than one-third in the past thirty-five years from what it used to be in the United States—or down to about 48,000 in 1948.

Suicide—the ultimate of "self-offenses"—is included in this chapter because under various religions (Catholic and Orthodox Jewish among them) and under common law in many countries, it is regarded as "wilful destruction of life" and therefore as a crime, with attempt at suicide being punishable as a misdemeanor. (Some psychiatrists maintain that suicide is indeed in many cases not the desire to die, but the desire to kill, which, for lack of some definable other victim, may cause the individual to act against himself. It may be the active expression of a childish impulse to say to an offending grownup, "You'll be sorry when I'm dead!")

With regard to possible hereditary influences, there have been a number of studies which have seemingly tended to give support to the popular belief that suicide "runs" in certain families. In a recent (1950) review of these studies, with the addition of new findings regarding the extreme rarity of double suicides among identical twins, Dr. Franz J. Kallmann and his associates tend to discount the theory that any special hereditary trait or particular type of "inherited personality deviation" is involved in suicidal tendencies. Considering the fact that *under present conditions one in fifty males in the United States ends his life by suicide,* they believe that statistical chance might allow for as many as 500 cases a year in which two brothers in a family committed suicide without there being any need to account for this on any basis other than coincidence.

However, other authorities have pointed to the fact that a high proportion of the suicides—perhaps as many as one-half—are linked with mental instability or diseases (chiefly manic-depressive insanity, and also schizophrenia), and that to the extent that heredity is involved in these conditions, it may be an indirect influence in individual suicides, and may in some cases account for a number of suicides in the same family. Moreover, in many cases where suicides are attributed to such causes as "unrequited love," "loss of honor," "overwork," "failures" of various kinds, etc., it is possible that hidden elements of mental disease, with some hereditary basis, may have played a part. But that there is any direct hereditary tendency toward suicide itself is highly questionable.

Environmental factors in suicide can be identified with little effort. One need hardly look for any "suicide" genes to account for the countless thousands of suicides during the Nazi reign of terror, when helpless individuals were faced with the certainty of torture and extermination. The great increases in suicides during depression periods in the United States are also as much the result of environment as are the drops in suicide during wartime and in periods of prosperity.

Less easily attributable to environmental factors in their entirety are the marked differences in suicide rates between males and females almost everywhere in the world. Year in and out in the United States the average for all ages is about four times as many suicides by men as by women, with the rate in the older-age groups (from 70 onward) being about six to seven times as high for men. Greater strains on men when they are failures, or are incapacitated, or "lose face," conditioned differences in attitude toward suicide, and other social factors, may account for part of the higher male suicide rate; but we have also seen that, genetically, men are more likely than women to be afflicted by degenerative diseases or other ills which may make life seem unbearable.

Both inner and outer pressures, therefore, must be considered as working together in producing suicides. Apart from this, the attitude toward suicide anywhere (as toward murder) has much to do with its frequency. Where the act is regarded as serious wrongdoing, or a confession of cowardice, suicides are at a minimum. (They are reported as almost unknown among the Arabs.) In contrast, where suicide is thought of as an honorable deed, as is the case among the Japanese (the Kamikaze pilots of World War II having provided many examples) the suicide rate is high. In our own country, the rise in suicides in recent decades, often attributed to increased tension of modern life, might be equally associated with growing "individualism" and a modification of the attitude toward self-destruction.

This brings us to the point that, in general, the whole subject of "right-" and "wrongdoing" among humans rests on the shifting sands of prevailing social viewpoints. Murder may at one time and place be condemned and in another time and place be extolled as a noble act—as, for instance, political assassinations in many countries.

Theft is a virtue among certain Bedouins. Prostitution has been and still is considered among some peoples a "respectable" or even noble calling. Taking of graft and bribes by public officials has been—or was, at least—accepted as "smart practice" among the Chinese (not to mention among many groups in the United States). There is probably not a crime, social breach or type of dereliction that in certain localities in the world, or at certain places in our own country, is not considered quite proper.

To sum up: Genetic studies of the possible rôle of heredity in human wrongdoing bog down because of our inability to disentangle any inherent crime tendencies from the environmental factors in which they are enmeshed. Only if and when we can definitely identify crimes of each type as going with specific behavior patterns, when we can measure degrees of these patterns even to the extent that we can measure intelligence, and when we can find these behavior patterns appearing spontaneously in individuals without regard to their environments or contacts—only when and if this becomes possible will the geneticist be equipped with the facts needed to prove that there are genes for "criminality." Until then we can only speculate that there may be such genes—though they would have to be of an exceedingly complex nature—which may work indirectly to produce degrees of "susceptibility" to criminal behavior, in the way that there are genes producing degrees of susceptibility or predisposition to other complex traits.

In the meantime, we have no proof of a direct correlation between any specific crime and any given type of body structure, physical characteristic, mental state or racial identity. On the other hand, it seems to be clear that an atmosphere of degradation, ignorance and poverty will breed crime, and that lax prosecution or public indifference to any type of crime will foster its development.

So, while the possibility remains that factors inherent in individuals may have something to do with inclining them toward criminal conduct, and while we should try to set up safeguards against any such tendencies, it is certain that our greatest immediate hope for cutting down the crime rate lies in changing the conditions outside of people.

CHAPTER 40

SEX LIFE

(Sex and Sexual Behavior)

EVERY summer a strange phenomenon occurs in several New England seacoast towns. The resident males are chiefly rugged fishermen, of the most masculine type. But as the vacation season opens, large numbers of a *special kind* of male flock in from the big cities. They tend to be more than ordinarily good-looking; they dress colorfully, though to extremes; they are many of them highly gifted in various talents.

To the unsophisticated girl vacationing there for the first time, the sight of so many attractive young single men may stir high hopes of romance. Alas for her! Very soon she will learn that they have no interest in her as a woman. *The romances of these males are reserved entirely for members of their own sex.*

Luckily, the young lady may presently find other male vacationers who are entirely "normal" from her standpoint. But the questions will linger: What causes the "queer" men to be the way they are? Were they *born* to be like that? Are they really "feminized" males—a biological cross between male and female? Or are they merely *acting* queerly as the result of some peculiar "conditioning"?

These same questions have been asked for centuries by human beings everywhere, for there is no place or time where males of this type have not been known. But there have been many more questions about sexual behavior. About other so-called "perversions" and how they occur. About sexual activity in children. About the great differences in sexual capacity among individuals—the failure of some persons to respond sexually, and the extremes of capacity and indulgence in others. About the differences in sexual behavior between women and men. And, of special interest to us in this book, about what is "natural" in sex—or what is *inherited*—and what isn't.

All of these questions are of the most vital importance in people's lives, for they bear directly on the individual's adjustment to himself and others, on the success or failure of many marriages, on all social relationships. Yet for a long time it was not thought "proper" to inquire into the intimacies of sex. Only in recent decades, with a relaxing of some of the taboos, have scientists begun to make searching investigations in the field. From their findings we will try to draw out here chiefly those facts which might relate to inheritance.

First, a distinction between "sex behavior" and "sexual behavior": The former refers to the general behavior of individuals as members of their sex—the behavior of a girl as compared with a boy, of a woman as compared with a man. The latter refers specifically to behavior in which the *sexual impulses* are expressed in one type of outlet or another. Both forms of behavior are of course closely related, and are in turn interwoven with the whole physical makeup, personality and behavior pattern of the individual. Thus, in sex and sexual behavior we are dealing with perhaps the most complex of all traits, where the problem of digging down to hereditary factors may be the most difficult faced in this book.

As with other traits, we might assume that it is simplest to look for evidence of heredity where there are marked deviations from the "normal." But almost immediately we learn that there are no *scientific standards* for determining precisely what is "normal" or "natural" in sex or sexual behavior. The definitions vary and have varied enormously among the different peoples of the world, being everywhere strongly influenced by training, laws, religions, taboos, customs, habits, etc. Even in our own country, within a few generations, we have seen radical changes in attitudes toward sex.

So without weighing the standards, let us see how the pattern of sex and sexual behavior develops in an average boy or girl—say "Johnny" and his little next-door neighbor "Mary."

In preceding chapters we have noted that as biological mechanisms Johnny and Mary come into the world with many differences. It would be expected, therefore, that their behavior would also show differences. But knowing that little boys and girls aren't ever reared in the same way, we can't be sure how much of their behavior differences result from the workings of their genes and chromosomes, and how much from the influences of their parents and others.

Whys and wherefores aside, evidence from many studies indicate that Johnny, as an average boy baby, will be more active, restless and aggressive than Mary, and, as he continues to grow, will utilize his bigger and stronger muscles in more physically exacting and rugged play. Mary, on the other hand, will show greater deftness in her hand movements, will begin to dress herself earlier and more expertly than Johnny, will be more interested in what she wears and in the colors, and will engage in more sedentary play (*preferring* dolls to his mechanical toys). She will be more keenly aware of people and of details regarding them and will be more jealous of attention, although she will be shyer in front of strangers. She also will be more nervous, being given to more nail-biting and thumb-sucking than Johnny.

These are only some of the many behavior differences which experts have found to characterize little boys and girls *on the average*. They are especially significant because much the same average differences are reflected in the behavior of adult males and females. Is it because the little ones are taught to imitate the adults of their sex? Or is it because the adult patterns evolve from *inherent* early sex differences? Some psychologists incline to the former theory. Other authorities believe that much of the divergence in the behavior of little boys and girls is of biological origin—that the sexes were *born to behave differently*. This would appear to be so not only from studies of infants at the Yale Clinic, but also from much evidence regarding lower animals.

Repeated experiments have shown that changing the hormonal balance in young animals, from the "male" to the "female" direction, or vice versa, automatically changes their behavior. Nothing is more amusing than to see how young female chicks, injected with "male" hormones, become more aggressive, flap their wings and crow with canary-like squeaks. In reverse, young roosters if castrated lose their (literally) "cockiness." If full-grown hens are given heavy dosages of "male" hormones, or full-grown roosters of "female" hormones, there may be a complete reversal of the sex pattern of behavior developed. So, too, experiments with guinea pigs, rats and mice have proved that sex-behavior patterns can be much modified or altered through hormonal treatment. But, in addition to the sex hormones, sex differences in the other hormones (pituitary, adrenal, thyroid, etc.) and in the entire genetic makeup of males and females contribute to their divergent behavior patterns.

Nevertheless, among human males and females it is not so easy to draw a direct line from their biological differences to their behavior differences, because always, in between, there are innumer-

THE "INK-BLOT" TESTS for "MASCULINITY" and "FEMININITY"*

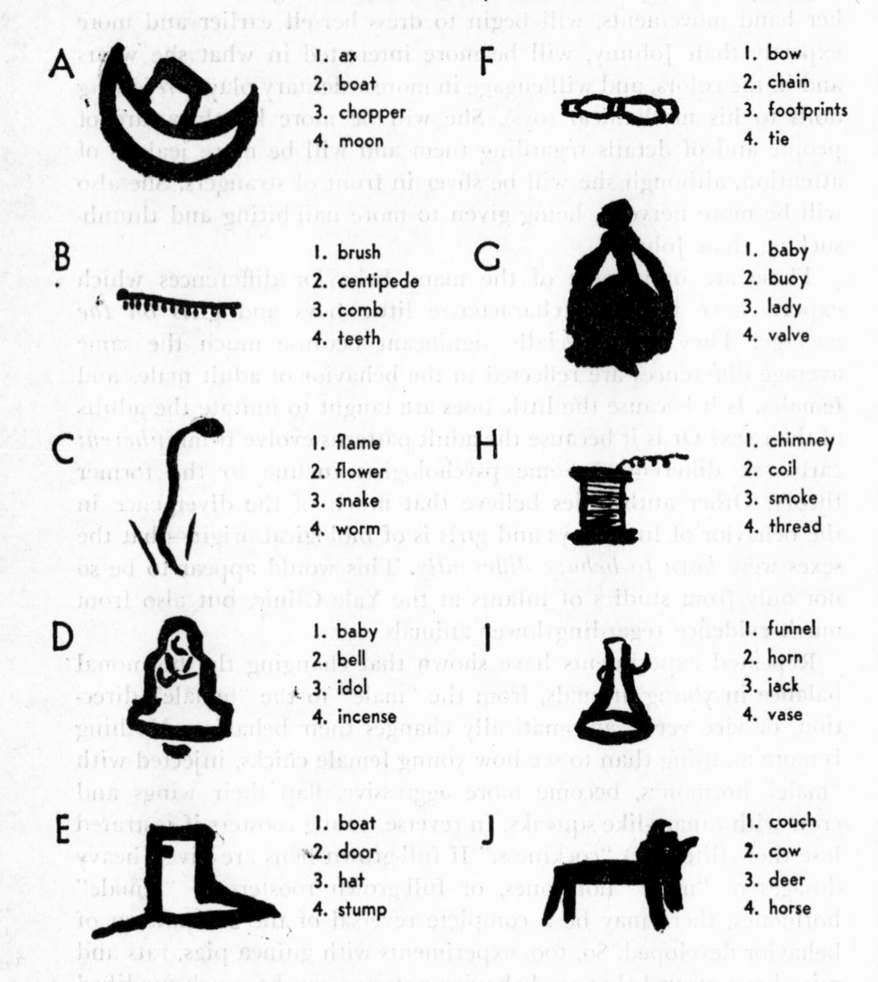

HERE IS HOW THE ANSWERS ARE SCORED:

PICTURE:	A	B	C	D	E	F	G	H	I	J
Masculine:	1, 2, 4	1, 2	2	1, 2	1, 3, 4	2, 3	1, 2, 4	2	3, 4	2
Feminine:	3	3, 4	1, 3, 4	3, 4	2	1, 4	3	3, 4	1, 2	1, 3, 4

* *From "Sex and Personality", by Terman and Miles*

able environmental influences. Most important is the fact that in every human group there is a prescribed behavior pattern considered "normal" for each sex, and that any too great departure from this pattern will bring with it social disapproval, and often punishment.

While it is true, as we said before, that the standards for sex and sexual behavior may vary greatly from one society or group to another, the main concepts of what is "masculine" or "feminine" have been surprisingly uniform throughout the world, among both civilized and primitive peoples, with very few exceptions. With "masculinity" are supposed to go strength, virility, bravery, aggressiveness, enterprise, interest in mechanical things, outdoor activity, adventurousness, etc. With "femininity" are linked domesticity, sedentary activity, softness, tenderness, emotionality, affection, sentimentality, etc. The patterns prescribed are certainly not always in accord with the facts—or with biology. But one must grant that they reflect, on the whole, traits which most women would like to see in their men, and most men would like to see in their women.

At any rate, it is on the basis of the accepted standards that tests of "masculinity" and "femininity" were devised by Professor Lewis M. Terman and his associates. These tests comprise a series of questions (the same for both men and women) to which an individual can give either a response considered "masculine" (netting a "+1" mark) or one considered "feminine" (netting a "— 1" mark). It follows that males on the average have fairly high "plus" scores, females fairly high "minus" scores. But as investigators have found (and as most of us know) there are great ranges of "masculinity" and "femininity" within each sex, some males being more "feminine" in their responses than a good many women, and some women being more "masculine" than a good many men.

The highest "masculinity" scores are reported made by college athletes and engineers; the lowest by clergymen, artists and journalists, with male "inverts" (extreme types of males who act like females) being way over on the "feminine" side. A real surprise is that policemen and firemen are reported rather low in "masculinity" scores—presumably because they tend to lack marked mechanical interests and financial objectives, are especially eager for "security" and are amenable to discipline—all rated as "feminine" traits. (Better not tell this to the cop on your street!)

Among women, the most feminine are reported to be domestics,

"MASCULINITY" AND "FEMININITY"

(How various classifications of men and women rank according to average scores in the "M-F" tests)

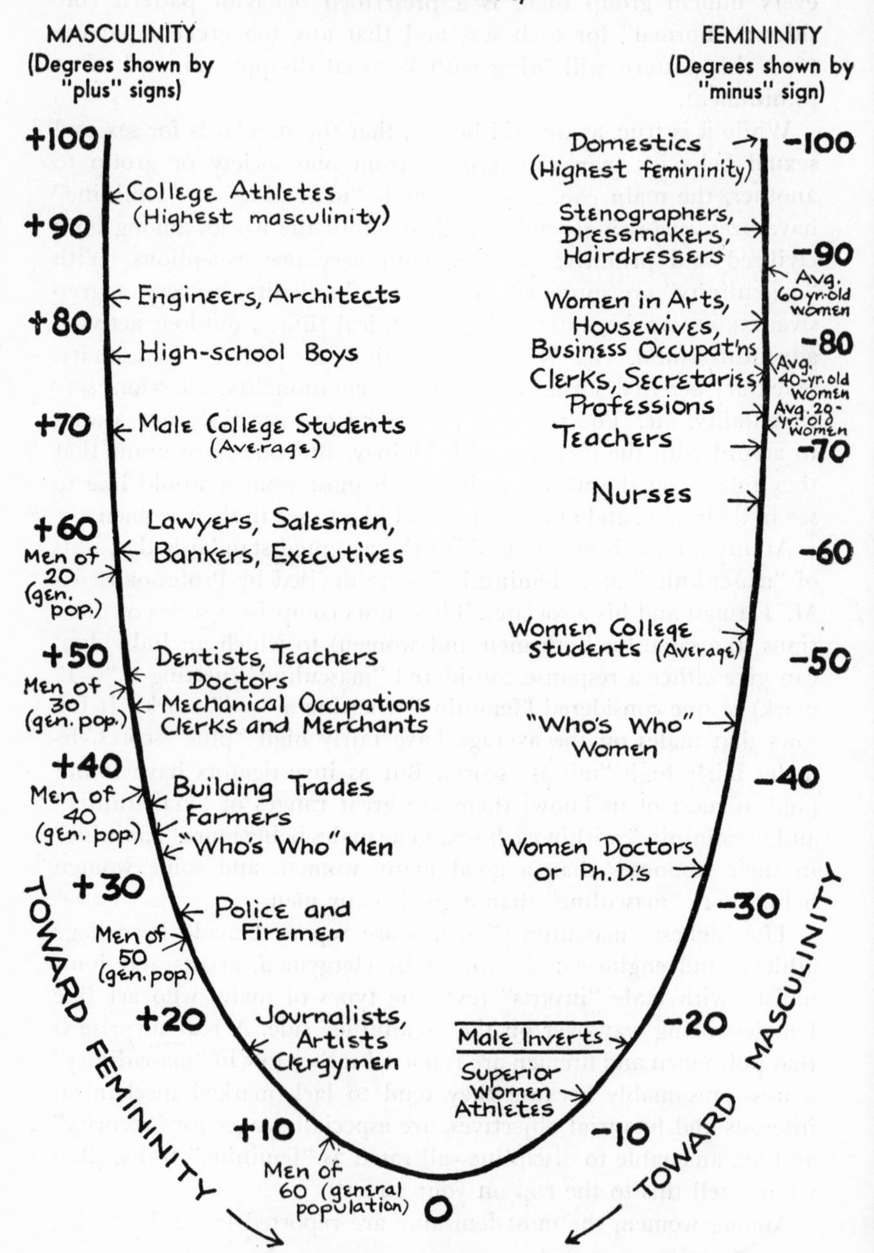

(Based on reports by Terman and Miles in "Sex and Personality")

the least "feminine," female athletes. The "M-F" ratings for other activity groups, as you will note in the accompanying Chart, are not too different from what one generally would expect.

These scores, while possibly indicative of a person's behavior at a given time, can hardly be accepted as an index of *basic* "masculinity" or "femininity." This is clearly shown by the fact that the "M-F" score changes greatly with age, men becoming much more "feminine" in their behavior as they grow older (the "masculinity" average at age 70 being only "—3"), while older women, too, become somewhat more "feminized."

Apart from aging effects, outward physical makeup may give little evidence of one's psychological "masculinity" or "femininity." A rough-looking, ruggedly constructed male, or a heavy-set, masculine woman, may each yet be soft and "feminine" in nature; and a delicate-appearing man, equally with a petite, baby-doll-eyed girl, may be ruthlessly "masculine" in character. Nor are the traits themselves, as measured in the tests, always indicative of true qualities. The man who is daring in physical exploits is not necessarily more courageous, and hence more "masculine" than the artist, writer, musician or clergyman, who, in pursuing their careers, are often called on to cope with mental hazards and situations which call forth the highest types of bravery. And who would question that many women, facing dangers of childbirth or confronting serious emergencies of everyday life, are as brave as the bravest men?

Up to this point we have been thinking chiefly of the behavior of males and females as individuals. Now let us consider another aspect of "sexuality"—social behavior in relation to persons of the opposite sex. So back to childhood again.

Awareness of one's sex is almost the first social fact impressed on a child. To a great extent it comes through conditioning, but even without that, it would soon develop among little boys and girls through the mere perception of the differences in their sex organs. In any case, before childhood is far along, boys and girls identify themselves, or are trained to identify themselves, with members of their own sex.

How the "Boy Meets Girl" story evolves is shown in the accompanying illustration (from the author's book, *Women and Men*) which depicts seven stages in social development, as reported in many studies. First, in infancy, preoccupation with one's self. Then undifferentiated play with children of both sexes. Then preference for one's own sex, with different games for each sex, reaching its height before puberty in marked distinctions and even antagonism between the sex groups. Thereafter the process reverses to some extent, boys showing interest in girls collectively, then in girls individually, and "going in couples" becomes general.

These are not merely "average" stages in the developing male-female social pattern. They are also thought of as *"normal" stages in sexual development.* For, when a boy or girl deviates too sharply from the pattern for each stage, or fails to pass from one stage to another, the beginnings may be there of sexual maladjustment in later life. As examples:

—The individuals who remain in the infantile stage of preoccupation with their own bodies, and who cannot transfer sexual interests to others. Classed with these are the chronic masturbators and the "narcissists"—persons "in love with themselves."

—Those who remain sexually in the "neutral" stage of sexual indifference. They are apt to be individuals very low in sex drives or feelings.

—Those who continue in their strong attachment to their own sex or feel aversion toward the opposite sex, which may lead to homosexuality. On the other hand, those who repudiate their own sex and identify themselves instead with the opposite sex (in actions and interests) may also become homosexuals, of the "invert" type. (They will be dealt with later.)

—Those who never "couple up" or form any strong attachment with an *individual* of the opposite sex. They include the chronic "Don Juans," or their female counterparts, the "Doña Juanas" (the habitual flirts). While seeming to be strongly sexed, they may actually be persons with no deep sex feeling, who never derive full satisfaction from their experiences.

The foregoing gives us, in brief, the main types of "sexual deviation." But what is it that leads individuals of each type to fall out of line at the different stages of sexual development? Are the causes entirely psychological, or are biological influences—and hence, hereditary factors—also involved?

That there must be differences in the biological makeup of individuals which affect their sexual behavior can be taken for granted. We know that in the case of any given person, the state of the body, as it changes or varies throughout life, constantly influences sexual behavior. So comparing different individuals, we can assume that

SEVEN STAGES IN BOY-GIRL RELATIONSHIP

INFANCY-BABYHOOD
Boy and girl interested only in themselves

EARLY CHILDHOOD
Seek companionship of other children, regardless of sex

ABOUT AGE EIGHT
Boys prefer to play with boys, girls with girls

AGES 10 to 12
Antagonism shown between sex groups

AGES 13 to 14
Girls become interested in boys, try to attract their attention; boys aloof

AGES 14 to 16
Boy group also shows interest in girls; some individuals begin to pair off.

AGES 16 to 17, ON
"Going out in couples" becomes general

basic differences in physical makeup, sensory structures and mechanisms, hormonal output, and other biological factors—*all of which are affected by heredity*—may also account for *some* of the differences in sexual behavior (always allowing for the many psychological influences). But this refers chiefly to the *quantity* of a person's sex drive, which might account for degrees of sexual capacity. Quite a different matter is the *direction* taken by the sexual impulses, especially with regard to the "deviations" previously mentioned. Are the persons who engage in these deviations, as we asked before, biologically different in any way from those who do conform to the prevailing sex standards?

An initial requirement is finding out precisely what *is* the sexual behavior of people in general. Many studies have attempted to throw light on this, but no study has ever approached in scope and intensity that undertaken by Professor Alfred C. Kinsey of Indiana University and his associates, Wardell B. Pomeroy, Clyde E. Martin, and others.

Their first published report, in 1948, of *Sexual Behavior in the Human Male,* was considered by many as so "revolutionary" as to require a complete change in all our sex codes, laws and attitudes. (In fact, at one conference, the venerable Dr. Robert L. Dickinson, dean of American sexologists, was moved to say, "From now on all of our sex knowledge will be spoken of as 'B.K.' and 'A.K.'—'Before Kinsey' and 'After Kinsey.' ") But there also have been some dissenting opinions.

Most of our readers know something by now about the Kinsey studies. With an eventual goal of 100,000 case histories, the first Kinsey report presented statistics regarding 5,300 American males, while a second report, awaiting publication at this writing, will present facts regarding about 8,000 females. Each of these persons was questioned in great detail concerning every phase of his or her sex life, bearing principally on the beginnings, nature and frequency of all types of sexual outlet. From the vast amount of data, many inferences and conclusions were drawn. Some of the general findings are in line with those from earlier studies. More startling are the new findings with respect to marked differences in male and female sexual behavior. But the real "dynamite" in the Kinsey report lies in the great incidences claimed for homosexuality and other types of sexual deviation, and in the Kinsey conclusions that the biological and social basis for this behavior is *entirely "normal" and "natural."*

The big questions, then, are whether the Kinsey statistics to date reflect the true *general* situation, and whether the conclusions derived from them are valid. Here there have been radical differences of opinion. Many authorities have taken an affirmative stand, as we said. Others have strongly criticized the report on the ground that its "sampling" is *not* representative, that it is heavily slanted toward the "abnormal" cases, that it concentrates too heavily on the purely mechanical aspects of sex, and that, in any case, the conclusions and interpretations go beyond the evidence. We cannot here take sides in the issue, but it should be kept in mind that Dr. Kinsey and his colleagues themselves regard their findings to date as only tentative —covering merely 13 per cent of the 100,000 case histories set as their goal.

Before taking up specific points in the Kinsey report (as they might concern us in this book), let us pave the way with certain further general observations regarding sexual behavior in males and females. For by knowing what patterns of sexual behavior are considered "normal" for each sex, and what differences are considered *basic* (and perhaps, genetic) in their sexual functioning, we may better understand the significance of individual deviations.

Of primary importance, then, is the fact that before the male can perform sexually, he normally must have the desire for the sex act, and must be in the required physical state to make it possible. This does not have to be the case with the female. (Stories to the contrary, no male can be "raped" by a woman unless he's physically responsive.) A second fact is that the completion of the sexual act by the male normally involves discharge of seminal fluid, whereas in the female no fluid is discharged (other than the mucous secretion). The act therefore demands much more from the male than the female, and limits much more his capacity for sexual performance. On the other hand, the sexual act has much more importance and seriousness to the female, in view of her reproductive rôle, and awareness of this in humans leads to much more sexual discipline and restraint for the female.

Keeping in mind these facts, here are some of the tentative Kinsey findings:

—The sex life of the average male is much more extensive than that of the average female. Sexual responsiveness develops earlier in males and reaches its peak much sooner—in the late 'teens—whereas in females an equivalent peak is not reached until almost age 30.

—Males are more easily aroused sexually than females (especially by psychological factors, sight or memories), are more readily conditioned by past sex experiences, and their sexual activity is more continuous than in females. Prolonged periods without sexual activity can be maintained much more easily by women than by men.

—While there are male "sexual athletes" whose sexual activity is vastly greater than that of average males, and while the average male has much more sexual activity than the average female, no male can approach some females in capacity for performance. Both in American males and females, however, the average individual's sexual performance is far less than his or her capacity for it, but with the activity being curbed much more in females than in males.

—Whereas impotency (or inability to respond and perform sexually) is extremely rare in males before old age, perhaps *30 per cent of the females are more or less sexually unresponsive.* Further, only a small fraction of 1 per cent of the males may go through life without some active sexual response, whereas *10 per cent of the females* go through life without ever having had any active sexual response. Also, in general, many more females than males are indifferent, or "anesthetic," to sexual performance.

The interpretations placed on these findings by Dr. Kinsey are of special interest to us. For it is his belief that inherent biological factors not only account for a good deal of the difference reported in sexual response between males and females, but also for some part of the great difference in sexual performance between individuals within either sex. This is in accord with what we brought out earlier in the chapter. Further, while the effects of psychological and social conditioning must also be considered in each case, Dr. Kinsey believes that there has been a tendency to overstress their importance in many cases of *frigidity* in women, as well as in some cases of impotency or low sex-drives in males. The assumption that "all unresponding individuals are 'inhibited,'" says the Kinsey report, "amounts to asserting that all people are more or less equal in their sexual endowments, and ignores the existence of individual variation. No one who knows how remarkably different individuals may be in morphology, in physiologic reactions and in other psychologic capacities, could conceive of erotic capacities (of all things) that were basically uniform throughout a population." Psychiatric "therapy," the report says, may often be wasted on some persons (especially females) who were "never equipped to respond erotically."

As a final note on sex differences (departing from the Kinsey report for a moment) there is the very important distinction that comes with later maturity—the *menopause* ("change of life") which occurs in women and has no precise parallel in men. The menopause marks the formal end of the reproductive capacity in women, although it often comes at a time when the woman is yet in full vigor, and need not at all be correlated with lessened capacity for or interest in sex. However, the sexual behavior of many women undergoes great change during and following the menopause—in some there being depressed sexual responses, in others, heightened responses—and while this may be influenced by their hormonal changes, psychological factors are perhaps most important. (Heredity has been reported as playing a part in the time of onset and the nature of the menopause. It has also been reported, though not entirely authenticated, that earlier puberty usually is a forecast of a later menopause.) While it has been claimed that men, too, undergo a "change of life," this is a quite different process from the one in women. For in men there is no abrupt cessation of reproductive capacity—this often continuing in some men until very old age—with the only change taking place being a gradual diminution in sexual capacities as an accompaniment of the general aging process. Whether or not degrees of decline in sexual vigor or in reproductive capacity in men are also influenced by heredity is still to be established.

Now we come to that aspect of sexual behavior (and of the Kinsey report) which has provoked the most controversy: *homosexuality,* and other forms of so-called "abnormal" sexual activity. The popular concept of the homosexual is of an individual who not only engages as a persistent practice in sexual relationships with members of his or her own sex, but even looks and behaves considerably like those of the opposite sex.* This isn't necessarily so.

* The term "homosexual" (as Dr. Kinsey points out) is derived not from the Latin word *homo,* for "man," but from the Greek word *homo* for "sameness" of two individuals involved in a sexual relationship. (The opposite is "heterosexual" ["mixed"] relations.) While homosexuality applies to women as well as men, the popular term in their case is "Lesbianism" (referring to the female homosexual relations, described in the poetry of Sappho, which were reported as having taken place on the Greek island of Lesbos).

Sex authorities classify many types, grades and intergrades of homosexuals, in which those conforming to the popular picture make up only a minority group. For instance, there are male homosexuals who look and act as thoroughly masculine as possible, and women homosexuals who are utterly feminine; there are individuals who are both homosexual and heterosexual, at varying periods or simultaneously; there are some who start out as homosexual and later become "normal," or vice versa; some who believe they are homosexual and live as such, although their true tendencies may be otherwise, and a great many who lead presumably normal lives without ever realizing that they are actually homosexual in tendency. Moreover, the classifications of homosexuals as "active" and "passive," in terms of some playing the "husband" and others the "wife" rôle, does not apply to a great many, and perhaps most homosexuals, who engage with each other in both types of activity.

Thus, in attempting estimates of the incidence of homosexuality, there must be an understanding of the types or degrees of behavior being dealt with. Prior to the Kinsey report, studies in the United States and Europe had placed the incidence of homosexuality among males at anywhere from 2 to 5 per cent, though employing definitions very loosely. During World War II the armed services in the United States reported a homosexual incidence of only about 1 per cent. The Kinsey report, however, says that military screening and detection for homosexuality was very inadequate, and makes these startling claims as to the more "probable" situation:

That about *4 per cent* of the American male population is *exclusively homosexual throughout its life.*

That about *13 per cent* of the males are *predominantly homosexual,* though engaging in opposite-sex relationships.

That if homosexuality is extended to include any kind or degree of active homosexual experience, at any time, *nearly half of the American males have had such experience.*

(For women estimates of the incidence of homosexuality is even more difficult than for men, because homosexuality can be more easily concealed or suppressed by a woman, and many more women than men homosexuals submerge themselves in marriage, or are forced to do so. However, some investigators have reported much the same percentage of "overt" homosexuals in women as in men—about 3 to 4 per cent.)

The most serious implications in the Kinsey report lie in the claim that homosexuality must be accepted as a biologically and socially "normal" and "natural" form of sexual behavior—in fact, *that most kinds of human sexual behavior previously considered as "perversions" must in this sense no longer be termed "abnormal."*

The contention has been violently disputed. Many critics believe, first, that the Kinsey reports have applied the term "homosexual" too indiscriminately, without sufficient distinction between those who may have indulged in some passing homosexual activity (often only during adolescence) and those who are confirmed homosexuals—especially the ones whose general behavior is "freakish." (We already have pointed out, in our chapter on "Crime," a parallel situation—the need of distinguishing between the minor or occasional lawbreaker and the hardened criminal.) It is further argued that no matter how great might be the incidence of homosexuality this would not necessarily prove that it is "normal," any more than the very high incidences of mental diseases, or neurological or other defects, and their effects on behavior, prove them to be "normal." In short, it is maintained that if the chronic, extreme, or freakish homosexuals cannot be called "abnormal," the very word "abnormal" would lose all meaning. The answer of the Kinsey group is that the latter points misinterpret the scientific issues involved, confusing moral values with biological facts.* To some extent, however, it may be a matter of semantics.

Why homosexuality as a confirmed practice has been regarded as "abnormal" should appear obvious. Morals or religious codes aside, one clear fact is that homosexuality defeats completely the functions of reproduction. True, we now recognize that sexual relationships among humans serve other important purposes (emotional, psychological and social) and that, even biologically, sex and reproduction do not necessarily, or even most of the time, go together. (Women are fertile only one or two days in each month; and in many men, as well as women, who are consistently sterile, the sex drive is as strong as in those who are fertile.) But whatever the objectives of sexual relationships, there is the further fact that the sexual structures of males and females are specifically designed to complement each other, and that those of the same sex are not. No amount of argument can therefore obscure the fact that homosexuality, as a

* The technical pros and cons of the question are discussed in detail in the chapter, "Concepts of Normality and Abnormality in Sexual Behavior," contributed by Dr. Kinsey and his colleagues to the book, *Psychosexual Development in Health and Diseases.* (1949).

preferred practice where opposite-sex relationships are available, goes contrary to Nature's design, and that socially and psychologically it sets the individual apart from the great majority of others.

Nor can we directly apply to human beings the evidence that homosexual activity occurs widely among lower animals and that it may be "natural" among them. For there are no groups among lower animals which deliberately *choose* homosexuality in *preference* to opposite-sex relationships when these are available. A further fact is that a behavior trait, or any other trait, can be "natural" without being normal, as we saw in the "Black Gene" chapters, where a great many of Nature's "abnormal" mistakes were described.

If we agree, then, that *chronic homosexuality* and certain other types of "deviate" sexual behavior are abnormal, we come to the question: *Is heredity in any way responsible?*

The evidence so far is scanty. There have been studies of homosexuality in twins (Theodore Lang, J. Sanders, etc.) which have reported that in almost every instance where one of a pair of "identicals" was homosexual, so was the other, whereas this wasn't true in fraternal twins. Other findings have been that 35 per cent of the homosexuals come from families in which the trait has appeared in other members, that the trait seems to "run" in certain families, etc. But the fault in most of these studies has been that of lumping together all types and grades of homosexuality, without distinction between the possible "conditioned" cases and the possible "biological" ones.

Where the presumption of heredity might be strongest is in the "invert" homosexuals—those in whom *exclusive* homosexual conduct is coupled with a complex behavior pattern radically different from that of normal males, and in certain respects approaching that of the female. Although almost anyone can identify these "inverts," professional observers have noted many special details: eccentric movements of the hips, shoulders, hands, feet and head, facial expressions, lisping or high-pitched voices, etc. Often the beginnings of the pattern are found well before adolescence, sometimes at ages of 5 or 6. What makes it difficult to believe that these behavior peculiarities are purely acquired is the fact that they appear in much the same form in individuals everywhere in the world, even among the most primitive peoples, from Eskimos to African cannibals. Thus, distracted American parents who now consult psychiatrists about their boys of this type have their counterpart among equally baffled primitive parents, although the latter sometimes regard the "feminine" boys as divine products, and delegate them to the priesthood. In certain other tribes these boys are inducted at puberty into the ranks of women, and are "married off" to men.

Looking for clues in the outward physical makeup of homosexuals, Dr. George W. Henry has reported that homosexual males tend frequently to show deviations from the average in certain secondary sex characteristics, such as having the "feminine carrying angle of the arm" (see illustration, Chapter 15), narrow hips, deficient hair on face, chest and back, feminine distribution of pubic hair, excess of fat on shoulders, etc. In many female homosexuals, conversely, he reported physical traits characteristic of males—less or firmer fat deposits, firmer muscles, excess hair on face and body, underdevelopment of breasts, low-pitched voices, etc. However, studies by other investigators have not found this to be so, and certainly the facts do not apply to all homosexuals, many of whom are more masculine-looking and virile than average men, and if women, may be extremely feminine in appearance.

One point to be noted, though, is that if a boy merely *looks* "feminine"—if he is regarded as "pretty" or delicate in features and body, or behaves in what is thought of as a "feminine" way—he may be inducted more easily into homosexual activity through the fact that girls may turn from him and older homosexuals may turn toward him; and that if a girl looks or behaves too "masculine," being thus less popular with men and more popular with certain women, she, too, may be inducted more easily into homosexual activity, regardless of what her inherent sexual tendencies may be. The ranks of male or female homosexuals might therefore easily be swelled by individuals resembling their opposite sex, without this proving that certain looks and homosexual behavior necessarily go together.

A theory advanced by Dr. Richard Goldschmidt, some years ago, was that the homosexual inverts might be the biological equivalents of the hereditary "intersexes"—individuals born part male and part female—as among certain insects. This theory has been given little support by subsequent investigations. Even some reported findings that male homosexuals tend to be abnormal in their hormonal production (less of the "male" hormones, more of the "female") have been disputed. The conflicting studies may have been made with different types of homosexuals. There is still the possibility that, in some of the "inverts," abnormalities in hormonal functioning or in biological sex development may have been involved. This follows from many experiments with lower animals (rats, mice, guinea pigs and poultry), which show that by changing the "male-female" hormonal balance, sexual behavior in these animals can be modified in any direction, causing males not only to behave like females, but to be attracted to and to attract other males sexually. On the other hand, with added "male" hormones male animals can be made more "masculine" in their sexual behavior. The corresponding situations, in reverse, occur among hormonally treated females.

In humans, hormone treatments have not yet been found to produce any such dramatic results. Drs. Jacob Kasanin and Gerson R. Biskind did report (1942) that by treatment with testosterone (a "male" hormone) a group of "somewhat effeminate, jealous, jittery young men with undeveloped male sex glands were dramatically transformed into 'he' men with an interest in girls." But these men had not previously been homosexuals. On the other hand, a group of army selectees classed as homosexual did not show evidence of lack of "male" sex hormones. In any case, while hormonal treatments have been shown to increase sex drive and capacity in some individuals, it remains to be proved that they can change the *direction* of the drive or sexual interests, as, for instance, in "curing" homosexuality. What seems likely is that once the psychological pattern for homosexuality is established, no biological treatment alone could eradicate it without psychological treatment as well.

When we turn to the homosexuals in whom no inner or outer biological characteristics offer clues to their sexual behavior, in what way could heredity be involved? The only possibility is that, if "normal" sexual behavior is in any way governed in human beings by inherited mental and nervous stimuli or reflexes, as it is in other animal species, sexual behavior might conceivably be deflected to the "abnormal" by inherited peculiarities in these mental and nervous mechanisms. This remains for the moment pure theory, for it has not yet been shown that the great majority of homosexuals are in any way different in their basic mental functioning from persons in the general population.

Spurning the biological explanation altogether, many psychiatrists maintain that homosexuality of all types is entirely conditioned. This, too, remains to be proved. What can be said only is that, beyond question, if there is or isn't any inheritance of a "predisposition," the development of homosexuality can clearly be traced in a great many cases to specific early influences and experiences. Here we have such facts as that mothers—the misguided, neurotic, emotionally frustrated ones—play a principal rôle, for a much higher than average proportion of homosexuals are sons (often only sons) of such mothers. (As Dr. Fritz Wittels phrased it, many of these sons have been "smothered" rather than "mothered.")

A "psychological formula" for developing homosexuality in boys is given by Professors Terman and Miles as having these elements: Too demonstrative affection from an excessively emotional mother, especially in the case of a first, last or only child; a father who is unsympathetic, autocratic, brutal, much away from home, or deceased; treatment of the child as a girl, coupled with lack of encouragement or opportunity to associate with boys and to take part in the rougher masculine activities; overemphasis of neatness, niceness and spirituality; lack of vigilance against the danger of seduction by older homosexual males."

Other factors that have been suggested as contributing to homosexuality are early psychic shocks; overly-strong childhood "fixations" on some older person of the same sex; rigid training to regard sexual intercourse as indecent or "loathsome"; and, in women, fear of pregnancy or, in men, fear of fathering a child. But, as Dr. Henry points out, "Whatever the external influences may be, the majority of persons do not succumb to them and the minority who do succumb appear to be fundamentally predisposed. Some of this predisposition may be inherited."

The two apparently conflicting schools of thought on the subject of homosexuality—the "biological" school and the "all-out psychological" school—need not be entirely in conflict. We have dealt with many conditions in this book, involving behavior as well as physical abnormalities, where a given condition may be either hereditary or environmental (abnormal intelligence, many physical deformities, many diseases, etc.), or where it may result from an interoperation of both forces. Thus, in summary, it is still possible that some cases of homosexuality may be chiefly (or entirely) psychological and environmental, and in between may be still other cases where degrees of "predisposition" are dependent on a "homosexual" environment. In fact, with more accurate classification it may be found that different types of homosexuality are really different conditions, rather than gradations of the same behavior pattern.

What to do about homosexuality is a question which can here be touched on only lightly, for we have been concerned only with the biological aspects of the problem, and not with the moral, religious or legal aspects. In individual cases, once "overt" homosexuality has become a fixed pattern in an adult, there is still a question at the present time whether it can be "cured." Hormone treatments, or other biological treatments have as yet proved of little effect, as we said before, except possibly in cases which were originally due to some biological abnormality in sexual development. Psychoanalytic treatment has been reported successful only in limited cases, but in most instances of "overt" homosexuality, many analysts believe the best that can be done at present is to adjust the individual to his pattern of life. However, there is every reason to believe that a high percentage of the cases of homosexuality *could have been prevented,* and that the general incidence of homosexuality could be greatly reduced, through better psychological and sexual conditioning of younger people.

The belief that something should be done, if possible, about homosexuality is well founded on the fact that, apart from religious or moral attitudes, the confirmed homosexual in our culture is hardly likely to be a well-adjusted or happy individual. But, at the same time, if it can be proved that this form of sexual behavior is indeed a *natural* one with many individuals—that they have either inherited the tendency or acquired it without any volition—and that nothing can be done to change them, the question arises as to whether the attitude of our society should not be changed.

Viewed from any standpoint, homosexuality calls for more sympathy and understanding than is now being given it by the public or the law. In the light of what we already know, the indiscriminate hounding of homosexuals as criminals, classifying them with degenerates of all kinds, exhibiting them on the stage as freaks and subjecting them to scorn, ridicule and ostracism, seem hardly in keeping with a supposedly enlightened age. If we find they are psychologically disturbed or sick people, we should treat them as such. If we find they are merely among Nature's deviations from the average, we should accept them as such.

CHAPTER 41

EVOLUTION

THERE is one question which overshadows all the others in this book.

How did all the different kinds of people and other living things there are in this world originate?

Whether you start far back before Adam and Eve, or with them—or long after with Noah and the animals in his Ark—the question would be essentially the same.

Back in 1859, Charles Darwin set off an explosion throughout the civilized world with the answers embodied in his startling new theories of *evolution.* The resulting avalanche of controversy has never quite stopped. Echoes reverberated during the famous Scopes trial in Tennessee, in 1925. More recently, another uproar over evolutionary doctrines was precipitated by action in the Soviet Union (which we'll discuss further on).

Originally, the most violent of the reactions to Darwin's theories were those occasioned, as everyone knows, by his implied assault on the biblical story of Creation. For Darwin dismissed the idea that man was dropped into the world ready-made. On the contrary, he advanced the belief that there had been a step-by-step development from the most elemental living things through fish, reptiles, lower mammals, up to apes, and then, by some "missing link," to man himself.

Despite continuing dissent, this aspect of the Darwinian theories eventually won acceptance from scientists, and has been steadily reinforced by a wealth of evidence to which modern genetics has greatly contributed. But in one conclusion it appears that Darwin fell into the same error as did others of his time. This involves the hoary old enigma:

Which came first, the chicken or the egg?

Or, from the standpoint of evolution, and thinking of chickens as symbolical of various species: Did a new kind of chicken arise, which then produced a new kind of egg?

Or did a *new kind of egg* originate, which then produced a new kind of chicken?

Darwin held that the chicken came first. However, it was decades before the science of genetics was born, and Darwin was merely taking for granted what almost every other contemporary scientist did—that heredity, and with it "upward evolution," was both an accumulative and a *blending* process. By such a process the changes or improvements that each generation made in itself or which were made by environment could be added to and blended in with those of the preceding one, the combined effects then being passed on to the next generation. Thus:

—Giraffes had gotten their long necks by stretching higher and higher for choice top leaves on trees, each generation benefiting by the stretching done by their parents.

—Apes had developed their brains and muscles by the effort of keeping up with their respective Joneses, and had passed on their accomplishments to their offspring.

—And conversely, in various species, certain organs had become atrophied or lost through disuse, the classic (supposed) example being that of the fish who swam into dark caves and by staying there generation after generation eventually gave rise to a race of blind fish.

All this is in line with the theory of the *inheritance of acquired characteristics.* It is a very old theory. Years before Darwin's time it had been widely promulgated by the French biologist, Lamarck, who maintained that the transmission of acquired traits had been the chief cause of evolutionary changes. But he offered no explanation as to *how* the process could work. (Nor could he say how a bird who wanted or needed a longer bill and fancy feathers suddenly got them from some evolutionary Santa Claus.) While Darwin considered the inheritance of acquired characteristics as of only secondary importance in the evolutionary process (placing his principal stress on "natural selection," as we'll explain later), he nonetheless subscribed to the old concept, as did virtually all the biologists of his day. To explain how these acquired traits could be transmitted, he offered his "gemmule" theory—that various cells of the body produce minute units called gemmules, which concentrate in the germ cells and transmit the acquired changes to offspring. This

WHICH CAME FIRST...?

ACCORDING TO DARWIN:

1. First there was a certain kind of bird,

2. It laid and hatched eggs,

3. Which produced offspring similar to itself. *But—*

4. As they developed, *different environments, habits, etc.* produced changes in the descendants,

5. Which ACQUIRED changes were communicated and PASSED ON THROUGH THEIR EGGS

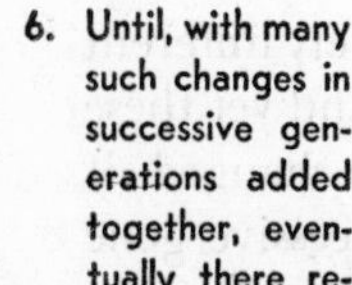

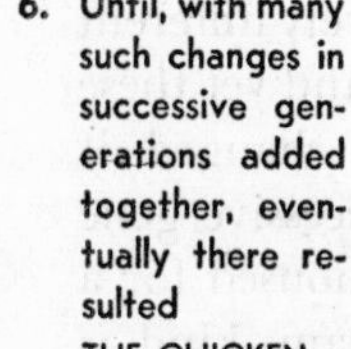

6. Until, with many such changes in successive generations added together, eventually there resulted THE CHICKEN

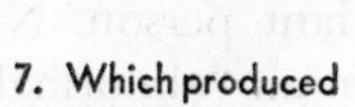

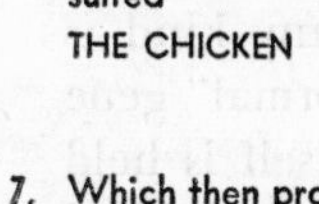

7. Which then produced the characteristic CHICKEN EGG

So by this reasoning THE CHICKEN CAME FIRST.

—BUT ACCORDING TO MODERN GENETICS:

1. First there was a certain kind of egg.

2. Which produced a characteristic kind of bird,

3. But in some of these birds something happened to produce MUTATIONS

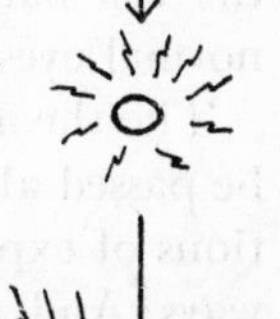

4. Which resulted in their laying eggs with certain CHANGED GENES

5. Which produced birds differing from their parents. And as mutations continued,

6. In the course of ages there resulted A NEW KIND OF EGG WITH NEW GENES

7. Which produced THE CHICKEN

Thus, as science now indicates, THE EGG CAME FIRST.

assumption was shattered by later findings; and also, in time, the whole theory of the inheritance of acquired characteristics became discredited among reputable scientists (as we noted at the very beginning of this book).

The process of disproof got under way even before Darwin's death (1882), when biologists began asking certain questions. Why hadn't the principle worked with regard to the binding of feet by the Chinese, circumcision by the Jews, tattooing by the savages, and the many other changes people had made in their bodies, through customs, habits, etc., for generation after generation—*with no effect on their offspring?* Skeptical biologists tried some experiments. August Weismann (in 1880) gravely cut off the tails of mice for twenty successive generations, but in the last litter—just as he expected—the mice showed not the slightest shortening of their tails as compared with their ancestors.

The "cave-blindness" theory was tested by keeping flies in pitch-blackness for sixty successive generations; and at the end, once again, the last batch of offspring, when born into the light, had just as normal eyes as ordinary flies.

The theory that acquired changes in thinking and behavior could be passed along by heredity was tested by training successive generations of experimental animals to do certain things or act in certain ways. And yet no effect of this training showed in their offspring (although for a time some experimenters thought it did, by confusing their own improved skill in training the animals with the capacities of the animals themselves).

The experiments made along these lines run into many hundreds. As the best evidence, however, geneticists stopped to reason: Recessive genes, paired with dominants, may be carried hidden for generations in bodies of persons with characteristics entirely different from those which the recessives would tend to produce, and yet these genes are never affected. The "blue-eye" gene isn't changed if coupled for generations with a "brown-eye" gene; a recessive gene for idiocy isn't in any sense "brightened up" by being housed for a lifetime in a brilliant person. No "normal" gene of any kind is affected by living in an "abnormal" body, and no "abnormal" gene is "normalized" by living in a normal body. This in itself is held *prima facie* evidence that characteristics developed by an individual cannot change his genes to *conform* to these characteristics.

One other fact should be apparent to every one. During the most important period of human life—from conception to birth—the individual lives in an environment exclusively conditioned by the mother. The only contribution from the father is through the genes brought into the egg by the sperm cell, matching the mother's genes. And yet, despite all the environmental influences that might come from the mother, children tend in no whit more to inherit—or acquire—their mother's general characteristics than their father's. (In a Negro-White mating, for instance, the results are the same whether it is the mother or the father who is Negro.)

In short, it was believed that the theory of the inheritance of acquired characteristics had virtually died with the tragic end of one of its principal exponents, Paul Kammerer, a Viennese zoologist, in 1926. It was in that year that a visiting American scientist, Dr. G. K. Noble, was amazed to find that some of Kammerer's experimental frogs had been "doctored up" and some of his records faked, to support the "acquired-inheritance" theory. Following this exposure, Kammerer went to Soviet Russia and, shortly after, committed suicide.

Why Kammerer, posthumously, then became a hero in the Soviet Union; why the theory of the inheritance of acquired characteristics was fervently revived and exalted there; and why, at the same time, Soviet authorities "vetoed" the science of modern genetics, is a long and sad story. But it involves not so much science as *politics.* For what the genetics storm in the Russian teapot boils down to is the attempt to prove that any science which does not fit in with Marxist-Soviet political philosophy must be wrong.

Briefly, certain Soviet plant breeders, led by one Trofim Lysenko, had scored considerable success in growing and improving grains in new environments, and through using grafting and crossbreeding techniques with various plants. (In this work they relied heavily on the methods of the old practical plant breeders, notably the American, Luther Burbank, and the Russian, Michurin—the inspiration of the latter, especially, leading to their calling themselves "Michurinists.") But Lysenko went on to claim that the environmental improvements had become *fixed and transmissible through inheritance;* that this constituted disproof of most of the theories of modern genetics; and—what most impressed the Soviet leaders—that his theories *were in complete accord with Marxist political principles,* whereas the theories of the "bourgeois-capitalist, ideological, American-Morgan-Mendelian geneticists" were anti-Marxist and "counter-revolutionary." He also convinced the practical-minded Soviet authorities that he was a man who got results quickly, whereas the "classical" geneticists were merely "piddling along with useless fruit-fly experiments." These contentions led presently not merely to the suppression of modern genetics teachings in the Soviet Union, but to a purge of many of the geneticists after Lysenko became overlord of the Soviet biological sciences.*

Yet the fact remains that none of the theories of Lysenko as to acquired inheritance could be established scientifically; that there were no results obtained by him which could not be explained quite simply by recognized genetic principles; and that a scrutiny of Lysenko's writings by some of the world's outstanding geneticists (Professor Julian Huxley, Professor Muller and others) has revealed them to be largely a mass of jumbled fallacies, evasions and misstatements. (One of Lysenko's most recent contentions, that Soviet agrobiologists had succeeded *in turning wheat into rye* by altering the environment—reported in *Izvestia,* December 15, 1949—is regarded by sober geneticists as just about as possible as causing a cat to give birth to puppies.) In fact, were it not for the crushing of Soviet geneticists and the grave threat to science generally, the Lysenko theories would have been briefly dismissed by scientists as unworthy of serious attention.†

* Lysenko's chief adversary, Nicolai I. Vavilov, a prominent geneticist (who had been named to head the World Genetic Congress in 1939), was reported as having been sent to a concentration camp in Siberia and to have died there in 1942; other Soviet geneticists also disappeared; others who did not renounce their "heresies" were removed from their positions; and finally, on an ominous day in 1948, Lysenko completed his sweeping triumph by announcing that the Soviet Central Committee had formally approved his theories, which made them the only "correct" and "acceptable" ones for Soviet scientists. (For detailed accounts of *l'Affaire Lysenko* and the issues involved, consult references listed in our Bibliography.)

† In seeking some justification for Lysenko's theories, certain of his sympathizers have grasped at recent findings involving *non-Mendelian,* or "cellular" inheritance (transmission of traits in exceptional instances not through the chromosomes but through other factors in the cell outside the nucleus—viruses, *"plastids," "plasmons," "plasmagenes,"* etc.). Thus, in the one-celled *paramecia,* Dr. Tracy M. Sonneborn's experiments have revealed a "killer" strain whose properties, poisonous to other paramecia of the "sensitive" strain, are carried by the *"kappa"* plasmagenes. Further, by environmental action, "killers" can be made to lose these inherited properties, and "sensitives," if placed in solutions of mashed-up "killers," can acquire and then transmit the poisonous traits. *But the "kappa" plasmagene is actually dependent for its maintenance on "Mendelian" (chromosomal) genes.* In short, Dr. Sonneborn has made it emphatically clear that his and other findings regarding cytoplasmic (non-chromosomal) transmission merely serve as *additions* to established genetic principles; that they in no sense challenge modern Mendelian genetics; that they offer no support to the theory of acquired inheritance as applied to the overwhelming majority of known gene-

What is most surprising is that the Soviet leaders fail to see certain grave implications in the Lysenko thesis as applied to human beings: If the acquired effects of a good environment could be inherited, *the effects of bad environment also could be inherited.* Were this true, Professor Muller points out that "individuals or populations which have lived under unfavorable conditions and have therefore been physically or mentally stunted in their development would tend, through inheritance of these acquired characteristics, to pass on to successive generations an even poorer hereditary endowment; on the other hand, those living under favorable conditions would produce progressively better germ cells and so become innately superior. In a word, we should have innate master and subject races and classes, as the Nazis blatantly insisted."

This erroneous concept, it should be noted, would hit particularly hard at the Russian people, who, for many centuries, lived under conditions markedly inferior to those of most other Europeans. Even though Russian theorists maintain that the harmful effects of bad environment for very long periods could be remedied in "two or three generations" of bettered conditions, Professor Muller notes further that "no explanation is offered of why the improvement should occur so much more readily than the deterioration." In short, the Lysenkoites have been rejecting one of the most important and socially constructive conclusions of modern geneticists, that peoples who have been continuously exposed to inferior environments are not "*ipso facto* inherently less capable."

We can hope, then, that in time the wiser men in the Soviet Union will see the wisdom of joining with scientists elsewhere in tossing the acquired-trait-inheritance theory onto the trashheap of discarded beliefs, and in viewing the whole "*Affaire Lysenko*" as merely a deplorable incident in the history of genetics.

So we come back to the point, if the material for evolution was not provided by acquired characteristics, whence *did* it come? It undoubtedly came, as geneticists are now agreed, through spontaneous changes in genes and chromosomes which we have referred to as "mutations." *Today the whole concept of evolution centers about these mutations.*

As geneticists look back, they see that mutated genes must have been responsible for innumerable new characteristics in all kinds of

---

controlled hereditary traits; and that far from upholding the Lysenkoists in any way, all of the results with paramecia are in opposition to their claims.

animals and plants within the last few hundred years. In 1791 a Massachusetts farmer found in his flock a peculiar lamb with very short legs. It offered him a distinct advantage: It couldn't jump the fences and get away. So from this single mutant (of course he didn't think of it as such) he bred the strain of sheep known as Ancon, which was so popular for many years and is still extant.

In 1889 a hornless Hereford calf appeared in a Kansas herd, and from this has been bred the present "polled" (hornless) Hereford cattle, valued because they suffer fewer injuries than horned cattle.

The list of comparatively recent mutations recorded among all sorts of animals could be greatly extended. Vastly more numerous are those that have been observed in the plant kingdom even within our own time. Many of these have given rise to unusual new types of flowers or of highly desirable fruits, vegetables and grains.

Geneticists are just as certain that mutations of various kinds have continued to take place in humans. In discussing *hemophilia* we noted that the gene for it which Queen Victoria passed along probably arose in one of her parents by mutation, and that many of the other cases of hemophilia in each generation also arise in this way. There seems little doubt that various additional hereditary defects and peculiarities which appear spontaneously from time to time in human beings, with no previous family history to explain them, are often similarly due to mutations. (Professor Muller estimates that at the very least *one in every ten* human sperms and ova, on the average, carries a newly mutated gene, and that any given gene mutates about once in 50,000 times. However, the great majority of mutations are of very slight degree.)

But what causes gene mutations? The easily recognizable ones—involving changes in surface traits—appear so infrequently under natural conditions that geneticists in former years had little opportunity to find out. Even among the carefully watched Drosophilae, thousands of flies had to be counted for every mutation that was found. One had to sit and wait for a mutation to show itself, and there wasn't a clue as to when, or how, it would appear.

Then, in 1927, came the epochal discovery by Professor Muller that *if flies were exposed to X-rays, the mutations would occur about 150 times as often.* Immediately, under X-ray bombardment, mutations in the Drosophilae began coming thick and fast. This discovery which eventually brought Muller the Nobel prize, in 1946, led to the speculation that perhaps some sort of *natural* emanations or atmospheric disturbances—for instance, *cosmic rays*—could also produce the mutations. Flies were taken up into higher altitudes, or into mines or regions where natural radiations were known to be more intense, and true enough, the rate of mutations was greatly speeded up. Subsequent discoveries showed that mutations could be induced by a variety of means—including not merely radiation of different kinds, but certain chemicals and gases, and various other strong influences—inside or outside an organism. Another important finding was that virtually every type of mutation which had been produced naturally could in the course of time be produced artificially, or vice versa, proving that the laboratory experiments offered the clue to what had actually been taking place under natural conditions throughout evolutionary history.

How a given gene is caused to mutate was roughly set forth in Chapter 10. It was pointed out that every gene is a large molecule made up of many atoms in a given arrangement, with the number of atoms and their arrangement in each gene governing its functioning. In the mutation process, then, something may happen to shake up the arrangement of the atoms in the gene, or to "knock out" some of the atoms entirely, or in other ways so to change the nature and/or number of the atoms and their workings that the gene thereafter will do things in a different way from what it formerly did. There are also, as we saw, *"chromosome"* mutations, in which chromosomes may tear apart and the pieces, with their strings of genes, may form new combinations with other chromosomes, so that the genes, in turn, might be influenced to work in new ways with their new companions. Still another type of mutation involves the *doubling* of the quota of chromosomes in given germ cells. This has been artificially produced in plants in recent years (through the use of *colchicine,* a strong chemical), resulting in greatly enlarged flowers or leaves. (Giant tulips—five feet high—have also been produced through radiation.) But the same phenomenon undoubtedly occurred naturally in animals in the early stages of their evolution, as we shall presently explain.

Perhaps you may ask here, "Why can't gene mutations be controlled so that specific genes can be hit in ways to produce specific *desired* effects?" The answer is that the production of gene mutations is an entirely haphazard process. Think of the chromosomes as they are tightly packed in the germ cells, with their genes all in a clump: Trying to single out a given gene with a bombardment of

X-rays would be like shooting a load of buckshot into a huge swarm of bees, with the purpose of hitting a certain bee in a certain way. To hit a given gene (even if we knew which one we were after) and make it change to suit our wishes would be infinitely harder. We can't say that such genetic sharp-shooting will *never* be possible, but it certainly is completely impossible now. All that the scientist can do is to greatly increase the chances that one or another gene, at random, will mutate (the heavier the dosage of radiation, for instance, the greater the number of mutations). But this is the important point:

Whether mutations of any kind are induced in laboratories or occur naturally, *in the great majority of cases they are of harmful types, leading to defects and abnormalities. Only once in many times does a mutation produce a change which can be considered beneficial.*

Nonetheless, it is through the rare instances of *favorable mutations,* of innumerable kinds and in countless numbers, occurring successively over very extended periods, that the whole process of evolution may now be explained. This does not mean that we are offering any theory as to how life originally began, any more than how the universe itself began. What the evolution theory attempts only is to begin with a spark of life in the form of a gene (or one type of gene) and follow through its development into many complex organisms. How that gene may have originated is another matter. Many scientists now think genes were originally derived from viruses, particles in the twilight zone between non-living and living matter. But no spontaneous generation of life, directly from non-living matter, has ever been observed. In any case, there is not necessarily any challenge here to belief in divine creation. For to say that a single bit of living substance, however and whenever it arose, should have been endowed with the potentiality for evolving into all the forms of life on earth, certainly implies no lesser miracle than that all living things were created directly, without any preliminary steps.

So, in applying the theory of evolution, we might start back in some infinite past with a single cell—a blob of the life-stuff, protoplasm—housing only one kind of gene. This one-type-gene cell, doing the simplest kind of work, proceeds to reproduce itself many times over (by the cell-division process described earlier in this book). All the offspring cells—each a separate organism, but with the same one-type genes as the rest—go on functioning in the same way. Then, in a flash, something happens to make one of the genes in a cell *mutate*. Now we have a cell with *two different types of genes*, able, in combination, to do something more complex than the others can do.

If the new two-type-gene cell can function more advantageously in its environment, it reproduces itself more prolifically than the simple ones, until there are proportionately many more like it. Additional mutations occur from time to time, increasing the varieties and numbers of genes within given cells. At the same time, the genes have been linking up in chains, forming *chromosomes*.

As the chromosomes grow longer and longer, and they twist and turn and multiply in their cell activities, individual chromosomes may break up to re-form into two or more separate and distinct chromosomes. In time there may be four, six, eight (or as in human beings, twenty-four different chromosomes) gathered within a single cell. *Chromosome mutations* of various types may also occur, as we pointed out previously, through exchanges of parts, rearrangement of genes, etc., all of which will alter their workings.

Something more has been happening. With increases in the number and complexity of genes and chromosomes, offspring cells begin to form into *clusters*, with cells at different locations working in different ways (as was explained in Chapter 10). For once a cell is working in *cooperation* with other cells, its power is greatly increased to do any one of many things, depending on where it finds itself with relation to the others, to the availability of oxygen, foodstuffs, needed chemical supplies, etc., and to the outer environment. Thus, although all the cells have the same genes, they would now begin to *specialize*. Starting with rudimentary specialization and becoming more detailed as organisms grew more complex, inner cells would form digestive apparatus and organs; middle cells, muscles and bones; outer cells, a nervous system, sense organs, skin and hair, etc. And, of course, the particular genetic makeup of each organism would determine the direction of its development.

So here we have the mechanism whereby, first, an endless variety of genes and chromosomes could have been produced, and, second, through these, an infinite variety of living things could have evolved, ranging from simple one-celled creatures to those more and more complex, with billions of cells and with every conceivable type of body construction and functioning. (In some respects you yourself, like every other human being, went through these evolutionary steps: from a one-celled creature at conception, to an individual with billions of cells at birth, with stages in between having much in common with the development of embryo fish, frogs, and other lower creatures.)

But also, as animals grew in complexity, there were several other important "biological inventions" which greatly speeded up evolutionary processes. Among these were the following:

Mobility. As animals developed various appendages for moving about, their possibilities were greatly increased for seeking out new environments and using the new conditions and materials for evolving into more efficient, complex and varied forms.

Sexual Reproduction. With the evolution of sexual mechanisms, including the production of sperm and egg cells, it became possible for two different individuals of a species to pool their genetic resources for transmission to their offspring, and to combine in them their genes in many new ways. Where, in self-perpetuating, single individuals, important evolutionary changes might require many generations, in the union of two parents an offspring with many new features could result immediately. (Just think how it would be if there were only mothers and no fathers—if all children were replicas of the mother, with only slight modifications—as compared with the highly varied offspring when there are two parents.)

Segregation. Groups of animals who became isolated from others of their kind for very long periods developed special characteristics; and, in time, changes in their chromosomes rendered them infertile with the others, resulting in new species. (Lions, tigers, leopards, jaguars and domestic cats, or the varied species in the horse, ape, bird and other families, are examples of segregation and evolution from common stocks.) Where segregated types developed different traits but remained fertile with one another, later crossbreeding produced further new types.

Parental Care. With sexual reproduction came the parental instincts which led animals of higher forms to take care of their young for longer and longer periods, permitting ever slower and more detailed development. Other instincts, such as those for *group behavior* and *cooperation,* which we discussed in our "Behavior" chapter, also contributed greatly to the evolutionary processes.

"Key" Mutations. As the biological mechanisms of animals grew more complex, a mutation in a single "key" gene could lead to very great bodily changes. In our "Black Gene" chapters, we saw how one

defective gene (singly or in a pair) could produce a whole series of defects. It follows just as easily that a single favorable "key" mutation—for example, in the brain or in the pituitary gland—might have led to some very big constructive change. Environment, too, could play a part in this, for often the potentialities of a gene or genes for doing important things may have been lurking for generations, awaiting the proper conditions. However, by and large, geneticists believe that the beneficial changes evolved in animals not by leaps and bounds, but by very small steps, with the development from one form to another coming through a slow and continuous process.

To accomplish the myriads of evolutionary changes, and to account for all the types and species of living things there are in the world, would have required hundreds of millions of years. But why not? Nature had an infinity of time behind and ahead of her, and needn't have been in a hurry. However, it is more than possible that in the earlier stages of evolution, when climatic conditions were more unsettled, temperatures higher and radiation perhaps more intense, mutations may have been produced at an exceptionally rapid rate.*

All the processes we have described provided only the *genetic raw materials* for the evolution of different species. But these raw materials were in themselves not sufficient. They had to be used properly, and first, they had to be tested and *selected.* For they weren't ordered in response to the needs of any individuals. Most often, in fact, the contrary was true. Throughout its long history, each species found new materials for its evolution continually dumped on its doorstep, so to speak, the good mixed up with a great deal that was bad, the usable with far more that was bizarre and unusable (somewhat like most of the gifts showered on winners of radio give-away programs!).

In this process of selection there also was the constant requirement of *adapting* to the environment. Hazards or peculiarities of climate, or natural enemies, or limitations of food supply, made it essential for animals of different species to have special kinds of

* If the latest theories are correct that (1) the mutation rate even under existing "natural" conditions is much higher than was previously estimated, and that (2) the great majority of mutated genes—even those classed as "recessive"—exert some degree of selective influence, positive or negative, this would contribute still more toward the possibilities of speedier evolution. (See footnote on Professor Muller's recent conclusions, p. 549.)

traits and equipment—particular types of fur, feathers or skin, toes or limbs, digestive apparatus, sensory mechanisms, etc.—in order to go on living successfully. The required assets didn't come all at once. Only by successive gene mutations, here and there, did individuals appear each with just a little more of what was needed. These individuals, better able to adapt to their environments, and therefore more likely to survive and *reproduce themselves* at higher rates, were thus selected by circumstances to lead the evolutionary procession, while the less favored ones dropped out of the ranks.*

In consequence, then, drawing always from the innumerable desired mutations perpetuated by the more favored individuals, each species and subspecies tended to develop the special kinds of *adaptive* characteristics which would add to its efficiency and safety under its existing conditions.† So came the hooves of horses, equipping them to run speedily over plains, and their teeth, adapted for grazing; the "camouflage" coloration of birds, or the stripes of the zebras and tigers; the antlers of deer, the horns of cattle, and the countless other biological devices and gadgets found in the animal kingdom.

This summarizes Darwin's brilliant theories of *natural selection* and *adaptation,* which in many respects have been greatly strengthened by the findings in modern genetics. But when we go further into his theories of the *"struggle for existence"* and the *"survival*

* A remarkable illustration of the evolutionary process of *selection* and *adaptation* is offered in recent experiments by Dr. M. Demerec (Carnegie Institution) with certain bacteria which exist in the colon of human beings and other animals. If exposed to the antibiotic, *streptomycin,* these bacteria are killed off. But of the billions in a given population, a few arise, through *mutation,* who, while they would die out in the normal environment, are resistant to streptomycin and actually thrive on it. These now take over and, by rapid propagation, in a short space of time create a new population of *streptomycin-resistant* bacteria. But if the environment is freed of streptomycin, there is a reverse process. While the "resistant" bacteria now die out, there arise among them, once more, through mutations, some of the old-type, "normal" bacteria, and in the "normal" environment these propagate rapidly and restore the population to its original "sensitive" form, vulnerable to streptomycin. (M. Demerec, *American Naturalist,* Vol. 84, Jan.-Feb., 1950.) It is probable, also, that in the reported development of DDT-resistant strains of flies, mosquitoes, and insects, a similar phenomenon occurs.

† To elaborate on the foregoing points, there are these observations drawn from Professor Dobzhansky's lectures: Environment controls evolution not as an inexorable force, but as a *challenge,* to which the organism may or may not respond with an adaptive change. The environment cannot impose a particular change on an organism (as was once believed), nor does the presence of a given environment guarantee that a certain type of animal will result. But mutations constantly appear which may prove useful in a given environment, which then acts as the *selective* agent.

of the fittest," we can see that they now call for certain modifications. (*"Neo-Darwinism"* is the term now applied to the combination of the acceptable aspects of the Darwinian theories and the modifications and additions contributed by modern genetics.)

It is clear that, without restrictive forces, infinitely more individuals of each species would be produced than there could possibly be room for. So Darwin held that there always was and had to be a constant battle for survival not only between individuals and their environment, but among members of each species themselves.* This we might grant. But Darwin held, further, that in this struggle for existence, the *"fittest"* would survive. Here we must ask, *"Fittest for what?"*

Unquestionably, as we have seen, certain favorable mutations made some individuals exceptionally well-fitted for surviving and gaining ascendancy, and certain defective mutations rendered other individuals "unfit" under almost any conditions, and destined to be weeded out. But there were also many mutations which produced merely minor adverse reactions to some special aspect of the immediate environment—its temperature, or a disease, or an enemy—and which could be overcome if the individual moved to another place (or, in the case of man, if he *changed* the conditions). Often, what in one environment might have been a handicap was in a different environment turned into an advantage, as with a heavy fur coat in a hot climate, and the same fur coat in cold regions. In fact, with a mere change in the outer environment, many lowly creatures whose genetic potentialities had previously been suppressed could become dominant.

On the other hand, what made some species or individuals supreme under certain conditions may have made it impossible for them to survive when conditions changed. The *dinosaurs* are the

* Darwin acknowledged that in formulating these theories he was initially influenced by the earlier doctrines of Thomas Malthus, who, in the famed *Essay on the Principle of Population* (1798), held that population increases in much higher ratio (geometric) than the means of subsistence (arithmetic), and, therefore, that there must be a constant "struggle for existence in which the weaker perpetually perished." Adopting this view, Darwin (*On the Origin of Species,* etc., first edition, 1859) went on to conclude that in the competitive struggle the individual with any special inherent advantages would tend to be *"naturally selected"* and to "propagate its new and modified form." However, in a later work, *The Descent of Man* (1871), Darwin strongly emphasized the principle of *cooperation* as an important element in evolutionary advancement. (The foregoing points are extensively treated by Professor Ashley Montagu in his recent book, *On Being Human* [1950]. We shall also deal with "cooperation" at some length in our Chapter 43.)

best examples. Long before man appeared, these and innumerable other species of animals, once highly "fit," had become "unfit" and had been wiped out by changes in their environment. Even within our own time dozens of species of birds and mammals have become extinct. And a great many others, including once lordly lions, tigers, buffalos, etc., exist now largely by the grace of man.

Thus, the "survival of the fittest" must be weighed not only in relation to the *inherent* capacities of species and individuals, but in relation to their environments at a given time—prescribed kinds of climate, terrain, bodies of water, vegetation, food facilities, the presence or absence of certain other animals, opportunities for expressing and developing their endowments, etc. Which would mean that the proper environmental stage always had to be set for whatever type of "fitness" was to make its bow and succeed; and even more, that if evolution, in retrospect, has been a continuously *progressive* movement toward the end results as we have them today, certain species and types of individuals in each species would have been predestined to survive and flourish *even before the environments which their descendants were to encounter had been created!*

We must therefore stop and consider whether or not the whole evolutionary process was indeed always working according to some plan as a constant movement *upward,* from lower to ever-higher forms, with Man as the ultimate goal. For this would imply that from the very inception of the universe, some great Force was directing the production of mutations and environments for the needs of an infinitely far-off future; and that when the most elementary creatures had appeared, back in the dim Proterozoic era, the changes taking place in them were designed for the millions of years hence when they would evolve into all the present living things on earth, and as the crowning achievement, into majestic Man himself. All this might be called the theory of predestination, or *purposive* evolution.

The theory is open to considerable question. While viewed from the end results, it might appear that the evolutionary process has generally pursued an upward plan, and that this plan might have in it the elements of "purpose," it need not follow that the specific stages and details fall into the pattern of "predestination." In fact, with the knowledge that mutations have apparently always been haphazard, that the vast majority of them are harmful and very few can be regarded as advantageous, we might have to conclude that man was no more foreordained among other animals than Pikes Peak, the Sahara Desert or the Thames River were foreordained among the earth's physical features.

So most modern scientists believe that man was a biological accident, happily able to survive in the environment in which he found himself. But what if there had been a different environment, if the water had still covered the earth, with only marshes sticking out here and there? Or what if today, through some cosmic cataclysm, there should be a radical change in the earth's surface, or in its temperature, or in the chemical composition of the atmosphere, making it impossible for man and other higher vertebrates to survive, while some lowly creatures could find themselves quite at home? Do we not, in contemplating such a dire possibility, have to revise our ideas of "fitness"? And do we not have to question whether man is inherently the "fittest" of all animals and predestined to always be the reigning monarch of the earth?

But we may not have to wait for the chance factors of evolution to alter our destinies. Until now man has been unique among all other animals in his power to purposely change his environment. Today we stand on the threshold of an ominous future, in which we also have the power *to change our heredity.*

Earlier in the chapter we spoke of the experiments in inducing mutations in fruit flies through X-rays. Almost from the beginning, geneticists foresaw that ordinary X-ray treatment might have similar effects on human germ cells if special precautions were not taken. There was evidence that some persons (among them early radiologists) who had been carelessly exposed to radiation had been rendered sterile for varying periods; and there was a strong presumption that in other cases gene mutations had been induced in the sperm cells of men or the ova of women.

But no one dreamed that within a few decades *the whole world might yet be turned into a vast laboratory in which human beings would wilfully subject themselves to mutation experiments. That is precisely what began to happen on the fateful day in 1945 when atomic bombs were dropped on Japan. For the effects of atomic radiation in inducing mutations may be even more intense than those of ordinary X-rays.*

True, the immediate *reproductive* casualties among the survivors in the bombed areas were no more than high incidences of sterility, miscarriages and the births of many defective babies who, as fetuses, had been damaged by the radiation. But while no great increase in *genetically* abnormal children was reported in the succeeding few years, this offered little comfort. Professor Muller, Professor J. B. S. Haldane and other noted scientists were quick to point out that the really serious genetic effects of atomic radiation would not be expected to assert themselves until at least several generations had elapsed.

Specifically, as with mutations generally, most of the human mutations induced by atomic explosions would probably be minor ones, with the great majority of them *recessive,* or of the *multiple-recessive* type, in their workings. This would mean that it might take some generations for the mutated genes to be combined in given descendants of the persons exposed to atomic radiation, and for the actual hereditary defects to come out. But there was no doubt among most geneticists that in the generations to come, descendants of persons in the bombed areas would show a much higher than average number of genetic defects and abnormalities, many of the same types that were discussed in our "Black Gene" chapters.

This belief seemed to have been confirmed through findings following the Bikini test explosions in 1946. In fruit flies and other experimental animals, and also in various seeds and plants, placed aboard the bombed ships, there occurred the same types of mutations, with a variety of defects and abnormalities, as had previously come through laboratory X-raying, or under natural conditions. Another finding was that, long after the Bikini explosions, some of the fish in the area, and some of the underwater plants, were still *radioactive.* Which leads to a further warning:

The effects of atomic radiation need not be confined to areas in which bombs are dropped. The ray particles set loose (alpha, gamma, beta, and neutrons) might find themselves carried by the wind, air and water for great distances; or they might find their way into fish and vegetation, and thence into people. So with any wide-scale atomic bombings, countless more persons than those in the bombed areas might be affected. For once the ray particles become imbedded in the human bone marrow (where they lodge, and from which science knows no way now of eradicating them), the rays might go on slowly bombarding the germ cells to produce mutations.

The prospect is a staggering one.* The first stages of human evolution were controlled largely by natural selection, with the assumption that those most "fit" did tend to survive. (Which may have been a wrong assumption: Many of the brainiest and most gifted individuals, or those with the most *human* qualities, but who were physically not so strong, may often have been killed by the brawniest and most brutal.) Later, with wars of extermination, human beings took a hand in deciding which of whole groups of people should survive and which should not, and it began to be more and more dubious as to whether the "fittest" were selected for survival, and whether the quality of our genes was steadily being improved. But what can we say now about *"upward"* evolution, with an overwhelmingly potent force in our fumbling hands which enables us not merely to destroy vast numbers of people—regardless of their "fitness"—but also to warp our genes irremediably?

Here are three warnings:

Professor Muller: "When an atomic bomb kills 100,000 people directly, enough mutations may have been implanted in the survivors to cause at least as many more deaths, dispersed through the population, over thousands of years. . . . Repeated exposure to radiation, generation after generation, could in time succeed in destroying the gene system beyond recovery."

Professor Haldane: "The killing of 10 per cent of humanity by an attack with atomic bombs might not destroy civilization. But the production of abnormalities in 10 per cent of the people by gene mutations induced by radioactivity may very easily destroy it."

Dr. George G. Simpson: "Man has caused the extinction of numerous other organisms, and is probably quite capable of wiping himself out, too. If he has not yet quite achieved the possibility, he is making rapid progress in that direction. What his future will be depends largely on him. In this matter he cannot place responsibility for rightness or wrongness on God or on nature."

* Much of what we have said here would be carried to enormously greater extremes if the still theoretical *"hydrogen"* bomb—immeasurably more potent than the "A" bomb—becomes a reality. Also claimed by some authorities is that various of the nuclear activities, quite aside from atomic-bomb construction or use, would, on any large scale, produce ineradicable radiation-poisoning of the environment; and, second, that the accumulative and probably *permanent* increase in environmental radiation over a long span of years, whether or not from bombing or peaceful use of atomic energy, or both, is likely to upset the whole economy of nature in ways not properly foreseen and potentially just as dangerous for man as any induction of human mutations.

Our evolutionary road ahead must remain uncertain. But we still have much to learn from looking backward. And so, in the next chapter, we shall try to throw light on how man arrived at his present stage from his first beginnings, and how to evaluate and utilize the qualities of all the different races, stocks and types of man that have already evolved.

CHAPTER 42

RACE: PART I

ORIGINS AND DIFFERENCES

THE history of race has long been a tragic one. But never have its pages been redder and grimmer than in our time, when theories regarding the *inherent "superiority"* of some peoples over others provided the excuse for the slaughter of millions of human beings, the uprooting and persecution of millions more, and the launching of a relentless war which almost brought our whole civilization to the brink of disaster. Nor have the persecutions, conflicts and discriminations in the name of race come to an end.

For at least one thing, though, we may be grateful: All of these evils have intensified the efforts of scientists to discover the true nature of the differences among human groups, how these differences originated and what they may mean. In the light of their findings, many of the most vicious of the race theories can be exposed for the fallacies that they are.

Our preceding chapter sketched roughly the processes by which the most elemental creatures evolved into the highest types of mammals. This, as we said, must have required tens of millions of years, but how many would be only a guess. The scientists prefer to talk about the vague pristine stretches in terms of eras divided into periods, subdivided again into epochs, and these in turn into ages. On this rough time scale we can then estimate that the first primate, our most remote ancestor, appeared at a point anywhere from forty to sixty million years ago.

The new creature that arose might have been distinguished from other mammals chiefly by its slightly more specialized brain, and its teeth. But this animal was not yet fully an ape, any more than it was a man. It still had a very long way to go to develop into either. In other words, anthropologists are now agreed that apes as we see them today didn't come first and men later, as was once thought, but that both these apes and men evolved separately from the same primate ancestor. The subtle distinction is that instead of thinking of ourselves as descendants of any existing type of apes, we may now consider them as merely our remote cousins. (This might or might not have brought comfort to the English bishop's wife, who—according to an old story—on first hearing of Darwin's theory of evolution, exclaimed, "Descended from the apes! My dear, we will hope it is not true. But if it is, let us pray that it may not become generally known.")

The precise steps by which the first primate turned into man are still not too clear. The most widely accepted theory is that there was a long, broad, evolutionary "primate" highway, from which branched off in turn, first, the lemurs and tarsioids; then the New World (American) monkeys; then the Old World monkeys (the macaques, baboons, etc.); and then, from one forked branch, the anthropoid apes (gibbons, chimpanzees, gorillas, orangutans), and at about the same time, man. Supporting this theory there are, on the one hand, the many similarities which both apes and men share with lower primates, in skeletal structure, control of facial muscles, color vision, blood components, etc.; on the other hand, there are many distinctive physical traits which are common only to man and the higher apes. Among these are broad and shallow chests (whereas monkeys have narrow, deep chests, like other mammals); erect or semi-erect posture; and the absence of tails. Man and the apes are also more alike in their blood groups, and in many details of anatomy and bodily proportion. In turn, man differs most radically from both apes and the other primates in the structure and relative size of his *brain*—the mechanism which has been most responsible for leaving all these others far behind in his development.

However, as we said, the pre-human creature had a very long distance to travel before he could accumulate all the mutations which enabled him to become a man. Not until late stages of the evolutionary journey do we catch our first glimpses of the true "missing links," which Darwin had sought in vain. The best evidence has come within recent decades through the findings by Professor Raymond Dart (in 1925), and later by Dr. Robert Broom, of fossil remains in South Africa of creatures who were in between ape and man: ape-like in brain size and skull structure, but man-like in teeth and many of their bones. These "ape-like men," as

THE EVOLUTION OF APES AND MAN

(ACCORDING TO CURRENT THEORIES)

Dr. Broom portrayed them, lived at the very least a million years ago, were about 4 feet tall, of graceful build, walked on their hind feet—almost erect, with head held high—and had known the use of fire and weapons.

A *giant* type of ape-man has also been added to the possible "missing links" through the finding by Dr. Broom, in 1948 (also in South Africa), of the fossil remains of a creature with an enormous, ape-like jaw and a skull with almost human brain capacity, who may have been double the size of a modern human being. The age of this ancient giant ("Swartzkrans Man") was placed at between one to two million years. Like his pigmy-sized distant relative, he too walked almost erect and might well have been on the threshold of the human race.

Later man-like creatures were the "Java Man," and the closely related "Pekin Man," whose fossil remains were discovered in Asia. These were believed to have lived anywhere from a half-million to a million years ago, and might conceivably have been more advanced descendants, or at least distant relatives, of the South African man-apes. At a later stage came the "Heidelberg Man," dated about 500,000 B.C. or less.*

Not until about 100,000 B.C., with the coming of the Ice Age, do the mists of man's past begin to really clear away. Now emerges the "Neanderthal Man," definitely of the genus *Homo,* whose remains were first found in the Neander River valley of Germany, in 1856. Since then the Neanderthal skeletons have been found widely distributed over Europe, and also in Asia and in North Africa.

Much evidence now attests to the fact that the Neanderthaler was about 5 feet 3 inches in height, thickset, beetle-browed, long-armed, with a massive jaw, little chin, big teeth, a large aquiline nose and other primitive features. Nevertheless, he could *think.* He fashioned wooden spears and chipped tools of flint (the latter by some process which still eludes us), he used fire and respectfully laid out his dead. It is with this man that our cultural history begins.

The days of the Neanderthaler, however, were numbered. For, beginning about 50,000 B.C., or well before, there was being fashioned in the crucible of evolution a new type of man. To the best

* The "Piltdown Man" and the "Swanscombe Man," whose fossil remains had been found in England, were also formerly regarded as oldsters in the 100,000 to 300,000-or-more year class, but Dr. K. P. Oakley of the British Museum, on the basis of certain new tests, now dates the former at no older than 10,000 years, the latter no more than 100,000 years.

of our knowledge this New Man arose in the region of Mesopotamia. Quite likely his ancestors had also been Neanderthalers. But of whatever species of *Homo* they were, they had stumbled into what was then one of the most favored habitats of the world. It had the best of climates, an abundance of game, fruits, nuts and foods of every kind. Compared to other regions where the scattered hordes of man-creatures battled for existence against great odds, this was a veritable Paradise. Here there was every opportunity for a species to thrive and develop, and by an accumulation of mutations, in the course of time to give rise to a new species.

Thus, if you are so inclined, you may think of this region as the Garden of Eden, and of the New Man that arose in its midst as Adam, first of the species *Homo sapiens.*

We must not assume that this Adam (the Hebrew for "man") sprang into being overnight. Various new genes had been arising over a long period, and, proving their worth, had been multiplying and coming together in individuals who supplanted those less favored. Even in this region of abundance there must have been a struggle for existence. But eventually *Homo sapiens* and his descendants reigned supreme—and alone.

For here is our second important point: That *every human being on earth today, civilized or primitive, descended from the same original stock and belongs to the same species.*

The first point we noted was that mankind descended not *from* apes, but *with* them, from some remote common ancestor. Together, then, the two points controvert earlier evolutionary theories, still cherished by some anthropological die-hards, that different divisions of men stemmed from different types of apes (the inference being, of course, that "superior" humans came from "superior" apes). The evidence to substantiate the theory of common origin is based not only on the biological similarity of all existing human beings in all important respects, but on the fact that wherever tested, people of all races and subgroups have been found fertile with one another. This is not true of apes which include a variety of species differing radically in their genes and chromosomes, making some types of monkeys or apes infertile with others. In fact, there are much greater differences between gorillas or chimpanzees and monkeys, than there are between gorillas and men.

To suppose, then, that starting from different species of primates and within a comparatively short evolutionary period, the various existing races of man could have achieved the biologic unity which they possess, is quite inconceivable. We can therefore safely assume that the history of all modern mankind begins with the same single group of the species *Homo sapiens,* clustered, as we believe, at the crossroads of Asia, Europe and Africa.

Favored by environment as this group was, it must have multiplied rapidly. Within five or six hundred years it is not impossible that from a single pair of humans (Adam and Eve, if you wish) there could have developed a population of one million. Inevitably, dispersal followed, for in those early days very little was required to set people a-moving. There was no strong sense of fixity in habitat, no dwellings, no cultivated fields, no domesticated cattle, nothing to hold people down.

So, following the hunt or good weather, or dispersed by quarrels or natural forces, bands of *Homo sapiens* fared forth among such other species of men as still roved the continents. We cannot say that the New Man was superior to all others, for some isolated species of man wiped out by ill chance might have been superior to *Homo sapiens* both mentally and physically. (Often, in fact, we have reason to wonder how well our species deserves the name "*sapiens,*" which means "wise.") The New Man may have killed off the men from whom he differed radically, or may have blended with those whom he found compatible. There is evidence that he did mate with some of the lingering Neanderthalers. But whether *Homo sapiens* exterminated or absorbed other men, before long, as we said, he had the world to himself.

Now came another period of integration. Large groups had drifted far enough apart to become isolated, and for a sufficiently long time (at least many thousands of years), so that various mutations could take place which would differentiate one group from another. Thus there developed in the region of China the "Yellow-Brown" or Mongolian race; in Africa the "Black" or Negro race; at the crossroads of Europe, Asia and North Africa the "White" or Caucasian race; and in the South Pacific the Australoid race, somewhat akin to the Negro, but whose derivation is not certain.

But these major race groups never remained (if they ever were) intact units, completely confined to areas genetically fenced off from one another. For always the process of isolation and integration—of "jelling" into distinctive large groups—was accompanied or followed by another process—the breaking away of small units to form

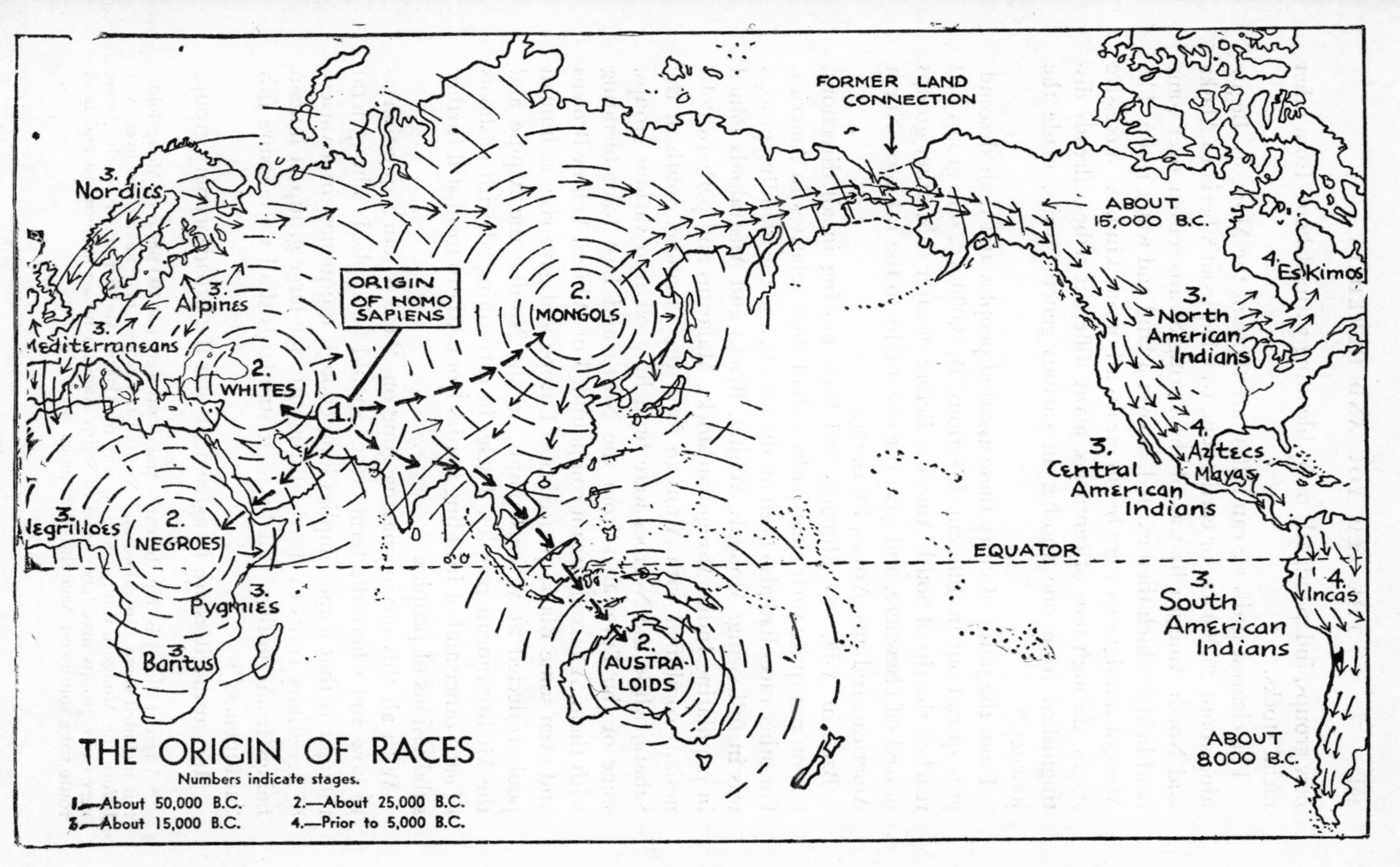
THE ORIGIN OF RACES
Numbers indicate stages.
1.—About 50,000 B.C.
2.—About 25,000 B.C.
3.—About 15,000 B.C.
4.—Prior to 5,000 B.C.
ORIGIN OF HOMO SAPIENS
1.
2. WHITES
2. MONGOLS
2. NEGROES
2. AUSTRALOIDS
3. Nordics
3. Alpines
3. Mediterraneans
3. Negrilloes
3. Pygmies
3. Bantus
FORMER LAND CONNECTION
ABOUT 15,000 B.C.
4. Eskimos
3. North American Indians
3. Central American Indians
4. Aztecs Mayas
EQUATOR
3. South American Indians
4. Incas
ABOUT 8000 B.C.

new groups, independently or by blending with offshoots from other racial stocks.

The clearest trails we can follow are those of the Mongols. Beginning about 25,000 B.C. or earlier, one trek led from Siberia to Alaska and North America by way of the Bering Straits, either over some land bridge which then existed, or over a land and water route. The Mongol immigrants were by no means all of one kind. At successive stages, through tens of centuries, many different tribes, already distinguished from one another in various genetic traits, made the journey.*

From the point of entry these assorted peoples and their descendants spread out in different directions. By 8,000 B.C. one group had reached the tip of South America. Before or after this, other groups moved off elsewhere, and gave rise eventually to the Eskimos, North American Indians, Aztecs, Incas, etc.

Back in Asia, too, Mongols had been moving in all directions, but on not quite such clear paths as had their relatives in America. For other races had also been on the march, and the blending process was in full swing. Mongols, Whites, Blacks and Australoids joined in populating India. Mongolian stocks, Malayans and perhaps Polynesians combined with Ainus to form the Japanese. South of the Sahara, while the Negroes were branching off into various groups, some of the Eurasiatics from the North and East were blending with them. A mixed stream compounded of Whites, Yellow-Browns and even some Blacks poured into Europe and gave rise, as human pools collected at various points, to the Nordic, the Alpine and the Mediterranean peoples. These, in turn, mingled with offshoots of each other and of invading hordes from Asia to form still further subdivisions of peoples.

With all this mixing having gone on, there is much question as to how and where the term "race" should be applied. The general thought is that a race implies long enough uniqueness in a variety of hereditary traits to clearly distinguish one large group of human beings from another. But by what standards shall we measure this "uniqueness"?

Most authorities are in agreement that the broad primary groups

* A recent theory is that the early Americans were not 100 per cent Mongoloids, but included some Australoid and Negroid tribes who may have come over even before the Mongols, though also by way of Alaska. Another theory is that some very early groups may have come to South America by a southern sea and land route from southwest Asia and Melanesia.

—the Mongolians, Caucasians, Negroes and Australoids—do meet the requirements for designation as "races." But there is much doubt as to whether the term "race" can also be applied to subdivisions of these main groups which developed at later stages, and within much shorter periods, as mixtures of different stocks, and continued their mixing process. For example, while some still speak of different White European races—the "Nordic race," "Alpine race," "Mediterranean race," etc.—there is increasing tendency to regard these as "ethnic" groups, differentiated from one another as much by cultural and environmentally conditioned traits as by biological factors. If you look at our accompanying Maps of the origins of different European nations, you may see that the genetic situation is something like a confetti shower at a New Year's Eve party.

Nonetheless, while there are no "pure" races, and while no rigid genetic boundaries can be set up separating all individuals of one division or subdivision of mankind from another, important *average differences* do exist in the way that various genes occur or are distributed. These differences, as Dr. Curt Stern points out, are of two kinds: (1) more or less *absolute* differences, whereby all, or nearly all, members of one group are distinguished from all, or nearly all, of another group by specific inherited traits, and (2) *relative* differences, whereby the frequencies of genetic traits differ in two groups, although the same traits may occur in both.*

What is now apparent, however, is that the relative differences, and a few of the absolute differences, go considerably beyond the surface traits which anthropologists in former years regarded as about the only important characteristics distinguishing races. Recent researches have shown that there also are significant average differences, even among ethnic groups, in blood types, disease inheritance and certain kinds of bodily functioning. We have touched on some of these differences in preceding parts of our book. Here we will summarize them and add a few other important details.

Features. Do race differences in features have any practical significance? Many authorities formerly doubted that they did, but

* Dr. Theodosius Dobzhansky believes, however, that no clear distinction can be made between "absolute" and "relative" race differences, and that these two represent nothing more than stages of divergence. He also stresses the point that "major races" and "ethnic groups" are not two distinct categories, but rather, that "ethnic" groups may diverge and become "major" races. In other words, that race is not a "frozen unit" but a stage in a process.

THE MELTING POTS OF EUROPE

These were the primary sources of your ancestry if your descent is—

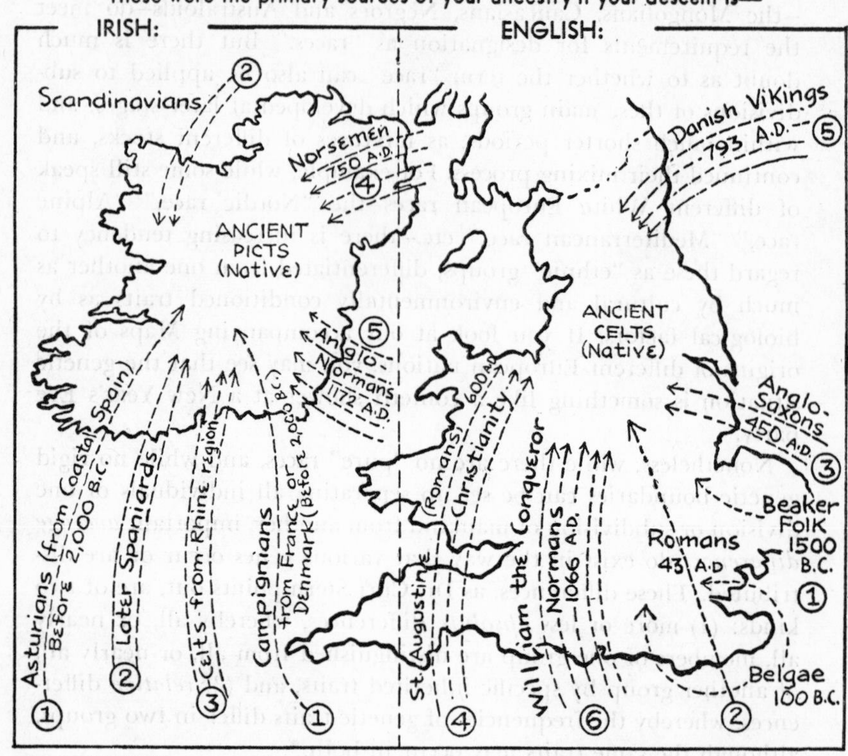

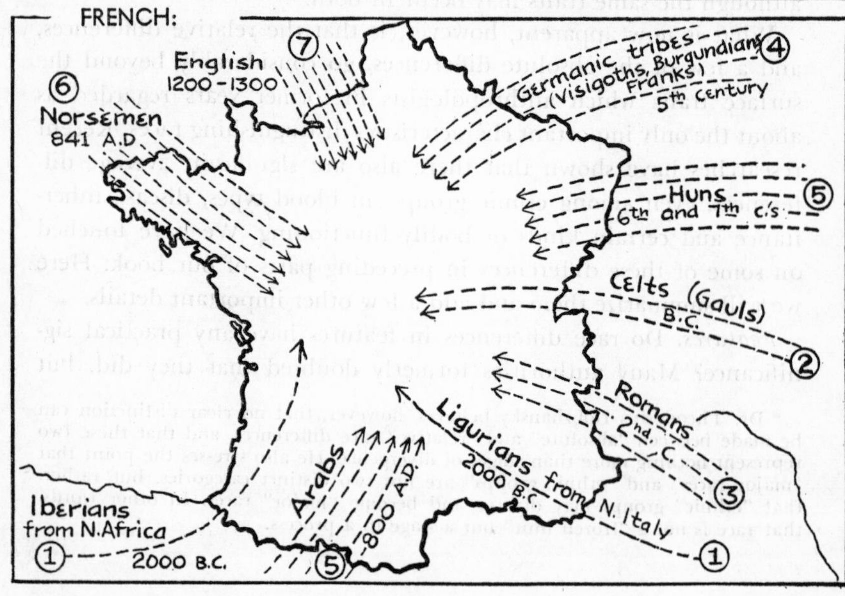

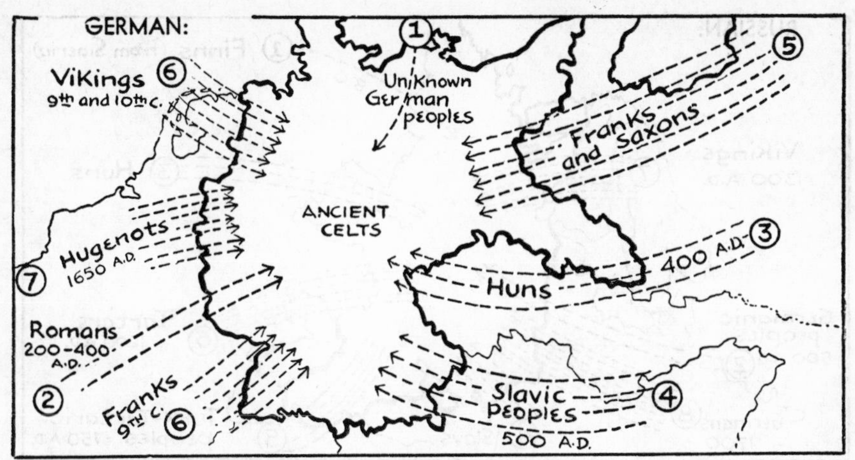
GERMAN:
1
Unknown German peoples
ANCIENT CELTS
Vikings 6
9th and 10th C.
5
Franks and Saxons
Hugenots
1650 A.D.
7
3
400 A.D.
Huns
Romans
200-400 A.D.
2
Franks
9th C.
6
4
Slavic peoples
500 A.D.

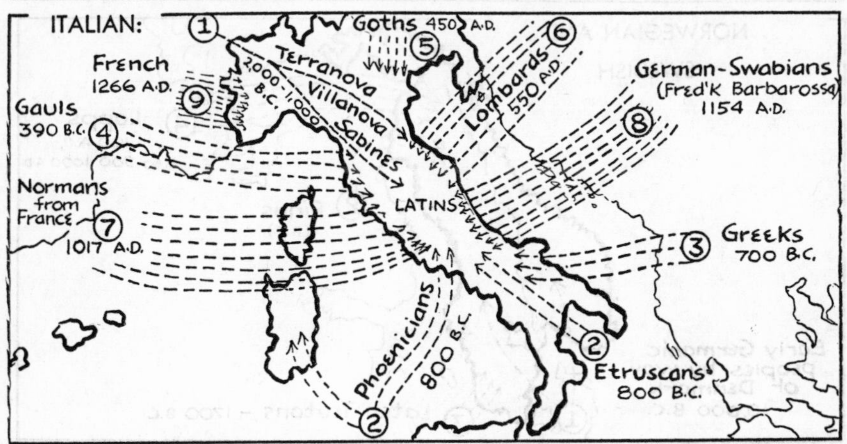
ITALIAN:
1
Goths 450 A.D.
5
6
Lombards
550 A.D.
Terranova
2,000 B.C.
Villanova
1,000
Sabines
French
1266 A.D.
9
German-Swabians
(Fred'k Barbarossa)
1154 A.D.
8
Gauls
390 B.C.
4
Normans from France
7
1017 A.D.
LATINS
3
Greeks
700 B.C.
Phoenicians
800 B.C.
2
Etruscans
800 B.C.
2

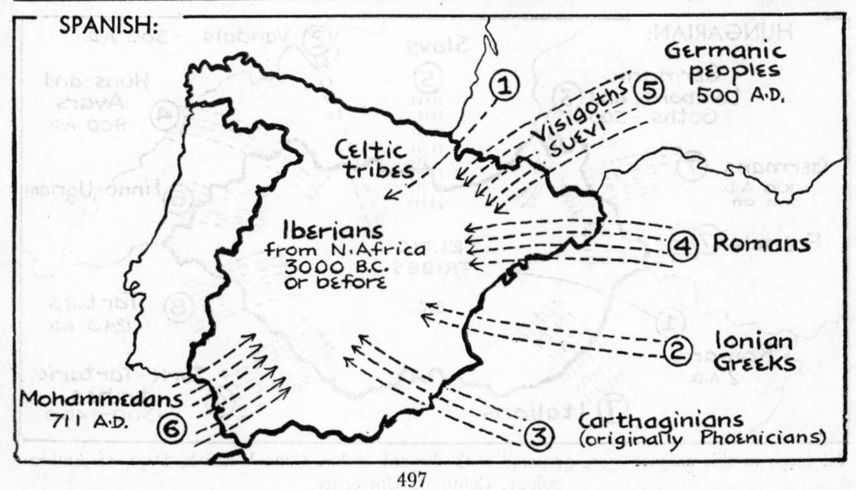
SPANISH:
Germanic peoples
500 A.D.
1
Visigoths
Suevi
5
Celtic tribes
Iberians
from N. Africa
3000 B.C.
or before
4
Romans
2
Ionian Greeks
Mohammedans
711 A.D.
6
3
Carthaginians
(originally Phoenicians)

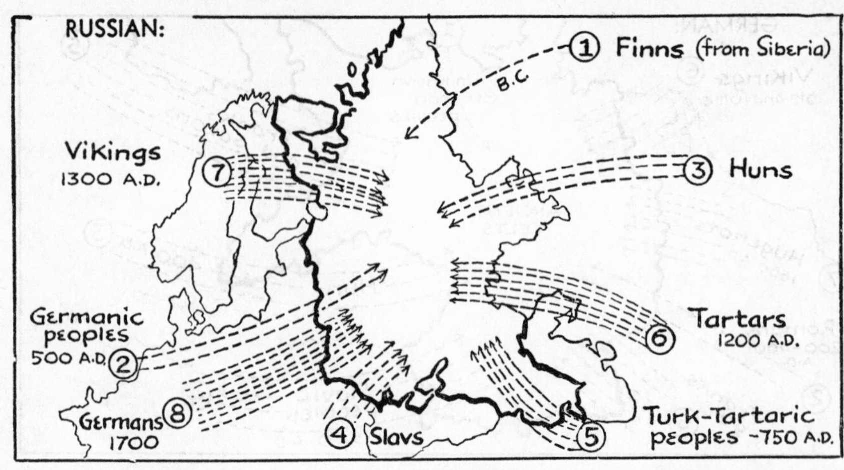

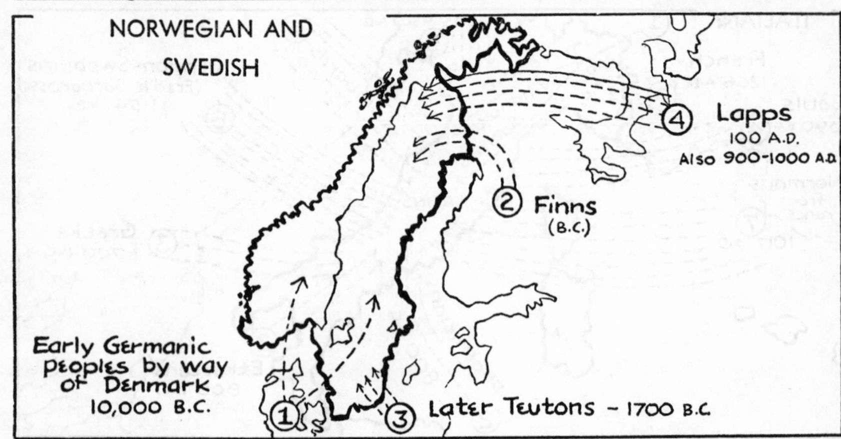

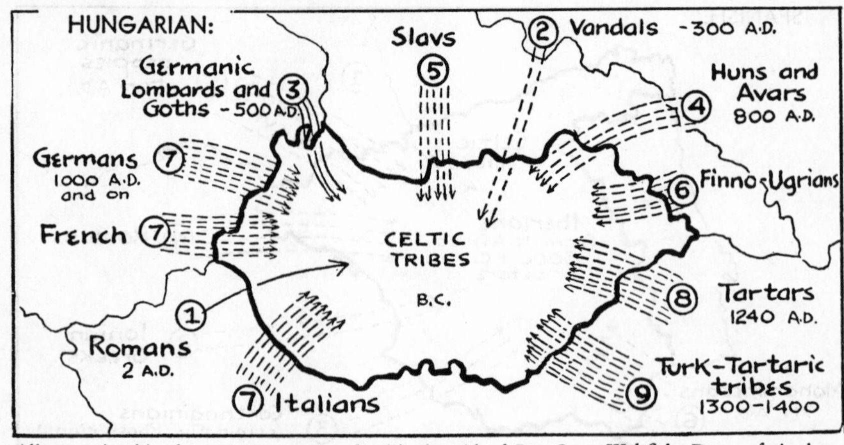

All maps in this chapter were prepared with the aid of Dr. Gene Weltfish, Dept. of Anthropology, Columbia University.

there is a growing tendency now to regard some of the features—for instance, the darker skins and broader noses of Negroes, in contrast to the lighter skins and narrower noses of Whites—as having evolved, originally, in relation to needs in different environments. Heavier skin pigmentation does serve as a protection against strong sunlight, so it is quite possible that as mutations in "skin-color" genes occurred, the more heavily pigmented individuals would have become concentrated in the hotter, tropical regions, whereas those with lighter skins would have moved off into the cooler climates.* Black, heavily pigmented eyes, and black hair, might also be considered as having some adaptive value where the sun or light was most intense. Likewise, there is the theory that the wider nostrils of Negroes evolved because they permitted better breathing in the hot, moist climates, whereas the smaller, narrower nostrils of Whites were better adapted to warming up cold air before it entered the lungs. (Of interest here is that Eskimos have among the narrowest noses.)

With the advances of civilization and the increase in means of adapting artificially to extremes of climate, differences in the biological makeup of humans may have less meaning with respect to their outer environments. Nevertheless, some selection is bound to continue. For example, a British authority, Dr. A. Grenfell Price, maintains that tropical Queensland is not inhabited by average specimens of British, but chiefly by those who could adapt to the heat, leading to the conclusion that biological selection takes place wherever Whites settle in the tropics. (During World War II it was reported that among the first United States soldiers to crack up in the tropics, there was an unduly heavy proportion of blonds.) It is therefore probable that, over long enough periods, people in regions or countries with marked extremes of climates would tend to become genetically differentiated to some extent through selection and adaptation.†

* One recent finding is that light-skinned people are much more prone to develop skin cancer on constant exposure to the sun than are dark-skinned people; another, that melanoma, or "black" cancer, seems more common among persons who do not tan.

† A Chinese biologist reported in 1945 that among the Chinese Shans there is some evidence that the people who migrated from a relatively cold and dry climate to a hot and moist region showed a slow increase in nasal index (the relative breadth of the nose) over successive generations. Also, from South America it has been reported by Dr. Carlos Monge that certain isolated tribes living high in the Andes show an evolutionary change in breathing apparatus and blood, adjusting the individuals to the prevailing oxygen insufficiency and to other conditions of their environment.

Other race differences in surface details are hard to explain on the basis of any practical value. Why in the same latitudes and climates, though in regions far apart, did some peoples develop kinky hair, others woolly, others curly and wavy, others straight? How could the specific hair forms help them? What advantage does a round head confer on an Alpine yodeler, a long narrow head on a Swede? What benefit is derived by Mongolians from the epicanthic fold which gives them their slant-eye effect? What use are the protruding rears of Hottentots? We don't know, and unless we can find reasons, we might gather that these various surface traits arose through the mere whimsy of Nature.

In any case, we must be extremely careful not to assume that certain features are evidence of a more "primitive" nature than others. Anthropologists point out that many of the peoples formerly considered most "primitive" in their features are further removed from the elementary types than are modern Europeans. The Negro's kinky hair and sparse body hair put him much further from the apes than the White Europeans who have straight or wavy hair and considerable body hair. The Negroes' skin color is also further away from that of the brown ape than is the Europeans'; and the full, fleshy lips of the Negro are a highly specialized and advanced human feature, for it is the thin lip that characterizes the ape. To point out, on the other hand, that Europeans may possess certain features less "ape-like" than those of the Negro would have just as little meaning.

Blood Types. While all races and racial subdivisions have individuals with blood types *O, A, AB,* and *B,* the incidence of each type varies considerably among them. Type *O,* generally the commonest, has an incidence of 100 per cent among some of the pure American Indian tribes (although the incidence is only 22 per cent among the American Blackfeet Indians). In other peoples type *O* occurs as follows: Ethiopians, 61 per cent; Spaniards, 49 per cent; English, 46 per cent; French, 43 per cent; Poles, 32 per cent; Japanese, 29 per cent; Egyptians, 27 per cent. Blood type *B* is most common in Asia (34 per cent among North Chinese), and is low in Europe, ranging from 23 per cent among the Russians to 7 per cent among the English and 5 per cent among the Spaniards (and even lower in the Basques). Blood type *A* incidences include: Italians 51 per cent; English, 44 per cent; Russians and Poles, 39 per cent; Filipinos, only 15 per cent.

The *M-N* blood types also have markedly different incidences. American Indians and Hindus have about 75 per cent *M*. In most other peoples *M* occurs with only slightly higher frequency than *N*, but there is, nonetheless, considerable variation.

Discovery of the "Rh" factor and its subtypes has led to the finding of some of the most striking genetic differences among racial groups. As we noted in our "Blood" chapter, the "Rh-positive" incidence is about 85 per cent in Europeans and Americans, 92 per cent in American Negroes and 99 per cent or over among most Mongolians, the remainder in each case being "Rh-negative." There are also differences in "Rh"-type distribution among subdivisions of each race, but these are slight, with one exception in Europeans: the Basques of the Pyrenees region, who are almost 35 per cent "Rh-negative." Dr. Alexander Wiener believes this is because the "Rh-negative" genes were originally much more prevalent than they now are among Europeans, and that when the Mongols invaded Europe, introducing into the populations heavy extra portions of "Rh-positive" genes, these didn't get into the isolated Basques. The latter observation brings up the point that just as the blood types offer clues in tracing paternity in individual cases, anthropologists are now often finding them useful in tracing the racial ancestry of whole groups of people.

Diseases. A number of diseases or abnormalities, wholly or partly hereditary, occur almost exclusively or with much higher than average frequency in some races or ethnic stocks than others. Among those we mentioned in the "Black Gene" chapters were *Cooley's anemia,* in Mediterranean peoples, and *sicklemia,* in Negroes. The proportions of genes for color blindness vary considerably: in White Americans and Europeans, 8 per cent; Negroes, 4 per cent; American Indians, 2 per cent; Eskimos, less than 1/10 of 1 per cent. Differences in the incidence of various major diseases (heart disease, cancer, diabetes, etc.) and in susceptibility to various infectious diseases have also been reported among races and ethnic groups.*

* At the International Cancer Congress in Paris, 1950, reports were given of marked differences in the incidence of specific types of cancer among peoples of various nationalities, ethnic groups and races: For example, in persons of India as compared with Americans and English; in Chinese of Sumatra as compared with Javanese living in the same environments; among Jews as compared with non-Jews (cancers of the cervix being comparatively infrequent in Jewish women, and cancers of the prostate in Jewish men, this latter possibly related to circumcision); and in people of some European countries and groups as compared

But a great deal of further research must be done before we can be sure that these differences are due to genetic factors and not to environmental influences. For the most part, *almost all important hereditary diseases and defects are found distributed among all peoples.*

Fingerprints show variations in the relative incidences of whorls, loops and arches in different races and their subdivisions. For example, in the English there are 25 per cent whorls, in Japanese and Indians, 45 per cent, in Jamaican Negroes, about 30 per cent. *Tasting* differences, with respect to the "PTC" chemical test (described in our "Behavior" chapter), are reported to range from 63 per cent of "tasters" among Arabs, to 94 per cent among Chinese and 96 per cent among African Negroes (as compared with 70 per cent "tasters" among American Whites and Europeans). *Singing voices* show marked average incidences among various European stocks, the proportion of men with basso voices, women with soprano voices, reaching a maximum of 61 per cent along the northwest coast of Germany and a minimum of 12 per cent in Sicily.

The aforementioned differences (and various additional minor ones we haven't mentioned) will probably in time be augmented by finding of further genetic distinctions among large human groups. But we must constantly keep in mind that these refer only to *average* differences. There is much overlapping of traits between any one race or group and another, and among individuals classified with any one racial or ethnic group there are many who are, in various respects, more like those of a different race or ethnic group than they are like their own relatives. Many Hindus, of the White race, have darker skins than many Negroes. Many Englishmen are darker and swarthier than many Italians. There are blond, fair-skinned Spaniards and Arabs, and red-headed Egyptians. There are very tall Japanese and very short Swedes. And so on.

However, the fact remains that when combinations of traits are taken together, it becomes fairly easy to classify individuals as of one major race or another; and when more and more specific traits are identified as occurring in different proportions in various groups, the chances of assigning persons to ever smaller subdivisions of mankind increase.

---

with others. Environmental factors might account for most, if not all, the foregoing differences, but contributory genetic influences are not ruled out. (Also see footnote, p. 499, on higher incidence of skin cancers among light-skinned people.)

So we come to our vital question: *How important are the average genetic differences among peoples?*

A few of the surface differences (in nose shapes, pigmentation or body build) may have practical value, as we noted in specific environments, but most others have no such value. The differences in blood types are important only in individual cases, where there are transfusions, or with respect to the "Rh" factor, when there are mother-child clashes. But these chemical differences in blood have no bearing on the over-all genetic makeup of peoples, and do not in any way indicate that the "blood" of one people is "better" than that of another. Likewise, the fact that the incidences of certain inherited diseases or defects vary among peoples also offers no evidence that when all conditions are taken together, any given racial stock is proved to be biologically the "soundest." And, of course, we need hardly add that such differences as those in fingerprints, singing voices or capacity to taste the "PTC" chemical have no great meaning, either.

The really significant aspects of race and group differences are those which we will take up in our next chapter.

CHAPTER 43

RACE: PART II

"SUPERIORITY" AND "INFERIORITY"

IF THERE are inherited differences in biological makeup and functioning among human races and subdivisions, are there not also *inherited* differences in temperament, behavior and mentality among them? And if so, can we thus grade racial groups in terms of *"superiority"* and *"inferiority"*?

The questions have the gravest implications, for any hasty or erroneous answers may contribute still further to prejudices which already have caused untold human suffering.

We can readily grant that peoples of different races and nationalities do show important differences in *ways* of thinking and behavior, and in achievements. But no scientific evidence whatsoever is as yet available to prove or indicate that these differences are hereditary. In our chapters on "Intelligence," "Behavior," "Personality," etc., we pointed out how extremely difficult it is to link inheritance with complex psychological traits in *individuals,* when we can't be sure of the rôle played by their environments. This applies in even greater degree to whole groups of peoples. Not until we can dig deep below all the layers of environmental and cultural influences, often piled up through centuries of living under distinctive conditions, can we be sure that what we are measuring in comparing peoples is the nature and quality of their genes.

At the outset, then, we might discount greatly the validity of what psychologists call "racial *stereotypes*"—sweeping generalizations such as that the Irish are inherently "pugnacious," the Japs "sly," the Chinese "inscrutable," the Negroes "primitive" or "childlike," the Swedes "stolid," the Germans "militaristic" or "craving regimentation," etc. We have seen very clearly in the United States that in a little space of time persons descended from every race and nationality take on common characteristics to such an extent that when they go abroad—particularly as in the case of our soldiers and sailors dispersed throughout the world—they are thought of by peoples elsewhere as all "typically" American, regardless of their origins.

No experiment could be more convincing than the actual stories of two young men now living in New York and personally known to the author: one, an American-Chinese; the other, a Chinese-American. (We'll explain the distinction.) In the first edition of this book, published in 1939, we told about Fung Kwok Keung, born Joseph Rhinehart (of German-American stock), who, at the age of 2, was adopted by a Chinese man on Long Island and three years later taken to China, where he was reared in a small town (Nam Hoy, near Canton) with the family of his foster father until he was 20. Returning then to New York (in 1938), he was so completely Chinese in all but appearance that he had to be given "Americanization" as well as English lessons to adapt him to his new life. A few years later, after the outbreak of World War II, he was drafted into the American army and sent to Italy. In many ways he was alien to the other American soldiers and tried continuously to be transferred to service in China, but army red tape held him fast in Italy until the war's end. Back again in New York, Rhinehart-Fung at this writing works as a compositor on a Chinese newspaper (an intricate job which few but Chinese could handle), and still speaks English very imperfectly, with a Chinese accent.

Now for the remarkably opposite case, that of a *racially* Chinese but *culturally* American young man: Paul Fung, Jr., another war veteran and now a comic-strip artist, whom the author has known since his infancy.* Of second-generation American-born Chinese stock, Paul, like his parents before him, was educated with and lived among White Americans all of his life. His thinking, behavior, speech, outlook and sense of humor are completely like that of any other American (and no profession requires this more than does that of an American comic-strip artist!). He has known little of the Chinese language and customs. So it was with the thought of becoming better acquainted with the Chinese people that, after enlistment in the air force at the beginning of World War II and a year of training, he asked for assignment to the American Chinese unit which had just been organized.

But Paul soon found that he was a stranger among the others of

* Paul has followed the profession of his father, the late Paul Fung, Sr., one of the best of the comic-strip artists, who had been a close friend and associate of the author in newspaper-syndicate work years ago.

Chinese stock. He couldn't understand them properly; his language and thinking were different; and—no small matter to a G.I.—there was a food problem, for he preferred American food and couldn't adjust to having Chinese food served him at virtually every meal. Most of the Chinese-American soldiers thought Paul was "putting on an act." Difficulties and conflicts ensued, and he had to seek companionship among White G.I.s from a near-by camp. His predicament was never fully realized by the military authorities, and it was only the misfortune of his father's death, calling him home just as the Chinese unit was about to go overseas, which led to his transfer to a regular unit of the air force. (Subsequently Paul served in the Pacific area for three years, being among the first air-force men to fly over Iwo Jima and Okinawa, and in the atomic-bomb flight over Hiroshima.)

Linking up these two stories, the author arranged for Joseph Rhinehart (Fung Kwok Keung) and Paul Fung, Jr., to meet at his studio early in 1950 (as shown in the accompanying photograph). After ten minutes with one another the same thought occurred to both: They were *culturally transposed.* Said Joseph, spontaneously, "He should be like me and I should be like him!" To climax the meeting, a further remarkable fact was brought out. You may already have noted that both men have the same family name, "Fung" (which in Joseph's case is given first, in the traditional Chinese way). So, for a real "believe it or not," it developed that *Paul Fung's grandfather had come from the very same town near Canton where Joseph had been reared and was a relative of Joseph's foster father!*

Think carefully about this story we've told. If ever you've believed, or still believe, that Chinese and Whites are born to be radically different in behavior, temperament and speech mannerisms—that the "sing-song" voice, or the "stoicism," or the eating habits of Chinese are traits produced in some way by special genes—let your mind dwell on these two young men whose "natural" environments were completely reversed. (Or merely imagine yourself in Joseph Rhinehart's place!) There may be just as much reason to believe that a Negro child, reared among Chinese, would be more Chinese than what we think of as "Negro" in behavior, or that a child of aristocratic European parents, lost and reared among jungle Africans, might grow up with all the traits of a typical cannibal. We might make similar comparisons in the case of an Eskimo

Photograph by M. Lasser

CULTURAL "TURNABOUTS"

Paul Fung, Jr. (left), racially Chinese but completely American in culture, is shown here with Joseph Rhinehart (Fung Kwok-Keung), White American by birth, but "Chinese" in rearing and basic culture. Photographed on the evening when they met at the author's studio (February, 1950), Paul, a professional cartoonist, has just completed a sketch of Joseph, and the latter has written below it his name in Chinese. (For further description of the two men, see text.)

child reared by a Hindu, or an Italian child reared by a Swede, or a Turkish child reared by a Boston Cabot.

Let us assume, however, that various genes influencing behavior and thinking are not distributed in the same way among all races and peoples, and that some of their average psychological differences are due, in a certain degree, to genetic factors. Might this not suggest that when all the genetic traits are added up, one subdivision of mankind may be "superior" to another?

The theory of "racial superiority," as it has been used by some peoples in a *biological* sense to justify their suppression or domination of others, is essentially a product of modern times. Before then, the concept of "superiority" was attached largely to degrees or types of civilization and culture. Although the ancient Hebrews did think that they were a "chosen people," it was mostly in the sense of their being a large tribal group with a divinely inspired religion and culture. They did not hesitate to absorb persons of alien stocks, and did not regard them as biologically inferior, as is best shown in the sympathetic treatment given in the biblical account to Ruth, the Moabite, great-grandmother of King David. (At no time since has there been any barrier among Jews to intermarriage with persons of other stocks who adopted their religion.)

Among other ancients, too, there was no race prejudice of the modern kind. Kings would often take as their brides princesses of different races. Mark Antony or Caesar would have had no qualms about marrying Cleopatra. The Greeks and Romans were ready to accept as equals individuals of any race who were up to them culturally. Coming closer to our own times, in the court of Peter the Great of Russia a Negro was such a favorite that he was vied for by the aristocratic ladies, and from his marriage to one of them was descended the famous poet, Alexander Pushkin. Where taboos or restrictions against racial intermarriages existed in earlier times, they were almost always on tribal, religious, or social grounds.

The attempts to classify *nationalties* or *ethnic groups* on the basis of "blood" (using "blood" in the fallacious sense of its carrying hereditary traits) and to identify those of one "blood" as biologically superior to those of other "bloods," began only about a century ago. First a Frenchman, Count de Gobineau, later a fanatical Englishman, Chamberlain, sought to show that Whites in general and "Nordics" in particular were superior biologically to other peoples. The theories were perverted to fantastic limits by the Nazis, to prove that the Germans (except for those they wished to exclude) constituted a special and exalted "race," authorized by nature to exterminate or subjugate "inferior" peoples and to dominate the world. This, fortunately, is for the most part history. But there is one fallacy, fostered by the Nazis, which persists: It involves the terms, "Aryan" and "non-Aryan."

In the 1880s, a German philologist, Professor Friedrich Max Mueller, had coined the term *"Aryan"* to apply only to a large group of *languages,* European and Asiatic, including the Celtic, Teutonic, Italic, Hellenic, Albanian, Armenian, Balto-Slavic and Indo-Iranian. Used in this sense, "Aryan" would have to take in a wide sweep of the most diverse peoples, ranging from the Irish to the *Vedda Negroes* of Ceylon (one of the most primitive tribes in existence). To make his meaning unmistakably clear, Professor Mueller wrote in 1883: "I have declared again and again if I say 'Aryan,' I mean neither blood nor bones, nor hair, nor skull. I mean simply those who speak an Aryan language. . . . To me an ethnologist who speaks of Aryan race, Aryan blood, Aryan eyes and hair, is as great a sinner as a linguist who speaks of a dolichocephalic [long-headed] dictionary or a brachycephalic [round-headed] grammar."

It is also worth noting that just a few years before Hitler came to power, the leading German treatise on human heredity, by Baur, Fischer and Lenz, included this paragraph (1929 edition):

"What we today term a nation or a people is, biologically considered, a mishmash of the most extraordinarily diversified elements. . . . It cannot be too emphatically insisted on that that which is common to the people of one nation, such as the German, the British or the French, and that which unites them as a nation, is not, properly speaking, their 'race,' but first and foremost, a common speech and culture."

Finally, other German authorities had long ago pointed out that the Germans were among the most highly mixed peoples of Europe, a blend of many ethnic groups—Nordics, Alpines, Mediterraneans and Slavs, with an admixture of Mongolian genes as well. (See our Map, p. 497.)

So it was in the face of all scientific findings that the Nazi leaders proclaimed that all persons of German *nationality* (excluding those of Jewish or Polish stock) were "blood brothers of the Aryan race"—even more, of a "super-Aryan race," to which persons of all other races were biologically inferior. The height of this absurdity was reached when the Japanese joined forces with the Germans, and

Nazi pseudo-scientists obligingly found evidence that their Oriental allies were also, in some way, "Aryans."

No more than there is an "Aryan race" is there a "Semitic" or "non-Aryan race," for "Semitic" also refers to a large family of languages, among them the Aramaic, Arabic and Hebrew. However, to classify the Jewish people—the chief objects of Nazi attack—as "non-Aryan" on the basis of their language is to compound the fallacy. For the great majority of Jews in the world (except for those now living in the new State of Israel) use Hebrew only in their religious services, as Catholics use Latin. The characteristic spoken and written alternative language of most European Jews has long been Yiddish, compounded largely with an Old German base, but much modified everywhere with words of the countries in which they reside. (American Yiddish, for instance, is in good part English. However, a great many second- and third-generation Jews in the United States and various other countries know neither Yiddish nor Hebrew at all.) Altogether, if judged by their language, most Jews would have to be properly included among the "Aryans."

Do the Jews in any sense constitute a "race"? Most authorities would say "No." While undoubtedly more homogeneous than many other large groups, the Jews are nonetheless compounded of diverse peoples. The Bible reveals that they were of highly mixed stocks of Eurasiatics, chiefly of Arabian and Mediterranean origins, to begin with, and their subsequent troubled history bears witness to the fact that they must have absorbed genes from a great many other peoples. Today Jews of many different types will be found throughout the world, as is strikingly shown among those collected in the State of Israel—Yemenite, Polish, Russian, German, Spanish, Italian Jews, etc.—whose features and various other traits show not merely the effects of centuries of living in different countries, but of differences in *genetic* makeup. While it is true that, in general, certain characteristics are more common among Jews than non-Jews, it is also obvious that large numbers of them do not have these characteristics, and that in every country many Jewish individuals are indistinguishable from their non-Jewish compatriots.*

As to what, then, constitutes a Jew, there is much disagreement.

* The so-called "Jewish nose,"—high-bridged and curved—is not "Jewish" but Hittite, as Dr. Harold M. Holden points out in his book, *Noses* (1950). But actually, the Bavarian Germans have the highest percentage of noses of this type, and similar noses are common in certain Scottish strains and among some American Indians.

Those who contend that Jews are merely a religious group must face the fact that there are wide differences in religious beliefs among them, from strictly orthodox to non-believers, and that even those converted to Christianity continue to be identified as Jews (as was the case with Disraeli, Heinrich Heine and Felix Mendelssohn, or with large numbers of converted Jews in Germany). Are Jews a "nationality"? Quite clearly not. Their nationality is that of the country of their birth or legal adoption: American Jews, British Jews, German Jews, etc. Nor has the establishment of the Israeli State (whose citizens, including also non-Jews, are identified not as Jews or Hebrews, but as "Israelis") made any change in the nationality of Jews elsewhere. Perhaps the best way to describe the Jewish people is as a *"kith."* This is the term applied by the late Dr. Ellsworth Huntington to certain large human family groups with a more or less common ancestry for a long period, and therefore some biological unity, but distinguished mostly by the effects of common cultural conditioning—religion, traditions, training, habits (including diet) and social experiences (to which, in the case of the Jews, might be added psychological reactions to oppression and discrimination). Among the examples of other "kiths" would be the Irish, Scotch Highlanders, Prussians and Roumanians.

This still leaves open the question of whether or not special combinations of genes for various "superior" traits might not be concentrated in certain kiths or racial groups, in greater degree than in others. Apart from doubts as to just what is meant by over-all "superiority," scientists are inclining more and more to the view that it can hardly be related to *inherent* capacities of different peoples until we can devise uniform standards of measurement that will apply fairly to all. (You will recall that this problem was touched on in our "I.Q." chapter.) One might say, "But look at the difference between advanced peoples and jungle savages! Can environment alone account for that?" The geneticist might answer, "Why not?" The difference is not nearly so great as between us and our Stone Age ancestors, and yet scientists are agreed that our basic intelligence is virtually no better than was theirs. (The remarkable drawings made by cave men give some hint of this.) Our cultural superiority over primitive men of the dim past would thus be attributed entirely to ages of accumulated experience, learning and environmental improvements.

Of course, there is still the question of why, on the same time scale, some peoples have lagged far behind others. The best answer might be, "Lack of equal opportunities." Just as there are underprivileged individuals, there are whole large groups of mankind who have been underprivileged, who never got the right start. Often it was a matter of having been settled in unfavorable climates, or in regions poor in natural resources.

We are here reminded of the Arctic explorer who was telling about the crude diet of the Eskimos, when a well-meaning but not too bright old lady expressed surprise that the Eskimos didn't drink milk.

"Madam," replied the explorer, "have you ever tried to milk a seal?"

There are many things, important to the development of culture, which one cannot "milk" out of an environment where they do not exist. People cannot learn to fashion metals where there are no mineral deposits, or cultivate crops in ground frozen solid, or breed cattle where only polar bears and walruses can survive. Think of the United States, and whether its people would ever have achieved their present position if their land had not been overflowing with natural riches.

But again, one might ask: Why did the American Indians do so little with the same environmental advantages, although they enjoyed them for thousands of years? Why did the Eskimos stay put instead of moving on to more favorable regions? Why did the cousins of the Indians and Eskimos, the Aztecs and Incas, reach such high stages of civilization—in many respects equal or superior to those of Europeans of the same periods—particularly in astronomy and mechanics? It is not easy to find all the answers in outside environments. Perhaps large groups of people are like individuals you know: With the same basic capacities, some make great headway, others stay in a rut, for many complex psychological reasons.

Too often, also, an entire people is judged by a few gifted members who, through inventions, developments of new techniques, or leadership in various fields, may have opened the way for tremendous broad-scale advances. To attribute to the mass the superiority of these few harks back to the eras when a champion was picked by one tribe to do battle with the champion of another, and the victory of either was regarded as proof of the superiority of all his fellows. (It's the same today when an anemic freshman rooter at a football game swells up with self-importance if his college team wins.) But no people has ever had a monopoly on inventive or creative genius. There is evidence that throughout the world similar ideas, inventions and cultural innovations arose independently, and repeatedly, among peoples far apart. This goes far to suggest that the basic capacities for achievement are spread fairly evenly among all racial divisions.

Thus, just as we may modestly concede that a sweeping victory by United States athletes in the Olympic Games doesn't prove the overall superiority of Americans, a temporary flurry of champions in any field of cultural achievement among the people of any nation or racial group doesn't offer proof of their total genetic supremacy. Commenting on the claim of "Nordic" supremacy, Professor Lancelot Hogben (himself an Englishman) has pointed out that the Black Moors were highly cultured at the time when the Nordics were little better than barbarians. He quotes a Moorish savant of Toledo as writing of the northern peoples, "They are of cold temperament and never reach maturity. . . . They lack all sharpness of wit and penetration of intellect." This, as Professor Hogben adds, was at a time when few priests in northern Europe could read or write and when washing the body was still considered a heathen and a dangerous custom.

History reveals countless instances where peoples who were on top at one stage were on the bottom at another, and vice-versa. It is of course possible that unusual genetic traits may have cropped out sporadically and at different times in different peoples, or that required combinations of genes for certain capacities may have been present in varying proportions. But the rapidity with which transitions have occurred, from dominant nations to subordinate ones, sometimes within a century, leaves much doubt on this score. So we may question now whether the reign of art among the Athenians, the era of conquest among the Romans, the exploits of the Vikings, the Renaissance among the Italians, and so on, had any more meaning from the standpoint of genetics than has the present American reign in business and industry, or the French reign in fashions and cuisine.

Even when we come back to such extremes as African jungle primitives in contrast with modern Europeans and Americans, we have no scientific evidence for ascribing the differences to genetic factors. However backward we may consider the primitives to be, anthropologists can tell us that they are far from being "uncivilized." Many of the African tribes (some united in nations of several million people) have highly intricate political, social and judicial systems, and in their arts, agriculture and many skills are superior to what many White Europeans were not so long ago. As to their genetic capacities, we have striking examples in the United States of how groups from the very same African stocks, uprooted and brought here as slaves, have within a few generations—and despite continued disadvantages—produced innumerable individuals of the highest caliber in the arts, sciences and professions, equal to the best in the country. The fact that Negroes in the mass are still lagging behind Whites can have little genetic significance so long as their environments and opportunities continue to be far from equal.

Here we might give some attention to the mixing that has taken place beween Negroes and Whites in the United Sates and in some other countries. First, the "Negro" genes in themselves are highly mixed, for it is a popular fallacy that the Negroes who were brought in as slaves were all pretty much the same. Actually, there were more genetic differences among groups of Negroes from widely separated African tribes than there were among White immigrants. The present American Negro population is therefore made up of mixtures of many kinds of "African Negro" genes, mixed in turn with genes from various White and Indian stocks (only a fraction of the American Negro population being today without other racial genes). In the aggregate, as Dr. Stern points out, American Negroes today comprise a more or less new single Negro race, genetically unlike any other existing Negro races.

But the Negro-White mixing has certainly not been all in one direction. Many Negro genes have also found their way into the White stream. First, it should be pointed out that the greatest amount of White-Negro mixing occurred not in the past few generations, but in the Colonial days and up to the end of the Civil War. In the earlier periods, however, the flow was mostly of "White" genes into the Negro population, with Mulattoes continuing to stay in the Negro ranks and adding their genes to make the Negroes lighter in color, on the average, and less Negroid. Subsequently, as individuals with some Negro ancestry were produced who could "pass" as Whites, many of these married Whites. This had a two-fold effect: It brought "Negro" genes (mostly for effects not on the surface) into the White population, and at the same time, it took "White" genes out of the Negro population. By this latter process, which is destined to continue, and with fewer reverse matings of Whites with Negroes than occurred in the days of slavery, it is very likely that American Negroes will for some time to come (so long as racial barriers are maintained) tend to *darken* again, and to become more Negroid.*

But again, it should be stressed that neither "Negro" nor "White" genes are confined to those for easily recognizable surface traits, such as skin color, features and hair form. Many of those who can pass as Whites may carry more "Negro" genes of other kinds than do some individuals who are distinctively Negroid in appearance. The selection of those who will pass over or be retained in the White population, and those who will remain in the Negro population, will therefore be carried out, as in the past, on the basis of the comparatively few surface traits. The end result may be that in their surface characteristics the Negro and White populations will continue to remain quite as distinct as they now are, for a long time to come, but that with respect to the less obvious, or internal genetic traits (for instance, blood types), the genetic differences will be narrowed down.†

The problem of Negro-White mixing, as of mixing between any other racial groups, becomes most serious when we ask: *Is "race-crossing," or interbreeding between peoples of different races, desirable?*

* Radical contrasts to the Negro-White situation of the United States are presented in the two other countries where the races have come together in large numbers, Brazil and South Africa. In Brazil, as Dr. Donald Pierson has pointed out (*Scientific Monthly,* March, 1944), although more Africans were imported than into any other region of the New World, the Negro, like the Brazilian Indian before him, is apparently disappearing as a racial unit. Slavery in Brazil was never on the same basis as in the United States, and disappeared not through any forced action but through gradual social changes. Likewise, barriers between Whites and Negroes were never very great, in large measure because they were not encouraged by the Catholic Church. While prejudice still exists in Brazil, Dr. Pierson interprets it as being on the basis of *class* rather than race. He quotes a commonly heard saying, "A rich Negro is a White man, and a poor White man is a Negro."

In South Africa, on the other hand, the discrimination against Negroes is far greater than in the United States, for they are not even recognized as citizens, and are kept under many severe civil and social restraints. A slight distinction, however, is made between the "coloreds," of mixed bloods, and the "Blacks," or full-Negro natives, the former being given somewhat more consideration in certain sections.

† Estimates as to the number of persons with "Negro" genes who have "passed over" or continue to do so yearly are extremely uncertain. Some claim that more than two million present-day Americans of Negro descent have crossed the color-line, with between 15,000 and 30,000 more going over to the White side every year; others claim that those "passing over" may number no more than 3,000 annually.

The question has two aspects, *biological* and *social*. From the biological standpoint, some of the objections that have been made to "race-crossing" are not well grounded, as has been indicated in various facts brought out in this chapter. For instance, if there is no real proof of the "inherent superiority" of some races or subdivisions, it cannot be said that they will be lowered in value, genetically, by having genes from other groups mixed in with theirs. It may be argued, though, that there is nonetheless an advantage in keeping races and groups "pure," retaining their distinctive traits (in the way that various breeds of livestock and domestic animals are kept "pure"). Here again, we have indicated that there are no genetically "pure" races or groups of people today, that all human beings are of highly mixed stocks, or in other words, "mongrels." The relatively "purest" peoples were those of thousands of years ago, and today the "purest" peoples are the isolated primitive tribes of Africa, Australia and the South Pacific. How mixed the European peoples are can be seen by another look at our Maps (and few would maintain that Europeans are genetically inferior to their "purer" separate ancestral stocks). If one stops to think, further, that Americans today are a mixture of these mixtures, one may have reason for doubting the old theory that the "purest" peoples have made the greatest advances.

Another argument formerly offered was that crossbreeding between peoples of markedly different genetic makeup would result in misshapen offspring–individuals with teeth too big for their jaws, or with other skeletal parts and organs that wouldn't fit or work together properly. This, too, has been almost entirely disproved. Mulattoes in the United States are the most obvious examples of individuals who are not biologically defective despite extremes of race mixture. In Hawaii, studies have shown that crosses involving Whites and Chinese or Japanese, as well as those of other racial stocks, have not merely not resulted in any structural abnormalities, but have generally led to the production of individuals with attractive and well-built physiques, superior in a number of respects to their forebears. In New Zealand, matings between the native Maoris and Whites have also resulted in well-built offspring who combine some of the best features of both stocks.

The contrary theory, that race-mixing might often be biologically beneficial, is based on some of the results of crossbreeding, or *hybridization,* in domestic animals and plants. "Hybrid vigor"–

greater size or strength, or greater resistance to certain diseases—comes frequently through the formation of new good combinations of genes or the breaking up of old bad combinations in the stocks which are crossed. While no clearly proven examples of such "hybrid vigor" in human beings as a result of race mixture can yet be offered, some theoretical situations might be the following:

Suppose some desirable trait (talent of a special kind, or improvement of physique) were dependent for its production on a four-gene combination, "A-B-C-D." If, then, only two of the genes, "A" and "B," were common in one racial stock, while the genes "C" and "D" were common in the other stock, crossbreeding would bring together the required four genes and prove advantageous. Similarly, where two racial stocks each carry combinations of harmful genes not found in the other stock, intermarriage would reduce the incidence of these combinations and the defects resulting from them.

Still another race-crossing situation involves the "Rh" disease, resulting from prenatal blood clashes between an "Rh-positive" fetus and an "Rh-negative" mother. Inasmuch as Mongolians are almost entirely "Rh-positive," their babies escape this danger. Among Whites, however, 15 per cent of whom are "Rh-negative," many babies are menaced. Accordingly, Chinese-White matings would have these effects: In China, any widespread matings with Whites would be detrimental to the Chinese on this score, for the introduction of "Rh-negative" genes would lead to many cases of the "Rh" disease which would not have otherwise occurred. But in a White population, the introduction of more "Rh-positive" genes through matings with Chinese would be beneficial to the Whites, because it would result in fewer cases of "Rh" blood clashes.

Within any nation or ethnic group itself, matings between persons of previously isolated stocks might similarly result in genetic improvement in some traits and deterioration in other traits, although in most traits there would probably be no significant changes.

Taking all the possibilities together, there might be just as much *genetically* in favor of mixed matings as against them. In any case, much of the argument for keeping people "racially pure" (to the relative extent that they may be so at a given time) is academic. Everything points to the fact that genetic fences between peoples cannot be long maintained. Moreover, regardless of what external barriers may be set up, *mutations* alone would constantly introduce into any supposedly "pure" strain many of the same genes which are found in other racial groups.

The social aspects of interracial marriages are, of course, another matter. The most serious argument against race-crossing is that where peoples of widely diverse types are mated, their differences in temperament, behavior, backgrounds and family connections may make for social conflict which will react unfavorably on their offspring. But this is something outside of the field of genetics, to be weighed only on the basis of individual attitudes and the prevailing cultural environment in given groups.

Perhaps no racial theory has been more insidious than another which reached its height among the Nazis: that periodic bloody conflicts between peoples are vital to human progress because they would supposedly lead to the purging of "inferior" human stocks and the ascendance of "superior" ones. This is a gross perversion of the Darwinian theory of the "survival of the fittest." In the earlier evolution of mankind, it might be granted that competitive struggles among *individuals,* as well as natural selective processes, did help to weed out some of the least "fit" genetically and promote the survival of the more "fit," in relation to their existing environments. But Darwin himself pointed out that what became most important in human survival and advancement was not bitter competitiveness, but social organization and *cooperation,* and the development of the capacity among people to live and work together peacefully.

This policy of cooperation—coming not through instinct, as in bees or beavers, but as a result of thought, deduction and learned experience—was the outstanding invention of human beings. It led, first, to cooperation of individuals within groups, a mutual respect for their differences and the utilization of the special capacities of each for the good of all. Second, it led to growing cooperation among whole groups on the same basis. It is true that there were continuous wars and conflicts. But far outweighing any gains which might have come through bloody clashes were the advantages that accrued to groups of peoples from peaceful contacts and the exchange of products, inventions and cultural developments.

Any lingering thought that wars and racial conflicts among human groups have any valid genetic meaning should have been dissipated by the experiences of our own time. While World War II was in progress, an American scientist, Dr. R. E. Coker, wrote in the *Scientific Monthly* (January, 1943): "The Axis powers have rendered a distinct philosophic service in reducing to an absurdity the idea that war is a means of effecting the survival of a superior kind of people. Who will be the victors—the supposed survivors? Whites? Yellows? Browns? They are on both sides, or may be. Teutons? Slavs? Mediterraneans? Caucasians? Mongolians? There was never more scrambling of races in the armies of two sides in a war."

As matters turned out, we can say no more than that victory came to the sides which had the greatest resources, the best equipment, the best organization—and the most luck. (Think of how different the results might have been if the Nazis had had the atomic bomb first!) Neither that war, nor any war which history records, can be said to have been fought out between "superior" and "inferior" genes, either on the part of groups or of individuals. To imply otherwise—that the "fittest" survived—would be to insult the memory of millions of men of the very finest types who gave their lives for others.

Adding up all the facts which both science and experience now offer us regarding racial or ethnic differences, it is clear that they invalidate many of the theories which have led, and still lead, to so much conflict, hatred and prejudice. The problem now is to get people to apply these facts constructively, in their thinking, feeling and actions.

Those who have sought to promote tolerance have so far concentrated largely on emphasizing the *similarities* among all peoples. There was good reason for this, in view of the fact that differences have always been too easily interpreted in terms of "superiority" and "inferiority" (with each group ascribing the "superiority" to itself). Nor has this ceased to be so. Nevertheless, there is reason to hope that increasing numbers of persons are becoming sufficiently mature to accept and view race differences in a more intelligent light.

Prejudices or antagonisms among human groups arise primarily from what is called *"xenophobia"*—the fear of, or dislike of foreigners, strangers or persons who look or act differently from those of one's own group. But there is abundant evidence that no natural basis for this exists.* For instance, so far as surface differences in

* In fact, the antagonism on the basis of race has been almost exclusively on the part of Whites toward those of other races. Neither American Indians, nor African Negroes, showed any aversion to Whites when they first saw them. It should also be kept in mind that some of the most violent and bitter hatreds among human groups have been between peoples of very closely related stocks.

features or coloring are concerned, one could easily prove that without conditioning no White child would feel any more aversion or hostility to a Chinese or Negro child than a white animal of any species feels toward a brown or black one—or that a member of any family feels toward a father, mother, sister or brother whose looks are different from his own. So, too, with differences in behavior traits within a family or group which are not considered as cause for hatred or hostility.

Suppose—which hasn't been proved—that genetic differences in certain capacities do exist among racial groups. This might only mean that if one large group has a slight advantage in a few genetic traits, another group may be superior in other ways. However, we are always speaking in terms of *averages,* and whatever the kind or degree of average differences among groups in given traits may be, this hardly entitles an individual to boast that because he is a member of a certain racial group, he himself is a superior human being. It would be quite as silly as for a Swedish midget to draw himself up to his full three-foot height and say, "Swedes are the tallest people in Europe. *I,* therefore, am taller than any Englishman, Frenchman or Italian!"

Whatever the genetic differences may be among races, ethnic stocks or kiths, our most important point is that human progress has been furthered not through conflict because of these differences, but through a proper respect for them and their use *cooperatively.* While the goal must certainly be to give all human groups everywhere equal opportunities to develop themselves to the fullest, we may yet welcome the possibility that each is endowed with capacities to make special contributions. Life would not be merely retarded, but very dull indeed, if all peoples everywhere lived, worked, behaved and performed in exactly the same way.

It has all been best summed up in a saying which you have heard, or have repeated yourself, hundreds of times:

"It takes all kinds of people to make a world."

CHAPTER 44

ANCESTRY

MR. REGINALD TWOMBLEY DUNN-TWERPP—who is not very bright, weighs 110 pounds and is the first to climb a chair at sight of a mouse—likes to boast that he is descended from William the Conqueror, and that the steel-blue blood of ancient warriors flows in his veins. To prove it he will show you his family tree and a beautiful hand-painted crest, prepared by a genealogist in Boston for fifty dollars.

Even in these United States there are still a lot of people like Reginald, who point with pride to some remote ancestor; and, no doubt, others who feel humbled because they haven't any to point to. You yourself may have been among them. We say "may *have* been" because by now you must have gathered that the whole ancestry business has been shaken pretty badly by our genetic findings.

The importance previously attached to ancestry rested on a number of fallacies. First was the pre-genetic concept that heredity was a process of passing on "blood"—the blood of the parents being blended together to form that of the child. No matter how far one traced back, therefore, there was always a little of the blood of any ancestor "flowing" in one's veins. Also, as blood was thought to carry factors that influenced character, the greater the percentage of "blue" or noble blood one carried, the more superior one would be; and the more "common" blood in one's veins, the more inferior one would be. Likewise, touches of genius, of great courage, of brilliance—or taints of criminality, shiftlessness and depravity—were thought to be carried in the blood. All that, of course, has been shattered by our knowledge that blood is merely a *product* of each individual's body and that not even a mother and her child have a single drop of blood in common.

Knowing now that all that we inherit are twenty-four *chromosomes* from each parent, ancestry has been reduced to a simple mathematical formula: With each generation further back the

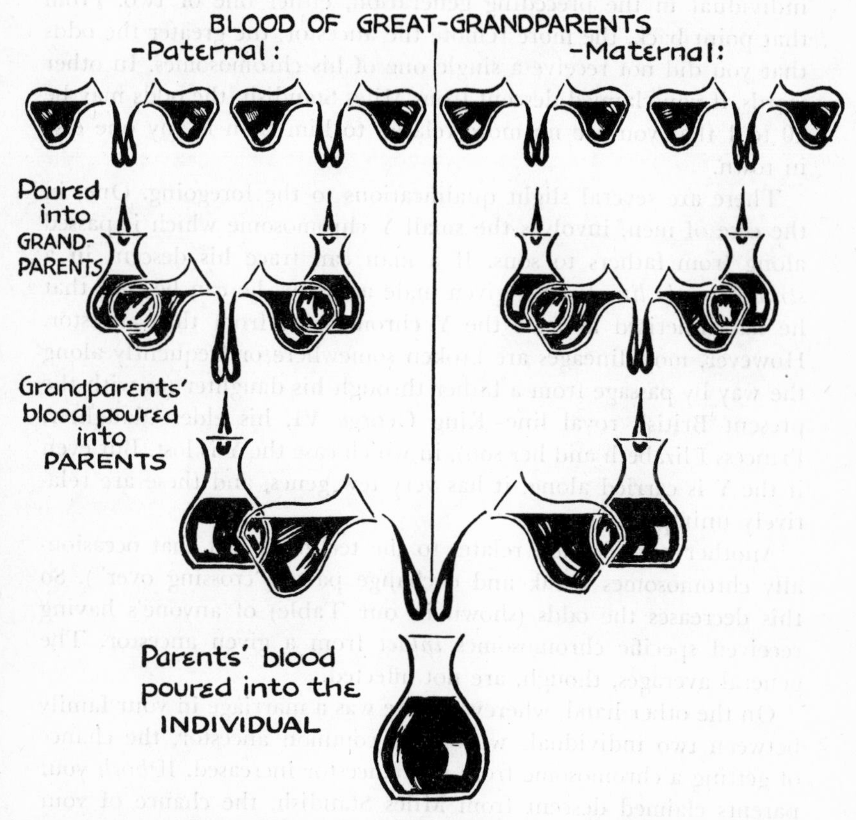

average number of chromosomes you may have received from any ancestor is reduced by half. Note the qualification "average number." You can be quite certain you received twenty-four chromosomes from each of your parents, but in the combination from your father, for instance, any number of these twenty-four may have been derived from *his* father, with the rest from *his* mother. On an *average,* however, you can assume that you received twelve chromosomes from each of your grandparents, that an average of *six* of these came from each great-grandparent, an average of *three* from each great-great-grandparent, and so on, the number from any ancestor being halved with each generation back.

Thus, as you will see by the "Ancestry Table" on page 524, when we get to the fourth generation you might have received from any ancestor on an average of three chromosomes, and from any specified individual in the preceding generation, either one or two. From that point back, the more remote the ancestor, the greater the odds that you did not receive a single one of his chromosomes. In other words, if you claimed descent from Miles Standish, the odds may be 20 to 1 that you are no more related to him than is any one else in town.

There are several slight qualifications to the foregoing. One, in the case of men, involves the small Y chromosome which is passed along from fathers to sons. If a man can trace his descent in a *straight male line* from a given male ancestor, he can be sure that he has inherited at least the Y chromosome from that ancestor. However, most lineages are broken somewhere or frequently along the way by passage from a father through his daughter (as with the present British royal line—King George VI, his eldest daughter, Princess Elizabeth and her son), in which case the Y is lost. But even if the Y is carried along, it has very few genes, and these are relatively unimportant.

Another qualification relates to the technical fact that occasionally chromosomes break and exchange parts ("crossing over"). So this decreases the odds (shown in our Table) of anyone's having received specific chromosomes *intact* from a given ancestor. The general averages, though, are not affected.

On the other hand, wherever there was a marriage in your family between two individuals with some common ancestor, the chance of getting a chromosome from that ancestor increased. If *both* your parents claimed descent from Miles Standish, the chance of your carrying one of his chromosomes would be increased to one in ten. Further, if there were marriages between other Pilgrim descendants further back in your ancestry, you might very likely be chock-full of "*Mayflower*" chromosomes. Thus, in families with considerable inbreeding, such as the European royalty, or in any peoples who have tended to hold together (the Irish, Scotch, Jews, etc.) the possibility of carrying one or more chromosomes of some vaunted ancestor increases. Nevertheless, Professor Haldane estimates that the odds are against King George of England having received *even a single gene*—let alone a whole chromosome—from William the Conqueror!

At the same time, with each marriage between related persons in your ancestry, the number of your ancestors is reduced. Were it not for this, you can readily see that the number of your potential ancestors, if you continued to double them with each generation back, would reach impossible figures. As the number of possible ancestors is limited, it has therefore been estimated that all persons of English descent are at least thirtieth cousins; and of course, if we go back far enough, we all have ancestors in common.

Even if one could be certain of carrying one or two chromosomes of some famous ancestor, the claim to distinction on that account becomes rather ridiculous when we recall that a full complement of forty-eight *chromosomes* is required to make an individual. Nor is there any guarantee that the one or two vaunted chromosomes which one might have received did not contain the very *worst* of genes.

A second fallacy is that of completely disregarding the unimportant ancestors, and in many families the remoter female ancestors. It is seldom pointed out, for instance, that while William the Conqueror's father was of royal blood, his mother was a humble tanner's daughter who bore him illegitimately.

In fact, with regard to all family trees the practice has been to lop off the ignoble branches in each generation, so that eventually only the limited few "distinguished" ancestors are left dangling. When a geneticist therefore is confronted with a lineage dating back, say, twenty generations, in which at best a selected few hundred out of a possible many thousands are listed, he may be pardoned for not taking it seriously.

A third fallacy in the ancestry field is that of comparing human families to strains of domestic animals—aristocrats to thoroughbreds and ordinary folks to mongrels. True enough, there are genetic aristocracies among horses, dogs, cows and cats; but bear in mind that they were derived only by the closest inbreeding—fathers with daughters, mothers with sons, brothers with sisters—and also by controlling every mating and by discarding those not wanted from every generation or litter. Human breeding, on the other hand, has been a haphazard process, and even the bluest of our blue-blooded families are a hodgepodge of unidentifiable genes. To quote the famed biologist, W. Johannsen, "From the point of view of a pure-bred dog, we are all curs."

We cannot deny, however, that there are families which by the consistent achievement of an unduly large percentage of their

YOU AND YOUR ANCESTORS

The only possible hereditary link which you can have with any ancestor is through inheritance of one or more chromosomes.* This table shows the *average* number of chromosomes which you might have received from any specified ancestor in any generation back, or the odds against having received even a single chromosome.† However, as noted in the text, marriages between relatives in your line of descent intensified your link with any preceding ancestor.

Generation Back	*Approx. Year and Generation*	*No. of "Potential" Ancestors*	*No. of Chromosomes from Each (Av.)*
First (Your parents)	1920	2	**24**
Second (Grandparents)	1890 (The "Nineties")	4	**12**
Third (Great g.ps.)	1860 (Generation of Lincoln)	8	**6**
Fourth (Great-great g.ps.)	1830 (Generation of Andr. Jackson)	16	**3**
Fifth (Great-great-great-g.ps.)	1800 (Generation of Napoleon)	32	**1 or 2**
			Odds Against Having Received Even One Chromosome from Any Given Ancestor
Sixth	1770 (Revolutionary War heroes)	64	**4 to 3**
Seventh	1740 (Benj. Franklin, etc.)	128	**8 to 3**
Eighth	1700 (William III)	256	**5 to 1**
Ninth	1670 (John Bunyan)	512	**10 to 1**
Tenth	1635 (The Pilgrims)	1,024	**21 to 1**
Eleventh	1600 (Capt. John Smith)	2,048	**42 to 1**
Twelfth	1570 (Mary, Queen of Scots)	4,096	**85 to 1**
Thirteenth	1535 (Martin Luther)	8,192	**170 to 1**
Fourteenth	1500 (Henry VIII)	16,384	**340 to 1**
Fifteenth	1470 (Columbus)	32,768	**680 to 1**

* The generations as given would apply to a young adult today.

† See text for minor qualifications to the above Table, relating to the Y chromosome in males, and also the passing on of fractions of chromosomes through the process of "crossing over."

members do suggest that they carry many "superior" genes. Among such families may be cited the Darwins and the Huxleys in England, and the Adamses, the Edwardses, the Jameses and the Roosevelts in the United States. But it is also clear that even in the greatest of families there are mediocrities who ride along, as in a trailer, pulled by their family influence, opportunity or wealth and who, left to their own power, would get nowhere.

"Ancestry" or "family" has significance only when individuals themselves show clear evidence of continued superiority. But, alas, all our records show that combinations of "superior" genes do not long hold together. Rarely do we find any dynasty of superior humans continuing for as much as four or five generations.

When we turn now to "inferior" ancestry we find that the same fallacies underlie the compilation of "bad" pedigrees as of "superior" ones. The motives, however, are quite different. As we might express it in verse—

There was a Bostonese
Who searched out pedigrees
Which she stored in the middle of her forehead;
And when they were good, they were very, very good,
But when they were bad—they were horrid!

Which is by way of saying that compilers of pedigrees may be motivated by the very human urge to prove extremes. Those who compile genealogies of persons of "superior" stock are out to show how very good all these people are. In the compilation of pedigrees of "inferior" stock, investigators may unconsciously yield to the opposite impulse.

Nowhere has the practice of gilding the lily and tar-brushing the weed been more clearly illustrated than in the classic cases of the "Jukes" and the "Kallikaks." Few studies in the field of social science have been more widely publicized, and few have had more profound effect on eugenic thought, than those of these two families. Although geneticists have for years rejected as unscientific the methods and conclusions of the studies, the ghosts of the "Jukes" and "Kallikaks" continue to go marching on through many textbooks and reference works, and hundreds of thousands of college and high-school students have continued to be taught about these horrible examples. But let's look into the facts.

First, the "Kallikaks." Early in this century Dr. H. H. Goddard, then at work in an institution for mental defectives in New Jersey, chanced on the strange fact that there were two family groups in the vicinity, distantly related to each other, and yet as different in character as the proverbial night and day. The one branch comprised upright, intelligent, prosperous citizens; the other abounded in degenerates, mental defectives, drunks, paupers, prostitutes and criminals. Struck with the contrast, Dr. Goddard coined for the family the name "Kallikak" (compounded of Greek words meaning "good" and "bad") and after some research into the pedigrees published this explanation (in 1912):

Both clans had stemmed from the same remote ancestor—Martin "Kallikak," a Revolutionary War soldier—*but through two different matings.* Martin Kallikak, himself, it appeared, was of good stock, and after the war had married a worthy young Quakeress by whom he had seven children—progenitors of all the *"good"* Kallikaks. But—

Before he had married, and while a-soldiering, Martin had met a feeble-minded girl in a tavern, and with her had had an affair. He went his way, and presently the girl bore an illegitimate male child *to whom she gave the name of Martin Kallikak, Jr.* This lad grew up to be so wicked he was known as "Old Horror," and to make matters worse, sired ten worthless offspring. It was from these that Dr. Goddard traced all the many hundreds of *"bad"* Kallikaks.

Clearly, looking first at the very, very good Kallikaks, and then at the very, very bad Kallikaks, their differences would seem to have been caused by the two radically different females from whom they descended—the worthy Quakeress and the feeble-minded slattern. For a long time this was held up as a fine illustration of "superior" ancestry and "inferior" ancestry. But remember, this study was made in the infancy of genetics and with the rudimentary psychological techniques of almost forty years ago. Today, with our much advanced scientific knowledge and thinking, we can view the situation quite differently.

The comparison rests largely on the *assumption* that the illegitimate child whom the feeble-minded mother chose to call Martin Kallikak, Jr., was indeed the son of the man she designated, which no court would accept as evidence (and which no court did pass upon at the time). If we reject this premise—that all the "bad" Kallikaks descended from the same man as all the "good" Kalli-

WHAT IS WRONG WITH THIS PICTURE?

In Revolutionary War times there was a soldier named

"MARTIN KALLIKAK"

While in service he dallied with a feeble-minded tavern girl

—after the war he married a worthy young Quakeress

She bore a son whom she called "Martin Kallikak, Jr." — later known as "Old Horror."

She bore him seven fine, healthy, upright children.

From "Old Horror" came ten children who spawned hundreds of the lowest humans, with the worst heredity.

From these came hundreds of the most worthy type of humans, with the best heredity.

kaks, by different matings—then the whole double-pedigree aspect of the Kallikak study, balanced precariously like an inverted pyramid on this one point, topples of its own weight.

But supposing the facts to be correct, a nice point in genetics intrudes itself: Granted that "Old Horror" (Kallikak, Jr.) was a degenerate because of *bad heredity* (though we have no evidence as yet that "degeneracy" is inherited), by what gene mechanism did he become that way? No *single dominant* gene could produce any such complex condition, nor is there any known gene that can singly produce even feeble-mindedness. *Recessive* genes would have had to be involved. Which means that as such genes must come from *both parents* for the effect to assert itself, no matter how chock-full of "black" genes the feeble-minded mother was, the *worthy Martin Kallikak, Sr., himself had to be carrying duplicates of the very same genes* if the condition of his presumptive son, "Old Horror," was indeed due to heredity. That would mean, in turn, that some of the "good" Kallikaks in all probability also received these genes! By what good strange fortune, then, did all the "good" Kallikaks—without an exception noted in the study—turn out to be such fine eugenic specimens?*

Before we go on to a number of other points that any geneticist might raise, let's look into the case of the "Jukes" (also a coined name).

The Jukes family, another unsavory clan abounding in every known type of human riff-raff, was investigated long before the Kallikaks. It was in 1874 that R. L. Dugdale, a New York Prison Association inspector, chanced upon this worthless aggregation, clustered in one locality. Tracing back, he discovered that they all had a common ancestry in two eighteenth-century brothers who had married a pair of disreputable sisters. Intensifying their relationship was the fact that the Jukes were much inbred.

In 1916 the Jukes study was brought up to date with an investigation of the ensuing generations. Degeneracy, immorality and defectiveness were still rampant among the new crop of Jukes, but to a smaller degree. Many of the family, in fact, were honest, hard-

* A defense of the Kallikak study, and a bitter criticism of those who had questioned its validity, was made by Dr. Goddard in *Science,* June 5, 1942. In reply this author (Scheinfeld) presented an analysis of the issues in the *Journal of Heredity,* September, 1944 ("The Kallikaks After Thirty Years"). We may add here that whatever the shortcomings of his Kallikak study with respect to genetics, Dr. Goddard was long in the forefront of American psychologists, highly honored for many important contributions to the study of mental defects.

working citizens, some even "superior" and prosperous. This improvement was ascribed to reduced inbreeding and the infusion of "good outside" blood.

If we now analyze the Jukes studies, we find them quite as questionable from a genetic standpoint as we found the Kallikak studies. When Dugdale investigated the Jukes, not only was nothing known of the mechanism of heredity, but sociology was in its infancy. Dugdale blandly assumed, as did others at the time, that "pauperism," prostitution and criminality—even the tendency to have illegitimate children—had an hereditary basis. His conclusions were that, starting with a bad heredity, the Jukes had created for themselves a bad environment and that this environment had produced bad traits which in turn became hereditary. (Or, in other words, that morals, habits and other *acquired* bad traits are inherited—which, of course, we now know is unfounded.)

We can well suspect that in the original study of the Jukes there were many errors in the dogmatic classification of individuals as "prostitutes," "criminals" or "degenerates" (especially when we consider that some of the individuals classified had been dead for anywhere from 25 to 100 years). But even more strongly can we question the data regarding mental defectiveness, for at that time there were not even IQ scores to go by. Nor were the diagnoses of the Kallikaks (made with the limited psychological techniques available in 1912) above suspicion—particularly with regard to those long-buried. In fact, most of the ratings of the mentality of the bygone Kallikaks were apparently based on *recollections* of aged neighbors. Another important shortcoming of both studies was that the individuals traced or reported represented only a *part* of all the descendants.

With all these reservations, however, there is no gainsaying that the bad Jukes who were observed, like the bad Kallikaks, were an unusually undesirable lot. We needn't argue how bad or how degenerate they were. What concerns us is the extent to which their degeneracy and their lowness can be blamed on *bad heredity*.

Let us try to picture one of the Jukes girls, at the time of Dugdale's investigation, in the seventies:

Mamie Jukes lived in a dark, squalid nest of hovels, with a drunken, thieving father, a slattern of a mother and a swarm of untidy, ill-fed brothers and sisters. Mamie didn't go to school, because there was no compulsory education and the district schoolhouse wouldn't take any of the brood. Decent folks kept away from the Jukes and whipped their children if they were even seen talking to Mamie. She was pretty lonely until, when she got to be about 14 or 15, some men who hung around a pool hall began to take an interest in her. Mamie was a little bewildered, and pathetically flattered by this sudden attention. She was too dumb to understand what was happening, or how it happened, but soon she became pregnant. . . . And one day, months later in a dark corner where Mamie cowered like a sick animal, another illegitimate, "unfit" child was added to the Jukes clan.

Yes, this is a synthetic picture, but no one who has studied the records would deny that it is a typical one. Can we still say that the new Jukes child—or any similar child—starting out life under such conditions was predestined to inferiority because of "black" genes? Or could we not equally predict a bad end, *regardless* of the genes that child carried, on the basis of its "black" environment?

It is because earlier investigators did not quite see this distinction that their studies are now so greatly discounted. This is not to deny the possibility that some or even a good part of the defectiveness of such clans as those of the Jukes and Kallikaks might have been due to heredity. We know that like tends to mate with like, and that in the course of time, with inbreeding, degenerate strains might develop. But we'll have to have a lot better evidence than was gathered in the past to prove that the "horrible example" clans cited were primarily products of "black" genes, and not of "black" environments.

To quote the late Professor Thomas Hunt Morgan:

"The numerous pedigrees that have been published showing a long history of social misconduct, crime, alcoholism, debauchery and venereal diseases, are all open to the same criticism from a genetic point of view, for it is obvious that these groups of individuals have lived under demoralizing social conditions that might swamp a family of average persons. It is not surprising that, once begun, from whatever cause, the effects may be to a large extent communicated rather than inherited."

And as a *coup de grâce,* we may add this from another famed geneticist, Professor Lancelot Hogben: "If social biology ever becomes an exact science, the dreary history of the Jukes will be regarded as we now regard alchemy."

CHAPTER 45

THE GIDDY STORK

"We hold these truths to be self-evident: that all men are created equal . . ."

So SAYS our Declaration of Independence. But everything we have learned about human heredity challenges this statement. Nor could our Founding Fathers have meant it literally. What they undoubtedly had in mind is that spiritually, and ideologically, every human being, as one of God's creatures, is born with the right to be treated equally and fairly under the laws of man. Under the laws of Nature, unfortunately, there is no such justice. The further our knowledge of genetics proceeds, the more apparent it becomes that from the moment of conception, individuals are started off with every type of inequality in body and mind and in their chances for life, liberty and the pursuit of happiness.

One can grant, also, that this inequality extends to the worth of people to society, and that by almost any standard, some types of people who are born into the world are more desirable than others. Hence our problem: When we take a broad view of the population, it is disconcerting to discover—or so we are told—that the kind of people who are most wanted are being created in lessening proportions, those who are least wanted in increasing proportions. Here is a new sort of population threat, involving the *quality* of human beings and the genes they are passing along to future generations.

Fears regarding *quantity* of population are of long standing. Back in 1800, when the world population had doubled in a century to what was then regarded as the staggering total of 750,000,000 souls, many feared that at this rate there soon wouldn't be enough food for everyone. So the Reverend Thomas Malthus, a British clergyman, came out with his theory which went something like this: "Population growth is biologically self-regulating. Whenever the numbers of people get too big for the available resources, wars, plagues or famines will come along to trim humanity down to the required size." (Unfortunately many persons interpreted this as meaning that war and the other calamities were not merely natural, but necessary and desirable.)

The Malthusian doctrines, popular for a long while, began to seem questionable when humanity went on to even more phenomenal growth, almost tripling again in the next century and a half. Yet through vastly improved methods and means of food production, and many technological and medical advances, people in general were better fed, healthier and longer-lived than ever. Odder still, the only places where population growth began to slow down were in those very countries in which food was most abundant and living standards were reaching their highest point. Not calamity, but prosperity, and the social changes that came with it, was levelling off the numbers of people through voluntary restraints on reproduction.

By about 1930, the fears in the more advanced countries were of not having *enough* population in comparison with the backward countries which were continuing to have high birth rates. In France and Sweden, as examples, births had actually dropped below the replacement level, and it looked as if this also might soon happen in the United States and England. In Germany, Italy and the Soviet Union—countries seeking to become more powerful—drives were under way to stimulate birth rates through bonuses and various incentives. Then came World War II. And again, in the face of old Malthus, despite all the millions of lives that were lost through bloody purges, battles, bombings, plagues and famines, populations increased as birth rates shot up to the highest point in decades and more than made up for the losses in the warring countries. Added to this, life expectancies were going up by leaps and bounds, so that more and more older people were swelling the population ranks.

So again there was the fear of *too many people*. Nor was hope held out this time that population growth would check itself automatically by anything Nature could do. Two startling books, by Americans, came out in 1948. William Vogt, in *The Road to Survival*, and Fairfield Osborn, in *Our Plundered Planet,* carried the same dire warnings: Mankind was threatened with disaster or, at least, with a fearful battle for survival, by the fact that populations were increasing beyond the capacity of the earth to support them—in large part because millions of acres of land and forests were being despoiled, streams were being dried up, and natural resources accumulated over long ages were being exhausted without replacement. The old specter of an earth choking itself to death with people would indeed become a reality, these experts said, unless there were drastic curbs on reproduction.

Are these warnings justified? Some of the more optimistic authorities say "No." They argue that the world's present resources, if properly utilized, can feed twice as many people, and that by the time there are more, new means will have been found to increase the food supply to what is needed. But the argument can be sustained only up to a certain point. Under conditions as they exist now, with infant mortality steadily dropping and longevity increasing, the world could easily double its population at least every thirty-five years, and certainly every fifty years. (Backward Puerto Rico has doubled its population in the past twenty-five years; Holland has doubled hers in the past fifty years, and many of its people are being encouraged to move elsewhere. In the United States, too, population doubled from 1900 to 1950, although immigration contributed somewhat to this.)

It would therefore be a matter of simple mathematics: two times two times two. Taking the lower estimate of a doubled population every fifty years, our present two billion world population would become four billion by the end of this century. Eight billion in 2050. Sixteen billion by the year 2100, and so on, into fantastic numbers within a few hundred years. Not even with the greatest reliance on science could anyone hope that the earth could support such numbers. Sooner or later the need for worldwide voluntary limitation on births must become inescapable.

But, as we said before, a check on reproduction has already been taking place. The worry is that, as with some ladies in the reducing class, the reduction is not in the right quarters. Specifically, first viewing the world as a whole, the peoples of India, Egypt, Indonesia, and, in general, the more retarded countries (including some in South and Central America) have been reproducing at far higher rates than those of the more socially and economically advanced European countries and the United States. The ratios being contributed to the world's population by different countries, races and ethnic groups are thus rapidly changing. Yet this would have meaning with respect to changes in the *inherent* quality of mankind only if it could be proved that the peoples of some races or countries are *genetically inferior* to those of others. No evidence for this exists, however, as we saw in our "Race" chapters.

Unless or until we do have evidence that the broad changes in the makeup of the world's population have genetic significance, they might be viewed with alarm only with respect to their social implications—the menace to the countries with slowing-down growths as compared with those whose numbers are swelling, and the possibility of bitter struggles for existence among people in the future. On the other hand, if the population checks in the more advanced countries have come through greater social and economic progress, one might argue that the raising of living standards in the more backward and now unduly populous countries will similarly bring down their birth rates. Whether this will happen soon enough to offset the threatened calamities, only time can tell.

For the immediate present, and much more easily discernible, are the changes in population makeup that are taking place inside our own country and many others. Here there is clear evidence that the individuals and groups which are more backward—intellectually, culturally, socially and economically—are breeding at a much faster rate than those more advanced. How is this affecting our population *quality?*

Disregarding for the moment the question of *why* some people are on a lower level than others, there cannot be much doubt that certain individuals will not make as good parents as other individuals. If we think of the qualifications for parenthood in terms of "plus" and "minus," we might picture two contrasting types:

The *"Pluses"* are intelligent, capable, hard-working, law-abiding, socially-conscious couples, eager to have as many children as they can afford to support, and to whom they can give every advantage possible.

The *"Minuses"* are the more unintelligent or uneducated, shiftless, unsocially-minded couples, living from hand to mouth in unwholesome surroundings, careless about the upbringing of their children and often looking upon them as necessary inflictions.

So we come to the complaint that the "Pluses" of the United States and of other advanced countries are having the smallest families, while the "Minuses," who may least desire children and offer them the worst start in life, are having the largest families. (Remember, we are referring to broad averages. It does not imply that all those with small families are "Pluses" and all those with large families "Minuses." Nor can we ignore the fact that some couples have large families because they love children more, while other couples in the same circumstances have few or no children because they are selfish.)

For our country at large, the highest birth rates are in the most impoverished rural areas, chiefly of the South and West. On the other hand, in the more favorable economic areas—which are chiefly urban—fertility is much lower. In most of the large cities fertility is less than 75 per cent of that required for replacement, and within the cities proper the fertility is highest among the poor, the least educated and those in the least favorable circumstances, and lowest among those in the higher income and cultural brackets. Likewise, among the farmers and small-town inhabitants, those most prosperous and most advanced have fewer children than their backward neighbors.

"What these differences mean," says Dr. Philip M. Hauser, a leading population expert, "is that unless the present trends are changed, a disproportionately large part of future Americans are now being born and reared in urban and rural slums which cannot be expected to produce physically, mentally and morally healthy citizens, adequately equipped to achieve the good life and to contribute to the future of the nation." But, he goes on to explain, "I think the evidence now available makes it amply clear that most of our contemporary problems of population quality, and most of those in the foreseeable future—within a span of the next century or so—would definitely depend on the kind of cultural, educational and economic opportunities afforded to our coming generations rather than on the character of the genes they have inherited."

Attention has also been given to differences in fertility among racial, ethnic and religious groups, but these differences are not nearly as great or significant as many imagine (nor have we any thought here of interpreting them in *genetic* terms!). For example, there is the belief that Negroes have much higher birth rates than Whites. Actually, comparing Negroes of the lowest social and economic levels with Whites of the same levels, their reproduction rates are even less; while, as with Whites, Negroes on higher levels have been greatly limiting their reproduction.

Are Catholics outproducing Protestants? Where there is any difference in birth rates it is more on a social and economic basis than a religious one. White Protestants in the rural regions of the South have higher reproductive rates than Catholics of the North, and in the North, among the poverty-stricken of both religious groups, the birth rates are about the same. In a 1945 study made by Drs. Clyde V. Kiser and P. K. Whelpton of families in Indianapolis, it was found that while in general the Catholic families were somewhat larger, their fertility declined as in other groups with successive rises in the economic and educational scale.

Are foreign-born Americans reproducing faster than those of native stock? Up to about 1920 their birth rate was about one-and-a-half times that of the native-born. Since then, with the aging of the foreign-born population and the checks on immigration, the birth rate among them has come down to almost the level of the native Americans (the foreign-born now contributing only about 5 per cent of the total births). But bearing on our main point, it is important to note that among the children of the foreign-born, who have been socially and economically more favored than their parents, the decline in birth rates has been very marked.

What we see, then, is that all groups of Americans are on the same reproductive see-saw: Lower living standards, higher birth rates; higher standards, lower birth rates. But before we translate this into terms of the effects on our population *quality,* we must keep in mind the two distinctly different aspects: the *environmental* and the *genetic.* In some cases they may be related, in others not.

Where parents are inferior only because they have been underprivileged, then their children are inferior purely because of the environment. In that case, social and economic improvements could easily improve the quality of the offspring (and this has been happening in a great many instances). But if and where persons are backward in achievement and living in depressed circumstances because they are *genetically inferior*—as with those suffering from inherited mental or physical handicaps—then the children they produce will be given bad starts both through bad heredity and bad environment. It is because of the high birth rates among these parents that many population experts believe the genetic quality of our population has actually been declining.

What evidence have we for this? To date the case revolves principally around the *intelligence* factor, and is largely inferential. In our "IQ" chapter we pointed out that there was a correlation between the measured intelligence of parents at different occupational levels and that of their offspring. Where the parents are in the professional and upper-level business groups, the IQs of their children average about 116. At the opposite end, children of unskilled laborers have average IQs of 96. But going with this also is the fact that the lower-IQ families in all groups have proportionately many more children.

For instance, in a British study in 1947, of 3,400 children at Bath, England, Dr. J. A. Fraser Roberts reported that the brightest 4 per cent of the children had an average number of less than two brothers and/or sisters, whereas the dullest 8 per cent had an average of more than four siblings. In other words, families with the dullest children averaged almost two-and-a-half times the size of families with the brightest children.* Further, going by the parents' IQs, Dr. Roberts reported that the chances of producing a child of the moron grade (with an IQ of less than 70, but exclusive of idiots or imbeciles) was only 1 in a thousand for parents with IQs of 130; 6 per thousand for parents with IQs of 115; 23 per thousand for parents with IQs of 100; 67 per thousand for parents with IQs of 95; and *160 per thousand for parents with IQs of 70.* (For feeble-minded parents, with average IQs of 44, the ratio of moron children was about one in three.)

Thus, if the IQs are any indication of inherited intelligence factors, there would be some basis for concluding that with proportionately fewer children among the upper-level parents and more children among the lower-level parents, fewer of the better "intelligence" genes and increasingly more of the lower "intelligence" genes are being passed along. On this assumption, many experts in the United States and Great Britain maintain that *the average IQs in these countries have been declining by at least one to two points each generation.*

Not all authorities concede this, and some offer these arguments: If any slight decrease in average IQ is actually taking place, this is more than offset by the fact that ever-larger numbers of people are being educated, so that whatever people's mental equipment, they are now able to do much more with it than they could in the past; and that, therefore, the mental *performance* of our population on the whole has really been improving. There is also the argument that as general advances are made in living conditions, more and

* Even in the Soviet Union it was reported in 1939 that parents with high IQs had considerably fewer children than those with low IQs.

more of those on the lower levels will be curtailing their reproduction. These arguments, however, do not affect the contention that for the time being the *genetic* quality of our population is being lowered.

Let us therefore look closer at some of the causes of the differential fertility which is causing so much concern. First and foremost is *birth control* (or to use a recently more favored term, "planned parenthood"). With the desire to insure as much care and education as possible for each child (and also to lessen the strain on themselves and to safeguard the health of the mother), the generally more enlightened parents are taking advantage of the knowledge and facilities for birth control now available. On the other hand, parents in the lowest social and economic levels are more likely to let Nature take its course.

(It might be pointed out here that birth control is not as new as some may think. Almost a century ago, evidence indicates that upper-class families in the United States were tending to limit their births more than those on lower levels. Nor is birth control solely a product of civilization. Among many primitive peoples contraceptive methods have long been practiced; and *infanticide*—killing of defective or unwanted children, as well as induced miscarriages—has been common among them, as it also has been among many lower-level Europeans and Asiatics.)

Comparing city and country, the pressure of limitation of families is not so great in the rural areas. Added children on farms do not mean having to move to new quarters with higher rentals (and finding the apartments), as in the cities. Also, schooling in farm areas is more limited, so that children do not remain dependent for so long; in fact, children on farms are often economic assets, especially among the most backward, where they are put at some task from the earliest ages. However, the ban on child labor, and laws making schooling compulsory up to age 16, have reduced the incentive in many areas to have large families.

Another cause of the disproportion in birth rates are the differences in ages at marriages. Persons in the upper levels have longer periods of education and training, and in turn tend to postpone marriage, or having children, or both, until they are established. This is particularly so among the more educated women. Not only does college training postpone for them the time when they begin bearing children, but in many cases it acts to forestall marriage altogether. Alumnae records of our leading women's colleges show a strikingly high proportion of graduates who remain unmarried, though not nearly as high as in former years. As an example, the alumnae register of Barnard College for Women (New York) shows that where only 9 per cent of the graduates of the class of 1900 had married, the proportion rose to 51 per cent in 1935 and to 64 per cent married in the class of 1946, with the promise of becoming even greater.

But the number of children per marriage for either male or female college graduates has remained consistently low—much below that needed merely to replace the parents. Various reports in the past few years have shown figures such as these: Twenty-five years after graduation, Harvard alumni (class of 1924) had produced an average of only 1.74 children each; Yale alumni, 1.70; Wellesley alumnae, 1.45; Vassar, 1.49. These figures are very close to the reproductive averages of graduates of seventy-six leading American colleges, as reported by Dr. Clarence J. Gamble in 1947: for men graduates, an average of 1.72 children each; women graduates, 1.35 children each. By way of comparison with the earlier times, Yale graduates of the eighteenth century had an average of better than 4 children each surviving to maturity.

However, among the male college graduates themselves, there is evidence that the more successful produced substantially more offspring that the less successful. On the other hand, among the women, those most outstanding in careers tend to have few offspring, collectively. Of the 2,400 women in *Who's Who in America* in 1949, 40 per cent were not married, and of those married, close to 40 per cent had no children. (It might be noted that most of these *Who's Who* women were graduated from colleges and embarked on careers a generation or more ago, when the idea of "marriage versus career" or "career versus motherhood" was widely prevalent, and one choice was believed to preclude—or did preclude—the other. The situation has changed considerably as increasingly more women are combining careers with both marriage and motherhood, although their average reproductive rate continues to be much below that of women not in careers.)

What should be emphasized, especially, is that in referring to the low birth rates among the more educated men and women we are not speaking of *class* differences. In all groups and in all families, from the poorest to the richest, and from the social "nobodies" to the "400," the brightest sons and daughters are the ones who, as a rule, go through college and are the most successful. And it is these who tend to have the fewest children—considerably fewer, evidence shows, than their own brothers and sisters who are less educated and less successful. So if the assumption is valid that persons of higher achievement are genetically superior in capacity, there is some reason to believe that their failure to reproduce themselves means a relative diminution of the "superior-achievement" genes being poured back into the human stream.

Altogether, what we may be experiencing is in some respects a reversal in the process of human evolution. Here is how many authorities would state the case: From the earlier stages of mankind until very recent times there was some degree of natural selection of the "fittest." Not only did those best endowed genetically, in mental and physical makeup, have the best chance of surviving and succeeding, but they were also most likely to reproduce themselves more and insure the survival of more children. As civilization has advanced this evolutionary process appears to have been checked and turned in an opposite direction. It is no longer necessary for each individual to prove his capacity for physical survival. Society, aided by medical science, is seeing to it that every one born into the world is kept alive, if possible. Moreover, not merely are the genetically inferior individuals not restrained in reproduction, but unless they are physically incapacitated or have to be institutionalized, they have the opportunity to reproduce themselves at even a higher rate than those better endowed. *The process of evolutionary "selection" is therefore now working in favor of the least "fit" and against the most "fit."*

Whether or not one accepts this interpretation, there can be no challenge to the basic facts presented in this chapter:

Ever-larger proportions of our most capable, most educated and most successful persons who are qualified to be the best parents, are voluntarily and drastically limiting their reproduction, in many cases below that needed for their replacement.

In contrast, a great many of the persons who are least qualified for parenthood are reproducing with little limitation.

Stated another way, among those whom society might wish to see with more children, there is *low "brood" pressure.*

Among those whom society might wish to see with fewer children, there is *high "brood" pressure.*

The Stork, it seems, has no sense of direction. What shall we do to steer it right?

CHAPTER 46

EUGENICS AND THE "UNFIT"

NOT so many years ago the word "eugenics" conjured up a picture of a muscular young man in a leopard skin being mated to a robust young woman in a bathing suit while over them, in an inset signifying "The Future," hovered a large brood of ruddy youngsters posed athletically (in their birthday suits) to show the effects of good heredity and a diet of cracked wheat and raw vegetables.

Later on the picture changed to one of determined reformers shooing the Stork away from slums and hovels while shouting their war-cry, "Sterilize! Sterilize!"

If "eugenics" still suggests to many minds "just another of those crackpot reform movements," the blame attaches to the earlier "eugenists" who got it off to a bad start. And this is unforunate, for eugenics, *properly interpreted,* may be one of the great forces for good on our social horizon.

"Eugenics" (based on the Greek word *eugenes*—"well-born") was the term coined by Sir Francis Galton in 1883 to designate his movement for improving the human race by scientific breeding. However, "eugenics" should not be confused with "genetics," which did not come into being until 1900. Thus, without knowledge of most of the important facts about heredity which we now have, Galton and his followers were motivated by many old fallacies concerning ancestry. They believed quite strongly that those on top were there largely because of "superior" heredity, while those at the bottom were there because of "inferior" heredity. These ideas were naturally very pleasing to persons who considered themselves as belonging to the "superior" classes, and won strong support from them, while at the same time arousing resentment among the more democratically-minded.

When the first genetic findings did come out regarding various "black" genes in human beings, the eugenists pounced on these as confirmation of their belief that most of the major ills in the world were due to bad heredity. The quickest and most effective way to improve the world, they argued, was by breeding better humans. This was violently contested by the "environmentalists," who insisted that hereditary differences were of little account, and that the way to produce a nearly perfect humanity was entirely through improvements in education, medical care and socio-economic conditions. Today we are finding both sides ready to compromise.

Recognizing that heredity and environment are always interoperating forces, the "hereditarians" have come to realize that many defects previously attributed to bad heredity are due primarily to outside influences, and that no matter how greatly we can improve our heredity, this will help little if we do not also provide good environment. The "environmentalists," on the other hand, faced with increasing proof that many ills, defects and undesirable characteristics are directly due to or influenced by heredity, must concede that no long-range plan for human betterment can ignore the importance of improving our genetic makeup. What should be stressed particularly is that most of the leading *geneticists* never aligned themselves with the extreme "eugenists," and have consistently been just as critical of radical measures advocated for human breeding as they have been of tendencies to ignore the factors of heredity.

Thus, as the facts have become clearer, there has been formulated this twofold "eugenics program" in which both environmental and genetic measures are included:

Negative Eugenics, embodying all measures that might reduce the proportion of "unfit" individuals.

Positive Eugenics, embodying all measures that might increase the proportion of "fit" individuals.

Not to give the impression that a definite platform has been drawn up (as by a political convention), we may say at once that the eugenics "program" we are presenting is merely a summary of various proposals made for improvement of the human stock. Some of these measures already are being carried out in this and other countries, some are still in nebulous form, some have met with general approval, and others are still being hotly debated.

First, "negative" eugenics: One important way to reduce the proportion of "unfit" children would be to reduce the birth rate among "unfit" parents. The cause of their unfitness is not necessarily of importance. For instance, couples who are insane, or low-grade morons, or who are criminal or degenerate, whatever the reason, are hardly likely to be "fit" parents. Nor need we question that a husband and wife living in squalor and ignorance, who already have a number of children not being reared properly, might well be considered unfit to have additional children. Yet many parents of these various unfit types keep producing unduly large numbers of offspring, chiefly because, through ignorance or indifference—and often against their will—they let Nature take its course.

To combat this situation, eugenists favor the spread of *birth-control* information. As was brought out in the previous chapter, the more educated and in many instances the more desirable individuals in our population are fully informed regarding birth-control techniques and are widely practicing them. Only by placing the same information and facilities at the disposal of the more backward couples (the contention is) can we prevent our population growth from becoming adversely one-sided. However, it is important to emphasize that modern eugenic objectives are not to keep anyone who wants children from having them, and not necessarily to limit the sizes of families, but to make sure that children are brought into the world under the best conditions possible. Like any guest in a home, it is felt a child should arrive only when *welcome.**

But what about persons who are considered unfit to have any children at all, and who cannot be relied upon to voluntarily refrain from reproduction? For these, the extreme form of birth control is proposed—that of *sterilization.*

Sterilization, as you may know by now, is not an *unsexing* operation. It in no way inhibits sex desires or interferes with normal sex-functioning. What it involves (with occasional exceptions) is a permanent blocking of the capacity for reproduction, by a quite simple operation: In a woman, cutting and tying the fallopian tubes which carry eggs from the ovaries to the womb; in a man, cutting and tying the tubes which carry sperms from the testes. The resulting condition, merely of sterility, is much the same as it is with many normal women and men who cannot reproduce.

Sterilization for eugenic reasons is not new. The first state laws, authorizing sterilization of mental defectives, were adopted in

* This is now expressed as the basic policy of the Planned Parenthood Federation, which operates or sponsors more than 600 clinics in American cities. Its work lies not only in providing birth-control information, but in helping parents to have children when they want them. *Inducing fertility* in previously barren couples through advice, or treatment, wherever possible, is an important activity of special clinics which it conducts.

Indiana and California in 1907 (although sterilization had already been performed in an Indiana prison some years earlier). Twenty-eight other states subsequently passed sterilization laws, but some states suspended them later. Many court battles had meanwhile taken place until the legality of the sterilization statutes was upheld in a Supreme Court decision in 1927, in which Justice Oliver Wendell Holmes made the now widely quoted comment, "It is better for all the world if, instead of waiting to execute degenerate offspring for crime or to let them starve for their imbecility, society can prevent those who are manifestly unfit from continuing their kind. The principle that sustains compulsory vaccination is broad enough to cover cutting the Fallopian tubes. . . . Three generations of imbeciles is enough."

By 1950 about 50,000 Americans of both sexes have been sterilized, more than a third of the operations having been performed in California alone (at a rate about seven times that for the country as a whole). In Europe, Denmark began practicing eugenical sterilization in 1929 (more than 4,000 persons, mostly feeble-minded, having been sterilized up to 1950), and Finland, Norway, Sweden and Switzerland followed. Germany, under the Nazis, went on to carry sterilization to fantastic limits (which we'll discuss presently). Canada now also provides for sterilization of some mental defectives.

Coming back to the United States, of the total of those sterilized to date, about half have been feeble-minded, about 47 per cent insane, and the remaining 3 per cent divided among criminals, sexual degenerates, epileptics, and certain types of hereditary physical defectives. (Also to be noted is that apart from the official state sterilizations, there are a considerable number of privately performed sterilizations each year. Some are on men and women who fear that they may transmit serious hereditary conditions, but more of the operations are on women for whom pregnancy would be dangerous.)

What has been accomplished, and how much more can be accomplished through sterilization?

The original thought was that sterilization provided a quick and easy method of wiping out all the serious hereditary conditions. The need for this would appear great. By conservative estimates there are in the United States today far more than a million persons with serious genetic defects, including tens of thousands of the blind and congenitally deaf, many thousands more of the paralyzed and deformed, and hundreds of thousands of the mentally diseased and low-grade feeble-minded—in addition to the large numbers with hereditary organic ailments. The cost of caring for these, many of whom require institutionalization for all or most of their lives, is tremendous. The toll in suffering is immeasurable. Even to reduce the proportion of the genetically afflicted by a small amount each generation would be an enormous gain.

We can start by assuming (but with great reservations to be noted later) that most of the 50,000 persons sterilized to date did carry serious "black" genes, and that thereby the birth of tens of thousands of defective children already has been prevented. But this is the merest beginning. Suppose from now on that we have a free hand to sterilize anybody and everybody, those in institutions and outside, who may be carrying serious hereditary defects the genes for which they are likely to transmit.

At the very outset, when we seek to eliminate any given "black" gene, we must consider the genetic mechanism involved—dominant, recessive, sex-linked, etc.—for in each case the problem is distinctly different. Let us see, then, what would be the effects of sterilization on the different genetic types.

Dominant gene conditions are the simplest to deal with. Where a single dominant gene is the direct cause, any hereditary disease or defect could be almost wiped out within one generation if all persons affected by it were sterilized. The "almost" refers, first, to the fact that new genes of the type often reappear through mutation; and, second, in such dominant conditions as Huntington's chorea, the more common adult glaucoma, and inner-ear deafness, which may not appear until middle life, the individual already may have had children and passed along the gene before he could be singled out for sterilization. (This problem may eventually be overcome if and when tests are devised to detect advance symptoms of conditions with late onsets.)

A special problem lies in the incompletely *dominant* conditions (or those due to "qualified" or "irregularly" dominant genes, or "dominant genes of low penetrance"). In these, the same gene sometimes asserts itself and sometimes doesn't, or may have different effects, from mild to serious, depending on circumstances. (Examples are cataracts, polycystic disease of the kidneys and many hand and foot abnormalities.) In such cases some persons with the gene may be completely normal or evidence only a mild defect, and may yet produce a seriously defective child. Without clues as to all the immediate carriers, it might take many generations to eliminate the incompletely dominant defects, although their incidence could be steadily reduced by sterilizing those in whom they did appear.

On the whole, the serious dominant conditions that could be easily eliminated (these including *some* types of hereditary blindness, paralysis, and muscle, skin and skeletal defects) are comparatively rare and would be of secondary importance in a sterilization program.

Sex-linked diseases and defects. Where a single gene produces its effects in males only, with two genes required to make a female defective, the problem with respect to sterilization becomes more complicated. In *hemophilia,* the best-known example, it is now dangerous to attempt sterilization of the victims because, being "bleeders," any operation might prove fatal. (New operational techniques may overcome this.) However, this disease is more dramatic than significant eugenically, as few hemophiliacs survive to maturity or reproduce, and few pedigrees of hemophilia run for more than a few generations. Mutations, it is believed, have been largely responsible for keeping up the supply of "hemophilia" genes.

In other sex-linked conditions, including a variety of serious eye defects and other conditions listed in our "Black Gene" Tables, sterilization of the victims (males, carrying one gene, and the much less frequent females, with two genes) would do much to reduce the future incidence of these defects. But there still would be the great number of cases of non-defective women each carrying a single, hidden, sex-linked, "black" gene. What are we to do about these women, in themselves perfectly normal, yet able to produce one in two defective sons, and also one in two daughters who are carriers?

First is the problem of identifying the carriers. In many cases this may not be possible until the woman already has borne a defective son (as where no affected males have appeared previously on the woman's side for several generations, or where the gene has arisen through mutation). Generally, however, the certainty or possibility of a woman being a carrier can be established quite easily. If her father was afflicted with a sex-linked disease, we know definitely she is carrying the gene for it (received through his X chromosome). So, too, if the woman has a brother with the disease (the gene having been received from her mother), there is a fifty-fifty chance of her being a carrier. Finally, where a suspicion exists, there is the likelihood that in some sex-linked conditions means will be devised of

WHAT STERILIZATION COULD ACCOMPLISH

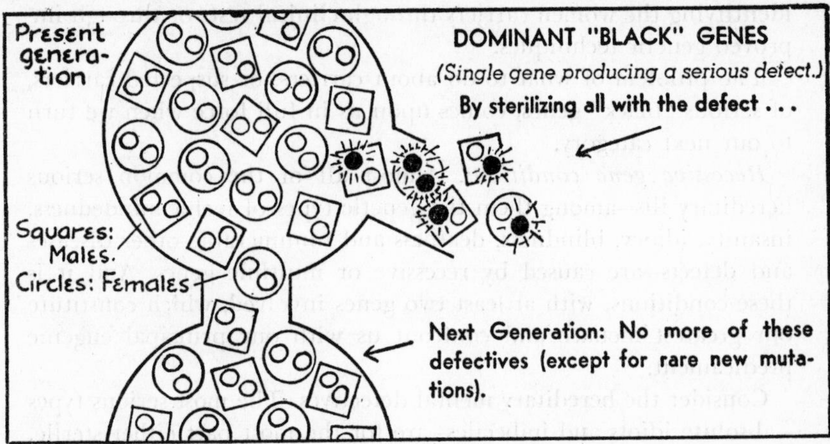
Present generation
DOMINANT "BLACK" GENES
(Single gene producing a serious defect.)
By sterilizing all with the defect . . .
Squares: Males.
Circles: Females
Next Generation: No more of these defectives (except for rare new mutations).

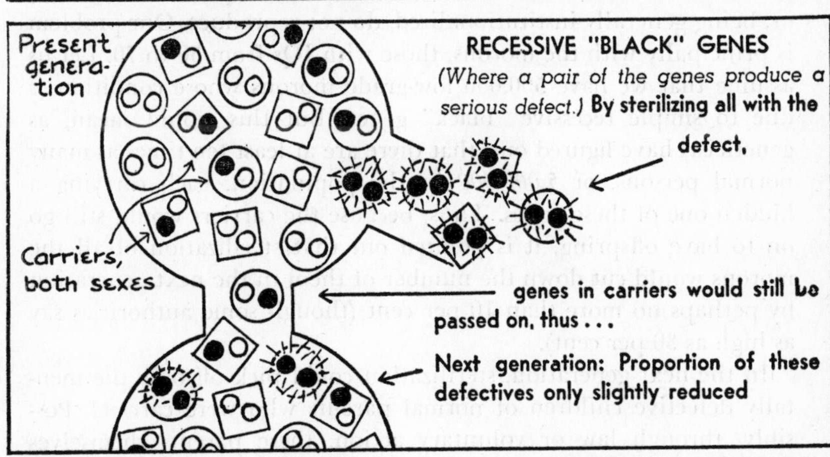
Present generation
RECESSIVE "BLACK" GENES
(Where a pair of the genes produce a serious defect.) By sterilizing all with the defect,
Carriers, both sexes
genes in carriers would still be passed on, thus . . .
Next generation: Proportion of these defectives only slightly reduced

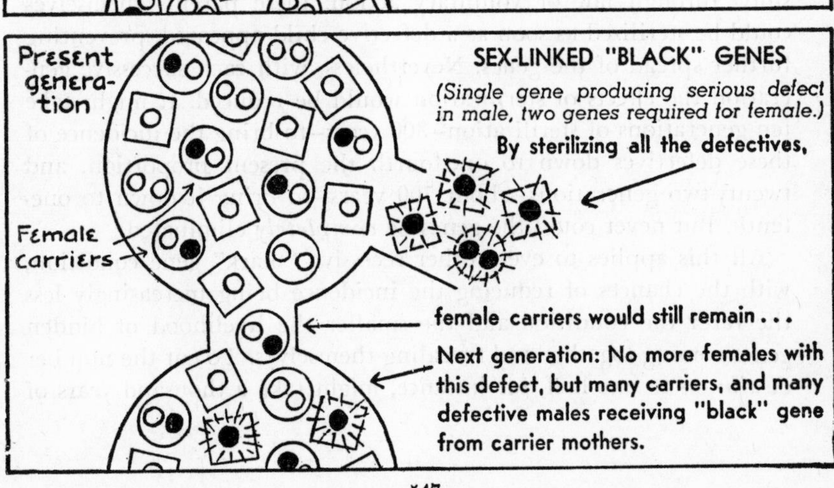
Present generation
SEX-LINKED "BLACK" GENES
(Single gene producing serious defect in male, two genes required for female.)
By sterilizing all the defectives,
Female carriers
female carriers would still remain . . .
Next generation: No more females with this defect, but many carriers, and many defective males receiving "black" gene from carrier mothers.

identifying the women carriers through clinical tests or through improved genetic techniques.

The problem of what to do about carriers, or suspected carriers, of serious "black" genes, comes upon us in full force when we turn to our next category.

Recessive gene conditions. Almost all of the common serious hereditary ills—among them the genetic types of feeble-mindedness, insanity, idiocy, blindness, deafness and innumerable other diseases and defects—are caused by recessive or multiple genes. And it is these conditions, with at least two genes involved, which constitute our greatest menace and confront us with our principal eugenic predicament.

Consider the hereditary mental defectives. The most serious types —absolute idiots and imbeciles—are for the most part either sterile, or, being generally institutionalized, do not reproduce. Our problem is principally with the morons, those with IQs from 50 to 70. Let us assume that we have 500,000 low-grade morons whose condition is due to simple recessive "black" genes. But this would mean, as geneticists have figured out, that there are at least ten times as many normal persons, or *5,000,000* in the population, each carrying a hidden one of these genes. Thus, because the carriers would still go on to have offspring, it is pointed out that sterilization of all the morons would cut down the number of them in the next generation by perhaps no more than 10 per cent (though some authorities say as high as 30 per cent).

In the next generation, sterilization could pick off only the mentally defective children of normal parents who were carriers. Possibly, through law or voluntary action, these parents themselves could be sterilized as soon as a defective child appeared, preventing further spread of the genes. Nevertheless, with each successive generation the effects of sterilization would be reduced. It might take ten generations of sterilization—300 years—to bring the incidence of these defectives down to one-fourth the present proportion, and twenty-two generations—about 700 years—to bring it down to one-tenth. But never could the genes be *completely* eliminated.

All this applies to every other recessive "black" gene condition, with the chances of reducing the incidence being increasingly less the rarer the condition and the smaller the likelihood of hidden genes coming together and revealing themselves. To cut the number of *albinos* to one half, for instance, might take a thousand years of sterilization. There also are various qualifications to be considered wherever environmental influences are a factor, or where genes are irregular in their manifestation or haven't been positively identified. This applies particularly to the major mental diseases, such as schizophrenia and manic-depressive insanity, the genes for which may be carried by many persons who are in themselves normal. In many other conditions which may be suppressed by a favorable environment or which do not assert themselves until after maturity (numerous examples of which were given in our "Black Gene" chapters), the possibilities through sterilization would be limited.

With no recessive defect could sterilization accomplish much in the long run unless all normal persons who were carriers could also be sterilized. And that would mean—assuming that the carriers could be detected, which is true now only in a small percentage of the cases—that *almost every one of us would have to be sterilized.* For virtually every individual carries some hidden recessive "black" genes.*

The limitations of sterilization, and the need for caution in its use, were pointed out in the notable report in 1937 by a committee of the American Neurological Association. Denouncing wholesale and peremptory sterilization, the committee held that the procedure was justified only in especially selected cases of insanity, feeble-mindedness, epilepsy and a limited number of other conditions showing every evidence of being hereditary. Regarding carriers the neurologists reported, "Our knowledge of human genetics has not the precision or amplitude which would warrant the sterilization of people who themselves are normal in order to prevent the appearance (of a condition) in their descendants." A kind word was said for the feeble-minded: "In a world which has much low-grade work to be done, there is still room for the people of low-grade mentality, of good character." And finally, "Any law concerning sterilization

* Professor Muller very recently (1950) offered these conclusions: (1) That the average individual carries at least *eight,* and possibly *scores,* of single ("heterozygous") genes, each of which is by itself capable of producing a significant but usually slight detrimental effect on him. And (2) in line with the foregoing, that a very high percentage of genes formerly considered purely "recessive," have, in fact, some degree of dominance. In other words, that even in the single state, and when coupled with a "normal" dominant gene, a great many of the so-called "recessive" deleterious genes might be producing some slight degrees of lessened vitality or mild defectiveness in the individual—effects not readily distinguishable from those of such environmental causes as dietary deficiencies, chronic infections, exposure, overwork, etc., or which might be the results of interaction between the genes and the environmental factors. (Data from "Our Load of Mutations," article by Professor Muller, awaiting publication.)

under the present state of our knowledge should be voluntary and regulatory rather than compulsory, and should be applicable not only to public charges but also to those in private institutions or at large in the community."

Leading geneticists of the world (including Professors H. J. Muller, J. B. S. Haldane, L. T. Hogben and others) also urged caution regarding sterilization in their "Manifesto" drawn up in 1939 on the eve of World War II, in which they stated that sterilization of the "unfit" offered no quick solution for the improvement of the human species. While recommending the measure to some extent, coupled with more and more birth control to curb defective childbearing, the geneticists warned that people and their governments would have to be a lot better informed about the causes of human defects before any strong measures to control human reproduction could be safely enacted and enforced.

That they were very wise and foresighted in cautioning restraint was proved by what happened in Nazi Germany when wholesale sterilizations began to be carried out. The first stage of the Nazi "eugenic" campaign, in which hundreds of thousands of defectives of all kinds were sterilized, was hailed with enthusiasm by many sterilization advocates everywhere. One well-known American eugenist announced, "This action of Hitler's stamps him as one of the greatest statesmen and social planners in the world," and suggested that it was "only lack of vision which is keeping the United States from doing the same thing." But before long it became painfully clear where the Nazi "vision" for eliminating those regarded as "unfit" was heading. There followed the ruthless killing of millions of persons, many of the highest types; and the Nuremberg trials laid bare the Nazi plans to sterilize untold numbers of others among conquered peoples.

Even in the United States we already had an inkling of what unprincipled sterilization might do when, in a Kansas reformatory some years ago, scores of girls were arbitrarily sterilized as punishment for everything from sex offenses to "misbehavior," "bad temper," and "getting into fights." A report at the time said that some of those in charge regarded sterilization as "roughly the equivalent of a slap on the wrist at the more conventional finishing schools." This was in spite of the fact that the state law specifically listed idiocy and social disease as the only legal grounds for sterilization.

Where sterilization also goes largely outside of genetic boundaries is in the operations performed in some states on habitual criminals, chronic sex delinquents, sexual degenerates or those guilty of serious sex crimes.* No proof yet exists, as we pointed out in our "Crime" chapter, that criminality is directly inherited or transmitted through specific genes. Thus, with respect to criminals or other persons of bad character, sterilization can be justified only on social grounds: That such persons, regardless of their genetic makeup, are certain to be "unfit" parents. The same principle can be applied, as we said earlier, to individuals who are feeble-minded or mentally diseased.

The case for sterilization as a eugenic measure is therefore considerably strengthened if it is based not merely on genetic threats, but also on the environmental handicaps that may be suffered by offspring of a given defective person. With growing emphasis on the importance of early home conditioning, one might ask what chance a child has of being "normal" if brought into the world by a mentally defective, badly psychotic, habitually criminal or physically warped parent. The mental institutions, the prisons and reformatories and the public relief rolls provide some of the answers.

Another argument is that few of the persons recommended for sterilization *want* children, and that of the thousands so far sterilized in the United States, the great majority have been benefited and made happier by the operation, as have been their families. This is particularly true of female sex delinquents of low mentality. A high percentage of these when committed to institutions already have borne illegitimate children, often defective ones, and if further tragedies are to be avoided, the wisdom is either to keep such girls and women locked up, or to sterilize them before they are released. As Superintendent Howard T. Ennis of the Delaware Colony for Feeble-Minded told the author:

"Very little opposition to sterilization is encountered after its prospective benefits are made clear to the individual and the family. For defective girls, there will be the freedom to marry without fears of having defective children, or of being burdened with strains of

* In two states, Kansas and North Carolina, *castration* is also authorized for some sex criminals and "perverts," who must consent to the operation as a prerequisite to their release from prison. However, while the operation may have psychologic effects, there is doubt as to how far it results in any biological curbs on perverted sexual impulses, inasmuch as men castrated in maturity may go on performing sexually for many years.

childbearing and childrearing for which they are not equipped. For the defective boys, who can expect no more than limited incomes as adults, there will be the freedom from the added burden and responsibilities of fatherhood. In proof, follow-up studies of sterilized individuals in our own state and elsewhere show a very high percentage of happy marriages and of much better adjustment than would otherwise have been the case."

While there is good reason, then, to proceed cautiously with sterilization, and to greatly scale down the exaggerated early notions of what it could accomplish, one should not go to the other extreme of minimizing or underestimating its possibilities. To say that sterilization cannot ever eliminate hereditary ills, and can at best reduce their incidence by only a small proportion annually, is not to deny that even this small reduction might be translated into tens of thousands fewer genetically defective persons in each generation, and the saving of the vast sums of money which would have been necessary for their care.

But all this is speaking in practical terms. For whatever the arguments in favor of sterilization, we must take note of the fact that many persons are strongly opposed to it on religious or moral grounds, as they may also be to any form of birth control as an officially sanctioned state policy. The contention is that there should be no man-made interference with the "natural processes" of human reproduction; that human beings are not wise enough to dictate which persons should or should not have children; that if it is divinely willed that certain defective individuals be born into the world, they should be accepted and provided for; and that even if there seem to be some immediate benefits offered by sterilization, these are greatly overshadowed by the menace to humanitarian, moral and religious principles. The foregoing represents in substance the official views of Catholic authorities, who are almost unanimously opposed to sterilization. Among Protestants, however, there are many church authorities who favor it. In England, the Bishop of Birmingham is among the many strong advocates of sterilization for eugenic reasons, and at this writing a committee of the Church of England is weighing the pros and cons of the problem with a view to determining its official stand.

Much of the present opposition to sterilization would undoubtedly be reduced if means were found to produce temporary sterility, or sterility that is not irrevocable (as it is under present methods). In women, also, some operation that is completely without hazard is advisable. Such measures, toward which medical experts are now working, would relieve sterilization of much of its drastic significance, would increase the number of those voluntarily undergoing sterilization, and would permit "probationary" sterilization of those whose hereditary defectiveness or social undesirability was in doubt.

With respect to birth control—the voluntary regulation by parents of the number and spacing of their offspring—it should also be pointed out that the strongest opposition is not to the *principle,* but to the *methods.* This was brought out in the report of the British Royal Commission on Population, 1949 (p. 158), in which representatives of the Roman Catholic Church were quoted as follows:

"The charge must not, however, be brought against Catholic teaching that it is in favor of what the fanatical defenders of birth control call 'avalanches' of babies. This attribution to Catholics of a desire of population growth to an alarming extent and at every hazard is a mere rhetorical flourish. It has neither sense or meaning. Catholic teaching, if loyally adopted, cannot possibly lead to an excessive and haphazard population, for the Catholic husband is taught, provided the moral law on marital relations is preserved, to exercise self-control in marriage, not to overtax the strength of his wife, not to procreate more children than he can hope to educate and rear healthily, and to make suitable provision for every child he has, so that all his children may become healthy, vigorous and loyal citizens."

Where Catholic opposition lies, the report continued, is chiefly to the use of *mechanical* or *chemical means* of controlling conception. Alternatives recommended by the church have been abstention from sexual relations or confining them to the so-called "safe" periods each month when the woman is unlikely to conceive, i.e., the periods preceding and following the week or so in the mid-point of a woman's menstrual cycle during which ovulation generally takes place. However, while adherence to the "safe period" principle (popularly referred to as the "rhythm" theory) can undoubtedly reduce the chances of conception, it is regarded by medical authorities as far from dependable, inasmuch as many women are highly irregular in their menstrual cycles and it may be difficult to determine when ovulation occurs.

In any event, the decision as to how, when and to what extent to practice or advocate birth control for eugenic reasons will continue to be governed by personal attitudes and circumstances. Likewise, any greater practice of sterilization either on a voluntary basis or through enforced action by states will depend on further genetic findings as to what it can accomplish, and the conviction of the public, in a democracy, that it is needed. (Opinion polls a few years ago showed that more than two-thirds of the American public did favor compulsory sterilization of mental defectives.)

For the time being, it may be interesting to the reader to test his attitudes on the complex problems involved. Here, then, we present a number of actual situations, two historical, the others based on recent news reports. How would *you* act in each case?

1. A young man in an eastern city lost an eye during childhood because of affliction with *retino-blastoma,* in some cases inherited through a *dominant* gene. He married and had two young children. The condition appeared in both. In 1949, the youngest, a boy baby 11 months old, was required to have both eyes removed. The other, a girl 2½ years old, had one eye removed and was threatened with the loss of another.

If you had known of the threat beforehand, what would you have advised for this man? Celibacy? Sterilization? Birth control? Or leaving everything to chance?

2. A widow in a western city in 1950 had *three hemophiliac sons,* aged 20, 16 and 13. The family has been on relief for years, receiving a large sum monthly, plus expensive free hospital and medical treatment because of the special needs. After the first hemophiliac son appeared, it might have been clear that the mother was a hemophilia-gene carrier, with a fifty-fifty chance that any subsequent son would be hemophiliac. Would you have advised sterilization under such circumstances? If so, consider the next case.

3. The British Queen Victoria, as we now know, was a *carrier* of genes for hemophilia which found their way to various descendants, including two sons of King Alphonso of Spain and the last Czarevitch of Russia, though not to any descendants in the British royal family. The disease in the Czarevitch helped to make his parents victims of the evil Rasputin, and was a factor in bringing on the Russian revolution—(as we explained in Chapter 22, p. 178). If you had lived at the time and known that Victoria was a hemophilia-gene carrier, *would you have advocated her sterilization?*

4. More than a thousand persons in the United States in the past

three hundred years have suffered the agonies of Huntington's chorea, the most terrible of hereditary afflictions, as a result of receiving the genes brought over and passed on by three English brothers in the seventeenth century. Many other descendants now living may still suffer this fate. If you had lived three hundred years ago, and could have looked into the future, *would you have favored sterilizing the three brothers, or "letting Nature take it course"?* Would you today advocate sterilizing all carriers of Huntington's chorea genes who could be identified? Would you extend this even to suspected carriers?

5. A delinquent girl in an institution in New England was turned loose without being sterilized because she was just over the borderline of "legal" feeble-mindedness (with an IQ of 72). Within a few years she had borne, illegitimately, first a feeble-minded child, then a pair of defective twins, who died in infancy. What would you have advised beforehand in such a case? That the girl should have been insured better follow-up guidance after she left the institution? That she should have been kept in the institution throughout her reproductive period? Or that the authorities should have been empowered to sterilize her before her release?

6. A few years ago there was the celebrated case of the daughter of an outstanding inventor (deceased), who sued her mother for having had her sterilized on the grounds of feeble-mindedness. The court verdict upheld the mother. But an interesting question is raised: Might not the girl also have been carrying valuable "superior" genes received from her gifted father? And in such a case, where there was no absolute certainty that the girl was genetically defective, would society have been justified in risking the passing on of "feebleminded" genes in order to perpetuate the rare "superior" ones?

7. Within the space of a month, at the beginning of 1950, there were these three cases in or near New York City: (A) A man and wife with seven children, in moderately comfortable circumstances, were arraigned for deliberately starving to death one of the younger children and almost causing the death of another, because they weren't interested in them. (B) A recently bereaved widow with six children was charged with killing her newborn baby, for whom she felt she couldn't provide. (C) A 34-year-old woman was found with her ten children in a terrible state of neglect and malnourishment, the husband having abandoned the family. Would there have been

justification for exerting pressure on all these parents to practice birth control, at least after they had had three or four children? And if so, what means should have been employed to insure this being done?

All of the foregoing cases, to be sure, are extreme examples, although one or more similar situations may exist in almost every community. They are cited only to dramatize the issues involved. We do not pretend here to offer the "right" answers. And we doubt that in view of all the ethical, moral, social and legal issues bound up in the question of limiting or preventing reproduction by given individuals, any conclusive answers could be given.

Where the uncertainty will continue to be greatest is on the question of what to do about known *carriers* of serious recessive "black" genes—persons in themselves normal, but who are likely to pass on one of these genes to some of their children, and to future generations. As was pointed out previously, there are so many of us in this situation that to talk of sterilizing carriers in general would be foolish. What can be done is to stress the fact that wherever a normal person carries a hidden "black" gene for some very serious condition, there is an immediate one-in-four chance that a defective child will result *if that person mates with someone carrying a similar "black" gene.* Thus, as one important means of reducing the incidence of defectives, marriages should be strongly discouraged between persons in whose families the same recessive condition has appeared (such as diabetes or some forms of idiocy, mental disease, blindness, etc.), and who can know in advance that they are both likely to be carrying a gene for the defect.

The foregoing caution applies particularly to marriages between cousins and other closely related individuals. This calls for some explanation, inasmuch as many aspects of this problem are misunderstood.

Cousin marriages, or *inbreeding,* may immediately suggest an array of idiots, imbeciles, monsters, weaklings, deaf mutes and other defectives among the offspring. To what extent does this accord with fact?

Genetically, the marriage of first cousins means only this: Having two grandparents in common, *at least one-quarter of their genes, on the average, will be exactly the same.* Thus, if their mutual grandparents were carrying any hidden "black" genes, there will be a much greater than average danger that these will come together in their children. In marriages between second cousins, the possibility of the same genes combining is much reduced, and it continues to decrease as relationship becomes more distant.

Much substantiating evidence is available. Some thirty years ago Alexander Graham Bell (inventor of the telephone) made a study of large numbers of the nation's blind and deaf, and found a high percentage of cousin marriages among their parents. Inbred families on the island of Martha's Vineyard had an incidence of 11 per cent of congenital deafness; great numbers of feeble-minded were found among the so-called hill-folk of New England; and many dwarfs were found in one of the peninsulas of Chesapeake Bay. In Switzerland, too, where there is much inbreeding, studies have shown disproportionately high incidences of hereditary defects of many types, both physical and mental. For instance, Dr. Ernst Hanhart places the incidence of congenital deafness (a large proportion hereditary) among the Swiss at 12 per thousand, at least five times the rate in the United States.

In general, the rarer the recessive condition, the greater is the likelihood that, where it appears, the parents are related. Various studies indicate, therefore, that the complete prohibition of first-cousin marriages, even though they may occur in less than 1 per cent of the population, would reduce the incidence of xeroderma pigmentosum (a fatal skin disease) by 50 per cent, albinism by 30 per cent, congenital deafness by 25 per cent, retinitis pigmentosa by 17 per cent, juvenile amaurotic idiocy by 15 per cent, and other types of recessive defects by varying percentages.

But we must not conclude from this that a ban on *all* cousin marriages is justified, or that inbreeding in itself is harmful, sinister or immoral. Existing laws or scruples against inbreeding date far back to times when nothing was known about the mechanism of heredity, and often stem from taboos and superstitions which had little to do with blood relationships. In the Middle Ages the ban on marriages between "related" persons was extended even to those who merely had had the same *godfather* or *godmother;* and in the appendix of a Bible printed in Philadelphia in 1803 by John Adams, we find that a man was enjoined from marrying his brother's wife, his wife's aunt or niece, or his *wife's grandmother* (just in case any man should have had such an impulse).

It is also incorrect to assume that there is a deep-rooted or instinctive fear against inbreeding among humans. In biblical times Jacob wedded his first cousins, Rachel and Leah, while Abraham married his half-sister, and Moses was the product of a mating between a nephew (Amram) and an aunt (Jochebed).* The Egyptian Pharaohs and Ptolemies mated with their sisters wherever possible—Cleopatra having been the offspring of six generations of such brother-sister marriages, while she herself, in turn, was married to her younger brother. The ancient Peruvian rulers also believed that the only bride royal enough for a king was his own sister. The Spartans were highly inbred; there were many cousin marriages among our Puritans; and coming down to the present, the sturdy Pitcairn Islanders are the highly inbred descendants of the famed mutineers of the *Bounty*. In most of the foregoing cases there is no evidence that inbreeding had any specially harmful effects.

This brings up the point that where no serious "black" genes are in circulation, and the family is of unusual stock, cousin marriages or other inbreeding may in fact result in *superior* children. As an example, Charles Darwin, married to his first cousin, Emma Wedgwood, produced many distinguished descendants. Turning to domestic animals, we have ample evidence that constant and intense inbreeding, far from being disadvantageous, has made possible almost all of our most valuable strains. However, as we noted in the chapter on "Ancestry," the breeder of domestic animals has the privilege of discarding the defectives that crop out and rigorously selecting for matings only the superior animals. If something like this could be done among humans (but we're not saying it should be done!), cousin marriages would in long-range terms be of immense eugenic value. For the present, however, we must conclude that unless a family is of unusually high quality, and known to be free of serious hereditary defects, cousin marriages should be discouraged. But equally to be discouraged, as we pointed out before, are matings between any unrelated individuals in whose families the same serious hereditary defects have occurred.

Hovering in the background, therefore, is the suggestion that just as pre-marital venereal disease tests now are required in most states, the passing of some form of eugenic test, in which the possibilities of having defective children will be explored, may also eventually be required of applicants for a marriage license. In this, as in all

* *Exodus*, 6:20: "And Amram took him Jochebed his father's sister, to wife; and she bare him Aaron and Moses. . . ." (Incidentally, to readers who may have wondered about the author's rather odd given name, Amram, this will explain its source.)

"negative" eugenic proposals, little account is taken of Cupid. We dare say that any stringent action to greatly hamper Cupid's activities will bring on an uprising in his defense.

In fact, when we look back over all the proposed curbs on human mating and reproduction for eugenic reasons, it seems pretty clear that any radical measures along these lines at this stage of our knowledge might invite more dangers than benefits, as was foreshadowed by the experience under Nazi rule. Whatever can or should be done in existing democratic societies to limit the production of "unfit" offspring would seem, for a long time to come, to depend largely upon the voluntary action of individuals themselves.

CHAPTER 47

PROGRAM FOR TOMORROW

EVERY farmer knows that improvement of crops or livestock depends on the two factors, "Seed" and "Feed." These are synonyms for what some biologists call "Nature" and "Nurture," others call "Heredity" and "Environment."

If the farmer is intelligent and his crops have been running down, he looks first to the "feed"—the soil or his agricultural methods—before he begins bombarding the state farm bureau for new "seed"; and if his cattle and sheep are below par, he looks first to their pasturage and care before he clamors for new animal "seed" (or strains). So in humans, the program of "Positive Eugenics," which seeks to increase the proportion of the "fit," turns first to "feed," or in other words, environment.

We saw in Chapter 45 that the reasons for the decline in births among the "fit" *of every group* were primarily social or economic. To remedy the situation, most "positive" eugenic measures proposed for the immediate future are also social and economic. For the most part they invite little controversy, because they might be included in almost any program for human betterment.

To illustrate these proposals, let us apply them to two hypothetical young people, John Smith and Betty Jones. Both are as "fit" as can be, healthy and intelligent. John is twenty-three, just out of college, and breaking into a profession on a small salary. Betty, two years younger, and with a high-school education, is working as a secretary. They're much in love and want to get married, but feel they'd better wait until John can properly support a wife.

Says Eugenics: Don't let them wait! Encourage parents to make substantial "setting-up" gifts to such young couples wherever possible (which may include a return to the practice of giving dowries). Have the state provide marriage loans or grants. Take more active steps to provide housing for newlyweds, with special rent concessions for the first years of married life. Urge employers to raise salaries of young men when they marry.

But couldn't outside aid be avoided if Betty planned to continue working after marriage until John was solidly established?

That, says Eugenics, would defeat our principal objective: *For Betty to begin having children as soon as possible.* Reason One: There will be more certainty of her fitness, and less chance of a miscarriage or of any child's being congenitally defective (for, remember, the still birth and defective-child rate is much higher in older than in younger mothers). Reason Two: The longer she waits the more chance there is of her becoming sterile, through various diseases or accidents (and the more chance there also is of John's becoming sterile). Reason Three: Younger parents can be closer to their growing children, understand them better, share their interests more.

So, if John and Betty have been encouraged to marry early, the next step is to see they aren't forced to delay having children because of fear of the extra expenses. Eugenics suggests: *Lower maternity costs,* through group hospital and medical plans, and perhaps also state subsidies to hospitals for the purpose. *Pre-maternal* care, to be provided by state-established agencies wherever needed. And after the arrival of babies, easing the burdens of mothers by establishing public diet kitchens, milk services and diaper laundries. Also, for mothers who have to go back to jobs, public nurseries and, later, pre-schools for young children.

All of these various measures should induce the Smiths not to wait too long to have their first child. But we want them to have *more* children. For this, inducements might be: *Rental concessions,* through public or private housing projects, offering a decreasing scale per room for larger families. *Tax cuts,* increasing with each child, as it grows up. *Educational grants* and scholarships, to relieve parents of worry about their children's future schooling.

Such proposals might have seemed visionary and impractical a few decades ago. But many of them are already in operation in the United States, and all of them are in some other countries.

As an impressive illustration of how effective a "positive" eugenics measure can be—even though it wasn't deliberately planned as such—consider the case of the New York City public-school teachers.

A few decades ago "teacher" was a synonym for "spinster," and, in truth, school teachers almost invariably were spinsters, because they *had to be*. When women teachers married they lost their jobs. But see what has happened:

In 1915, after the issue was fought through the courts, the New York Board of Education was forced to rescind the ban on married women teachers. Today, out of the city's 28,000 women teachers (graded and high school) *almost 50 per cent are married.* Of the rest, many more are still young enough to be quite sure of marrying. And as for their having children (where once this meant quitting their jobs), the New York system provides maternity leaves for teachers with no loss of seniority. The result is that large numbers begin having children in their best years, while many, as soon as their husbands are able to carry on alone, resign to increase the size of their families.

The story of the New York teachers (which is paralleled in many other cities) is emphatic proof of how "social sterility" factors, which have been operating to prevent many eminently qualified individuals from marrying and having children, can be easily eliminated.

Another "social sterility" factor is that which forces many women to postpone marriage, often until it is too late, in order to care for old or sick parents or younger members of the family. Liberal pensions for aged or sick parents (already on the way) and educational grants for younger brothers and sisters, would set many of these women free. In fact, when we think of the millions of fine women who are forced to remain unmarried, a great proportion for no justifiable reason whatsoever, we can be very sure that many other "social sterility" factors are at work which should be uncovered and rooted out.

Now back to John and Betty. Suppose, after trying to have a child, they find they apparently *can't* have one? This, it is now estimated, is the situation with about one in ten couples. Formerly barrenness was usually blamed on the woman, but it now appears that in at least one-quarter of the cases where couples have been unwillingly childless, the cause is the man's failure to produce any sperm, or a sufficient amount of sperm, or properly fertile sperm. While this may have resulted from some disease, it may be equally possible that some inherent defect in the man's sperm-producing mechanism is involved, and that in all other respects he is and has been perfectly healthy and normal. (Nor need sterility be in any way related to *virility* or potency.) Another possibility (rare) is that some of the husband's genes may be in conflict or "incompatible" with the wife's genes, or that both may be carrying hidden recessive genes which together may prevent the conception of a child.

However, in the majority of cases the trouble, if not due to the husband's sterility or low fertility, lies in the wife's inability to produce fertile eggs (through disease or defect, for reasons similar to a man's failure to produce fertile sperms), or in some defect, deficiency or obstacle in her reproductive mechanism which prevents conception or carrying a child past the initial stages. What can be done, then, in these cases?

Fortunately, the situation for sterile couples has become increasingly brighter. Modern treatments, by means of hormones, radiation, operation or even "psychological conditioning," have been making it possible for a considerable proportion of previously sterile couples —perhaps about 25 per cent of them—to have children. Thus, if the Stork refuses to come to John and Betty, they may now seek examination and treatment at many special "fertility" clinics throughout the country (some conducted by the Planned Parenthood organization), or by doctors specializing in this field, to be found in most large communities.

But suppose the medical verdict is "No." To our Smiths, as to tens of thousands of other barren couples wanting children, one might then say:

Adopt a child, for an adopted child may often be reared to be quite as much like you as a child of your own.

What, by the way, is meant by a child "of one's own"?

We have seen how, with regard to its hereditary factors, every child is a gamble. No one can predict to what extent a child will be genetically like or unlike its parents. True enough, we can make some forecasts about physical characteristics, and here and there about defects. But no one can predict the character, disposition, mentality or behavior of any given child of normal parentage. These traits are determined or influenced by such a multitude of genes, interoperating with so many environmental factors, that as individuals we can't possibly expect to reproduce ourselves. A true "chip of the old block" in humans is a genetic myth.

But while the genetic makeup of any child of yours is to a great extent unpredictable, you do have considerable power to control the environment which you will provide for it. Thus, in the opinion of many authorities, if you took any healthy child of genetically normal stock, and raised it carefully, it might in many respects turn out to be as much like you in character and in degrees of *social* resemblance as many a potential child of "your own."

So, encouragement of adoptions constitutes another plank in the "Positive Eugenics" platform. But the demand for adoptable infants in the United States now exceeds the supply, to such an extent that a "Black Market" for babies to adopt has existed for several years—some couples paying enormous fees to those who can secure a baby for them. One suggestion, then, to relieve the adoptable baby shortage, would be this: There are now vast numbers of babies who are kept from being born every year through *abortion*. A rough estimate is that about one in four pregnancies in the United States annually is terminated in this way. (In about three-fourths of the cases the women involved are married, in a minority of the instances the babies being sacrificed because of disease in the mother or fear that childbirth would be dangerous.) But in a great number of the cases, undoubtedly, the expectant mother would be happy to bear the child if she could do so under favorable conditions, and could be sure the baby would have a happy future. Arrangements to this effect already are being carried out through reputable agencies and institutions in many large cities. If this were done to a greater extent, there would be no shortage of fine babies for adoption.

There is another possibility for bringing babies to many couples who now want them. We have postponed telling about it because it involves a number of delicate problems, and has evoked strong opposition in many quarters on the ground that it goes counter to religious, moral or legal codes. We refer to *artificial insemination,* the process by which a wife is impregnated with sperms from some unknown donor, without any physical contact between them.

Artificial insemination has long passed the experimental stage in human beings. Many thousands of children (perhaps as many as 20,000) now growing up in the United States are the results of this procedure. But where it has so far been most extensively employed is in the breeding of cattle and horses. To be sure, no direct comparison can be made between the breeding of lower animals and human beings, but it might be interesting to note, first, how and why the method has been of value in livestock.

The principal advantage of artificial insemination in livestock breeding is that the services of a prize bull or stallion can be vastly multiplied and carried over wide areas. First, the sperms from one ejaculation by a pedigreed bull (containing about five billion sperms) can be divided into about thirty portions, each of which will be sufficient to impregnate one female. Second, the sperms, transferred to vials and refrigerated, can be kept active for days and shipped by airplane to almost any point. (Sperms from pedigreed South American prize bulls are frequently flown to the United States, and, in the United States itself, one leading cattle breeder operates a "flying service" which delivers sperm from his pure-bred bulls anywhere in the country in twenty-four hours.) Third, females can be impregnated in their most propitious times, with their chances of conception being increased.*

How successful artificial insemination in cattle has proved to date can be gathered from these facts: By the end of 1949, more than 2,000 prize bulls were in artificial insemination service in the United States, each servicing an average of about 1,250 cows; 10 per cent of all the dairy cows in the United States had been bred artificially (in some states up to 25 per cent); and in Great Britain there were more than 100,000 first-generation "test-tube" cattle. One famed Holstein bull, Red Apple, who died in New York in 1948, was credited with having sired more than 15,000 offspring through artificial insemination during a period of three and a half years—about 150 times the number he could have sired in the natural way.

Now how can artificial insemination be applied to human beings —or rather, how has it already been applied?

We'll return to our typical couple. Suppose, after examination, it has been found that *Betty is in all probability fertile, but John is definitely sterile*. This would be one situation in which artificial insemination could be considered. (Some other situations will be discussed later, when we shall also take up the objections.)

The procedure, once the husband has given formal consent, is fairly simple. The doctor engaging in the practice (there are many such doctors throughout the country) has on file a number of prospective sperm donors—mostly young college men—each of whom has been thoroughly investigated with respect to health, character, mentality and genetic background. From this list the doctor selects

* Artificial insemination has also been used in dogs, particularly where there is any "temperamental incompatibility" between male and female. A notable example was the case of Fala, famed Scotch terrier pet of the late President Franklin D. Roosevelt. Attempts in 1945 to mate Fala romantically with a female (Buttons) having failed, because she bit him badly, artificial insemination was employed, which resulted in the birth of twins.

a donor who is as close as possible to the husband in coloring and physical makeup, and of the *same basic blood type* (to avoid any question of paternity which might come up later). The doctor then determines the nearly exact time of the month when the woman is likely to be fertile, and introduces sperms obtained from the donor. The process may have to be repeated for several successive months, but as a rule, unless the woman turns out to be infertile, conception results. Also, it is reported as a general fact that "artificial-insemination" babies tend to be of physically superior type, presumably because of their above-average "substitute" fathers and the unusual care given to the mothers.

Here, then, is a means whereby a wife who might otherwise be doomed to complete barrenness could have the experience of motherhood; where she and her husband could have children—as many as any average couple—each of which would be at least "half theirs," but which the outside world would consider completely their own; and where no child need ever know that there had been anything unusual about its birth.

But there are also situations in which the husband is not sterile, and where artificial insemination *using his own sperms,* may be of value. Here are examples:

1. Where impregnation in a woman is difficult under ordinary circumstances, for organic reasons, in which case artificial insemination of the husband's sperms may solve the problem.

2. Where a woman is of "low" fertility, and it is essential that she be impregnated under the most propitious circumstances, artificial insemination of her husband's sperms during her precise period of ovulation (as determined by a medical expert) will greatly increase her chances of conceiving.

3. Where the husband (in unusual cases) is impotent or unable to impregnate his wife in a normal way, but yet produces fertile sperms, in which cases his sperms might be obtained and introduced through artificial insemination.

4. Where the husband has some serious hereditary condition which he might transmit to a child; or where husband and wife know or are fearful that they each carry the same recessive "black" genes (as with first cousins).

Taking all the situations together, from a purely practical and eugenic standpoint there would appear to be much in favor of employing and greatly extending the use of artificial insemination among human beings. First is the fact that if one in every ten couples is barren, and the husband's sterility is responsible for at least one-fourth of these cases, the way is opened for hundreds of thousands of the now barren couples to have children through artificial insemination of the wife with a donor's sperm. In addition are the thousands of other cases, of the types previously mentioned, where the chances of conception could be increased by artificial insemination of the husband's sperm. Yet the process has been used to only a relatively small extent. A principal reason is, understandably, the opposition of many husbands (and perhaps wives, too). But this is bound up with the strong antagonism to the method on religious, moral and ethical grounds, and also with the legal problems in the background.

The religious opposition has come chiefly from the Catholic Church, and also from some authorities in the Church of England. Pope Pius XII, in September, 1949, issued a statement condemning artificial insemination "as entirely illicit and immoral" with a single exception—when serving "as an auxiliary to the natural act of union of the spouses and of fecundation." The latter may be assumed to apply to some of the special situations we have presented, where the husband's own sperms are used. The Reverend Geoffrey Fisher, Archbishop of Canterbury, also, in 1949, condemned insemination with a donor's sperm as "wrong in principle and contrary to Christian standards."

The legal questions raised by insemination of a woman with a donor's sperms are extremely complex, and remain to be settled. Is the wife under such circumstances, having borne a child not her husband's (though with his consent), guilty of *"technical adultery"?* Our legal experts say "No," on the assumption that American courts would not uphold any "adultery" charge if there had been no sexual contact. Is the child that results *"illegitimate"*—or at least not legally the husband's child? Courts haven't decided this to date, although in one case in New York, in 1948, Justice Henry Clay Greenberg offered the *dictum* that the "insemination" baby was not illegitimate, and was as legally the husband's as if it had been formally adopted by the couple. A major question, however, is what the status of a "test-tube" baby would be with respect to inheriting a noble title (or throne), or an estate or legacy, if the intent was that the heir be the "issue" or actual blood-relative of the deceased.

Another problem (one raised in the British House of Lords in 1949): If artificial insemination becomes common, and if the same sperm donor is used frequently in a given community, might there not be danger that many young people so conceived, and who, unknown to their parents or themselves, were biologically half-brother and -sister, might some day fall in love and get married? However, if doctors restricted their use of the same donor to a few inseminations, this danger would be minimal.

Finally, fears of psychological complications between husband and wife if she bears an "insemination" child through a donor's sperm do not seem to be borne out by actual experiences. For one thing, couples are not likely to undertake the procedure unless they are strongly bound to one another and have a strong desire for a child. Apart from this there is no more reason, and probably less, why a man shouldn't be as fond of an "insemination" baby as he can be of a child not his who comes to him through marriage to a widow or divorced woman. By and large, doctors in touch with insemination cases say the couples have been made much happier.

Marked for a distant future is the possibility held out by a number of geneticists that human beings may some day benefit by the principle employed in highly pedigreed livestock: of having highly "superior" men or geniuses father very large numbers of children. (That in itself wouldn't seem such an original idea to some Oriental potentates, or here and there to certain other men.) But the thought carries beyond fatherhood during a man's lifetime. If means are found to preserve human sperms for long periods—theoretically, for many decades—the sperms of some outstandingly great men could be used to father large numbers of children *long after the sires are dead.*

Earlier notions were that a genius could posthumously father "as many as 50,000 offspring" by this means. But that is now much discounted by findings of the enormous quantity of sperms required for each human insemination (as many as forty or fifty million), and the improbability of securing more than a certain amount from any one man before his death—especially at an age when he had proved himself outstanding. However, it is not impossible that some hundreds of offspring might some day be fathered posthumously by a genius. As stated by Dr. Hudson Hoagland (who, with Dr. Gregory Pincus has been experimenting in keeping human sperms alive, so far for periods of several months), "Possibly institutions which now store the memorabilia of our great departed may one day also store their vitrified sperms."

What may seem even more fantastic in the human breeding picture of the future is another possibility: *Some women may be enabled to have children without bearing them.*

Incredible as this may seem, something already approaching it is being done with lower animals. First there were the laboratory experiments (by Dr. Gregory Pincus and others), in which fertilized eggs were withdrawn from females of various species (rabbits and mice), and then introduced into the fallopian tubes or wombs of other females, who nurtured the fetuses through to birth. One important outcome of these experiments was the finding that the resulting offspring were identical in all hereditary traits with what they would have been if the same female who had produced the eggs had also mothered them. For example, when an egg from a white rabbit was nurtured in a black foster-mother rabbit, the offspring were all white, and took on none of the genetic traits of the foster mother. (Another proof against the theory of inheritance of acquired characteristics.)

Practical applications to livestock of the foregoing experiments are already under way. The ultimate objective is to enable a prize cow to produce not one calf in a season, as she normally does, but twenty or more calves, and perhaps a hundred or more calves in her lifetime. The procedure, as outlined by biologist Raymond E. Umbaugh, who has been attempting it with cows in Texas, is as follows: *One,* induce "super-ovulation" in the blue-ribbon bossy by causing her to mature at one time not the usual single egg, but at least twenty and possibly up to a hundred eggs. *Two,* have the cow bred or artificially inseminated. *Three,* withdraw the fertilized eggs by flushing from the tubes. *Four,* implant one each of the eggs, separately, in a different "scrub" cow.

By mid-1950, biologist Umbaugh's actual experiments had gone far enough so that a number of "scrub" cows had carried calves, conceived by blue-blooded cows, through several months of the fetal stage, although all of these calves were miscarried before their full term. (However, confidence was expressed that eventually such calves would be carried through to birth.) In another direction, with dogs, complete success has been achieved by Dr. Leon F. Whitney, collaborating with Dr. Harry S. N. Greene of Yale. Working in Connecticut, these men transplanted not merely eggs, but entire ovaries, from aged pure-bred female dogs to young mongrel females. (One purpose of this experiment was to show that wornout ovaries might be rejuvenated by being transplanted from an older female to a younger one.) After being bred to pure-blooded males, the foster, mongrel, mothers produced *pure-blooded* puppies, exactly like those which the donor of the ovaries herself would have produced.

Can these experiments eventually be applied to human beings? The experts who have been carrying on the work have no doubt about this. First (if and when the techniques are employed with humans), innumerable women who have healthy ovaries but cannot produce children because of defective reproductive mechanisms or hormonal deficiencies, or to whom pregnancy may now be dangerous because of kidney, heart or other diseases, could be able to have children through "proxy" mothers. The procedure would simply be to transfer a fertilized egg from any such woman to the womb of another woman, who could volunteer for a consideration to bear the child. Second, complete ovaries might be transplanted from an older woman (still fertile, but for whom childbearing might be considered unwise), to a younger woman (perhaps one whose own ovaries weren't functioning properly). The woman with the transplanted ovaries might then be able to bear a succession of children, who would be *genetically not her own* but those of the ovary donor. (In either of these two cases, won't we then have legal complications, even greater than with the "insemination" babies!)

But also—stretching theory to the farthest—if a great man's sperms could be kept for long periods, a woman who was outstanding or a genius could have her eggs—or her *ovaries*—stored for decades, and mother hosts of children after her death!

Back of all the more radical human breeding proposals hovers the thought that we might some day be able to produce a race of "superior" people, or, in another direction, that we might breed distinct types of human beings for specific purposes, as we now breed lower animals. That this *could* be done—once we have determined the exact genes responsible for the manifold and complex human traits—is hardly doubted by any geneticist. What it would demand, however, is the assumption by the state of supreme power over all human reproduction—the decision as to who should be allowed to reproduce, who should mate with whom, which children

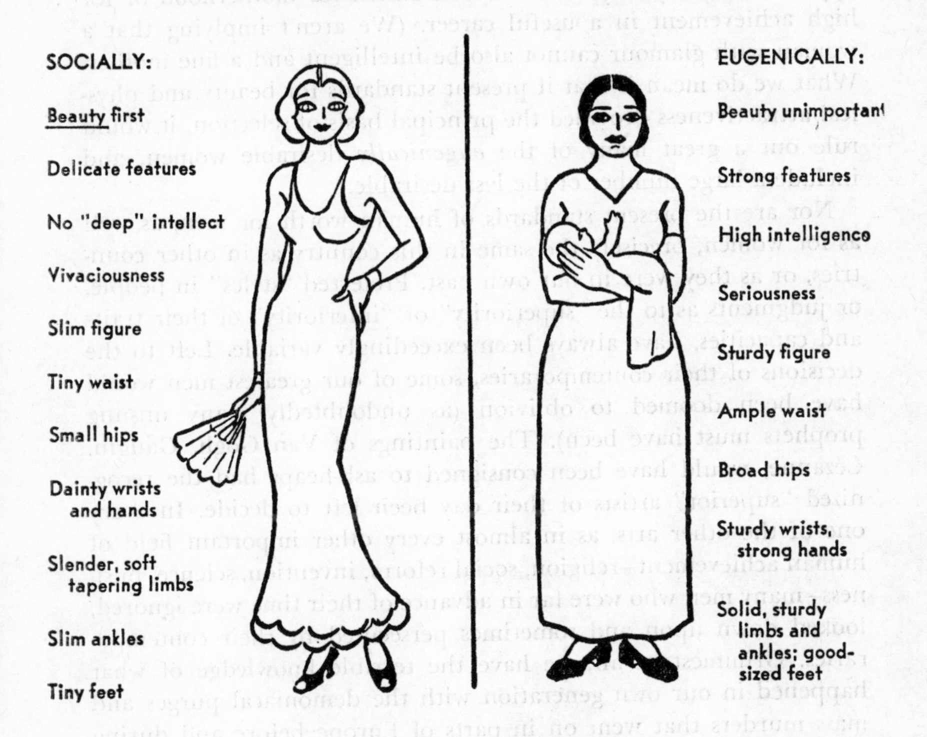

should survive, and how each child should be reared, graded, trained, and bred in turn. An unwelcome idea, but not an impossible one. It virtually happened in Sparta long ago, and it came very close to happening in Nazi Germany.

But the questions inevitably come up: How sure are we of what types of human beings to breed (if we are not referring merely to those free from serious defect)? And, if "superior" humans are our goal, what do we mean by "superior"?

For example, consider women (always a fascinating subject). If we had the power to breed women to order, what type would we aim at—leaving it to both men and women to decide? In the United States, by present popular standards of "desirability," it might be as close as possible to the slim, bathing-beauty type, with other traits going with the "glamour" girl, as shown in the accompanying illustration. Yet, as our Chart shows, these characteristics would be quite opposite in many ways to those best suited for motherhood or for high achievement in a useful career. (We aren't implying that a woman with glamour cannot also be intelligent and a fine mother. What we do mean is that if present standards for beauty and physical attractiveness provided the principal basis of selection, it would rule out a great many of the *eugenically* desirable women, and include a large number of the less desirable.)

Nor are the present standards of human worth for men, as well as for women, precisely the same in this country as in other countries, or as they were in our own past. Preferred "styles" in people, or judgments as to the "superiority" or "inferiority" of their traits and capacities, have always been exceedingly variable. Left to the decisions of their contemporaries, some of our greatest men would have been doomed to oblivion (as undoubtedly many unsung prophets must have been). The paintings of Van Gogh, Gaugin, Cézanne, would have been consigned to ash-heaps had the recognized "superior" artists of their day been left to decide. In every one of the other arts, as in almost every other important field of human achievement—religion, social reform, invention, science, business—many men who were far in advance of their time were ignored, looked down upon and sometimes persecuted by their contemporaries. Grimmest of all, we have the terrible knowledge of what happened in our own generation with the demoniacal purges and mass murders that went on in parts of Europe before and during World War II. Pre-existing standards of human worth were horribly warped and often completely reversed. Tens of thousands of individuals who in other countries, or in the very same countries a few years before, would have been regarded as of the most "superior" types—scientists, intellectuals, humanitarians—were destroyed as if they were vermin, while many individuals whom we may now think of as degenerate and inferior were exalted and idolized.

Even under average conditions and among persons each of us knows, it is far from easy to evaluate qualities and rate individuals according to their value to society. The lying child with an overdeveloped imagination may *sometimes* be the forerunner of a gifted writer; the boy who balks at discipline may *sometimes* develop into a blazer of important new trails. Extreme righteousness may often be coupled with intolerance, and bravery may sometimes mean callousness. The requirements for success in many fields may go with such undesirable social qualities as ruthlessness, insensitivity, unscrupulousness and selfishness. As human beings, many obscure little men who never get anywhere may be superior to some of those on top.

We might also keep in mind that the plans for improving the human breed have to date been concerned chiefly with physical fitness, and with intelligence as measured by IQs. But we cannot be sure that these are the traits in human beings which are the most important, or that if we concentrate on them we may not often be doing so at the expense of traits more desirable. Qualities such as sympathy, kindness, decency, tolerance and consideration for others —which, too, may be influenced by heredity, although we haven't yet identified the genes for them—may in the long run prove the most essential for human survival and progress. If these traits had been present among us in greater proportion within the past few decades alone, far more could have been done to prevent or reduce defectiveness, disease, degeneration and untimely death than could be accomplished through generations of intensive breeding merely for superior physical or mental endowment.

So, having sifted the various eugenic proposals, both "negative" and "positive," we may be left with these conclusions: No radical change in the genetic makeup of human beings can be expected for a long, long time. Nor are we justified, with the limited knowledge of most of our genes and their workings, and with our still uncertain and short-sighted viewpoint, to plan any drastic change. We can and should try to root out the most serious of the "black" genes which do not appear to have anything at all in their favor; we can and should restrain reproduction of individuals who at any stage of civilization would be considered undesirable; and we can and should encourage propagation among those individuals, to be found in all classes and among all peoples, who by every broad rule of human existence can be considered fit and desirable.

In short, modern eugenics places its greatest hope for improvement in the human stock on such changes in the social environment as will bring about the most eugenic distribution of births. Better education, better hygiene, better standards of living, can far more easily and more rapidly reduce the number of "unfit" than can any arbitrary process of breeding. Such genetic improvements as we can effect, short of those possible through the comparatively limited employment of compulsory sterilization, must depend at present on voluntary action. To go much further, and by ban and edict of the state to launch into a program of breeding human beings to order, might bring upon our heads a deluge of evils that might far outweigh the good to be derived.

We were talking about John Smith and Betty Jones at the beginning of this chapter. They signify to us an average desirable American couple. If we can correctly interpret the aims of American eugenics we believe these aims would be to bring to all the Johns and Bettys the kind and number of sons and daughters that their own minds and hearts and longings would prescribe for them.

CHAPTER 48

"YOU AND HEREDITY"

THIS book began, as you may recall, with "Stop and think about yourself."

Now that you are reaching its end we hope that you have indeed thought of yourself in relation to all the facts presented regarding the whys and wherefores of human beings, and what they inherit and what they do not. But you may rightfully ask, "How can this knowledge be applied in a practical way to my own life?"

For instance, there are the facts about the inheritance of features and surface details. They may help to satisfy a natural curiosity as to how you got your looks, or how your children got theirs—or, if your family is still to come, what you may expect your children to look like. Should you be concerned about beauty, you may also be more certain now as to what aspects of features and body build are dictated by heredity, and to what extent environment can make improvements. Other than this, the knowledge regarding inheritance of looks has as yet little practical value to the layman, except in doubtful paternity cases. If you are single, your choice in marriage would hardly be affected by the possibility of your offspring having such or such hair or eyes. And we doubt that you would jilt your sweetheart because you knew your alliance might result in a child with attached ear lobes or a slightly protruding underlip.

But, as you will remember, the study of the inheritance of surface traits, initiated by Mendel with his peas, has led to all the other findings about genetics which we have presented. In time, also, the facts regarding inherited human features, coloring and unusual surface abnormalities may have increasingly useful value when geneticists discover how the genes for these traits are linked on different chromosomes with genes influencing specific body functions. Your eye color, your hair form, the curves of your ears, the shape of your fingers, etc., might then offer important clues as to whether or not you are carrying the linked genes for certain diseases and defects, or for certain types of behavior. This is still for the future. So we'll go on with the knowledge already at hand, taking up now the "black"-gene conditions, and how you can apply the facts regarding them.

Let us assume that some serious hereditary defect or disease is present in you or runs in your family. (You are indeed fortunate if this is not the case.) What light have our studies thrown on your course of action?

We have previously brought out what society should, might or can do about the more serious of the hereditary conditions. But the problem confronting you as an individual when a "black" gene strikes home cannot always be viewed from the broad and impersonal standpoint of society. To you the problem is not one of tens of thousands of matings, with results predictable in terms of averages, percentages and ratios. Everything in your case may be staked on a single turn of the wheel of chance. It will not lessen your worry to know that there was only a one-in-sixteen chance that someone in your family would inherit a rare, multiple-gene defect—if you happen to be that one. Nor can it comfort you to know that the odds are one in four that you and your mate will have a defective child. For your very first child might be that defective one—which would be calamity enough—and the possibility lurks that you might have two in succession.

You must be governed, therefore, by the special circumstances or considerations which apply to your case. As examples, take these hypothetical situations:

You yourself are afflicted with some serious hereditary condition. Should you risk having children?

If the condition is a dominant one, where a single gene from one parent can cause the damage, you know that there is a straight *fifty-fifty* threat that the condition will reappear. With the odds so great you must act as if it is almost a certainty that you will have a defective child. Your decision then must be based on the seriousness of the condition, the degree to which it has hampered your own life or impaired your happiness, the willingness of yourself and mate to have a child similarly afflicted and your capacity to compensate it for the handicap. In the few unqualified dominant conditions so serious that many sufferers have said, "I wish I had never been born," your answer could well be "No."

(For *sex-linked* conditions, if you are an afflicted male, the chances of transmission are discussed in the chapter, "The Poor Males." Fortunately, the serious sex-linked conditions, as shown in our "Black Gene" Tables, are also very rare.)

In the recessive conditions, produced only when two of the same genes come together, the problems are more numerous and more involved, although usually all for the good. That is to say, while the range of odds and circumstances to be considered are much more varied than in the simple dominant conditions, the probability of transmitting a recessive defect is in most cases much less. The threat is further diminished if a "recessive-*plus*" mechanism is involved (a pair of recessives plus some other gene), or if the appearance of the condition is governed by something adverse in the environment.

Has there been anyone among your near relatives with inherited feeble-mindedness, idiocy, congenital blindness or deafness? Diabetes? Albinism?

Whether or not you are carrying a hidden gene for any one of these or some other *recessive* conditions, or are yourself afflicted with it, *no child of yours could inherit such a defect unless it received exactly the same gene for it from your mate.*

Here is one of the most far-reaching, important and constructive findings of genetics. How many hapless individuals, parents of a defective child, have had salt poured on their wounds or been scourged by their mates with the words, "You know the child inherited it from you! You know it runs in your family!" What you cannot impress on yourself and others too strongly, therefore, is that wherever there is a child with any recessive defect, the inheritance has stemmed from both parents, and wherever a marriage or conception is being avoided for fear that such a child may result, the family histories on both sides should be considered with equal thoroughness.

The foregoing applies in large measure to our next question:

Is there insanity in your family?

Only in the cases of the extremely rare Huntington's chorea and Pick's disease is there any evidence that insanity can be transmitted through one parent alone. The most common mental disease, schizophrenia (or *dementia praecox*), requires for its appearance at least a pair of recessive genes (plus, possibly, some other gene and perhaps, also, an unfavorable environment). In manic-depressive insanity the genetic factors producing susceptibility are still not clear, but even if, as some authorities think, "dominant-*plus*" genes are responsible (a dominant gene and one or more other genes), the probability is that one parent alone could not contribute the necessary genes. Thus, the situation in the common insanities would be much the same as with the recessive conditions: If there is an insane child and both parents are normal, although insanity has appeared in relatives of one of them, there is no justification whatsoever for the other parent saying, "The child inherited it from *your* family!" Whatever the inherited factors might be, the accusing mate must also be carrying one or more of them.

In any case, wherever the inheritance of a condition must come through both sides, the immediate threat lies in the mating of two "carriers." Often the facts are quite clear. If both you and your mate had a parent with the same recessive affliction, each of you is a carrier of the gene for it. The odds then are one in four that you will have a child with the defect. If the condition hasn't appeared before in your immediate family, but it appears in one of your children, then you can again be certain that both you and your mate are carriers, and that the same one-in-four threat will face the next child. If one of you is himself or herself afflicted with the recessive condition, and the other mate is a carrier, the odds for any child are one in two. But, most dangerous of all, if you and the person you marry both have the same recessive condition, *every one of your children will inherit it.* For instance, if you have hereditary diabetes and you marry another such diabetic, every one of your children will inherit the diabetic tendency.

So to this problem:

You are in love or engaged, and have just learned that the possibility of having a seriously defective child lurks in your contemplated marriage.

If children are not important to you, the situation can resolve itself easily. But if having children is a primary objective, you may have to weigh the "black"-gene odds against your affections—even to the point, where the risk is menacing, of considering marriage to someone else. However, as you have learned, in only a small proportion of cases (among them, sometimes, those involving first cousins) need such a predicament arise. Generally, where the risk is not too great, you are justified in being swayed by the advantageous prospects of the marriage.

You are already married, and a genetically defective child has appeared. What should you do about having other children?

First, you must consider the type of defect; second, how it is inherited. If the condition is serious and due to a dominant gene, the straight fifty-fifty chance of its appearing again ought to deter you from having another child. A man in Boston had "lobster-claw" hands (see illustration on p. 197), a dominant abnormality. After a son was born with the same condition, the man went on to have a second son, and then a third, similarly afflicted. We might wonder about a parent in such cases.

Where the condition is recessive and a child with the defect has appeared, the fact that the *statistical* chances call for one in four defective children shouldn't be misinterpreted. Some parents have foolishly thought that, having already had the "one-in-four" defective child, there would be no risk for the next three. But there have been many cases of two amaurotic idiots, or two or more genetically blind or deaf children, coming in succession. Once it has been shown that parents can produce a child with a serious hereditary defect, they must be prepared for the possibility that others may follow.

We assume next that your problems of mating are in the past: *You already have a child, or all the children you expect, and no hereditary defect has as yet shown itself. What good will it do to worry about defects appearing later?*

The foreknowledge of threats offered by your family history may prove of tremendous importance, as was pointed out in our "Black Gene" chapters. In various serious conditions—heart, cancer, diabetes, severe allergies, certain functional disorders, etc.—awareness by your doctor of any hereditary threats offered to your children may help him greatly in early detection, diagnosis and treatment, leading in many instances to prevention and cure. To cite some specific cases:

—Where *childhood* rheumatism lurks in family backgrounds, notably among the poor, its development in many children may be prevented by assuring them plenty of fresh air, proper living conditions and periodic medical examinations of their hearts and nervous systems. In the adult forms of heart and arterial conditions, if these are known to run in families, various tests can now often reveal those members who have the tendencies or predispositions, and special precautions in the way of diet and avoidance of overstrain may help to reduce the dangers.

—In *cancer,* the previous appearance in parents or near relatives of breast, intestinal, rectal or stomach cancers should be special reasons for periodic examination of the children when they reach maturity. Particularly in *rectal polyps,* which may occur in childhood, the appearance of the condition in one member of the family should immediately put others on their guard. We may recall here that perhaps as many as 40 per cent of cancer cases may be treated successfully if detected early enough.

—Where *diabetic* inheritance is suspected, tests may now confirm the presence of the tendency well in advance of the serious manifestations, and control of diet, abstinence from overeating, keeping down of excess weight and frequent medical inspection may thwart the development of the disease or greatly impede its progress.

—In *insanity,* the foreknowledge of a familial tendency may make possible various precautionary steps, either through medical or psychiatric treatments already available or foreshadowed, or through avoidance of undue environmental stresses. Abnormal behavior in a child whose family has some history of mental disease should immediately call for a psychiatrist's attention.

—Where special kinds of *allergies* run in families, and there is a possibility that these may be inherited, parents who are on the alert for any unusual reactions in their young children to given foods or substances may forestall serious disorders.

Current medical literature cites many instances of children or older persons who were saved from death or serious disease by prompt action based on knowledge of inherited tendencies. (Some specific examples were given in Chapter 31.) This brings us to another point. You may have been thinking that all of this searching into one's hereditary background, with a view to knowing whether any threats confront a child, may take the joy out of parents' lives and arouse many undue fears. In some instances this might be true, but on the whole we believe that the knowledge of what your children may or *may not* inherit can do far more to allay fears than to arouse them.

Just before Christmas, 1949, a man in Virginia shot and killed his three young children "because I didn't want them to grow up and inherit my mental condition." Some years before, a mother on Long Island slew her two young children because she feared they had inherited cancer from her. The facts in both cases showed that the unhappy parents were much mistaken. Quite probably they were unbalanced, but there have been innumerable other instances where persons who were rational have taken their own lives or looked with terror at their children because of groundless fears that some hereditary doom was hanging over them. Sometimes the very fear of having inherited a disease may actually produce some of its symptoms through *psychogenic* (mentally-induced) effects. This is especially true of mental or emotional disorders, and various *psychosomatic* conditions which are brought on or worsened by mental disturbances.

Finally, several important points brought out in previous chapters should again be stressed here. One is that even if a condition *is* hereditary, this doesn't mean that it can't be cured or successfully treated. Many serious hereditary ailments, including diabetes, various glandular disorders and other conditions due to metabolic or functional defects, have had their effects minimized by medical treatment. Some of the hereditary eye and ear defects are now being successfully corrected by operation. In time, too, there is hope that some of the inherited mental diseases and mental disabilities may respond to treatment.

Another point to be emphasized is that a host of conditions formerly considered hereditary have now been proved otherwise, and in the case of many more, adverse environment has been shown to be the principal cause of the worst effects. On the other hand, there are few conditions not formerly considered hereditary which have been added to the "black gene" list. Much has been done to clear up the confusion between congenital defects and diseases which are inherited and those which are purely acquired (such as syphilis, some forms of congenital deafness and blindness, and many structural abnormalities). Also, one of the most notable contributions of medical genetics has been the discovery of how the "Rh" disease is produced prenatally, and how babies can be saved from its more serious consequences. Altogether, genetic findings have swept away so many former fears that an average couple can today have children with less worry regarding the threats of heredity than ever before.

Turning to the social traits, of intelligence, behavior, character, personality, etc., limited as may yet be our genetic knowledge, it is sufficient to also allay a host of long-standing fears. Many of the undesirable social traits in human beings have been indicated as due primarily to environment, and there has been much to challenge prevalent beliefs and suspicions regarding the hereditary "criminality," "immorality," or general "undesirability" of members of this or that group, class or race. These findings, too, may be of use in your own life. If you have had the uneasy feeling that one of the aforementioned traits, or some crudity, unpleasant mannerism, inability to "get along" or other social deficiency in you was due to an inherited and incurable "streak," you may see by now that your suspicions were probably unfounded. Again, in marriage, employment, friendship or any other relationship, if any individual you have in mind is personally desirable and of good character, you need not be greatly worried because he is of this or that stock or nationality, or be much concerned because a grandfather had a penchant for abducting horses, or a great-aunt was no better than she should have been.

This does not imply that you should ignore the important rôle that genes obviously play in the development of mind, character and personality. But in these complex social characteristics, only where an individual himself shows some markedly adverse trait, or where it consistently appears in his family with no evidence that it is due to environment, can we consider him genetically suspect. Among members of your own family, and your intimates, where there are great differences in behavior and achievement which cannot be traced to environmental influences, you are justified in ascribing them in considerable measure to different gene combinations. Practically applied to your children, such knowledge might lead you to deal more sympathetically with the "black sheep" and to endeavor to make up to them, by guidance and training, for any inherited deficiencies.

Further, with the strong indication that special talents, capacities and aptitudes are inherited, you may avoid forcing specialized training on a child not inherently fitted for it, while at the same time encouraging the child who does reveal such capacities. We may add that with our knowledge regarding the inheritance of social traits constantly growing, problems of child guidance and training and of adapting individuals to the work and life for which they are best fitted will be increasingly simplified.

So far we have been dealing with the practical application to your life of *genetic* facts. But, as we have seen, in all major aspects of our lives we cannot dissociate the effects of heredity from those of environment. It is of interest to note, therefore, that the technique developed for sifting hereditary factors can be admirably adapted to the analysis of environmental influences.

In much the same way that our genetic makeup is determined by *biologic* genes passed on from one generation to another, we may consider that our social makeup is determined by *"social genes,"* also passed on from one generation to another. These "social genes" would include all the factors that go to make for education, technical knowledge, habits, customs, mannerisms, attitudes, beliefs, etc., and also for the physical effects of our social environment. Thus, you, like every other person, are the product of both biologic genes and "social genes," with this difference between them: The biologic genes were passed on to you through the stream of germ plasm which has flowed from the dawn of life, with the only changes made being those produced by mutation. No human force has ever had the power to change a single one of these biologic genes in a given direction; and not even today can we do more than cast out a limited number of the most defective ones, and that only by controlling reproduction.

But our "social genes" are no inherent part of our germ plasm or of our makeup. They were every one of them *acquired.*

Suppose for a moment that you and your mate were set down, like another Adam and Eve, on an uncharted island where no man had ever been before and which no other human could ever reach. And suppose, at the same time, that you were struck by some force that blotted out completely every thought, every memory, everything you had learned from the moment of birth, and all consciousness of the past. Would you be able to talk, think, act or cope with existing conditions any better than did the most primitive Stone Age man? Science, as we have observed, says "No!" For your biologic genes would be hardly different from his, and deprived of all the "social genes" acquired and accumulated in twenty thousand years, you and your descendants would have to travel the same long road of social evolution that stretched ahead of the Stone Age man. You would have to begin all over again learning the simplest facts by trial and error or accident. Generations and scores of generations would pass before your descendants would learn to build dwellings, plant seeds, fashion the simplest mechanisms and develop a written language.

So if you, or any one of us living today, differ from men of any previous generation in mental development, behavior or other social characteristics, or in the possession of any superior inventions, appliances or objects, it is because we have had passed on to us an accumulation of "social genes" from the past, with their many resulting products. But this does not mean that *all* of the "social genes" of each generation were passed along, or that the best of them were carried over. Each generation has been the heir of all the preceding generations, and from what we know of heirs we have little reason to doubt that in many instances some of the best "social genes" in the successive legacies were lost, destroyed or tossed foolishly away. When we think of all the wars, barbaric invasions and blotting out of whole civilizations, of the whims and judgments of ruling despots that often dictated the course of culture as it is being dictated even today, we have good reason to believe that numerous "social genes" of inestimable value were not passed on, while some of the worst were.

Just as we have identified many biologic "black" genes, we can easily point to "social *black* genes" linked with or producing poverty, ignorance, social and contagious diseases, injuries from accident, vice, crime, suicide, corruption, strife, conflict and finally war. Look back through our pages and you will find little to suggest that these blights on mankind are inherent in our germ plasm. Those who point to them as part and parcel of "human nature" ignore the fact that the impulses of the vast majority of people are toward sociality, kindness, peacefulness, tolerance, the desire to be and let be. We have only to think of the sacrifices of parents for their children, of the spontaneity with which we respond to our fellow creatures in time of fire, flood, disaster or distress, of the millions praying each day to be made better and worthier, of countless individuals working throughout the world to uplift others. Back of these impulses we can find many of our superior "social genes."

Herein, then, lies the hope for whatever improvement can be made in mankind, or that you, as an individual, can in your restricted sphere help to make in your children:

1. Through the selection, by regulating and controlling human breeding, of the biologic genes which we pass on.

2. Through the selection, by education, laws or other measures of the "social genes" which we pass on.

As for our biologic genes, we have brought out in preceding

chapters what might be accomplished eugenically. By sterilization and birth control we might reduce somewhat the proportion of the "unfit," and by stimulating births in other quarters we might increase somewhat the proportion of the "fit." This is on the basis of our present knowledge of human genetics, which is little compared to what we know about the breeding of plants and domestic animals.

The application of genetic principles to agriculture and livestock breeding has been so sweeping that there is today hardly a fruit, grain or vegetable which you eat, and no egg, poultry or meat from the better farms or ranches, in whose production genetic principles have not been employed. "Double-breasted" turkeys and chickens, juicier steaks, more abundant milk, more flavorsome fruits, are today coming to you as the result of applying genetic knowledge. Better corn breeding alone has increased the crop yield in the United States by about 20 per cent, with an increased value of almost a billion dollars yearly. Production of penicillin has been much increased—five- to seven-fold—through the genetic breeding of high-yielding strains of the mold organism. And if you still have any doubt about the reality of genes and chromosomes, and what the knowledge of their workings can accomplish, you need only consult some of the publications of the United States Department of Agriculture, telling of the genetic mechanisms of every important cultivated plant and food animal—facts which every alert farmer and breeder is applying today.

If the knowledge of human genetics has lagged behind, it is not entirely because of our inability to experiment with human beings. Also responsible is the fact that the importance of human genetics has not yet been popularly realized and that our all too few trained geneticists have been forced, by practical considerations, to devote themselves chiefly to the problems of crops and livestock in which state or national governments are immediately interested. Another great shortcoming is the failure of most colleges to give adequate training in human genetics. (Only about eight colleges in the United States at this writing offer special courses in the subject, and in only a few medical colleges are there courses in medical genetics.) Once we know proportionately as much about the genetics of humans as we do about the heredity of plants and livestock, there is no predicting what we may be able to do.

However, at the moment we have no need to stake our hopes

for an improved mankind on future genetic findings or on radical changes in our biological makeup. We can consider that we have not even begun to tap the genetic resources at our command. We have in our biologic genes now in circulation, scientists tell us, all the potentialities for a race of supermen—*if we can properly direct and control our environment.* In other words, all our studies have led to renewed confidence in "human nature"—in our inherent impulses and capacities—and to the belief that not our biologic genes, but our acquired "social genes," are responsible for most of our social ills.

We noted in the chapter on "Race" that large groups and whole peoples have been praised for the virtues of the few gifted individuals who have raised the general level of those about them.

Similarly, the many have been damned for the excesses of the few. If the advancement of mankind has come through the efforts of a handful, civilization has again and again been hurled back by a few individuals, who, like cancers, have corrupted the rest. We have no more right, therefore, even in these questionable times, to condemn all civilization as hopeless because of some of its evil specimens than we have to consider that all persons are diseased because a few have hemophilia or Huntington's chorea.

Today, evil "social genes" as embodied in the acts of malignant individuals present a greater menace than ever. Mankind has been brought so closely together that it must now be considered as one body. Whatever happens to a group of humans anywhere in the world can sooner or later affect others. *"Il faut cultiver votre jardin"* ("Cultivate your own garden"), said Voltaire. Which was another way of saying, "Look to your own backyard!" But if that was ever good advice, it is so no longer. We cannot ignore what is happening in the backyards of our neighbors or of our fellow men, be they ever so far away. We have learned that a malarial swamp on one man's farm may menace others for vast stretches around, that a plague in China may reach us here, that a bank crash, a crop failure, a strike, a financial depression and most certainly a war, no matter where, may start a chain of effects spreading throughout the world and ultimately to you. There is no "social *black* gene" that might not some day strike at you and yours and no biologic "black" gene that might not find its way to your children or your grandchildren.

So, if you are concerned with the practical application of genetic findings to yourself and to your children, you must think both in biologic and in social terms, and not only of your own family, but of others. Biologically, your action is limited by the children you have or do not have. Socially, even if you are childless, there is no limit to the influence you can exert. But nothing that is done toward biologic or social improvement can have permanent meaning if it is confined to one family, one group, or even to one nation. All that we have learned proves that one section of mankind cannot long maintain a corner on "superior" genes, biologic or "social," or rid itself and keep free of the "inferior" genes in circulation. Only by improving others also can we improve ourselves, and only by promoting progress on a broad front, throughout mankind, can we give our own advancement significance or permanency.*

That something should and can be done to improve humanity is the view of many of us who do not consider that this is the best of all possible worlds and that it can run itself without planning. We have seen and are seeing that the good, the superior, the "fittest" in genes, persons or doctrines are not automatically being swept on to survival, and that the bad, the inferior and the most "unfit" are not automatically swept into the discard. Those of us who are at the top of the social heap can no longer smugly ascribe this all to our greater intrinsic worth, diligence and perseverance. And where, as individuals, we have failed in what we have set out to do, if we have not reached the heights in our profession, business or in one of the arts, we cannot so easily blame ourselves. No one fully aware of the findings of genetics and related sciences can still cling to the old theories of predestination, or, contrariwise, to the belief that the individual is the "master" of his fate and the "captain" of his soul. Knowing that our lives are governed, if not dictated, by both biologic and "social genes," we may look at both

* To those new readers who may find here familiar echoes of many public pronouncements and world developments of recent years, this might be of interest: The paragraph marked with the asterisk, and the three immediately preceding and all those following to the end of the chapter, have been retained exactly as they were written in 1938, and as they appeared in the original edition of this book, published in 1939 on the eve of World War II. The author makes no claim to having been prophetic, for he was merely expressing the consensus of many others at the time. But in the light of events which transpired after the book appeared, some of the statements regarding the unity of mankind may take on new meaning. One may find in them the answer to those who thought that the United States could be kept out of World War II; the essence of the late Wendell Willkie's "One World" philosophy; the underlying principles of the United Nations; and, most recently, President Truman's program with regard to helping backward nations.

the shining successes above us, and at the criminals, the paupers, the drunkards, the misfits at the bottom and well say, "There but for the grace of my genes go I."

But if we today are the products largely of chance, our descendants do not have to be. We have had a long enough spell, all the thousands of years since *Homo sapiens* made his appearance, of leaving our destinies to the fates or to the tides of circumstance, largely because we were ignorant of what otherwise to do. But here at last we have the first glimmers of true light as to why we are what we are, and what we can do to make the world better. Genetics and the related sciences have proved beyond question that we can guide, if not control, the destinies of those who follow us by selecting the units of biologic and social inheritance which we pass on to them. To make this selection intelligently, we must first understand ourselves, the sources of the good and the bad in us. It has been the lack of such understanding in individuals, and between one person and another, between man and woman, parent and child, class and class, nation and nation, race and race, that has been responsible for much of the strife, misery and unhappiness in this world. If we are called on to decide what first to include in our legacy to succeeding generations, our wisest choice might well be whatever genes there are, biologic and "social," that make for better human understanding.

SUGGESTIONS
FOR
FURTHER READING
AND
INDEX

SUGGESTIONS FOR FURTHER READING

To list the many thousands of articles and hundreds of books drawn upon in the preparation of THE NEW YOU AND HEREDITY would require a sizeable volume in itself. So what we are presenting here is no more than a highly selected list of "key" references, which we believe will prove most useful to readers seeking further information on human heredity in general, and on specific topics of importance. Almost all of these references carry bibliographies which will open the way to additional reading channels.

Because the popular literature in the field is very limited, most of the books and articles are of a technical nature, mainly for college students and professional people. However, wherever possible we have included books or articles written especially for laymen, and these are identified by a preceding asterisk (*).

For easier reference, the reading list throughout has been arranged by topics which follow more or less the plan of this book. Also, for simplification, and to conserve space, *titles of articles are often paraphrased, condensed, or in some cases omitted.* With all of these articles, then, look up the references (1) by journal and date, (2) by author and/or subject.

In selecting both books and articles for this list, preference has been given to those of most recent date, with the knowledge that as a rule, their bibliographies will cite the important earlier treatises. (Many of the principal references prior to 1940 will be found in the Appendix of the first edition of *You and Heredity*. These references, with few exceptions, are not repeated here, but the old book should still be obtainable at most libraries.)

At the end of this reference section will be found a list of periodicals, and also a list of colleges offering courses in human or medical genetics.

GENERAL

Genetics in the Twentieth Century. (Symposium, "Golden Jubilee of Genetics.") L. C. Dunn (Ed.). Macmillan, 1951.

Human Genetics. R. R. Gates. (2 vols., with extensive bibliographies. For *specialists.*) Macmillan, 1946.

Principles of Genetics. E. W. Sinnott, L. C. Dunn, Th. Dobzhansky. (4th ed.) McGraw-Hill, 1950.

Principles of Heredity. L. H. Snyder. (3rd ed.) D. C. Heath, 1946.

Principles of Human Genetics. Curt Stern. W. H. Freeman, 1949.

*"Progress and Prospects in Human Genetics." H. J. Muller. *Am. J. Hum. Genet.*, Sept., 1949.

**Genetics—The Science of Heredity.* Publ. Affairs Pamph., No. 165. 1950.

CHROMOSOMES

Nucleolar chromosomes in man. Jack Schultz, Patricia St. Lawrence. *J. Hered.*, Feb., 1949.

Chromosomes, genes, photographed with electron microscope. D. C. Pease, R. F. Baker. *Science*, Jan. 7, 1949.

The Chromosomes of Vertebrates. Robert Matthey. (*See* rev., *J. Hered.*, Apr., 1950.)

HUMAN EGGS, SPERMS

Series of potentially abortive ova. A. T. Hertig, John Rock. *Am. J. Obstetr. & Gyn.*, Nov., 1949.

"In Vitro Fertilization and Cleavage of Human Ovarian Eggs." M. F. Menkin, John Rock. *Am. J. Obstetr. & Gyn.*, Mar., 1948.

"Human Spermatozoa, Morphology: Observations with Electron Microscope." O. S. Culp, J. W. Best. *J. Urology*, 61(2), Feb., 1949.

PRENATAL DEVELOPMENT

**Ourselves Unborn.* George W. Corner. Yale U. Press, 1944.

Mother's age and stillbirths. H. H. Strandskov, Sara Einhorn. *Am. J. Phys. Anthrop.*, June, 1948.

Stillbirths, among "Whites" and "Colored." H. H. Strandskov, Doris Ondina. *Am. J. Phys. Anthrop.*, Mar., 1947.

SEX DETERMINATION AND RATIO

Changes in sex ratio, upper social strata. M. E. Bernstein. *Hum. Biol.*, Dec., 1948.

Same-sex families. R. J Myers. *J. Hered.*, Oct., 1949.

Sex ratio of human stillbirths. H. H. Strandskov, J. A. Roth, Henry Bisaccia. *Am. J. Phys. Anthrop.*, 7(1, 2), 1949.

See also: Women and Men. Amram Scheinfeld. Chs. 1-4. Harcourt, Brace, 1944.

GENES, THEIR NATURE AND WORKINGS

What Is Life? Erwin Schrödinger. Macmillan, 1946.

"The Gene." H. J. Muller. *Proc.* Royal Society (Gt. Britain), Vol. 134 (1947).

"Precision of Genetic Adaptation." H. J. Muller. N. Y. Ac. Med., *Harvey Lectures,* Series 43 (1947-48). Subsequently published by C. C. Thomas, 1950.

"Genes and the Chemistry of the Organism." G. W. Beadle. *Am. Scientist,* Jan., 1946.

MENDEL AND BEGINNINGS OF GENETICS

The Birth of Genetics. Supplement to *Genetics,* 35 (5), 2, Sept., 1950.

*Gregor Mendel. Hugo Iltis. *Sci. Month.*, May, 1943; *J. Hered.*, June, 1947.

*"I talked with Mendel." C. W. Eichling, Sr. *J. Hered.*, July, 1942.

FEATURES, COLORING

Up from the Ape. E. A. Hooton. (Rev. ed.) Macmillan, 1947. (*See* Index for various topics.)

Eye color, studies. W. J. B. Riddell. *Ann. Eugen.,* 1941, 1942, 1943.

—Genetic analysis of. A. M. Brues. *Am. J. Phys. Anthrop.,* 4(1), 1946.

Red hair, inheritance. J. V. Neel. *J. Hered.,* Mar., 1943.

Skin color. E. A. Edwards, S. Q. Dunley. *Am. J. Anat.,* 65 (July, 1939).

*"Is the American Negro Becoming Lighter?" W. M. Kephart. *Am. Sociol. Rev.,* Aug., 1948.

*The "Black baby of White parents" myth. Curt Stern. *J. Hered.,* Aug., 1945 (p. 233).

Eye, anthropology of. W. M. Krogman. *Ciba Symposia,* Nov., 1943.

Hair structure, form. S. M. Garn. *Am. J. Phys. Anthrop.,* 4(2), 1946.

—Types, distribution. S. M. Garn, in Symposium, "Growth, Replacement and Types of Hair." *Annals,* N. Y. Ac. Sci., 53(3), 1950.

—Size, shape of head hair, six racial groups. Morris Steggerda, H. C. Seibert. *J. Hered.,* Sept., 1941. Age changes: *J. Hered.,* Nov., 1941.

BODY FORM, STATURE

Stature: Toronto children, half-century ago, today. H. V. and E. M. Meredith. *Hum. Biol.,* May, 1944.

—Increase in American men. Metrop. Life Ins. *Bull.,* Nov., 1944.

—In U. of Toronto freshmen. J. Allan. See *Biol. Abstr. (H),* June, 1950: 14099.

—Mt. Holyoke College freshmen (women), physical measurements, 1918, 1943. Marion Gillim. *J. Am. Statist. Assn.,* Mar., 1944.

—Weight and height changes in Great Britain. W. F. F. Kemsley. *Ann. Eugen.,* 15(2), 1950.

—Height, weight, Ottawa children of two socio-economic strata. J. W. Hopkins. *Hum. Biol.,* May, 1947.

—*See also:* Hooton, *Up from the Ape,* pp. 531 ff.

Hereditary obesity (in mice). G. E. Dickerson, J. W. Gowen. *Science,* 105(2732). 1947.

"HEREDITY AND ENVIRONMENT"

Symposium on above, *Psych. Rev.,* 54(6), Nov., 1947. *Also* articles: E. L. Thorndike, *Eugen. News,* Sept.-Dec., 1944; Anne Anastasi and John P. Foley, Jr., *Psych. Rev.,* Sept., 1948.

"The Interaction of Nature and Nurture." J. B. S. Haldane. *Ann. Eugen.,* 13(3), 1946.

*"The Genetic Approach to Human Individuality." L. H. Snyder. *Sci. Month.,* Mar., 1949.

*"Does Heredity Make You What You Are?" A poll of experts, conducted by Arthur Kornhauser. *Am. Mag.,* May, 1946.

TWINS (AND OTHER MULTIPLES)

**Multiple Human Births.* H. H. Newman. Doubleday, Doran, 1940.

Rule for predicting multiple births. S. Peller. *Am. J. Phys. Anthrop.*, Mar., 1946.

Sex ratios, single and plural births, among Whites, Negroes. H. H. Strandskov, G. J. Siemens. *Am. J. Phys. Anthrop.* 4(4), 1946.

"Five Little Dionnes and How They Grew." (Review) G. C. Schwesinger. *J. Hered.*, Mar., 1940.

"Genetics of Quintuplets." (I) J. W. MacArthur; (II), with Allan R. Dafoe. *J. Hered.*, Sept., 1938, Sept., 1939.

Quadruplet studies. H. H. Newman, I. C. Gardner. *J. Hered.*, June, 1939; July, Oct., 1940; Sept., Oct., 1942; Sept., Oct., 1943; Mar., 1944.

Handedness: "An Application of Gene Frequency Analysis," etc. D. C. Rife. *Hum. Biol.*, 22(2), May, 1950.

DISEASE AND DEFECT INHERITANCE (GENERAL)

Genetics, Medicine and Man. H. J. Muller, C. C. Little, L. H. Snyder. Cornell U. Press, 1947.

Genetics in Relation to Clinical Medicine. F. A. E. Crew. Edinburgh: Oliver and Boyd, 1947.

Human Genetics. R. R. Gates. (2 vols.) Macmillan. 1946.

Constitution and Disease. Julius Bauer. (2nd ed.) Grune & Stratton, 1945.

"Medical Genetics and Public Health." L. H. Snyder. N. Y. Ac. Med., *Bull.*, 2nd Ser., 22(11), Nov., 1946.

"Detection of Genetic Carriers." James V. Neel. *Am. J. Hum. Genet.*, Sept., 1949.

"Eponyms of Hereditary Diseases." M. D. Schweitzer. *J. Hered.*, Oct., 1941.

DISEASE AND DEFECT INHERITANCE (SPECIFIC)†

Heart, Arteries

"Essential Hypertension and Nephrosclerosis." P. Søbye (Copenhagen). See *Biol. Abstr.*, July, 1950:17316.

Atherosclerosis, genetics of. David Adlersberg, A. D. Parets, E. P. Boas. *J. Amer. Med. Assn.*, Sept. 24, 1949.

Rheumatic fever. M. G. Wilson, M. D. Schweitzer, Rose Lubschez. *J. Pediatr.*, Apr., May, 1943. Also, *Am. J. Med.* (2), 1947.

–Decline in England, World War II. J. A. Glover. *Lancet*, July 10, 1943.

Cancer

Genetics of cancer. W. E. Heston. In: *Advances in Genetics.* M. Demerec (Ed.). Academic Press (N. Y.), 1948.

"Biology of Cancer." A. C. Ivy. *Science*, Nov. 14, 1947.

Heredity in breast cancer (also leukemia). Articles by Th. Busk, L. S. Penrose, *et al.*, M. N. Karn. *Ann. Eugen.*, 14, 1947-1949.

Cancer of (1) breast, (2) lower digestive tract, in family groups. E. J. Gardner, F. E. Stephens. *Am. J. Hum. Genet.*, Mar., 1950.

† Detailed discussions of most of the rarer inherited diseases and defects, with extensive bibliographies, will be found in Gates, *Human Heredity* (listed under "General"). Because of the many technical aspects, however, this treatise is recommended only to specialists.

**Cancer.* Beka Doherty. Random House, 1949.
See also Metrop. Life Ins. *Bulls.*, Jan., 1949 (cancer among children); Aug., 1948 (improvement in female cancer mortality); Feb., 1947 (sex differences in cancer).

Diabetes

The Treatment of Diabetes Mellitus. E. P. Joslin, *et al.* (8th ed.) Lea & Febiger, 1946.
"Survey of a Scottish Diabetic Clinic." H. N. Munro, J. C. Eaton, A. Glen. *J. Clinic. Endocr.*, 9. Jan., 1949.
"The Familial Distribution of Diabetes Mellitus." H. Harris. *Ann. Eugen.*, 15(2), 1950.
Diabetic incidence, surveys. *J. Amer. Med. Assn.*, Sept. 27, 1947; *Sci. News Let.*, Oct. 4, 1947.

Tuberculosis

Twin studies on resistance factors. F. J. Kallmann, David Reisner. *J. Hered.*, Sept., Oct., 1943.
Familial susceptibility. R. R. Puffer. Harvard U. Monogr., Public Health Report No. 5. 1946.
*Decline in tuberculosis. Metrop. Life Ins. *Bull.*, Nov., 1949 (p. 3).

Goiter

Hereditary exophthalmic goiter. N. F. Boas, W. B. Ober. *J. Clinic. Endocr.*, 6(8), 1946. (See also *Biol. Abstr.*, Aug., 1947:16341.)

Ulcers

Hereditary factors in peptic ulcer. R. Doll, J. Buch. *Ann. Eugen.*, 15(2), 1950.

Sex-Linked (Sex-Limited) Conditions

Hemophilia, mutation rate. J. B. S. Haldane. *Ann. Eugen.*, 13:262 (1947).
*"The Royal Disease." Hugo Iltis. *J. Hered.*, Aug., 1948.
Hemophilia in dogs. K. M. Brinkhous, J. B. Graham. *Science*, June 30, 1950 (p. 723).
Baldness. J. B. Hamilton, A. E. Light. "Patterned Loss of Hair in Man." Symposium, "Growth, Replacement and Types of Hair." *Annals*, N. Y. Ac. Sci., 53(3), 1950.
—Inheritance of premature baldness. H. Harris. *Ann. Eugen.*, 13(3), 1946.
Color blindness, sex differences, etc. R. W. Pickford. *Nature* (London), 159, 160. 1947.

Structural Abnormalities

Congenital Malformations. D. P. Murphy. (2nd ed.) Lippincott, 1947.
**Family Skeletons.* D. D. Whitney. U. of Nebraska Press, 1946.
Dwarfism: Size, proportion of midgets. C. W. Dupertuis. *Am. J. Phys. Anthrop.*, 3(2), 1945.

–Differentiation, inheritance, different types of dwarfism. H. Grebe. See, *Biol. Abstr.,* Jan., 1949:121.

Gigantism. On Robert Wadlow (the "Alton giant"): *Time* Mag., Mar. 1, 1937; death of, *N. Y. Times* Sunday science section (Kaempffert), July 21, 1940.

Hand abnormalities. *J. Hered.,* Jan., 1948 (fused fingers); Nov., 1947 ("lobster claw"); Feb., 1947 (familial variations); Dec., 1946 (stub fingers); Feb., 1943, Mar., 1946 (extra fingers); Nov., 1943 (malformations of hands, feet).

"Brittle bones" (blue sclerotic). C. S. Kellogg. *Arch. Int. Med.,* 80(3), 1947.

Cleft palate. See *Biol. Abstr.,* May, 1948:10635 (Krantz); Feb., 1948:2787 (Hanhart); Feb., 1949:2700-A (Phair); July, 1949:3316 (Schorr).

Teeth Defects

Familial and individual variations in teeth anomalies. C. P. Oliver. *Genetics,* 33(6), 1948.

*"Bad Teeth by Inheritance." Jane Stafford. *Sci. News Let.,* Apr. 19, 1947.

Missing teeth. W. G. Erwin, R. W. Corkern. *J. Hered.,* Aug., 1949.

Caries (tooth decay), familial. Henry Klein. *Publ. Health Repts.,* 62(35), 1947.

Malocclusion. S. E. Stoddard. *J. Hered.,* Apr., 1947.

Skin Defects

Birthmark inheritance. S. J. Denaro. *J. Hered.,* July, 1944.

"A Human Mosaic." (With striking photograph) M. Zlotnikoff. *J. Hered.,* June, 1945.

*Birthmarks in relation to skin cancer. E. F. Traub. *Hygeia,* June, 1940.

"Albinism in Negroes." S. B. and C. Pipkin. *J. Hered.,* July, 1944.

White forelock inheritance. A. M. Cromwell. *J. Hered.,* Feb., 1940.

Psoriasis. Charles Lerner. *J. Invest. Dermat.,* 3(5), 1940. See also *Biol. Abstr.,* Apr., 1949:11073 (Romani).

Muscles, Nerves

Hernia (inguinal). B. R. Weimer. *J. Hered.,* Aug., 1949.

Muscular diseases. E. Thomasen (Denmark). See *Biol. Abstr. (H),* July, 1950:17320.

Progressive muscular dystrophy. J. W. Boyes, *et al. Ann. Eugen.* 15(1), 1949.

Hereditary periodic paralysis. C. P. Oliver. *Am. J. Dis. Childr.,* Nov., 1944.

Cerebellar atrophy (ataxia). R. B. Richter. *Am. J. Hum. Genet.,* Mar., 1950.

Spastic paraplegia. J. B. S. Haldane. *J. Genetics,* 41(2, 3), 1941.

Eye Defects

"Some Genetic Aspects." P. J. Waardenburg. Ch. in: *Modern Trends in Ophthalmology.* Arnold Sorsby (Ed.). (2nd ed.) Hoeber, 1949.

"Heredo-familial Degenerative Diseases." F. B. Walsh. Ch. 9 in: *Clinical Neuro-Ophthalmology.* Williams & Wilkins, 1947.

Astigmatism. See *Psychol. Abstr.*, Oct., 1948:4572 (Birö).
Atom-bomb cataracts. D. G. Cogan, *et al. Science,* 110(2868):654. 1949.
Cataract. C. L. Anderson. *J. Hered.,* June, 1949.
Cross eyes (strabismus). L. S. West. *J. Hered.,* Nov., 1939.
Missing eyes (anophthalmos). L. M. Ashley. *J. Hered.,* June, 1947.
Myopia (hereditary). K. C. Wold. *Arch. Ophthal.,* 42:225. 1949.
Nystagmus. Mary Allen, M. L. Billings. *J. Hered.,* Dec., 1942.
Optic atrophy (Leber's disease). See *Biol. Abstr.,* Feb., 1947:2563 (Bhaduri).
Retinablastoma (glioma). H. F. Falls. *J. Am. Med. Assn.,* 133(3):171. 1947.

Speech Defects

*Speech Handicapped School Children. Wendell Johnson, *et al.* Harper, 1948.
Stuttering. In twins. S. F. Nelson, *et al. J. Speech Disorders,* 10(4), 1945.
—General incidence. Wendell Johnson. *Rev. Educ. Res.,* 14. 1944. See also *Psych. Abstr.,* Nov., 1949:5638 (Henderson).
*—Treatment. "Miracle with Mirrors." J. D. Radcliffe. *Hygeia,* July, 1947.

Deafness

Deafness and the Deaf in the U. S. H. Best. Macmillan, 1943.
*"Heredity in Congenital Deafness." M. T. Macklin. *Hygeia,* Aug., 1949.
Otosclerosis. E. W. Amidon. *J. Hered.,* Aug., 1948.
Hereditary nerve deafness. F. E. Stephens, D. A. Dolowitz. *Am. J. Hum. Genet.,* Sept., 1949.
Deaf-mutism. Harold Lindenov (Denmark). See *Biol. Abstr.,* Aug., 1947: 16343.
Ear-nose-throat diseases. P. H. G. van Gilse, *et al.* See *Biol. Abstr.,* June, 1947:13381.

Metabolic Chemical Disorders

Allergies. Respiratory. K. A. Stiles, E. J. Johnston. *J. Allergy,* 17(1), 1946.
—Familial nonreaginic. A. P. Locke, M. G. Meyer. Symposium, "Allergy." N. Y. Ac. Sci. 50(7), 1949.
—Migraine. W. G. Erwin, Jeanette LaFleur. *Proc.* Louisiana Ac. Sci., 12:23, 1949. (*Biol. Abstr.,* Dec., 1949:28194.)
Gout. C. J. Smyth, C. W. Cotterman, R. H. Freyberg. *J. Clin. Invest.* 27(6), 1948. *Also,* C. J. Smyth, R. M. Stecher, W. Q. Wolfson. *Science,* Nov. 5, 1948.
Alkaptonuria: W. K. Hall, *et al. J. Hered.,* Jan., 1950.
Obesity, infantile excessive. Laurence-Moon-Biedl syndrome. E. Jaso, A. A. Curbelo. *Am. J. Dis. Childr.* 70(1), 1945.
—Hereditary, in mice. G. E. Dickerson, J. W. Gowen. *Science,* May 9, 1947.
Smell-blindness. P. M. Patterson, B. A. Lauder. *J. Hered.,* Oct., 1948.
Taste-blindness. Josef Cohen, D. P. Ogdon. *Psych. Bull.,* Nov., 1949. Also, *Science,* Nov. 18, 1949.

Blood Diseases

Sickle-cell anemia. J. V. Neel. *Science,* July 15, 1949. *Also,* Linus Pauling, *et al. Science,* Nov. 25, 1949.

Cooley's (Mediterranean) anemia. E. Silvestroni, I. Bianco. *Am. J. Hum. Genet.*, Sept., 1949.

Leukemia, familial. Aage Videbaek. *Acta. Med. Scand.*, 127. 1947. (See *Biol. Abstr.*, Nov., 1947:21317.)

MENTAL DISEASES

Schizophrenia. *Dementia Praecox.* Leopold Bellak. Grune & Stratton, 1948.

—Genetic concepts, treatment. F. J. Kallmann. *J. Hered.*, Nov., 1948. Also, *Psych. Quart.*, 21. 1947.

—In monozygotic twins. E. J. Gardner, F. E. Stephens. *J. Hered.*, June, 1949.

—Adrenal influences. "Nature of the Adrenal Stress Response Failure in Schizophrenic Man." Hudson Hoagland, Gregory Pincus. *J. Nerv. Ment. Dis.*, 111 (1950). *See also*, Pincus, *et al.*, *Psychosom. Med.*, 11(2), 11(3), 1949.

—In childhood. Charles Bradley. *J. Pediatr.*, 30. 1947.

Mental Health. Symposium. Amer. Assn. Adv. Sci., Sect. III. Science Press, 1939.

Statistics. Analysis ages of first admissions to mental hospitals, N. Y. State. Benjamin Malzberg. *Psychiat. Quart.*, 23. 1949.

—Mental disease among aged, N. Y. State. B. Malzberg. *Ment. Hyg.* (N. Y.), 33. 1949.

Chemical, biological influences in mental disorders: Enzyme kinetics, etc. Hudson Hoagland. *J. Comp. & Phys. Psych.*, June, 1947.

Psychopathic personality. A. J. Arieff, D. B. Rotman. *J. Crim. Law & Criminol.*, 39. 1948.

*"*Folie à Deux.*" F. J. Kallmann, J. S. Mickey. *J. Hered.*, Oct., 1946.

Huntington's chorea: A family history. C. P. Oliver, B. C. Schiele. Dight Inst., U. of Minnesota *Bull.*, 3. 1945. *See also* note, Schiele, *J. Hered.*, Dec., 1946 (p. 383).

—Prediction of Huntington's chorea. R. M. Patterson, *et al. Am. J. Psychiatry*, 104:786. 1948.

Psychoneurosis in the armed forces: E. D. Fisher, *Bull.* U. S. Army Med. Dep., 7. 1947. See also *Psych. Abstr.*, June, 1947:1869 (Moriarity).

"War Strains and Mental Health." A. B. Stokes. *J. Nerv. Ment. Dis.*, 101. 1945.

Manic-depressive insanity. *Hereditary and Environmental Factors in Causation of Manic-Depressive Psychoses and Dementia Praecox.* H. M. Pollock, Benjamin Malzberg, R. G. Fuller. State Hospitals Press (Utica, N. Y.), 1939.

"Inheritance of EEGs in Children with Behavior Disorders." M. A. Kennard, *Psychosom. Med.*, 11(3), 1949.

"Intelligence in Mental Disorders." Anne Roe, David Shakow. *Annals*, N. Y. Ac. Sci., 42(4), Jan. 31, 1942.

*Treatment: *How Psychiatry Helps.* Phillip Polatin, E. C. Philtine. Harper, 1949.

**You and Psychiatry.* W. C. Menninger, Munro Leaf. Scribner's, 1948.

Mental Defect (Feeble-mindedness, Idiocy)

The Biology of Mental Defect. L. S. Penrose. Grune & Stratton, 1949. (Note: This book contains almost all important data and references on mental defect to date of its publication.)

"Birth Injury as Cause of Mental Defect." L. S. Penrose. *J. Ment. Sci.,* 95. 1949.

Mongolism. Some statistical aspects. Benjamin Malzberg. *Am. J. Ment. Def.,* 54. 1950.

"Constitutional Factors in Institutional Children." Frank Bodman. *J. Ment. Sci.,* 96. 1950.

"What is a moron?" E. A. Doll. *J. Abn. Soc. Psychol.,* 43. 1948.

Epilepsy

Epilepsy. P. H. Hoch, R. P. Knight (Eds.). Grune & Stratton, 1947. (Section on Heredity by F. J. Kallmann, Gerhard Sander.)

"Heredity of Epilepsy as Told by Twins." W. G. Lennox. *J. Am. Med. Assn.* (In press, Nov. or Dec., 1950.)

*"Marriage and Children for Epileptics." W. G. Lennox. *Hum. Fertility,* 10(4), 1950.

*"It's Time to Talk About Epilepsy." Marguerite Clark. *McCall's* Mag., Feb., 1945.

Audiogenic seizures (in mice). C. S. Hall. *J. Hered.,* Jan., 1947.

Sexual Abnormalities

Genital Abnormalities, Hermaphroditism, etc. H. H. Young. Williams & Wilkins, 1937.

"Sex Chromosomes in a Human Intersex." A. E. Severinghaus. *Am. J. Anat.,* 70, Jan. 15, 1942.

"True Hermaphroditism." J. C. Weed, *et al. J. Clin. Endocrin.,* 7(11), 1947.

*Hen into rooster. Note by R. E. Arndsdorf. *J. Hered.* Oct., 1947 (p. 320).

Blood Groups, Factors, Applications

Blood Grouping. Symposium. *Annals,* N. Y. Ac. Sci., 46(9), Nov. 8, 1946.

Blood Groups and Transfusion. A. S. Wiener. (3rd ed.) C. C. Thomas, 1943.

Blood groups, race differences. *See* W. C. Boyd, under "Race" references.

Rh factor. "Heredity of the 'Rh' Blood Types." A. S. Wiener, *et al. Am. J. Hum. Genet.,* Dec., 1949.

—*"Rh" nomenclature.* I. B. Wexler. *Am. J. Hum. Genet.,* Dec., 1949. *Also,* W. B. Castle, M. M. Wintrobe, L. H. Snyder, *Science,* Jan. 9, 1948 (p. 27).

Erythroblastosis fetalis. Philip Levine. In *Blood Grouping,* Symposium, N. Y. Ac. Sci. *See* reference, above.

Kell-Cellano factors. Philip Levine, *et al. J. Hematol.,* 4(7), 1949.

Disputed Paternity Proceedings. S. B. Schatkin. (2nd ed.) Matthew Bender, 1947.

—Observations on series of 500 cases. A. S. Wiener. *Am. J. Hum. Genet.,* June, 1950.

LONGEVITY

Length of Life. L. I. Dublin, A. J. Lotka, Mortimer Spiegelman. Ronald Press, 1949.

"Twin Studies on Senescence." F. J. Kallman, Gerhard Sander. *Am. J. Psychiatry,* 106(1), 1949. (Also, *J. Hered.,* Dec., 1948.)

*"Biology of Old Age." Florence Moog. *Scientif. Amer.,* June, 1948.

Longevity. In relation to country of origin in N. Y. State. Massimo Calabresi. *Hum. Biol.,* Dec., 1945.

—In social classes (England). Christopher Tietze. Milbank Mem. Fund *Quart.,* 21(2), Apr., 1943.

—Per capita income and mortality. M. E. Altenderfer. U. S. Pub. Health *Reports,* 62. Nov. 28, 1947.

—"Prolonging Life." E. R. Long. *Science,* Mar. 26, 1948.

*—Animal longevity. "Man Outlives Animals." Frank Thone. *Sci. News. Let.,* Jan. 24, 1948. *Also,* Farm animals. I. M. Lerner, *J. Hered.,* July, 1944.

Aging and Degenerative Diseases. Biol. Symposia, 11. J. Cattell Press, 1944.

*"Why Grow Old?" A. C. Ivy. *Hygeia,* June, 1945.

**Live Long and Like It.* C. Ward Crampton. Publ. Affairs Pamph. 139. 1948.

INTELLIGENCE

Differential Psychology. Anne Anastasi, John P. Foley, Jr. Macmillan, 1949. (Excellent general discussions and bibliographies.)

Twin studies. *See* Chapter 11, above, with references.

Definitions: "Cognitive, Conative and Non-Intellective Intelligence." David Wechsler. *Am. Psychologist,* Mar., 1950.

*"Testing Intelligence and Aptitudes." L. L. Thurstone. *Hygeia,* Jan., 1945.

*"Theories of Intelligence." L. L. Thurstone. *Sci. Month.,* Feb., 1946.

"Prediction of Intelligence at College Entrance from Earlier Tests." R. L. Thorndike. *J. Educ. Psychol.,* Mar., 1947.

—"Growth of Intelligence During Adolescence." Thorndike. *J. Genet. Psych.,* 72. 1948.

"Consistency, Variability in Intelligence, Birth to 18 Years." Nancy Bayley. *J. Genet. Psych.,* 75. 1949.

IQ changes in U. S.: Soldiers, World Wars I, II. R. D. Tuddenham. *Am. Psychologist,* Feb., 1948.

"Schooling Makes a Difference." Irving Lorge. Teachers' Coll. *Rec.,* Columbia U., May, 1945.

Race differences. On the Negro IQ, *see* articles by M. D. Jenkins, *Sci. Month.,* May, 1948, and (with C. M. Randall) *J. of Soc. Psych.,* 27. 1948. *Also,* by Paul Witty, *J. Abn. & Soc. Psych.,* 40(4), Oct., 1945.

Effects of war on IQ (Holland). A. D. de Groot. *J. Abn. & Soc. Psych.*, July, 1948.
Sex differences: *Women and Men*. Scheinfeld. Chs. 8, 24.
—*See also,* articles, J. R. Hobson, *J. Educ. Res.* 41. 1947; W. D. Lewis, *Psych. Abstr.*, Mar., 1948:5492.

HIGH IQ, TALENTS, GENIUS

**The Gifted Child Grows Up*. L. M. Terman, M. H. Oden. Stanford U. Press, 1947.
Music talent inheritance. Articles by C. E. Seashore.* *Sci. Month.*, Feb., 1942; May, 1941; Apr., 1940; and On vocal talent, Oct., 1939. See also, *Science,* Apr. 24, 1942.
—"Assessment of Musical Ability." James Mainwaring. *Brit. J. Educ. Psychol.*, 17. 1947.
Artistic aptitude. N. C. Meier. *Psych. Monogr.*, 51. 1939.
Creativity. J. P. Guilford. *Am. Psychologist,* 5(9), Sept., 1950.
Mathematical talent. G. Révész. *Acta Psychol.* (Hague), 1940:5. (See *Psych. Abstr.*, June, 1949:2586.)
—"The Memory of Salo Finkelstein." J. D. Weinland. *J. Genl. Psych.*, 39. 1948.
Chess: "The Thought of the Chess Player." A. D. de Groot. *Psych. Abstr.*, Mar., 1948:1090.
—"Chess Men—and Chess Mentality." E. Lasker. *N. Y. Times* Sunday Mag., Apr. 24, 1949.
Abnormality in Genius. (A survey of the literature.) Anne Anastasi, John P. Foley, Jr. *Annals,* N. Y. Ac. Sci., 42(1), Aug., 1941.
"Idiot Savant." (A case study.) M. Scheerer, E. Rothmann, K. Goldstein. *Psych. Monogr.* 58(4), 1945.

BEHAVIOR

Instinct: Report on symposium, Princeton. W. S. Hunter, *et al. Psychol. Rev.*, 54(6), 1947.
*"Growth Potentials of Human Infant." Arnold Gesell. *Sci. Month.*, Apr., 1949.
—"Human Infancy and Ontogenesis of Behavior." Arnold Gesell. *Am. Scientist,* 37(4), 1949.
"Prenatal Development of Behavior." Leonard Carmichael. *Psychol. Rev.*, 54:316. 1947.
Hormones and Behavior. Frank A. Beach. Hoeber, 1948.
Heredity and behavior. J. P. Scott. *Science,* Dec. 22, 1944. Also, *Sociometry,* 8(1), Feb., 1945; *J. Hered.*, Jan., 1942; *Comp. Psych. Monogr.*, Feb., 1945.
Inheritance in Dogs. Öjvind Winge. Comstock Press (Ithaca, N. Y.), 1949.
—Differences in reactivity. J. L. Fuller. *J. Comp. Physiol. Psychol.*, 41. 1948.
—Shyness, inheritance. F. C. Thorne. *J. Genet. Psychol.*, 65. 1944.
Fear, on nature of. D. O. Hebb. *Psych. Rev.*, Sept., 1946.

"Self-regulation of Diet in Childhood." C. M. Davis. *Hlth. Educ. J.* (London), 5, 1947. (*Psych. Abstr.*, Feb., 1948:638.)
Taste sensitivity: Chemical specificity in genetical differences. H. Harris, H. Kalmus. *Ann. Eugen.*, 15(1), 1949.
—Taste-blindness to P. T. C., as function of saliva. Jozef Cohen, D. P. Ogden. *Science,* 110(2864):532. 1949.
—Army finds differences. *J. Hered.*, Nov., 1946 (p. 330).
Handedness. *See* under, "Twins."

PERSONALITY

Personality, Society and Culture. Clyde Kluckhohn, H. A. Murray (Eds.). Knopf, 1948.
Personality and the Behavior Disorders. J. McV. Hunt (Ed.). Ronald Press, 1944.
Culture and Personality. S. S. Sargent, M. W. Smith (Eds.). Viking Fund (N. Y.), 1949.
The Biological Basis of Individuality. L. Loeb. C. C. Thomas, 1945.
"Personality Organization in Children." J. E. Anderson. *Am. Psychol.*, Sept., 1948.
"Shirley's Babies after Fifteen Years." Patricia Neilon. *J. Genet. Psychol.*, 73. 1948.
*Twins and personality. *Case of Millan and George.* F. E. Stephens, R. B. Thompson. *J. Hered.*, Apr., 1943.
—Twins T. and C. from infancy to adolescence. Arnold Gesell, Helen Thompson. *Genet. Psych. Monogr.*, 24(3), 1941.
*—Quadruplet studies. I. G. Gardner, H. H. Newman. *J. Hered.*, July, Oct., 1940; Oct., 1942; Sept., 1943; Mar., 1944.
Temperament, factorial analysis. L. L. Thurstone. (Abstract.) *Science,* Apr. 28, 1950:254. (To be publ. *Proc.* Natl. Ac. Sci.)
—Factorial analysis and body measurements. L. L. Thurstone. *Am. J. Phys. Anthrop.* 5(1), 1947; 11 (1), 1946.
Obesity, psychological aspects. Hilde Bruch. *Bull. N. Y. Ac. Sci.*, 24(2), 1948.
*Coloring: Coat color, physique, temperament. C. E. Keeler. *J. Hered.*, Sept., 1947. Also, *J. Comp. & Physiolog. Psych.*, Apr., 1948.
*"The Astrology Racket." A. E. Meyer. *Am. Mercury,* Jan., 1945.
*—"Scientists Look at Astrology." B. J. Bok, M. W. Mayall. *Sci. Month.*, Mar., 1941.
*Sex differences in personality. See *Women and Men.* Scheinfeld. Chs. 9, 17, 18.

SEXUAL BEHAVIOR

Sexual Behavior in the Human Male. A. C. Kinsey, W. B. Pomeroy, C. E. Martin. Saunders, 1948. Also, scheduled for 1951, *Sexual Behavior in the Human Female.* (Extensive bibliographies in both books.)
—Symposium on Kinsey Report. (A.A.A.S.) *Sci. Month.*, May, 1950.
—Critiques of Kinsey report. L. M. Terman, *Psych. Bull.*, Sept., 1948; A. H. Hobbs, R. D. Lambert, *Am. J. Psychiatry,* June, 1948; Paul

Wallin, *Am. Sociol. Rev.*, Apr., 1949, and (with Claude C. Bowman) *Am. Sociol. Rev.*, Aug., 1949 (p. 548).

Physiological and Psychological Factors in Sex Behavior. (Symposium.) *Annals*, N. Y. Ac. Sci., 47(5), May 9, 1947.

Sex and Personality. L. M. Terman, C. C. Miles. McGraw-Hill, 1936.

The Sexual Perversions and Abnormalities. Clifford Allen. (2nd ed.) Oxford U. Press, 1950.

See also: *Women and Men.* Scheinfeld, Ch. 19, and Bibliography, pp. 421 ff. Also, *Psych. Abstr.*, Oct., 1948:4498 (Darke); Dec., 1948:5485 (Bergler), and 23868 (Lang).

CRIME

Principles of Criminology. E. H. Sutherland. Lippincott, 1947.

—"White Collar Crime." Sutherland. *Am. Soc. Rev.*, Apr., 1945.

**Unraveling Juvenile Delinquency.* Sheldon and Eleanor Glueck. Commonwealth Fund, 1950.

*—*Crime and Justice.* S. and E. Glueck. Little Brown, 1936. Harvard U. Press, 1945.

Mental defect and crime. In, Penrose, *The Biology of Mental Defect* (see under "Mental Defect." refs.), pp. 209 ff.

"Heredity and Crime." A. N. Foxe. *J. Crim. Law & Criminol.*, 36. 1945.

*Twins and crime: Rev. of Rosanoff studies. Gladys Schwesinger. *J. Hered.*, Jan., 1942.

"A Decade of Serious Crime in the United States." A. L. Porterfield. *Am. Soc. Rev.*, Feb., 1948.

—Suicide and homicide indices. Porterfield. *Am. Soc. Rev.*, Aug., 1949.

Suicide, in twins and only children. F. J. Kallmann, *et al. Am. J. Hum. Genet.*, Dec., 1949.

Alcoholism: Biochemical factors in. R. J. Williams, *et al. Arch. Biochem.*, 23(2), 1949.

—"Adult Adjustment of Foster Children of Alcoholic and Psychotic Parents." Anne Roe, Barbara Burks. *Quart. Jour. Studies in Alc.* (Yale U.), Dec., 1945.

—Cultural differences in alcoholism. R. F. Bates. See, *Psych. Abst.*, Aug., 1946:2797.

Negro-White crime rate differentials. E. R. Moses. *Am. Soc. Rev.*, Aug., 1947.

Sex differences in crime. See, *Women and Men.* Scheinfeld. Ch. 20.

*—"Belligerency Not Inborn." (UNESCO report.) *Sci. News Let.*, Nov. 6, 1948.

*—"Are Wars Inevitable?" J. R. Swanton. Smithsonian Inst., War Background Studies, 12. May 11, 1943.

EVOLUTION

**The Meaning of Evolution.* G. G. Simpson. Yale U. Press, 1949.

Natural Selection and Adaptation. Symposium (Muller, Wright, Jepsen, Stebbins, Mayr). *Proc.* Am. Phil. Soc., 93(6), Dec., 1949.

"Genetics in the Scheme of Things." (Nature and origin of life.) H. J. Muller. *Proc.* Eighth Intl. Congr. Genetics. *Hereditas,* suppl. vol., 1949.

*Acquired characters, "pangenesis": early history. Conway Zirkle. *Trans.* Amer. Phil. Soc., 35(2), 1946.

The "Lysenko" theories: **Heredity, East and West.* Julian Huxley. Schuman, 1949.

*—*Death of a Science.* Conway Zirkle (Ed.). U. of Penna. Press, 1949.

*—The Russian purge of genetics: Collected articles. *Bull.* Atomic Scientists, 5(6), May, 1949.

*—Articles by H. J. Muller. *Sat. Rev. of Lit.,* Dec. 4, Dec. 11, 1948.

*—"Heredity, Environment and Politics." T. M. Sonneborn. *Science,* May, 1950.

*—"Lysenko's Wonderful Genetics." R. C. Cook. *J. Hered.,* July, 1949.

Mutations: H. J. Muller. "Our Load of Mutations." *Am. Jour. Hum. Genet.,* June, 1949.

Plasmagenes. Jack Schultz. *Science,* Apr. 21, 1950 (p. 403).

Radiation (atomic, X-ray, etc.), genetic effects. "Radiation Genetics." Symposium, Oak Ridge Natl. Lab. *Jour. Cellular & Comp. Phys.,* 35, Suppl. 1. June, 1950.

—"Radiation Damage to the Genetic Material." H. J. Muller. *Am. Scientist,* 38(1), 1950.

RACE

Races: A Study of Problems of Race Formation. C. S. Coon, S. M. Garn, Joseph Birdsell. C. C. Thomas, 1950.

Origins and Evolution of Man. Cold Spring Harbor Symposium, XV. 1950.

**Heredity, Race and Society.* L. C. Dunn, Th. Dobzhansky. New American Library, 1946.

Genetics and the Races of Man. William C. Boyd. Little, Brown, 1950.

Human evolution. J. B. S. Haldane. In: *Genetics, Paleontology and Evolution.* G. L. Jepsen, G. G. Simpson, E. Mayr (Eds.). Princeton U. Press, 1940.

See also: Curt Stern, *Principles of Human Genetics,* W. H. Freeman, 1949, Chs. 25, 26, 27. *Also,* E. A. Hooton, *Up from the Ape.* (Rev. ed.) Macmillan, 1947. Parts IV, V.

South African ape-men: *Finding the Missing Link.* Robert Broom. London: Watts, 1950.

*"The Great Aryan Myth." Knight Dunlap. *Sci. Month.,* Oct., 1944.

"American Negro, Origins." Ashley Montagu. *Psychiatry,* May, 1944. (Also, *Sci. Month.,* July, 1944.)

—"Racial Ancestry, Mississippi College Negro." August Meier. *Am. J. Phys. Anthrop.* 7(2), 1949.

See also, references on Negro under "Coloring" and "Intelligence."

Kiths (*also,* Climate effects on race). *Mainsprings of Civilization.* Ellsworth Huntington. Wiley, 1945.

*Jews. "Who are the Jews?" Melville J. Herskovitz. Ch. 30 in: *The Jews,*

Their History, Culture and Religion. Louis Finkelstein (Ed.). (2 vols.) Harper, 1949.

POPULATION DIFFERENTIALS ("THE GIDDY STORK")

Overpopulation threats: **Road to Survival.* William Vogt. Sloane, 1948.

*—*Our Plundered Planet.* Fairfield Osborn. Little, Brown. 1948.

—UNESCO "Food and People" discussion. *"The Double Crisis." Aldous Huxley. *Sci. News Let.,* Mar. 26, 1949.

—Differential birthrate and future quality of population. Symposium, "Population Conference," Princeton. *Eugen. News.,* Sept.-Dec., 1947.

—The college birthrate. C. J. Gamble. *J. Hered.,* Dec., 1947.

—Birthrates by religious groups. C. V. Kiser, P. K. Whelpton. Milbank Mem. Fund *Quart.,* Jan., 1944.

Declining intelligence, supposed threat. L. S. Penrose. *Am. J. Ment. Def.,* 53:114. 1948.

—"Note on Trend of Scottish Intelligence." *J. Hered.,* Feb., 1950 (p. 47).

Report, Royal Commission on Population. London: H. M. Stationery Office, 1949.

*Does genetic endowment vary by socio-economic group? Discussion. B. J. Stern vs. Curt Stern. *Science,* June 23, 1950 (p. 697).

"Women in Who's Who." (Marital, reproductive status.) C. V. Kiser, N. L. Schacter. Milbank Mem. Fund. *Quart.,* 27. 1949.

"Biological Factors Affecting Family Size." F. A. E. Crew. *Brit. Jour. Soc. Med.,* 3(1), 1949.

EUGENICS

**Preface to Eugenics.* Frederick Osborn. Harper, 1940. (New edition scheduled, 1951.)

Inbreeding—association of characters, etc. J. B. S. Haldane. *Ann. Eugen.,* 15(1), 1949.

See also discussions on eugenics in: Curt Stern, *Principles of Human Genetics,* Ch. 24. *Also,* in: L. S. Penrose, *Biology of Mental Defect* (1949 ed.), pp. 231-240.

Sterilization: In the U. S., 1948. Clarence J. Gamble. *Eugen. News.,* Mar.-June, 1949.

—*Sterilization in N. Carolina:* A sociological, psychological study. Moya Woodside. U. of N. Car. Press, 1950.

In Denmark. Tage Kemp. *Eugen. Rev.,* 38(4), 1947.

—In Sweden. Nils von Hofsten. *J. Hered.,* Sept., 1949.

—Female sterilization techniques. R. J. McNeil. *Calif. Med.,* 69(1), 1948.

Birth control: **Voluntary Parenthood.* John Rock, David Loth. Random House. 1949.

*—The birth control debate (including Catholic view). *New Republic,* Dec. 11, 1944.

Fertility in Men. R. S. Hotchkiss. Lippincott, 1944.

—*Fertility in Women.* S. L. Siegler. Lippincott, 1944.

—*Human Fertility, and Problems of the Male.* E. J. Farris. Author's Press, 1950.

Abortions, report on a series. Christopher Tietze. *Hum. Biol.,* Feb., 1949 (p. 59).

*Ovaries, transplanting of. Sam Matthews. *Sci. News. Let.,* Apr. 1, 1950 (p. 202).

Artificial insemination: Legal aspects (human). S. B. Schatkin. *Hum. Fertility,* June, 1948. (In same issue, analysis of 100 cases, M. P. Warner.)

—*Artificial Insemination of Farm Animals.* Enos J. Perry (Ed.). Rutgers U. Press, 1945.

Eugenic counseling. L. H. Snyder. "Medical Genetics and Public Health." *Bull.* N. Y. Ac. Med., 2nd Ser., 22(11), Nov., 1946.

"The Geneticists' Manifesto." (On improvement of mankind by breeding.) *J. Hered.,* Sept., 1939.

PERIODICALS

For continuing references on new findings in the field of human heredity, as they appear, the best sources in English are the following publications. They will be found in most large public libraries, college libraries and medical libraries.

American Journal of Human Genetics (Quarterly)
Journal of Heredity (Monthly)
Human Biology (Quarterly)
Eugenical News (Quarterly)
The Eugenics Review (Quarterly, England)
Annals of Eugenics (England)
The Treasury of Human Inheritance (England)

Also see: *Biological Abstracts,* Section H., and *Psychological Abstracts* (both monthlies), under desired topics.

COLLEGE COURSES IN HUMAN GENETICS

The following is the list to date of colleges in the United States and Canada offering courses in Human Genetics (H), Medical Genetics (M), or both (H-M):

Bowman-Gray School of Medicine (Winston-Salem, N. Car.): M
University of California (Berkeley): H
University of Chicago: H-M
Dartmouth College: M
McGill University (Canada): M
Michigan State College: H
Ohio State University: H-M
University of Oklahoma: H-M
College of Ozarks (Clarkesville, Ark.): H
University of Rochester: H
University of Toledo: H
Tulane University: H-M
University of Utah: M
Western Reserve University: H

INDEX